D1601981

Wildlife of Mexico

By A. STARKER LEOPOLD

ILLUSTRATED BY *Charles W. Schwartz*

Wildlife of Mexico
The Game Birds and Mammals

Berkeley, Los Angeles, London: 1972

UNIVERSITY OF CALIFORNIA PRESS

UNIVERSITY OF CALIFORNIA PRESS
BERKELEY AND LOS ANGELES, CALIFORNIA
UNIVERSITY OF CALIFORNIA PRESS, LTD.
LONDON, ENGLAND
© 1959, BY
THE REGENTS OF THE UNIVERSITY OF CALIFORNIA
SECOND PRINTING, 1972
ISBN: 0-520-00724-7
LIBRARY OF CONGRESS CATALOG CARD NUMBER: 59-6865
PRINTED IN THE UNITED STATES OF AMERICA
DESIGNED BY JOHN B. GOETZ

Foreword

Because of its varied topography and its situation at the juncture of the Nearctic and Neotropical zones, Mexico is endowed with a rich and varied fauna. Since the initial faunistic studies by Francisco Hernández, doctor at the court of King Philip II of Spain—who traveled extensively in Mexico in the period 1570 to 1577—the natural history of the country has continued to interest naturalists.

Contributions to our knowledge of the Mexican fauna have been made over the years by various expeditions and field investigations. Some of the more important of these were the royal expedition sent by the Spanish Crown at the end of the eighteenth century under the command of Martín Sesse; the studies of the "Scientific Mission to Mexico" conducted during the transitory reign of the Emperor Maximilian, the results of which are presented in various volumes; the compilation of materials of great interest that served as a basis for the *Biología Centrali-Americana;* and extensive collections of birds and mammals assembled by E. W. Nelson and E. A. Goldman for the United States Bureau of Biological Survey. These and countless lesser undertakings have laid the foundation of knowledge of Mexican wildlife.

Until now, however, there has been no investigation of adequate scope focused specifically on the game animals of Mexico and their importance in that country. There have been efforts in this direction, the first of which was a book by Don Pedro Blazquez, published in 1869 under the title *El cazador mexicano*—an interesting work, deserving of praise in its time but now only a bibliographic curiosity.

Early in the present century two authors residing in central Mexico in the state of San Luis Potosí, Srs. Carlos López and Carlos M. López (who were not related), published their classic volume, *Caza mexicana*. This work, carefully edited and well illustrated, gives evidence of the authors' profound understanding of the game animals but suffers nevertheless because of their lack of biological training. Later, the senior author, Carlos López, became associated with the Dirección de Estudios Biológicos, Departmento de Taxidermia, and in this position—where I had the pleasure of knowing him well—he acquired much zoölogical knowledge that would have been of great help to him had he possessed it while he was preparing the book.

In 1938 Arturo Imaz Baume published his *Cacería*, which merited a second edition in 1949. Although an elegant and interesting treatise on hunting, it is not a contribution to zoölogical or ecological literature, nor did the author intend it as such.

The only book about Mexican hunting and Mexican game that has been written with a biological slant is *El cazador y la vida silvestre*, by Morelos Herrejón, published in 1952. In that volume is clearly manifest the zoölogical background of the author, who is Professor of Zoölogy in the Escuela Normal Superior, and who has been a lifelong hunter.

But there is still urgent need for a complete treatise on our game animals, such as is presented here by A. Starker Leopold. The author, a scholar of unquestioned competence in the field of zoölogy, has dedicated more than twelve years to the preparation of this work, including extensive periods of field investigation in all parts of Mexico.

To say that the present book is the "best" in its class is an understatement. Indeed, it is the "first" in which an author has been able to combine an adequate biological background with thorough, firsthand investigation of wildlife problems as they exist in the field. In effect, this volume fills a real vacuum that has existed in the literature on Mexican wildlife.

The hunting of wild game has always been an important activity in Mexico, and wildlife, if properly conserved and managed, can be further developed into a productive future resource. There has been lacking, however, an authoritative summary or guide to the problems of wildlife management in Mexico, to the needs of future wildlife research, and to the broad field of wildlife education.

In 1934 it was my privilege to establish in the Escuela Nacional de Agricultura at Chapingo a course in "Wildlife Zoölogy." It was hoped that this orientation course, designed specifically for inclusion in the forestry curriculum, would interest future foresters in wildlife problems, at least to the point that they might help gather data and specimens and perhaps consider wildlife needs in their professional practice. There was the possibility, too, of developing a few wildlife specialists. But this course was dropped from the curriculum and for many years now the foresters in Mexico have had no chance to become oriented in wildlife biology. The Escuela de Agricultura offers an interesting and valuable course in "Wildlife Administration," but this lacks the biological approach necessary as a foundation for wildlife management. Perhaps the present book, when it becomes available in the Spanish language, will make the resumption of university training in wildlife biology easier.

The parts of this volume that treat of the individual species of game mammals and game birds are excellent; these accounts will serve far into the future as an authoritative reference work. The first part, in which Leopold discusses the fundamentals of game management is in my judgment equally well done.

The author makes continual reference to the dynamic and ever-changing character of ecologic problems, a point of view that can scarcely be overemphasized. He expresses this idea clearly in the paragraph of chapter 1 which states: "But landscapes are not stable entities. A forest can be cleared and planted to corn so that it no longer is habitat for deer but becomes a home for doves, quail, and rabbits. The cornfield in turn can erode into a series of raw gullies that support no animals at all. The impact of human activity upon the land may substantially alter the native animal life."

We are accustomed to thinking of forest protection chiefly in terms of regulating excessive logging, as though this were the only or the principal cause of forest destruction. Yet the clearing of trees and brush from the land to make it suitable for farming, or the inadvertent clearing by burning or overgrazing, may be even more significant.

In exactly the same way, it is usual to think that the destruction or loss of wildlife is primarily a result of overhunting, when changes in habitat may actually be of much greater importance. Leopold emphasizes this point in another paragraph, which states: "A serious defect of much of the past effort in wildlife management has been the overemphasis on protecting animals from obvious sources of loss, such as hunting and predation, and a corresponding underemphasis on preserving a proper home in which the populations can live and reproduce."

The wildlife of Mexico has to date been of no small importance as a source of food for our rural peoples and as a source of recreation for our sport hunters. Unfortunately, far too little attention has been given to the development and perpetuation of our wildlife riches. It must be realized that, in many situations, sport hunting, with its attractions for tourists and its implications for commerce, may be a higher and more productive form of land use than the usually recognized activities of agriculture, forestry, and livestock production. When this fact is realized by the people and government of Mexico, wildlife management will take its rightful place in the rural economy of the country.

ENRIQUE BELTRÁN

México, D. F.
Summer of 1957

Contents

Wildlife of Mexico

Introduction

The doughty old soldier Bernal Díaz del Castillo, being the first visitor to record his impressions of Mexico, was the first to note the striking variety in altitudinal and vegetational land types of this new land. The route of the Conquest actually offered a fair cross section of the country. In the long hard struggle of 1519–1520 the Conquistadores progressed from the steaming swamps of Veracruz up jungle slopes and over the escarpment to the arid hills of Tlaxcala, thence through lovely pine uplands to the frozen shoulder of the volcano Popocatepetl, and finally into the green valley of Tenochtitlán, the heart of Montezuma's empire. Now in one day we can retrace the route in a whizzing automobile. The vegetation has been much altered, but the basic types remain in vivid contrast as Díaz described them.

Variety in Mexican topography, climate, and vegetation has given rise quite naturally to an equally varied animal life. Tropical and temperate faunas come together in unexpected combinations. For example, I recall sitting on a rimrock high in the Sierra de Tamaulipas one clear spring morning, with a level mesa of oak-grassland at my back and a lush tropical barranca at my feet. Among the oaks a wild turkey gobbled, bobwhites were whistling and Montezuma quail "buzzing," and a pair of black-bellied tree ducks explored the more venerable trees for nesting hollows. A white-tailed doe slipped over the rim seeking her bed in the cool brush below.

Down in the *monte* the monotonous whistles of tinamous and the soft cooing of red-billed pigeons and white-fronted doves echoed up to the rimrock. A handsome cock curassow sailed down the canyon on set wings, perhaps seeking his lady. And a gray fox slipped across a clearing. Where else in all North America could such an assortment of wildlife be observed from one rock?

But this animal wealth is shrinking in both variety and abundance as the Mexican landscape is cleared and put to economic uses. Overhunting likewise is contributing to the impoverishment of the fauna. Some of this loss is inevitable, of course, but not all. A strong program of wildlife conservation could guarantee for Mexico the perpetuation of much of the natural richness with which the country has been so generously endowed. Toward that end an initial step would seem to be an appraisal of the animal resources of the country, with formulation of ideas on possible ways to conserve and manage the various species and their habitats. This book is intended to be a contribution along that line.

In preparing this report, I have had in mind as my most important audience the people of Mexico who are interested—or might become so— in natural history, hunting, or conservation. There is no popular book available in Mexico that brings together what is known today of the native game animals. Such a volume, it would seem to me, is prerequisite to public understanding of the problems of wildlife conservation. To be sure, my report in its present form, being in English, will find only scant use in a Spanish-speaking country. However, a Spanish translation is planned for immediate publication in Mexico. The English edition, I hope, warrants publication for its interest to American conservationists and sportsmen.

I hasten to point out that a great many scientific papers have been written about the Mexican fauna, as the incomplete bibliography attached hereto will attest. These, in fact, were one of my principal sources of information. But most scientific writing is both unavailable and unintelligible to the average reader, and most of it concerns the problem of taxonomy, or animal classification, which is a field of science beyond the scope of all but a handful of specialists.

The idea for a survey of Mexican wildlife originated with William Vogt when he was Director of the Conservation Section of the Pan American Union. In 1944 I was employed by the Union to initiate such a survey, and I traveled in Mexico for two years, investigating local wildlife conditions in various parts of the Republic, from Sonora to Yucatán. A branch of the Mexican government gave financial support to the field work. In the fall of 1946 I joined the staff of the Museum of Vertebrate Zoölogy of the University of California, and the field program of the Museum has permitted continued work in Mexico to the extent of approximately one trip of a month or so each year. Gaps in the original survey have been filled one

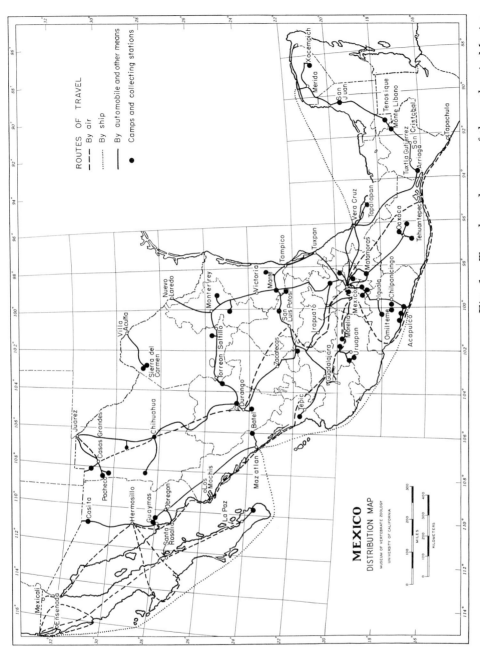

Fig. 1. Travels and camps of the author in Mexico.

by one, until it now seems time to draw together the materials into the long-planned volume.

FIELD PROCEDURE

My travels in Mexico, with principal camps and study sites, are shown in figure 1. Most travel was by automobile, but to attain desirable campsites or to cross gaps in the highway system it sometimes was necessary to travel by other means of conveyance—airplane, railroad, boat, bus, chartered truck, oxcart, pack train, or afoot with native porters carrying the luggage. The surveys of migratory waterfowl were made in January, 1951, and January, 1952, in an airplane of the United States Fish and Wildlife Service, piloted by Robert H. Smith. These trips were of about a month's duration

Fig. 2.   Arrival by oxcart at a camp near Galeana, Nuevo León.

and offered an opportunity to see from a low-flying airplane most of the Pacific Coast of Mexico and much of the interior.

The average length of stay at a campsite was about a week. After a camp was established I usually went first to officials of the local municipality to present my credentials and to explain my mission. This prevented much misunderstanding. Moreover, local residents could often give valuable information about the species of game in each locality and where to find

Fig. 3.   A pleasant camp near Acuña, Tamaulipas. A wild turkey hangs in the oak tree awaiting preparation as a specimen.

them. Notes on hunting practices, logging of the forests, farming, grazing, fire, and many other pertinent points could be picked up in these conversations. A fair share of the data included here were obtained in this way. I owe a debt of gratitude to the many *comisarios, alcaldes,* and other local officers who supplied information and who helped along my field work in innumerable other ways.

At each camp I spent most of my time walking over the country with shotgun, field glasses, camera, and notebook, observing the range and the animals themselves and collecting specimens. I attempted to preserve at least one specimen of every kind of game bird and small game mammal in the vicinity of each camp. These served as positive locality records for the various species and also yielded information on weights, food habits, breeding condition, and general biology. In most camps no effort was made to collect deer or other large game mammals, even when they were numerous, since sight records are entirely reliable and it did not seem worth while to take the time to kill and prepare the specimens. Plants were collected which were either dominant species in the local floras or were serving as food for game. Before leaving a camp I attempted to have in my notes and in the specimen cases (1) a complete record of the game species present and the relative abundance of each; (2) information on the local flora—both its present composition and its probable composition at its climax; (3) notes

Fig. 4.   Preparations at Tenosique, Tabasco, for a flight into the rain forest of eastern Chiapas. Photograph by D. L. Spencer.

on land use as related to game range; (4) notes on hunting as practiced by the local people and by visiting sportsmen; and (5) photographs of the country showing the types of range and the effects of land use on the habitat.

These field data were then supplemented with information derived from the voluminous scientific literature on Mexican fauna and flora and from some of the principal collections of Mexican vertebrates housed in museums of the United States and Mexico. The range maps for each species are based on the composite records of my own observations, museum specimens, and published records of occurrence.

PLAN OF THE BOOK

The writing of this book was begun in 1947 when a Guggenheim fellowship permitted me a period of freedom from regular university duties. But the job was not finished then, and perhaps it is just as well, for knowledge of the Mexican fauna has advanced greatly since then. The work of many field parties, both American and Mexican, has served to clarify countless problems of animal distribution and status that were vague a few years ago.

The finished volume, as it finally turns out, consists of three parts. Part I, "The Wildlife Resource and Its Management," presents a general account of the topography, climate, and vegetation of the country, both original and man-determined. As previously implied, the impact of human use upon the landscape is perhaps the dominant influence determining wildlife populations, and only through an understanding of the demands of agriculture, grazing, and forest practice can one grasp the basic problems of wildlife conservation. In this part of the book, after outlining the situation as I see it, I analyze the current government program of wildlife conservation in Mexico and suggest possible ways in which it might be strengthened.

Parts II and III present the accounts of individual species of game birds and mammals, respectively. One of the initial problems was to decide which species to include and which to omit. This was not as easy as it sounds, for there is no fixed definition of "game species." In most parts of the world, animals are considered "game" if they are taken for sport, for food, or (using the broadest possible definition) for usable products, such as fur. But so inclusive a concept applied to the Mexican fauna would yield a list of practically all the birds and mammals of the country, since nearly all are used for something. I have gone out with local hunters after parrots, herons, cormorants, anhingas, and many other marsh birds—for sport as well as for food. One night in Guerrero I joined a group of men and boys who, with slingshots and pine torches, were hunting songbirds on their roosts. They killed orioles, towhees, sparrows, and a few doves, all of which were later prepared for the kitchen. In some localities most men and boys of six years or more carry slingshots to supplement the bean pot with a little meat. Any bird or mammal that can be killed with a pebble is considered fair game. Pocket gophers are trapped regularly for food in many parts of the central upland; in fact, some villages have special gopher catchers (*tuzeros*) who do nothing else. Hummingbirds are taken for their supposed medicinal properties.

Extending the concept of game to include all the species actively hunted in Mexico would seem to me to be going a little too far. Yet, a useful volume on Mexican game can scarcely be limited to the species traditionally sought by sportsmen, for there are many birds and mammals of considerable interest and some economic importance—many of the predators, for example—that would be excluded.

As a basis for my list I finally settled upon the 1954 version of the Mexican game law, which enumerates all the families and many of the individual species considered in Mexico to be game. Even within this list I took the liberty of making some exceptions. Among the rails, I have accorded a full account only to the coot. Since the shore birds are utilized but sparingly in Mexico, I have only mentioned them briefly under a collective heading which considers all the families together. The smaller or rarer doves and pigeons are merely listed, without individual accounts. For diverse reasons the parrots (Psittacidae) and bats (Microchyroptera) are mentioned in the game regulations, but I have omitted them. Otherwise my list follows the regulations fairly closely.

In presenting general accounts of the species, it has often seemed desirable to lump closely related forms into a single account, although the species are listed separately and their individual ranges are delineated on the map. Thus, the tree squirrels, a confusing array, are treated by subgeneric groups, following Nelson's classification. The fox squirrels (Araeosciurus), consisting of six species according to current listing, are treated in one account. The ten kinds of gray squirrels (Echinosciurus) are discussed collectively in another. The two species of *Bassariscus* are considered together, as are the tree quails (*Dendrortyx*), the white-fronted doves (*Leptotila*), the white-sided jackrabbits, and so on. This arrangement is not intended to have any taxonomic significance whatsoever. Further collecting and study may show that two of the "species" mentioned actually intergrade and should therefore be listed as races under a single specific name. Other very similar species may prove to be indeed distinct, without hybridization. The plan of grouping used in this book does not imply prejudgment on my part as to ultimate taxonomic arrangement. Rather, it is entirely a matter of convenience in avoiding duplication in life-history accounts of closely allied forms, and of simplification of grouping for purposes of identification by the layman who might be using this book. It is better to be able to place an animal in its proper group than to become hopelessly confused by a long and complex list of finely subdivided forms, however accurate the list might be. For this reason I have included no mention of subspecies or geographic races.

Under the individual accounts are presented (1) criteria for identification—a brief description of each species, approximate weights and measurements, a plate of drawings by Charles W. Schwartz, and photographs when available; (2) a range map on which actual records of occurrence are plotted; (3) an account of the natural history of the animal; and (4) a report on present status of the species and problems of its management. In some instances, status and management of a related group of species are treated together under the family heading which precedes consideration of individual species. The purpose again is to avoid duplication. For example, the status of migratory waterfowl and problems of waterfowl conservation are discussed collectively rather than species by species.

If this book is long and involved, I like to think that it is by reason of the richness and variety of the Mexican fauna and not of my own ineptitude in condensing the materials it has seemed necessary or desirable to include. In a little Ozark cemetery I once saw an inscription on a headstone that paid this simple tribute: "She done the best she knowed." In presenting my account of the wildlife of Mexico I have tried to emulate this lady's accomplishment.

ACKNOWLEDGMENTS

My initial debt and still my greatest is to William Vogt, who raised the money to get this undertaking started, and who directed its formative years. With funds contributed by the International Committee for Bird Preservation I was employed by the Pan American Union for two full years. Travel and field expenses, and the salary of my field assistant, were supplied for that period by the Comisión Impulsora y Coordinadora de la Investigación Científica. Subsequent financial support of the project has come from the University of California through the Museum of Vertebrate Zoölogy and the Associates in Tropical Biogeography, the Guggenheim Foundation, the California Duck Hunters Association, and from Mr. Edward Grassmann, whose generous personal grant has carried me through this last year of compiling and writing.

Of the many persons who aided my cause in a multitude of ways, I am especially grateful to three of my very good friends in Mexico—Luis Macías Arellano, Chief of the Departmento de Caza; Enrique Beltrán, Director of the Instituto Mexicano de Recursos Naturales Renovables; and Bernardo

Villa R., mammalogist in the Instituto de Biología. My demands on their patience and hospitality were outrageous; yet they unfalteringly responded to my every call for help.

With the following *compañeros* I shared many a cheerful campfire: Leopoldo Hernández M. and Helmut Wagner, who were my assistants during the first year and a half; James D. Anderson, William Burt, William H. Elder, Wynn G. Freeman, Norman Hartweg, Floyd Johnson, Chester Lamb, Victor Lewin, Robert A. McCabe, Alden H. Miller, A. Wendell Miller, Frank A. Pitelka, Ward C. Russell, Peter Schramm, Charles W. Schwartz, Aaron J. Sharp, Robert H. Smith, and David L. Spencer.

The manuscript was read, in part or in whole, by Rollin H. Baker, Enrique Beltrán, Seth B. Benson, Walter F. Crissey, Emmett T. Hooper, Luis Macías Arellano, Alden H. Miller, Oliver P. Pearson, George B. Saunders, Charles W. Schwartz, and Bernardo Villa R. These friends and professional associates eliminated many a technical error from the text. Miss Dorothy Huggins of the University of California Press did a superb job of editing the manuscript. Gene M. Christman is largely responsible for the excellence of the maps and for the careful labeling of the figures. Don R. Medina and George Bryan, Jr., assisted in putting the manuscript in shape for the printer and in reading proof.

Perhaps the man who helped me the most was the *campesino* who always appeared in camp before the first tent stake was driven, who guided and directed and assisted me in everything I wanted to do, and who sat on his heels for hours watching me skin specimens and answering my every question expansively and with gracious good will. In him I had the fountainhead of knowledge about local wildlife.

PART I

The Wildlife Resource
and Its Management

CHAPTER 1

The Mexican Landscape

In all the world there is no kind of wild animal that is universal in its distribution or uniform in its abundance. The realization that all wild species are adapted to live only in specific environments comes to each of us at an early level of education. Thus, any schoolboy can tell you that tigers creep about in the jungle and polar bears are found bobbing along on cakes of ice in the Arctic. At a more advanced stage most people learn that deer live in forests and brushlands and antelope frequent the open plains. The outdoorsman goes still farther and comes to know that deer prefer certain types of forest, and should he be a hunter he will go to those very choice spots to seek his quarry, recognizing them at a glance as superior deer range. The scientist who studies wild animals pursues the point yet one more step and tries to analyze item by item the components of the habitat that make it possible for various kinds of animals to exist there; he is coming to understand how the particular combinations of food, cover, and water govern the composition and density of animal populations.

Thus, everyone, at his own level of understanding, recognizes that the nature of the landscape affects the distribution of animals.

But landscapes are not stable entities. A forest can be cleared and planted to corn so that it no longer is habitat for deer but becomes a home for doves, quail, and rabbits. The cornfield in turn can erode into a series of raw gullies that support no animals at all. The impact of human activity upon the land may substantially alter the native animal life.

In considering the status of wildlife in a large and varied region such as the Republic of Mexico, one should start with an understanding of the major types of habitat as they originally existed. It is the purpose of this chapter to describe these habitats. The second chapter of the book considers the significant changes in the vegetation, soil, and water that have accompanied man's occupation.

The importance of this approach to the study of animal distribution and animal conservation cannot be overemphasized. A serious defect of much of the past effort in wildlife management has been the overemphasis on protecting animals from obvious sources of loss, such as hunting and predation, and a corresponding underemphasis on preserving a proper home in which the populations can live and reproduce.

PHYSIOGRAPHIC REGIONS OF MEXICO

As a basis for dividing Mexico into component types of game range I have used natural vegetation zones. Since the vegetation pattern is governed by topography and climate, I shall give a brief exposition of these physical features of the habitat. Figure 5 presents a rather simplified classification of the main physiographic regions of Mexico.

The states of Sonora and Baja California in northwestern Mexico are mostly low desert with very little mountainous country. In northern Baja California the Sierra Juárez and Sierra San Pedro Mártir are essentially southward extensions of the Laguna Mountains of southern California, and practically the whole flora and fauna of the Lagunas enters this corner of Mexico. On the southern tip of the peninsula is a small uplift, called the Sierra San Lázaro. There is a low escarpment along the eastern slope of Baja California—the Sierra de la Giganta—and a few scattered volcanoes rise above the sweltering sands of Sonora; but otherwise the northwest corner is flat, hot, and dry.

The Central Plateau of Mexico is a slightly tilted tableland the lowest part of which is along the United States border and the highest part in the southern sector, from central Jalisco to western Hidalgo. This plateau is characterized by low rainfall, which produces a desert type of vegetation for the most part; but it is broken by many small mountain ranges a number of which are high enough to have somewhat more luxurious plant growth. It is bordered by two substantial mountain chains—the Sierra Madre Occidental on the west and the Sierra Madre Oriental on the east, each of which drops down more or less steeply to coastal plains on the Pacific

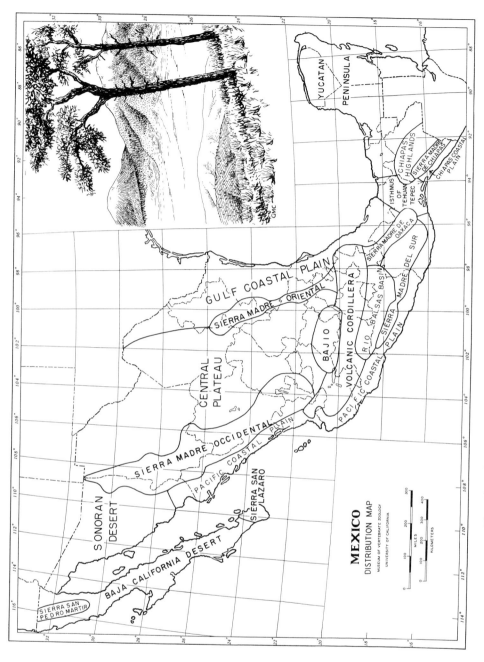

Fig. 5. Physiographic regions of Mexico. Modified from Tamayo, *Geografía general de Mexico*, 1949. Mexico may be grossly divided into twenty physiographic regions.

Map labels

MEXICO
DISTRIBUTION MAP
MUSEUM OF VERTEBRATE ZOOLOGY
UNIVERSITY OF CALIFORNIA

MILES
KILOMETERS

SONORAN DESERT
BAJA CALIFORNIA DESERT
SIERRA SAN PEDRO MARTIR
SIERRA SAN LAZARO
SIERRA MADRE OCCIDENTAL
PACIFIC COASTAL PLAIN
CENTRAL PLATEAU
GULF COASTAL PLAIN
SIERRA MADRE ORIENTAL
BAJIO
VOLCANIC CORDILLERA
RIO BALSAS BASIN
SIERRA MADRE DEL SUR
SIERRA MADRE DE OAXACA
ISTHMUS OF TEHUANTEPEC
CHIAPAS HIGHLANDS
SIERRA MADRE DE CHIAPAS
CHIAPAS COASTAL PLAIN
YUCATAN PENINSULA

and Gulf sides, respectively. The northern tip of the Sierra Madre Occidental falls off to the Sonoran Desert.

To the south, the Central Plateau dips into a shallow basin called the Bajío—one of the richest agricultural areas in Mexico. The Bajío in turn is bounded on the south by the Volcanic Cordillera, a transverse zone of recent volcanism in which occur all the great volcanoes of Mexico and literally thousands of smaller ones. The Valley of Mexico is one of many closed basins within this galaxy of cones. Yet to the south of the Volcanic Cordillera is the great inland basin of the Río Balsas, draining to the Pacific. It in turn is bounded on the south by the Sierra Madre del Sur and on the east by the Sierra Madre de Oaxaca.

The coastal plains of the east and west merge in the Isthmus of Tehuantepec, a narrow strip of land between the two oceans so low in elevation that it has been considered from time to time as a possible site for an interoceanic canal. In terms of plant and animal distribution the isthmus is quite obviously the connecting link between the biotas of the two coastal regions.

To the east of the isthmus, the Chiapas highlands and the Sierra Madre de Chiapas (another area of considerable volcanism) adjoin the mountainous zone of Guatemala. North of this uplift is the great Yucatán Peninsula, a flat limestone country, most of it scarcely above sea level.

Adding up these various physiographic units, one finds that most of Mexico, west and north of the isthmus, is high country well above sea level (above 5,000 ft.), where the climate is temperate and the winter season well marked. Even below the isthmus there is a substantial temperate upland in Chiapas. Thus, in spite of the southerly latitude, the frost-free tropics are confined chiefly to the coastal strips and to the Yucatán Peninsula, with the exception of the Río Balsas Basin, which represents a deep penetration of the tropics into the interior. Figure 7 shows the distribution of tropical and temperate regions. By planimeter measurement it appears that only about 30 per cent of Mexico is tropical, 70 per cent of the country supporting the types of vegetation characteristic of temperate northern regions.

The animal populations are distributed correspondingly. In most parts of the country the birds and mammals are those of the temperate zone, and a good many of them range into the United States. Some typical examples are the coyote, the jackrabbits, the scaled and Montezuma quails, the mourning dove, and the band-tailed pigeon. The strictly tropical fauna, although rich in species, is limited to a much smaller range. The monkeys, brocket deer, tapir, tinamous, curassows, and many others are specifically restricted to the tropical zone as shown. There are in addition a few highly adaptable species that seem to thrive in both zones—the white-tailed deer, mountain lion, bobwhite, and white-winged dove, for instance; but in

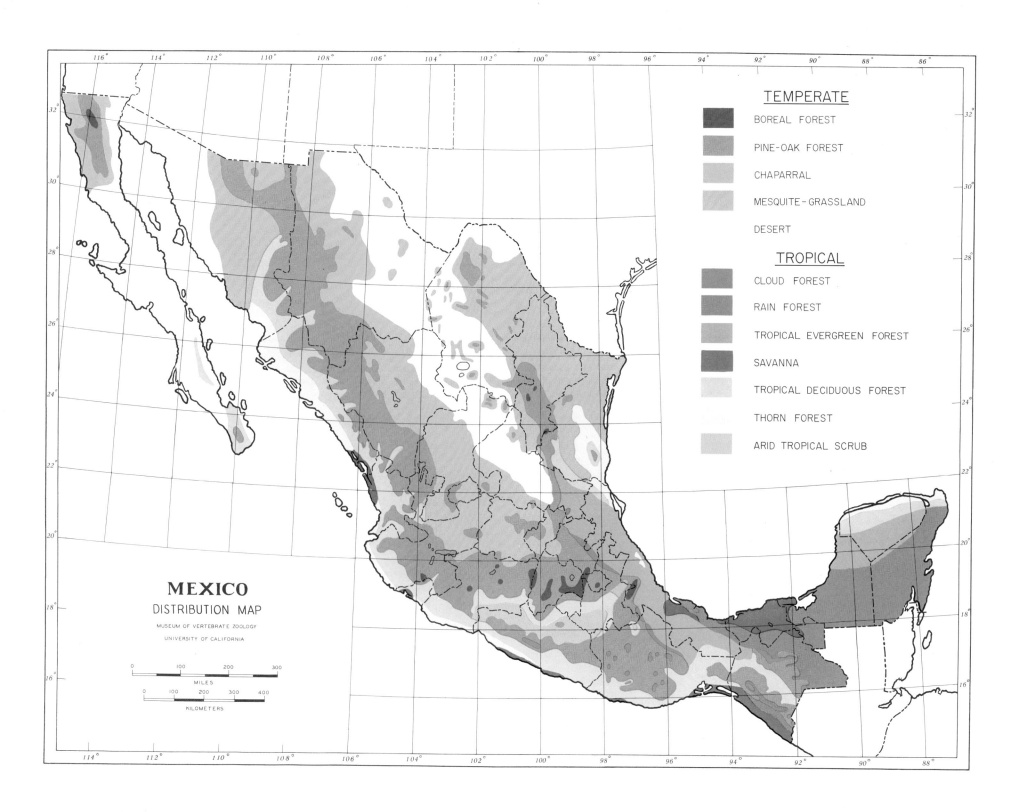

TEMPERATE

BOREAL FOREST

PINE-OAK FOREST

CHAPARRAL

MESQUITE-GRASSLAND

DESERT

TROPICAL

CLOUD FOREST

RAIN FOREST

TROPICAL EVERGREEN FOREST

SAVANNA

TROPICAL DECIDUOUS FOREST

THORN FOREST

ARID TROPICAL SCRUB

MEXICO

DISTRIBUTION MAP

MUSEUM OF VERTEBRATE ZOOLOGY

UNIVERSITY OF CALIFORNIA

0   100   200   300

MILES

0   100   200   300   400

KILOMETERS

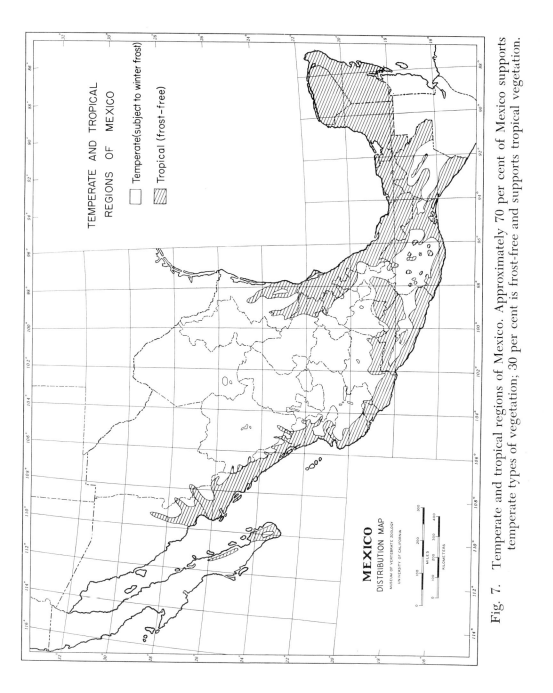

TEMPERATE AND TROPICAL
REGIONS OF MEXICO

☐ Temperate(subject to winter frost)

▨ Tropical (frost-free)

MEXICO
DISTRIBUTION MAP
MUSEUM OF VERTEBRATE ZOOLOGY
UNIVERSITY OF CALIFORNIA

MILES

KILOMETERS

Fig. 7.   Temperate and tropical regions of Mexico. Approximately 70 per cent of Mexico supports temperate types of vegetation; 30 per cent is frost-free and supports tropical vegetation.

Fig. 6.   The vegetation zones of Mexico.

general these are in the minority. In short, as a result of topographic uplift one can characterize the Mexican fauna as chiefly temperate and only locally or secondarily tropical.

DISTRIBUTION OF RAINFALL

As implied above, temperature is the determining factor separating tropical from temperate zones, and temperature is governed as much by altitude as by latitude. But within both the tropical and the temperate zones there is a gradient in rainfall which greatly affects the vegetation and hence the nature of the habitat for animals.

Figure 8 is a simplification of the detailed rainfall map prepared in the office of the Secretaría de Recursos Hidráulicos for inclusion in Jorge L. Tamayo's fine atlas of 1949. It can be seen at a glance that northern Mexico is dry, the southeastern region is very wet, and the central sector is a mixture of dry and wet areas conforming to the complications of topography already discussed. I shall make no effort here to elaborate the meteorological and orographic causes of this distribution of moisture—for that the reader is referred to Tamayo (1949, Vol. 2). Our concern is with the result, as expressed in plant growth. Looking ahead to the vegetation map (fig. 6), one can see in the rainfall pattern (fig. 8) a dominant regulatory force that molds the biotic nature of the countryside. The pattern is echoed in the range maps of many of the individual game species.

VEGETATION ZONES

The present classification and map of Mexican vegetation were byproducts of the first few years of the wildlife survey. The objective has been to subdivide the country into natural biogeographical units, thereby simplifying consideration of the problems of wildlife distribution and wildlife conservation. Selection of the twelve vegetation types was governed mainly by my own observation in the field. But in tracing the distribution of types, full use was made of the botanical literature and of generous personal advice from several field botanists thoroughly familiar with the Mexican flora, particularly Aaron J. Sharp, Charles L. Gilly, Howard S. Gentry, and Faustino Miranda. Results of this endeavor were first published as a separate article in the journal *Ecology* (Leopold, 1950). A Spanish translation by Luis Macías Arellano appeared two years later in the *Boletín de la Sociedad Mexicana de Geografía y Estadística* (Leopold, 1952). The account which follows is an abbreviated summary of the original article.

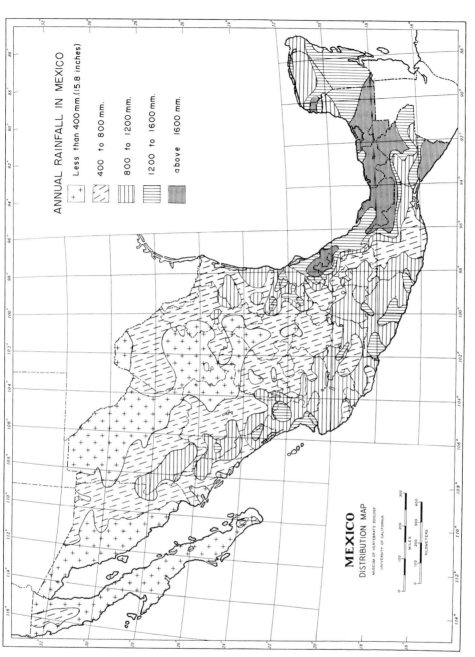

Fig. 8. Distribution of annual rainfall in Mexico. Map drawn from data presented by Tamayo (1949).

The map (fig. 6) has been corrected in a number of details but is essentially unaltered in its general form.

Each vegetation type, as defined here, is actually a composite of many recognizably distinct plant communities, some of which are described hereafter. I admit to having made many arbitrary decisions concerning the line of division between adjoining types and the type in which to include a given community. Also, there are countless areas of intergradation between types which are not shown on the map. Local juxtaposition of types is of great importance to game, as where fingers of mesquite reach across the desert or patches of manzanita occur on dry south exposures within the pine-oak uplands. These conditions must be understood, but they cannot be indicated on a small-scale map.

TABLE 1

ApproxImate Areas and RainfALL of the VegetaTion Zones

Zone	Percentage of total land area	Approximate area (in sq. mi.)	Range of annual rainfall (inches) [a]
TEMPERATE			
Boreal forest	0.5	3,800	30– 74
Pine-oak forest	25.8	195,600	18– 70
Chaparral	1.2	9,100	14– 30
Mesquite-grassland	21.6	163,700	9– 36
Desert	23.1	175,100	2– 15
TROPICAL			
Cloud forest	0.5	3,800	70–200
Rain forest	7.3	55,300	60–200
Tropical evergreen forest	5.5	41,700	36–112
Savanna	0.9	6,800	34–100
Tropical deciduous forest	9.1	69,000	24– 60
Thorn forest	3.2	24,300	16– 34
Arid tropical scrub	1.3	9,800	12– 28
	100.0	758,000	

[a] From data presented by Contreras Arias (1942).

Nor are the changes in vegetation resulting from human occupation shown on the map. The Valley of Mexico is designated as "pine-oak forest" although it is now stripped of its trees (as are also the hills around Zacatecas, Pachuca, Taxco, and several hundred other cities). The tropical forests of Yucatán have been almost entirely reduced to second-growth scrub by the age-old Mayan system of rotating milpas (Paynter, 1955 : 14). These secondary changes in the landscape are considered in chapter 2. The map is meant to show original climax vegetational types.

Certain well-defined types of unquestioned ecological significance are not recognized, because their distribution is too limited to map in small scale. Some of these are listed on the following page.

1. Arctic-Alpine meadows on the crests of major volcanoes.
2. The xeric vegetation of lava flows (under edaphic rather than climatic control).
3. Littoral communities such as salt marsh, mangrove swamp, and dune grassland.
4. Aquatic communities.

The mangrove swamps in particular are of importance as game habitat; they extend up the Gulf coast to southern Tamaulipas and up the Pacific coast to Tiburón Island, Sonora, and Santa Rosalía, Baja California.

The accompanying table lists the twelve vegetation types and the area in Mexico occupied by each. The areas were ascertained by planimeter from the map.

The temperate and tropical series are each arranged roughly in order of decreasing humidity. On the whole, the frost line can be said to divide the two series, as suggested above; but this concept cannot be adhered to rigidly. In southern Tamaulipas, for example, where the temperate and tropical regions meet, there occurs an overlapping of the arid types in each series, with the result that temperate mesquite-grassland occupies a hot inland basin (the Río Guayalejo valley) surrounded by tropical deciduous forest and thorn forest on the cooler and more humid foothills. In southern Sonora the tropical deciduous forest reaches far up the Río Yaqui valley, but the Yaqui delta is temperate mesquite-grassland. Cloud forest and pine-oak forest intermingle in many places. In short, exact lines of demarcation between the temperate and tropical types are not always as evident in the field as the map might imply.

TEMPERATE VEGETATION TYPES

Boreal Forest

The Boreal zone in Mexico is confined to the high volcanic peaks that range across the country in the Volcanic Cordillera and to a few scattered peaks in the northern mountains—Sierra Madre Oriental, Sierra Madre Occidental, and Sierra San Pedro Mártir. Included in this zone, under the loose term "boreal forest," are all associations above the Transition Zone of Merriam (1898)—principally forests of the Canadian and Hudsonian zones. A few alpine meadows exist on the tops of the highest volcanoes, but the areas are too small to warrant separate treatment here.

Some of the dominant trees in the boreal forest of central Mexico are fir (*Abies religiosa*), Montezuma pine (*Pinus montezumae*), white pine (*Pinus ayacahuite*), Douglas fir (*Pseudotsuga mucronata*), alder (*Alnus* sp.), and the stunted alpine junipers (*Juniperus* sp.). Many of the forest stands are very dense; in these the ground cover is mostly mosses and lichens. But elsewhere the trees may be well separated with a heavy understory of shrubs or coarse bunchgrasses, the latter commonly referred to collectively as *zacate* or *zacatón* (genera *Festuca, Muhlenbergia,* and *Agrostis*).

In the Sierra San Pedro Mártir of northern Baja California the highest points support an impoverished version of the boreal flora of California, with such trees as white fir (*Abies concolor*), lodgepole pine (*Pinus contorta*), and aspen (*Populus tremuloides*) as dominants.

The boreal forest is of little importance as wildlife habitat, partly because it is of limited extent but also because few of the Mexican game species are adapted to live at high altitudes. The volcano rabbit (*Romerolagus diazi*) of the Volcanic Cordillera is the only species really typical of this zone, and it is very local in its range.

Fig. 9.   Boreal forest on the rim of the Valley of Mexico. The dominant tree is the fir, *Abies religiosa*.

Pine-Oak Forest

From the standpoint of game, and likewise of human economics, the pine-oak zone is the most important vegetational type in Mexico. It is also the largest. Many distinct communities are included, from oak scrub bordering the northern deserts to high pine forests intermingling with the lower fringe of the firs. Standley (1920–1926) lists 112 species of oaks in Mexico,

Fig. 10.   Pine forest (*Pinus montezumae*) with an understory of *zacatón*. View near Tres Marías, Morelos.

all of which occur somewhere within the zone. Likewise, of the 39 Mexican pines enumerated by Martínez (1945) all except a few boreal species occur here. Because of the great number of species and the numerous combinations in which they occur, I cannot offer a complete list of the communities comprising the pine-oak zone. All, however, fall into four general types: pine forest, pine-oak woodland, piñon-juniper woodland, and oak scrub.

Pine forest.—Dense forests within the pine-oak zone are usually made up chiefly of pines; oaks are subdominant where present at all. In central and southern Mexico, the commonest pine and the one most generally occurring in tall dense stands is *Pinus montezumae.* This species is important as far north as Durango in the western mountains and Nuevo León in the east. In the great pinelands of Chihuahua the closely related *Pinus chihuahuana* is dominant, and in the Sierra Madre del Sur the main species is *Pinus herrerai.* These are all yellow pines, similar in appearance and ecological requirements to the Ponderosa pine of the western United States. The white pines are in the main limited in distribution and importance in Mexico.

Pine-oak woodland.—Open, scattered stands are dominated by pines in some places, by oaks in others. Usually these woodlands occur between the oak scrub of low elevations and the high pine forest of the upper ridges. So many different species grow in this association that it is nearly impossible to call any particular combination typical. Between Chilpancingo and Omilteme, Guerrero, for example, the oak woodland is comprised of three species of oak (*Quercus acutifolia, Q. lanigera,* and *Q. candicans*), with scattered yellow pines (*Pinus herrerai*) on the more moist sites.

Piñon-juniper woodland.—The piñon pines (*Pinus cembroides* and related species) normally occur in scattered woodland stands on arid foothills or low desert ranges of northern Mexico. In some places they are mixed with junipers, or more rarely with scrub oaks or elements of chaparral (manzanita especially).

Oak scrub.—At the lower fringe of the pine-oak zone there is often a belt of stunted oaks, growing more like large shrubs than trees. In some places the oak scrub extends well into the interior foothill zone of Mexico, which is predominantly mesquite-grassland. Although the vegetation appears sparse and poor, this region often supports many or most of the game species characteristic of the upper pine-oak zone. For example, I have found the Montezuma quail (*Cyrtonyx montezumae*), a characteristic bird of the whole pine-oak zone, in little outpost clumps of oaks far out on the dry, treeless foothills.

Since early times, most of the human population of Mexico has lived in the pine-oak zone, with its healthful, temperate climate suitable for the cultivation of corn. As a result of this concentration, the forests, soils, wildlife, and other natural resources of the southern uplands have been severely taxed and in some localities almost wholly destroyed, while great areas of the tropics remain virtually untouched. The conservation problem in Mexico is greatly aggravated by reason of the uneven distribution of people and the heavy demands made on the pine-oak zone.

Chaparral

Typical California chaparral extends approximately two hundred miles down the outer coast of Baja California, between the mountains and the Pacific. In the coastal fog belt south of that point the brush gives way gradually to desert vegetation which paradoxically is laden with epiphytic lichens.

Fig. 11.   Oak woodland near Chilpancingo, Guerrero.

Some of the dominant genera of shrubs found in this formation are manzanita (*Arctostaphylos*), coyote bush (*Baccharis*), chamise (*Adenostoma*), wild lilac (*Ceanothus*), sage (*Artemisia*), and scrub oaks (*Quercus*). Several of these occur widely in other vegetation types, as for example the manzanitas and scrub oaks in the pine-oak zone; but nowhere else in Mexico except in the northwest corner does true chaparral cover a large enough area to be shown on the map.

As one might suppose, the wildlife of the chaparral zone is essentially that of southern California.

Fig. 12.   Chaparral near La Cienega, Baja California. The dominant shrubs here visible are of the genera *Ceanothus* and *Arctostaphylos*. Photograph by A. E. Borell.

Mesquite-Grassland

Included in mesquite-grassland are several well-marked plant communities which have in common a ground cover dominated by grasses, usually species of grama (*Bouteloua*). Along the eastern base of the Sierra Madre Occidental and on some high ridges and plateaus of Chihauhua and Coahuila the grama grasses form an almost continuous sod in which there are few woody plants or succulents. In northeastern Mexico and in some parts of Sonora the grama sod has always been interspersed with shrubs

Fig. 13.   Mesquite-grassland interspersed with oak scrub on moist slopes (foreground) and cottonwoods along a river near Casita, Sonora.

and low trees, the most important being the mesquite (*Prosopis*). Transitional between these two communities and the desert proper may occur a mixed desert-grassland vegetation which includes many species of cacti and yucca along with the grama and mesquite. The mesquite-grassland association was the original stronghold of the pronghorn antelope and the burro deer, but it is much depleted now from overgrazing by livestock.

An ecologically distinct kind of grassland, the Gulf coast bluestem prairie, is included in this type. Originally, the tall prairie grasses of southern Texas—mostly bluestems of the genus *Andropogon*, with cord grass (*Spartina*) in the low spots—extended well into northeastern Tamaulipas; but grazing and other disturbances have in many places destroyed the grass and permitted an encroachment of mesquite and shinnery oaks, so that much of the region now is brushland.

Desert

The great desert areas of northern Mexico support a good deal of vegetation and a surprising amount of game. Several kinds of desert communities are recognizable. Cactus desert, the richest in both plant and animal life, usually adjoins the lower edge of the mesquite-grassland. Dominant plants are the cacti and yuccas, and among them various kinds of shrubs and grasses are interspersed. In parts of San Luis Potosí, cactus desert offers fine deer hunting, and the so-called desert quails (scaled and Gambel) are especially typical of this vegetation.

The vegetation on the more arid desert is chiefly creosote bush (*Larrea*) and shrubs of similar habit. Closed basins subject to seasonal flooding support no vegetation whatsoever. Parts of these llanos or *bolsones* that are not subject to flooding may be covered with almost pure stands of *Hilaria mutica,* a rather wiry, unpalatable grass of little value to either wildlife or livestock.

TROPICAL VEGETATION TYPES

Cloud Forest

The cloud forest in Mexico is made up of two distinct elements—temperate montane hardwood or pine-oak forest and a tropical undergrowth of low trees, shrubs, herbs, vines, and epiphytes. Such combinations occur on temperate peaks or escarpments (usually above 5,000 feet) that are swept by moisture-laden air currents rising from tropical lowlands. Because the dominant trees are temperate species, the formation might well be included in the temperate rather than the tropical vegetation series. It is often called "subtropical forest" or "temperate rain forest" (Beard, 1944). Even though I well realize that designating cloud forest as tropical is equivocal, I include it in this category because the greater part of the biota consists of species usually identified as tropical. The character of the forest is determined more by the heavy tropical understory than by the overstory. Also, most of the vertebrates found in cloud forests are of tropical genera. The climate is usually cool and decidedly moist but the temperature never reaches the freezing point.

The total area in Mexico occupied by cloud forest is small. The most important distributional units, and those most resembling true Andean cloud forest, occur along the crest of the Sierra Madre de Chiapas and in the Chiapas highlands just to the north. Other sizable belts are along the eastern escarpment from Oaxaca to Tamaulipas and in the Sierra Madre del Sur of Guerrero. Local, unconnected islands occur on various peaks scattered over the Oaxaca uplands and in the Tuxtla range of southern Veracruz.

The montane element of cloud forest usually is dominated by species of

Fig. 14.   Desert near the city of San Luis Potosí.

pine or oak but may contain many temperate hardwoods of the Appalachian flora such as *Liquidambar, Fagus, Nyssa, Tilia,* and *Cornus* (Sharp, 1946). Typical of the understory are tree ferns (which sometimes attain a height of 30 ft.), *Podocarpus,* giant *Equisetum,* begonias, bromeliads, and orchids, along with various species of lianas and other vines.

Tree ferns are perhaps the best plant indicator species. The emerald toucanette (*Aulacorhynchus prasinus*) is a good avian indicator of the vegetation type since its distribution in Mexico conforms almost exactly to the area of cloud forest as I have mapped it.

Rain Forest

The low, humid tropics are here divided into three vegetational zones—two forest types and savanna. Rain forest has the higher rainfall and more

Fig. 15.   Cloud forest near Tutotepec, Hidalgo. Tree ferns are good indicators of this type of vegetation. Photograph by A. J. Sharp.

Fig. 16.   Rain forest on Volcán San Martín Tuxtla,
Veracruz. Photograph by C. W. Schwartz.

luxuriant growth of gigantic forest trees. Tropical evergreen forest is a little less humid, with dense but low stands of broadleaf trees. Here and there along the coastal plains these forest types are broken by patches of savanna. Many elements of fauna and flora occur in all three formations.

Rain forest extends into Mexico from the southeast, halfway up the Yucatán Peninsula and along the Gulf coast to southern Veracruz. Lundell (1934) gives an excellent description of the rain forest in northern Petén. Although several hundred tree species are represented, the three largest trees and the species "which characterize the major climatic climax associations in the northern Peten forests" are mahogany (*Swietenia macrophylla*), zapote (*Achras zapota*), and *ramón*, the breadnut tree (*Brosimum alicastrum*). Of these, the zapote is the most characteristic of the whole zone (Lundell, 1934). Many other trees, shrubs, palms, lianas, bamboo, and a host of epiphytic herbs occur in the understory.

Fig. 17.   Interior of tropical evergreen forest near Niltepec, Oaxaca. Photograph by A. J. Sharp.

Tropical Evergreen Forest

The tropical evergreen forest is much like the rain forest but not quite so tall or so dense. The two principal areas of this type are the coastal plain and foothills of Veracruz and Oaxaca, and the belt of low forest crossing the Yucatán Peninsula between the interior rain forest and the comparatively dry tip of the cape. The original climax type of forest has been almost entirely destroyed in Yucatán and has been greatly reduced in Veracruz and Oaxaca, with the result that these areas are now occupied chiefly by secondary stages of scrub forest.

The original type was probably a dry phase of the zapote forest with little or no mahogany and *ramón*. Many genera of trees are represented, a few of the dominants being, in addition to zapote, the "red cedar" of commerce (*Cedrela*), copál (*Bursera*), pochote (*Ceiba*), and various figs, palms, and legumes.

A good part of the tropical game fauna exists only in the rain forest and tropical evergreen forest associations. For example, the monkeys, tapir, brocket deer, pacas, and agoutis, and various pigeons, tinamous, and curassows flourish in such forests. In order to preserve all of these species it will be necessary to maintain in their undisturbed state some blocks of the heavily forested tropics.

Savanna

Tropical savanna is not a climatic climax type of vegetation. Savannas occur in only a few parts of Mexico—on flat coastal plains or in marshy interior basins—either as a result of edaphic conditions (poor drainage, etc.) or as an aftermath of early clearing, cultivation, grazing, or burning of rain forest or tropical evergreen forest. Man-caused savannas are not new; they apparently were extensive along the Gulf coast when the Spaniards first arrived. Bernal Díaz recounts some brisk battles fought with the natives near the present city of Coatzacoalcos in open savanna plains. This formation may occur in the heaviest rainfall belts, as along the coast of Tabasco, or in relatively dry situations, such as coastal Nayarit.

The dominant plants are coarse tropical grasses. Scattered trees may grow in the grasslands; these are most commonly palms or palmettos. The trees on a coastal savanna in northern Nayarit are palms and calabashes (*Crescentia alata*) and, along watercourses, figs.

Tropical Deciduous Forest

In the semiarid tropics the vegetation is of two principal types: tropical deciduous forest and thorn forest, the thorn forest growing in the more arid regions. These types are found mainly in the western coastal plain and foothill region, from southern Sonora to Chiapas. In general, the thorn forest grows near the coast, the deciduous forest on the more humid foothills below the pine-oak uplands. Smaller areas of deciduous forest exist around the periphery of the arid interior basin of the Río Balsas and along the borders of tropical evergreen forest in southern Tamaulipas and north-

Fig. 18.   Savanna near Santiago, Nayarit.

ern Yucatán. As the name implies, the deciduous forest loses its foliage during the dry period of the year.

In general aspect the tropical deciduous forest is an open, relatively low forest of stocky, broad-leaved trees, rather lightly draped with epiphytes and vines but assuming the tall, dense character of tropical evergreen forest along watercourses. A few of the dominant trees are the *copales* (*Bursera*), amapa (*Tabebuia*), morning-glory tree (*Ipomoea*), which is a favorite food of deer, palo blanco (*Lysiloma*), and various legumes.

Thorn Forest

Typical thorn forest in Sinaloa is a dense but scrubby vegetation, often only 20 to 30 feet high, dominated by thorny leguminous trees, particularly acacias. This type is characteristic of the coastal plains of Sinaloa and Nayarit, and continues down the coast at least locally to Acapulco, Guerrero. Other patches of thorn forest grow in Tamaulipas, Veracruz, and along the arid tip of Yucatán. Like the tropical deciduous forest, the thorn forest loses its leaves in the dry season and assumes a dreary and uninviting aspect. But with renewed moisture, many of the plants burst into bloom, and when the new leaves show, the countryside is sometimes exceedingly attractive.

Fig. 19.   Tropical deciduous forest near Acatlán, Puebla. Photograph by A. J. Sharp.

In addition to the dominant species of *Acacia*, a variety of other legumes grow in the thorn forest. Among these are members of the genera *Caesalpinia, Cassia*, and *Mimosa*, often interspersed with ponderous branching organ cacti.

Arid Tropical Scrub

The Río Balsas valley is a tropical inland basin, cut off from the sea by highlands. Rainfall is low, and the vegetation is decidedly xeric, resembling cactus desert in some places. Patches of thorn forest and tropical deciduous forest occur locally. There are also some extensive stands of tall bunchgrasses. But the sparse vegetation is dominated for the most part by organ

Fig. 20.   Thorn forest along the railroad north of Culiacán, Sinaloa.

cacti, opuntia, and thorny leguminous shrubs, among which the acacias are prominent.

The types of vegetation described above were the raw material of which Mexico was made. Of course even before the advent of man, the climax types I have described were not necessarily developed uniformly, for many natural influences tend periodically to disturb vegetation and to start new periods of succession. Fires, hurricanes, floods, ice storms, lava flow, ash fall from volcanoes, and the grazing of herd animals are some of the normal disturbances which always prevent stagnation of vegetation. Nevertheless, it is safe to say that throughout all the recent past these twelve climax types of vegetation have been present in most of Mexico, and in these the native animals of the country have evolved and flourished.

The activities of man inevitably have altered the natural habitats. In order to live, man must crop the products of the land—both natural and cultivated—and in so doing he reconstitutes the landscape.

Fig. 21.   Arid tropical scrub, heavily grazed, near
Poliutla, Guerrero.

CHAPTER 2

Land Use

The Mexican biota no longer conforms to its original or "natural" pattern. The mountains are still there, in jagged silhouette just as Cortés found them. The dry plains shimmer in the midday sun as they did when Cabeza de Vaca crossed them. The climate has modified only slightly, as far as we know. What has changed is the thin skin of topsoil and the plants rooted therein. All animal life is extremely dependent on vegetation, and the vegetation in turn is a product of soil and water. Man through his agriculture, grazing of livestock, clearing of forests, damming and diverting of rivers, draining of lakes, and building of cities, roads, and canals has so altered the face of Mexico that Montezuma, if he returned today, might not recognize his domain.

These changes have radically altered the habitat for wildlife. Some species, like the jackrabbit, have spread and multiplied as a result, but most are much reduced in range and numbers. Not only has the immediate nature of the vegetation and game habitat been altered, but over considerable areas the topsoil has been eroded, and the capacity of the land itself to produce vegetation and game has been reduced accordingly. Like other crops of the land, wildlife grows best on rich soils, and the productivity of game range declines as the soil loses its fertility.

THE HUMAN POPULATION OF MEXICO

The most serious problems of erosion and land destruction have developed as a result of the uneven distribution of the human population. Even before the Conquest, certain of the upland areas were heavily populated and agriculture was locally intensive. The Valley of Mexico was the center of the Aztec nation, and many thousands of people derived a living from the crops tilled on surrounding slopes and in nearby communities. Timbers, firewood, and other forest products were removed from the higher hills. Even at that early date the natural vegetation and virgin soils were being altered. Throughout the central uplands, where the climate was temperate and healthful and the soil was reasonably productive, the situation was similar. The mountains and arid lands of northern Mexico, where conditions for agriculture were relatively poor, never were densely populated. The tropics, on the other hand, were rich in moisture and level land, but life there was precarious by reason of the hot climate and the ravages of tropical diseases. Certain tribes, such as the Mayans, flourished in the lowlands; but on the whole, the tropics were not heavily populated.

After the Conquest, the European population tended to build up in the pattern established by the original Indian population. The Spanish ensconced themselves in the existing major communities, for only there could they obtain the labor and tribute which they sought. The Valley of Mexico became more and more congested as the capital grew. Dozens of other cities developed on the southern highlands, where the Indians already were living and where the gold and silver deposits happened to be. The countryside was intensively farmed, and the original pine-oak forests gave way to cleared fields, even on rocky and precipitous terrain. But the population in the arid and mountainous northern areas and in the tropics increased slowly. Thus today we find the greater part of the population of Mexico living in a transverse belt across the center of the country, from Jalisco and Michoacán to Veracruz (see fig. 22). It is here that the basic resources have been most severely taxed, and it is here that the decrease in wildlife has been most pronounced.

For an agricultural country, Mexico is woefully deficient in rich and well-watered soils. As a result, it has been the custom for centuries to clear mountain slopes, plant the new milpas to corn until the topsoil has washed away, and then abandon them for new clearings higher on the mountain. Some such plan of living is necessary for feeding the people, even at a subsistence level. It would be difficult indeed to change this custom in Mexico, even if the population were stable. Unfortunately it is not stable but is increasing more rapidly than that of any other country in the New

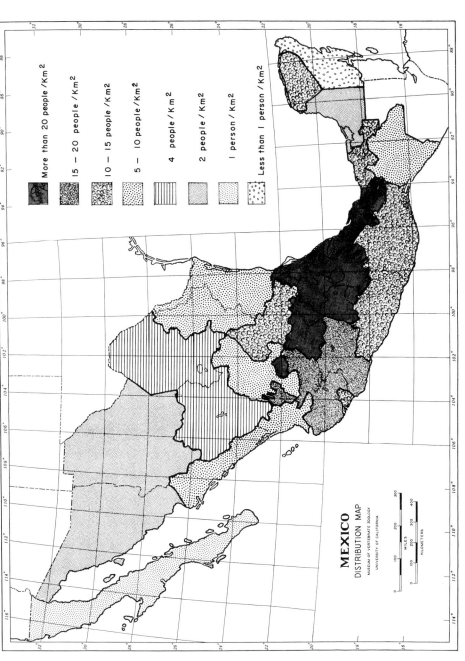

Fig. 22.   Distribution of the human population in Mexico. From Tamayo, 1949.

World. It has essentially doubled in the past fifty years. Table 2 shows the census figures from 1895 to 1952.

TABLE 2

THE HUMAN POPULATION OF MEXICO, 1895–1952
(From *Compendio estadistico—1953*, Dir. Gen. de Estadistica, México, D.F.)

Year	Population
1895	12,632,427
1900	13,607,272
1910	15,160,369
1921	14,334,780
1930	16,552,722
1940	19,653,552
1950	25,791,017
1952	27,283,148

This means that the demands upon the land are more severe each year. The people require not only more food but more fuel, more water, more fiber and lumber and power. In small part the need is being met by bringing into exploitation new areas in northern Mexico and in the tropics that were lightly used until recently. Thus the scourge of resource exhaustion is not only being intensified in the central uplands but is spreading throughout the nation.

Wildlife is affected not only by habitat deterioration but by direct use as well. When people are hungry they will use every facility to get the next meal. As a rule, in Mexico game is taken at any time and in any quantity that can be had, game laws notwithstanding. Thoughts about saving a breeding stock for next year are academic. Thus the problems of population underlie all the woes of game conservation in Mexico.

AGRICULTURE

Land can be classified into categories of best use from the standpoint of long-term human welfare. According to slope, depth and structure of soil, inherent fertility, rainfall, and drainage wc can designate the highest use to which each acre should be put to yield the maximum values over an indefinite period of time. Thus a piece of flat rich soil may yield good agricultural crops forever if the crops are rotated and soil fertility is maintained, and if rocks and gravel do not wash down from surrounding uplands and cover it. Gently rolling bunchgrass hills in the semiarid interior can support moderate numbers of livestock indefinitely if the sod is not broken by overgrazing or by ill-advised attempts to convert the land to agriculture. Forest-covered mountains will yield timber products and dependable supplies of water for power and irrigation if the timber is harvested wisely and not destroyed by clearing, repeated burning, or overgrazing. The productivity of each of these land types for game is dependent upon the manner in which the land is used, the highest game populations being sustained by land that is used conservatively and preserved from erosion and desiccation. Good agricultural lands yield quail, doves, and other small

Fig. 23.   Rich agricultural land in the Bajío, near León, Guanajuato.

game as long as the soil remains fertile and productive. Arid grasslands and mountain forests support antelope, deer, and other game species if the vegetational cover which protects the soil is maintained intact. Soils that erode and lose their fertility no longer offer the food and cover needed by the game, and populations inevitably decline.

Unfortunately, the pressures of immediate human needs frequently impose upon the land destructive and shortsighted plans of use which in the long run are enormously deleterious to human interests as well as to wildlife. Once erosion is allowed to start, it is difficult to curb. And the effects may be ramified and complex. For example, a mountainside which should be retained in forest is cleared to grow corn because the people in the

Fig. 24.   Poor agricultural land near Teloloapan, Guerrero.
This cornfield has lost nearly all of its soil. The
land should never have been plowed .

nearby village are "land hungry"—they have not enough valley land on which to raise food for all the people of the village. The shallow layer of rich soil which supported the forest and was held in place by it soon washes down to the valley floor. Temporarily the valley fields are enriched; but subsequent floods carry gravel and raw subsoil and deposit them in a sterile blanket over the good land, thereby reducing the productivity of the valley itself. The original clearing on the mountainside no longer will grow crops; so new slopes are cleared of forest to compensate for the fields just abandoned and for the reduced yield of crops in the valley. Floods and erosion increase, and each year the village is worse off from the standpoint of food. Finally, all the mountains within reach of the village are cleared—there is no new land. The stream which originally ran throughout the year now is a roaring flood during the wet season and disappears during the dry period. The village itself gradually disappears as the people drift away to apply this design for living to some new area. Downstream other villages are plagued by recurrent floods, and the irrigation and power dam built at great expense by the federal government fills rapidly with silt. The siltation of the impoundment and the loss of the productivity and buying power of the village eventually will affect industry and the whole national economy. This is not a hypothetical case but is precisely what is happening in many parts of the Mexican highlands.

How does this process relate to game conservation? It is manifest to any hunter that there are few if any deer on bare, gutted mountain slopes, only scattered coveys of quail in the gravel beds of the valley where formerly there were hundreds around the edges of rich fields, and no ducks in the drought-ridden lowlands where ponds and irrigated fields used to be. In this situation, game laws and administrative decrees are of less than academic interest. Conservation of game is dependent first and foremost upon conservation of the game environment—the land, the vegetation, and the water.

By searching the early literature for original descriptions of Mexican localities and revisiting these spots one could track down dozens of specific instances in which forest lands have been reduced to impervious rock or hardpan by cultivation. For example, when Alexander von Humboldt visited the Valley of Mexico in 1803 he described in detail the beautiful pine and oak forests that covered the hills north of the valley. At that time only the lower slopes had been cleared. Subsequently the forests were completely removed from the hills, and agricultural crops were grown until the soil would no longer support them. Initially, corn or wheat probably was planted on the new fields. When the topsoil was gone, the land was planted to maguey, the sturdy agave which can grow even in parched subsoil. Years of maguey culture finally reduced the land to bare and impervious hardpan, and cultivation was abandoned. Since then, burros and goats have grazed the scant xerophytic vegetation, until no recovery of the natural flora is possible. Thus the hills where Humboldt passed through lofty forests have been turned into the wastelands shown in figure 25. There is now, of course, no game at all.

Hernando Cortés characterized the Valley of Oaxaca as the most beautiful valley he had seen in Mexico; today it is a badland of red gullies. Early descriptions of the mines of Pachuca, Zacatecas, and Taxco speak of easily available timber near by for mine props and firewood; now it is many miles from any of these cities to the nearest remnant of forest. For additional voluminous evidence of land degeneration in the Mexican uplands the reader is referred to Vogt (1946), Beltrán (1946), and Gill (1951).

In parts of Mexico other than the southern uplands, erosion resulting from agriculture is spotty and less universal. Some of the steep slopes

Fig. 25.   Site of a rich pine forest near Mexico City described by Humboldt in 1803. Erosion following clearing, plowing, and grazing has left a biological desert.

along the eastern escarpment are being gutted by transitory agriculture of a sort fully as damaging as anything to be found on the temperate uplands. A traveler on the Pan-American Highway will see between Tamazunchale and Jacala mountainsides approximating 100 per cent in slope (45°) stripped of their forests and planted to corn (fig. 26). These fields are abandoned in four to five years and new lands are cleared, in the manner described above.

In Yucatán, the Mayan system of rotating milpas has been in effect for centuries; but the over-all damage to the land is less devastating here, because of the flatness of the terrain. Near Xocempich, Yucatán, where we camped for two weeks, the rotational period is about twenty-five years. A cornfield is cut out of the *monte* and the slash is burned. For two years thereafter corn will grow with little or no cultivation. During the third and fourth years vines and brush choke the field, greatly reducing the yield. The field is abandoned by the fifth year and is then left for twenty-five years,

Fig. 26.   Transient cornfields on steep slopes above Chapulhuacán, Hidalgo. Photograph by A. J. Sharp.

during which time the forest becomes reëstablished and some organic matter is restored to the soil. Thereupon the cycle is repeated. In mountainous country this system would be disastrous; but on the flat, pock-marked terrain of the peninsula, erosion results merely in the shifting of soil into hollows and coves in the limestone surface. Since there is no surface drainage, the soil does not reach the sea. Nevertheless, the second-growth forests are poor in vertebrate life and yield no timber.

The semiarid regions of northern Mexico are sparsely populated, but around each village are fields many of which are eroding. In the mesquite-grassland and oak-scrub of the foothills, "dry farming" is practiced extensively, often resulting in destruction of the soil. Fields that are too flat to suffer from water erosion are subject in the dry seasons to wind erosion such as occurs in the climatically similar dust bowl area of the west-central and southwestern United States. In northern Mexico as a whole, land destruction resulting from poor agricultural practices is local and of minor importance compared with that in the southern uplands.

Where water is available in the semiarid areas the flatlands are irrigated, and in these situations crop yields may be high if irrigation is done properly. Some extensive and important land-reclamation projects have been developed in central and northern Mexico in recent years by the wise use of available water resources. The Yaqui Valley in southern Sonora is an outstanding example. Waters from the Yaqui River were diverted onto a flat cactus and mesquite plain southwest of Ciudad Obregón, and a rich agricultural community has developed in an erstwhile barren desert. This represents real progress in Mexico's agricultural program, and from the standpoint of wildlife conservation it has been an important gain. Migratory waterfowl by the thousands winter in the rice and other grainfields of the Yaqui Valley where formerly a duck could not so much as get its feet wet. Gambel quail are numerous along ditches and around field borders. Similar but less extensive irrigation projects are being developed elsewhere in northern Mexico, both along the coasts and in the interior. In the arid tropics of the Río Balsas Basin, and likewise on the southern coastal plains, are great sugar and rice plantations, irrigated by waters from the temperate uplands. The national Secretaría de Recursos Hidráulicos is quite properly emphasizing land reclamation through irrigation. But it must be remembered that the future of all irrigation projects is contingent upon a continuing supply of water, and it is not enough merely to build dams and ditches on the assumption that existing rivers are permanent fixtures of the landscape. The mountains from which the rivers spring must be protected from erosion and desiccation in order to safeguard the sources of the water supplies. Rivers that are running now will not necessarily be running a hundred years hence if the watersheds are destroyed by careless lumbering and fly-by-night farming.

Fig. 27. Irrigation ditch near Ciudad Lerdo, Durango. Some flat desert lands can yield good agricultural crops if irrigated; they will also support abundant wildlife.

Although parts of the arid tropics are cultivated by irrigation, other areas in the higher rainfall belts are tilled without the addition of artificial water supplies. Coffee is an important crop in the mountains of southeastern Chiapas and locally in Oaxaca. Bananas, pineapples, and coconuts are grown on the southern coastal plains, and sesame and chick-peas (*garbanzos*) along the western coast from Sinaloa to Guerrero. Sisal for rope fiber is the major crop on the tip of the Yucatán Peninsula. Smaller acreages of corn for local consumption are raised along with these cash crops. Where steep lands are tilled, erosion invariably results; but most agriculture in the tropics is on the relatively flat coastal plains, where the soil is subject to little washing. Furthermore, there are still extensive flat areas in the tropics which have not been cleared and which profitably could be developed for agriculture if adequate local labor were available. The overpopulation of the southern uplands is in great contrast to the sparse population of the low tropics. Mexico can look forward not only to the irrigation of arid valleys and basins but to some agricultural expansion in the lowlands, contingent upon the control of tropical diseases and the encouragement of gradual migration of farm labor down from the uplands. But many tropical soils are fragile and must be used with the utmost care and reserve.

In summary, the human population and agricultural production have for four centuries or more been concentrated on the pine-oak uplands of southern Mexico. The continued increase of this population is forcing the cultivation of mountain slopes in the uplands and a spread of agriculture to the north and coastwise to the tropics. Shrinkage of the mountain forests is endangering the water supply, on which any permanent agricultural development must depend. The future welfare of wildlife is fully as dependent upon solution of the agricultural dilemma as is the welfare of the human population.

GRAZING

For the purpose of discussing grazing in relation to land conservation I shall divide the livestock operations into two types: those carried on by the big cattle outfits of northern Mexico, and the grazing of small herds of miscellaneous stock around farming communities anywhere in the country.

The major range for large-scale cattle operations is the mesquite-grassland and adjoining pine-oak zone in central and northern Mexico. Large-unit holdings of land (haciendas) are common and the raising of cattle is the principal industry. In this area, overgrazing is general but by no means universal. Around each ranch headquarters, near existing water sources, and on some llanos and flat mesas overgrazing is severe; the grama grass sod and the stands of desirable browse plants are deteriorating and in some places will soon be completely destroyed. In some localities erosion is severe; yet throughout the same region there are scattered areas that are grazed lightly or not at all. There has been no concerted effort to achieve better distribution of water, and numerous areas that lack natural water are unavailable to cattle. I have seen stretches of beautiful grama grass prairie in Sonora, Chihuahua, and Durango that are virtually untouched by grazing (see fig. 28). The same conditions of uneven utilization of forage were observed in northern Coahuila by Taylor *et al.* (1945). Although I have no real data at my disposal, I estimate that the total number of cattle now grazed on the rangelands of northern Mexico is not far in excess of the carrying capacity of the forage. But the range suffers because of the poor distribution of the stock. Some areas are overstocked; others, often on the same ranch, are understocked.

Overgrazing is not so serious a problem in the rangelands as in the vicinity of cities, villages, and agricultural communities in the southern uplands and arid tropics where countless small units of livestock are turned out to graze. This presents one of the most critical problems of land utiliza-

Fig. 28.   Scene west of Pacheco, Chihuahua. There remain some rich native grasslands in the mountains of northern Mexico, so far little altered by grazing. Photograph by R. A. McCabe.

tion in Mexico, and it will be very difficult of solution. Practically every *campesino* owns a few head of stock—perhaps a burro or a couple of cows or oxen or a small band of goats. As a rule, the *campesino* lives in a village, cultivates a few acres near by on which he raises his own beans and corn; and he turns his stock out to graze where they may on the *ejido*, or communally owned tract surrounding the village. There is no control of the number or distribution of this stock on the range. As a result, the environs

Fig. 29.   Pock-marked hills near Toluca, Estado de México, which are eroding because of continued overgrazing.

of practically every village in Mexico are critically overgrazed. Where villages are close together the whole countryside may be picked clean by stock, so that regeneration of forests, perennial grasses, or palatable browse species is entirely precluded. Hillside erosion is serious, and the animals themselves usually are poor and emaciated. Near Lake Rodeo, Morelos, I saw boys who were herding small bands of goats spend several hours each morning cutting branches from the acacia trees for the animals to eat—there was no other food in the countryside, even for these voracious and unselective beasts. The fallen acacia branches were eaten down to stubs an inch or more in diameter, which the boys then carried home for fuel. Such hundred-per-cent utilization of all plant growth greatly accelerates the formation of secondary deserts, described above in the discussion of agricultural practices.

Needless to say, there is little game on the grazing lands near villages. Were it not for the fenced milpas there would be no small game whatsoever in many of the agricultural communities, except jackrabbits and ground squirrels, which thrive on overgrazed rangelands.

In the wet tropics, grazing is not a serious problem. The vegetation is so rank and grows so rapidly that stock cannot keep ahead of it. Also, most breeds of cattle do poorly in the tropics, and it is only recently with the introduction of Sabu and Brahma strains that any number of cattle have been kept in the wet tropics. Ticks are a pest on these ranges, both to the stock and to the human population.

Considering Mexico as a whole, the grazing problem, like that of agriculture, is centered on the southern uplands and adjoining parts of the arid tropics where the human population is the highest.

FOREST PRODUCTS

Mexican economy is dependent upon several types of forest products. In the realm of commerce, lumbering is a big industry and the gathering of chicle a minor one. Of greatest importance to the people as a whole, however, is fuel. All cooking and heating in the typical community is done with wood or charcoal, and the volume of wood consumed annually on the hearth fires of Mexico must run into millions of cubic feet. Moreover, houses of most of the inhabitants are constructed of unmilled wood products in combination with adobe.

Cutting of logs and timbers started long before the Conquest, but it had little effect on the distribution of forests until the Spaniards initiated large-scale mining operations. At an early date, logging for mine props resulted in local timber shortages. Vogt (1946) quotes Fray Juan Agustín Morfi, who in traveling through Mexico in 1777–1778 observed numerous mining communities that were suffering because timber and firewood were no longer to be had in localities that once were completely forested. Humboldt speaks frequently of the alarming shrinkage of forests evident to him in 1803–1804. Until 1890, however, there were no commercial lumber companies in Mexico; production and utilization of timber products was merely a local matter. In the era of President Porfirio Diaz, when most of the rail lines were laid (1885–1910), commercial lumbering was initiated in the pine forests of Mexico, and the industry has continued to grow in scope and importance. For a time, transportation problems limited the extent of these operations, since railroad facilities were needed to move the logs and

Fig. 30.   Scene near Poliutla, Guerrero. Small game may be abundant in fenced milpas (right) and virtually absent from heavily grazed lands outside the fence.

lumber out of the forests and much of the timbered area was too rough for the laying of track. The recent introduction of the logging truck, which operates on inexpensive and rough roads, has made nearly all the pinelands accessible and has greatly accelerated the rate of utilization of the temperate forests.

Current logging practice is to strip an area of merchantable timber and leave the problem of forest regeneration to nature. In spite of an admirable set of forestry laws, logging in Mexico is still exploitative and there is no general public concern over the future of the forests. Few of the timber companies own any land. Logging rights are obtained by contract from the federal government or municipalities, and even under government

Fig. 31.   Forest land in eastern Michoacán being cleared for agriculture.

supervision cutting is wasteful and destructive, since the only objective is immediate profit. Even under this system of cutting, the pine forests would recover if left alone after the mill moved on, but this does not often happen. The penetration of a virgin pine forest in southern Mexico often is followed by local settlement of itinerant farmers along the logging roads— farmers forced to abandon their former lands because of erosion. Small fields are cleared in the cutover forest (and later are abandoned in turn when the topsoil is lost) and livestock are grazed throughout the year on or around these temporary farms. Woodcutters take advantage of the new roads to haul charcoal and firewood to the communities in the valleys. Fires occur with monotonous regularity, and as a result the forests do not recover and revegetate the mountains. There commences a rapid deterioration in the quality and quantity of forest products produced on the area and in the watershed cover. This process cannot be charged entirely against the logging operation as such but merely reflects the overpopulation of the southern uplands and the shortage of tillable land. The result, however, will be the eventual self-elimination of the logging industry when all the virgin stands of pine have been exploited.

The principal remaining virgin pine forests in Mexico are in isolated parts of the Sierra Madre Occidental and in some remote mountain areas of Michoacán, Guerrero, Oaxaca, and Chiapas. Mills now are operating in all of these areas and every effort is being made to get out lumber (currently selling at high prices) for the expanded program of building and industrialization being sponsored by the government. And rather large quantities of lumber are being exported to the United States and other countries.

It should be emphasized again that forests best serve human welfare when the timber products are used, and that there is no fundamental objection to logging as such. The point I wish to make here is that logging should be so conducted that it is a periodic harvest of the timber crop, not destruction of the forest. Future profitable harvests depend upon preservation of a growing stock of trees and a rich soil. Wildlife and watershed values are dependent upon the same conditions in the forest.

The logging of tropical woods, of which mahogany and red cedar are the most important, is generally a selective process and is accompanied by less obvious permanent harm to the forest. Transportation difficulties in the wet lowlands have prevented even the initial cutting of many valuable stands; but where logging has been carried on, the stands tend to regenerate more rapidly than in the dry uplands. The Department of Forestry checks logs at points of exit from the forest (usually at the mouths of rivers in which the logs are floated out) and is rather successful in enforcing the logging regulations that prohibit cutting of trees smaller than a certain diameter. Great areas of tropical forest have been cleared for agriculture.

Where rich flatlands are thereby brought under cultivation, the economic gain to the country far outweighs the loss of the forest. Steep lands and poorly drained bogs, however, should be retained in forests.

Chicle is an important forest product in the Yucatán Peninsula. The zapote trees (*Achras zapota*) are tapped by cutting a herring-bone pattern through the bark, much as rubber is harvested. The sap is then gathered in buckets and cooked down into chewing gum. The trees are left to recover before they are cut again. Too-frequent tapping is said to have killed some good stands of zapotes, but the tree is one of the dominant

Fig. 32.   Scene near Apam, Hidalgo. Local depletion of forests necessitates transportation of firewood for long distances.

species in the rain forest and it reproduces readily. Its fruit is an important food for wildlife.

No one who has traveled in Mexico need be reminded of the importance of firewood in the ordinary Mexican home. The pack trains of burros bringing *leña* or *carbón* from the mountains, the women gathering sticks to carry home in bundles, and the haze of blue smoke over each village in the morning are constant reminders that firewood, like water, is one of the basic necessities of Mexican life. In populous communities, again mostly on the southern uplands, the constant daily demand for wood has resulted in local depletion of the forests and in some places total annihilation of even the shrubs. Oak, being the most desirable fuel, both as charcoal and as split wood, usually is cleaned out of the forest first. When all the available oak is gone, pine and other inferior woods are utilized until they too become scarce. The only tree species to be seen on many of the hills around Mexico City is the introduced Peruvian pepper tree (*Schinus molle*), which because of its aromatic odor is considered unusable as firewood. All other trees have been cut.

Much of the deforestation of the southern highlands must be charged against the demand for firewood in greater quantities than the local forest can produce it.

WATER

Of all the resources of Mexico, water is perhaps the most precious. Even the best soils will not produce crops without it. Great quantities of water are needed for domestic use, for industry, and for power. And in the southern pine-oak uplands, where the demand is greatest, water is scarce indeed. In northern Mexico, where irrigable desert lands extend in all directions, there is hardly any water at all. Only in the tropical southeast is Mexican soil thoroughly saturated.

The natural deficiency of water in Mexico is being greatly aggravated by the misuse of land in the manner just discussed. Forested mountains and well-grassed foothills once soaked up the scant rainfall and fed it evenly into flowing streams or into the underground supplies. Today much of the sponginess of the earth has been lost and rain runs off the raw subsoil as off a tile roof. And while water tables are falling, destructive floods are increasing.

The Mexican government has been making a valiant effort to overcome the water shortage by building complicated and expensive dams and impoundments, power stations, canals, tunnels, and irrigation systems. Although these engineering structures offer immediate relief for some types of problems in some areas, they cannot in any way alter the basic problem of reduced infiltration and falling water tables. Nor can these improvements be looked upon as permanent, for if erosion and the silt load continue to mount, the reservoirs will soon be smothered in silt.

In any event, the vast bulk of agricultural land in Mexico will be unaffected by any of the structures now built or even being contemplated. For every hectare that will be irrigated below a new dam there are upstream in the highlands 1,000 hectares on which crops are baking in the Mexican sun. Therefore we must fall back on a program of land management, of revegetation of the slopes, and of erosion control on agricultural lands. The water must be controlled where it falls.

The steady desiccation of the uplands has had an enormous effect on wildlife. Drying of the rivers and springs has of itself rendered a good deal of former game range sterile and unproductive. The waterfowl, of course, have been most severely affected. The great interior wintering grounds

Fig. 33.   Silt-filled reservoir at Tuxpango, Veracruz,
its utility ruined by upstream erosion.
Photograph by A. J. Sharp.

of former years have shrunk almost to insignificance with loss of the marshes and lowering of the lakes. The Valley of Mexico was once a winter haven for clouds of ducks and geese; now only a few thousand visit there. The same is true of the lakes and marshes of the Bajío, the Jaliscan lakes, and the interior *bolsones* of Durango, Chihuahua, and Coahuila. Rivers that once fed these interior basins have of necessity been diverted for irrigation, leaving alkali flats where formerly the land was perennially wet. And so, because of the depletion of its water resources, central Mexico today has less game of all kinds and only a small fraction of the former waterfowl population.

WILDLIFE IN RELATION TO LAND USE

It is a safe generalization that vertebrate populations, including human populations, can exist in the highest density and in greatest health only on rich, well-watered soils. Erosion of the soil and deterioration of soil fertility inevitably reduce the capacity of the land to support livestock, and people. So also does loss of the water resource. Therefore, land use which leads to desiccation of the soil and depletion of soil fertility is a form of race suicide for the human population, and wildlife populations are dragged down in the process.

When the problems of soil and water conservation are considered from the standpoint of national economy, the need of adopting an adequate program of resource management is obvious. Wildlife, which is one of the secondary products of the land, would profit accordingly. For the permanent good of the country itself the mountains must be kept protected with forests in order to yield water for power and irrigation, and also lumber and firewood. The rangelands must be retained in sod to hold the soil and to feed the largest possible number of livestock. Only the relatively flat lands should be tilled, and if these are irrigated with water from the highlands, they can be cultivated intensively and profitably. This plan of land use would also result in the highest sustained populations of game. The expression "good land use is good game management" applies as well in Mexico as elsewhere in the world.

Until a general conservation program of this kind is adopted in Mexico, the other measures of game management discussed in subsequent pages will be effective for a short time only, if at all. In certain places and with some species, control of hunting is immediately necessary. Refuges will be useful in preserving migratory waterfowl and failing populations of big game. But these steps are only stopgaps when the forests, soils, and waters are dwindling away. No form of protection will produce game where the environment has been destroyed.

CHAPTER 3

Utilization of Wildlife in Mexico

Sport hunting in Mexico has throughout history been mostly a prerogative of the wealthy. The first Spanish viceroy, Antonio de Mendoza, seems to have been somewhat of a sportsman, for in 1540 there was organized a great hunt in his honor at a point in western Hidalgo where deer and antelope were abundant. The site of this excursion, now a stop on the national railroad, still bears the name Cazadero. The hunting tradition carried on through the centuries among the landed gentry, the well-to-do in the cities, and the governing classes. A good many Mexican presidents have indulged to some extent in hunting, among the most recent being Miguel Alemán. In the past thirty years, with the growth of a substantial middle class in Mexico, sport hunting has become more popular and much more democratic than formerly.

Hunting for food, on the other hand, has always been of considerable consequence among the poor of Mexico. It still is. The ordinary *campesino* cannot afford the guns and ammunition used in sport shooting, but he has long been adept at capturing game with primitive traps and weapons to supplement his meager diet. It is interesting to note in the 1953 *Compendio Estadístico* published by the federal bureau of statistics that 58 per cent of the wage earners of Mexico are classed as making a living in "agricultura, silvicultura, caza y pesca." The fact that hunting and fishing are considered part of the way of life of many rural residents, inseparable from farming and forest work, is a reflection of their economic importance.

In past years, game was hunted extensively for commercial purposes as well as for home consumption. Deer, ducks, hares, doves, and quail were sold on the markets for meat, and the hides of many native mammals were marketed for fur or leather. Commercial sale of game or game products is now prohibited by Mexican law, and although it still goes on, the amount of market hunting is shrinking steadily.

Of these three types of hunting—for sport, for food, and for commerce— hunting for food is by far the most important drain on wild populations. Sport hunting and commercial hunting have a comparatively minor effect on these populations. López and López (p. 594) in 1911 reached essentially this same conclusion.

But each type of hunting has its own significance. I shall discuss them separately in the pages that follow.

SPORT HUNTING

The upper-class hunting fraternity of Mexico developed high standards of sportsmanship and field conduct at an early date. The classic book on the subject, published in 1911 by López and López, expounds not only the joys and methods of the hunt but the ethics and mores of the true sportsman. This volume has been the bible of Mexican sportsmen ever since. Subsequent books on hunting by Imaz Baume (1938) and Morelos Herrejón (1952) have added strength and substance to the creed of López. The serious Mexican hunter generally has the best of equipment and knows how to use it. In Mexico, fine dogs are as much of a tradition as fine horses. And in marksmanship the Mexican sportsman is unexcelled.

But for all the venerable tradition, sport hunting is still limited to a comparatively small group in the country, although, as stated above, the number is growing rapidly. By way of comparison, the following figures on license sales in Mexico and the United States are offered.

	Sale of Sport-Hunting Licenses, 1954	Population, 1950 Census	Licenses per 10,000 Persons
Mexico	8,162	25,791,017	3
United States	13,746,861	150,697,361	912

Admittedly, the figures are not really comparable. In the United States, strict enforcement of the game laws has made it advisable—in fact, nearly mandatory—for virtually all hunters to purchase licenses, even landowners hunting in their own neighborhoods. Conversely, in Mexico the vast majority of the hunters cannot afford to purchase licenses and hardly need worry about the matter anyway, for the paucity of enforcement officers makes apprehension of unlicensed hunters most unlikely. Thus the number of permits (8,162) sold in Mexico in 1954 is no measure at all of the number of hunters in the country. However, it does suggest that a much smaller proportion of the public hunts for sport than in the United States. The multitude of unlicensed rural hunters are in general more concerned with meat than with recreation in their outings.

Deer are perhaps the most important game animals in Mexico in terms of sport hunting. The widely distributed whitetail is pursued by sportsmen everywhere in its Mexican range. Hunters from all parts of the Republic and from the United States make long and often expensive trips to reach localities where deer are abundant. Some of the more publicized deer hunting areas are the western mountains from Zacatecas to northern Chihuahua and Sonora, and sections of Coahuila, Nuevo León, Tamaulipas, and San Luis Potosí. However, deer are hunted for sport in every state in the country to some degree.

Peccaries are hunted along with deer but are rarely the primary objective

Fig. 34.   Jaguar killed near Santiago, Sinaloa, by a visiting sportsman. Big-game hunting often improves the economy of rural areas. Photograph by S. F. Ferreira.

of any hunting trip. The antelope, bighorn, and tapir were once popular game animals, but hunting them has decreased because they are now scarce and all three are legally protected. A few fortunate men of means enjoy the sport of hunting jaguars, mountain lions, and bears, with hounds. This is one of the more expensive forms of hunting and certainly one of the most exciting.

Waterfowl are second only to deer in the amount of hunting they attract. Near Mexico City there are many duck-shooting clubs that control the hunting rights on the best lakes and marshes. Along the United States border, especially in Baja California, Sonora, and Tamaulipas, American hunters enter Mexico in some numbers to shoot ducks and geese. There are clubs to accommodate these visitors. Elsewhere in the country wherever waterfowl congregate there is some hunting for sport, but the demand for shooting privileges is so slight that organized clubs are generally not necessary. The total number of waterfowl killed by sportsmen is negligible in terms of the hunting that goes on in the United States.

The hunting of upland game birds and small game mammals for sport is becoming increasingly popular. Quail, doves, hares, and rabbits are much sought by the newer generation of hunters, especially those who cannot afford to hunt ducks or big game or who are not in reach of them. Jackrabbits are perhaps the most important of the small game species. In various parts of Mexico, especially near Mexico City, Monterrey, Guadalajara, and Puebla, week-end rabbit hunts are coming to be a common form of recreation for city dwellers. It was partly for this reason that market shooting of jackrabbits —a fairly brisk business a few years ago—has been declared illegal. Most of the commercial shooting was close to the larger cities mentioned above, where the demand for sport hunting is greatest. Along the border, quail and dove hunting attracts a good many American sportsmen. Californians, especially, cross to northern Baja California for this type of sport, lured by the abundance of game and also by the long seasons, which extend at least two months later than corresponding seasons in California.

Considering collectively all forms of sport hunting in Mexico, the number of participants is still small and the levy upon the wildlife of the country is slight. Hence the generous seasons and ample bag limits, often commented upon by American sportsmen, are more than justified.

In terms of the economy and welfare of the country as a whole, it would seem that sport hunting could profitably be encouraged to expand. Wherever sportsmen congregate they spend money, and the local people profit accordingly. Payments for room and board, guides, services of all kinds, and rental of horses, boats, or other equipment all put money into circulation. Consider, for example, a village on the shores of Lake Texcoco, close to a concentration point for waterfowl. If a shooting club is organized and the birds are guarded for the recreational use of city sportsmen, the village in the course of a shooting season may profit by tens of thousands of pesos. If, however, the birds are shot by the villagers for food, or even for the market, the net gain is but a fraction as much. In other words, villages that utilize the wildlife of the vicinity as a lure for sportsmen are better off economically than those that use it locally for food. The greatest social value and cash value of wildlife lies in its recreational potential, not in the meat or salable products.

In the United States, recreational hunting and fishing are coming to be recognized as truly big business, influencing major industry as well as local economy. It has been calculated that in the year 1955 American outdoorsmen spent three billion dollars in pursuit of their sport. Much of this went to local communities where the game and fish were raised. Another large part went directly into industry for such things as automobiles, tires, gasoline, sporting equipment, and outdoor clothing. The whole economy of the country is favorably influenced by the strong development of this type of recreation.

In Mexico at the moment, sport hunting and fishing are still of limited importance, but they are growing. Everything possible should be done to encourage this growth. Sportsmen can become a medium for distributing wealth from the cities, where most of it is concentrated, to the rural areas where it is most needed. Even more important, perhaps, is the outside money that might be attracted into Mexico by visiting sportsmen. The Mexican government, of course, is fully aware of the economic value of the tourist industry, and much is being done to attract visitors—and dollars—into the country. But a large part of this effort is directed to improving transportation, hotel accommodations, and certain kinds of attractions, such as art galleries and archaeological sites. The interest of Americans in the out-of-doors is in most places being ignored. To be sure, the sports fisheries of La Paz, Guaymas, Mazatlán, Acapulco, and Tampico are well advertised, but little or nothing is being done to study their proper utilization or safeguard their future productivity. By the same token, the possible value of wildlife as a tourist attraction, to be hunted or just to be seen, is neither being properly exploited nor even investigated.

I can envision in Mexico a strong program of wildlife administration which would change the status of native animals from an incidental value to a major resource. The keystone to such a development is the management of most of the game for recreational hunting. Other objectives might be (1) preservation of abundant wildlife in well-distributed national parks and reserves where people can observe the native animals in their natural surroundings; and (2) a first-class natural history museum and a first-class zoo in Mexico City, with emphasis in both on the native animals. In my opinion these several ways to exploit the native richness of the Mexican biota would have incalculable value to the country—both economically and culturally. There is little indication as yet that Mexico is aware of this natural asset.

Fig. 35.   Beginning of a hunt at Tapalapan, Veracruz.
Photograph by C. W. Schwartz.

WILDLIFE AS FOOD

As things stand now in Mexico, the principal use of wildlife is as a supplement to the diet of farm folk. Few, if any, of these hunters purchase licenses. There are no records of their numbers or of the game they kill. The weapons may be bows and arrows, spears, simple homemade traps, slingshots, muzzle-loading shotguns and rifles, or modern breech-loading guns, especially the .22 rifle. But the aggregate drain upon the wildlife resource, especially upon deer and other big game, is enormous.

In virtually every community where we established a camp during the field survey we found one or more local hunters who did little else but hunt. Often we employed these men as guides or commissioned them to collect specimens. Most of them knew all about the kinds and distribution of local game and how to find it. Ordinarily they sold their kills for just enough to pay for ammunition and give them a scant living. Semiprofessional operators of this sort probably account for the most game.

The majority of *campesinos* hunt only occasionally, when conditions are favorable and farm work permits. But because there are so many such hunters the aggregate kill is very large.

Needless to say, year-round hunting of this type is carried on with little regard for the game laws. Most rural hunters, in fact, are in complete ignorance of the regulations and have no occasion to be troubled about the matter, since enforcement is virtually nonexistent in inaccessible areas. For the most part there are no self-imposed limitations on when, how much, or by what means game may be taken. In a few places local customs dictate the season of hunting. On Lake Pátzcuaro, Michoacán, the Tarascan Indians hold their first communal duck hunt on October 31, the day before the feast of Todos Santos, which corresponds approximately to the date of arrival of migratory waterfowl and bears no relation to the opening of the federal duck season, which is November 16. In the Sierra de Tamaulipas we detected a mild reluctance on the part of local hunters to shoot hen turkeys during the breeding season, although gobblers are hunted the year round. Generally, however, game is taken when it can be had, without regard to sex, age, or season.

The white-tailed deer is perhaps the most important species hunted for food as well as for sport. As a generalization it can be said that local deer populations are inversely proportional to human populations, the determining factor being hunting. Fawns and does are shot as freely as bucks almost everywhere in Mexico. Although deer have an astonishing capacity to persist under even the heaviest hunting pressure, their numbers can be severely curtailed by overhunting, as indeed they have been in most of

Mexico. With even a fair degree of protection, deer could be maintained in good numbers in much of the cutover forest land, both in the pine-oak zone and in the tropics. The potential yield of larger breeding herds would then be very much higher, both for sport hunting and for meat. Consider,

Fig. 36.   A successful hunter of southern Veracruz. This brocket deer will supply meat for several families. Photograph by C. W. Schwartz.

for example, the pinelands on the rim of the Valley of Mexico. They could support a substantial deer population that would bring income to the local villages from the city hunters in the vicinity and a substantial supply of meat as well. But as things are at present, continual persecution holds the number of deer at a very low level; thus no city hunters are attracted and the local hunters get few animals. In other words, a potential resource is being wasted by communities that can ill afford to waste anything.

Most other big game species in Mexico are less resistant than whitetails to overhunting and have therefore fared very badly. Antelope and bighorn have slowly but steadily been brought to the point of extermination in northern Mexico, mostly by meat hunters. Only a few remnant bands are left, most of them in inaccessible parts of Baja California and Chihuahua. Desert mule deer in the north and tapirs in the southeast are in nearly as severe straits.

It can be said, of course, that overhunting of big game is a socioeconomic problem, arising directly out of the low living standards of most rural Mexicans and the desperate need of those people for supplementary protein in the diet. As true as this is, the fact remains that a little husbandry of the wild ungulates would put far more protein on the kitchen table, and perhaps some pesos as well. A protection program for big game would necessarily begin as an educational undertaking, to show the people how they can profit personally by conserving the local breeding stocks of deer and other attractively large animals.

Though big game is universally overhunted for food, waterfowl and small game are not—the apparent reason being the discrepancy in yield of meat per cartridge expended.

Ducks, coots, and a few geese are taken for home consumption when they are down from the north. The kill consists of many small bags taken usually with one or two "pot shots" into flocks resting on the water. I watched a hunter near Alpuyeca, Morelos, discharge his muzzle-loading shotgun into a flock of pintails and teal after an elaborate stalk on the pond where they rested. He went home contentedly with three ducks. One day on Lake Rodeo, also in Morelos, a local farmer approached a flock of Mexican ducks with the aid of a stalking horse and killed two with his single charge. Near San Juan del Río, Querétaro, Helmut Wagner and I saw a youth stalking teal by stripping off his clothes and slipping through the water with tules tied to his head; he took six birds with two shoots. Much of the waterfowl hunting consists of small operations of this nature.

Small game contributes substantially to the supper pots of Mexico—more so than waterfowl, because of its more general distribution and availability. Practically all the species listed in this book, and many nongame species as well, are hunted to some extent for food. Cranes, turkeys, curassows, guans, chachalacas, tinamous, and all the quails and doves are considered delicacies. The larger rails and shorebirds are utilized locally. Opossums, monkeys, armadillos, agoutis and pacas, rabbits, hares, squirrels, and raccoons are trapped or shot in large numbers. Even the predatory animals, especially the cats, are eaten with relish. Every conceivable method of capture is used in taking these birds and mammals. I have seen box traps set for quail, clapnets used to catch mourning and white-winged doves,

Fig. 37.   Squirrel hunter near Omilteme, Guerrero.
The gun is a muzzle-loader.

horsehair nooses to snare small birds, and slingshots, spears, clubs, bows and arrows, and even hand-thrown rocks to kill other species.

Some of the species not usually classed as game are actually preferred items of food. On Laguna de Coyuca, Guerrero, our guide showed a decided preference for great blue herons and roseate spoonbills in his hunting, although ducks were abundant. Elsewhere in Guerrero, and also in San Luis Potosí and Chiapas, we learned that macaws and the larger parrots were preferred to many game forms. Songbirds, pocket gophers, wood rats, iguanas, and alligator tails are on the list of comestibles. The meat and eggs of sea turtles and some of the fresh-water turtles are eaten. Even large insect larvae, particularly of the maguey worm, and grasshoppers are painstakingly collected for the table. (Some of these insects, fried in deep fat and well seasoned are delicious.) Less appealing, to me at least, is the well-known liquor, *mezcal con gusano,* made in Oaxaca of maguey worms and the juice of an agave.

When one ponders the amount and variety of food obtained by the people of Mexico from native wildlife, it becomes clear that here is an economic resource of some importance. Many people obtain a fair share of their meat from wild sources. In places this drain on the number of smaller birds and mammals is grossly excessive, as it is on big game, resulting in local scarcity of many species. And yet over much of Mexico the aggregate kill is not really greater than the productive capacities of most species, which on the whole are far more fecund than is generally believed. The status of small game is usually dependent on the condition of the range, and the primitive and ineffective hunting by the local residents scarcely harvests the normal surplus. Could the people afford more ammunition, the harvest undoubtedly would be excessive over more of the country.

In other words, the use of wildlife for food need not be eliminated in Mexico, for this is one of its great social values. Certainly, however, it should be regulated.

COMMERCIALIZATION OF WILDLIFE

Under the third category of wildlife uses are included all organized business operations that involve the sale of wild animals or products derived from them. At the time this survey was begun, certain types of commercialization of wildlife were legal. The hides of deer and peccary could be marketed freely, hares and rabbits could be sold on the open market, and live quail could be shipped out of the country for restocking in the United States. Under the general game law of 1952 all trade in wildlife was declared illegal. The mere passage of a law, however, does not necessarily put an end to customary business transactions, and there is still enough

Fig. 38. Young hunters in southern Veracruz. Boys with
slingshots kill small mammals and birds for food.
Photograph by C. W. Schwartz.

commerce in wildlife products to be worth considering here. The present commercial kill of game in Mexico is limited and is by no means as important as the kill for home consumption. Much of the following account relates to conditions of a few years past when market hunting was more of a problem.

At one time, deer were hunted commercially in many parts of Mexico and venison was not an uncommon item on restaurant menus. To be sure, I saw it listed only once in Mexico City, but deer are scarce in that region. In Mérida, Yucatán, venison was served regularly in the best hotels, and I am told that it still is. A good deal of deer meat undoubtedly is sold locally, in the villages and pueblos; shooting for local sale thus adds to the general overhunting of deer.

Deer hides were legal items of commerce until 1952, and they found their way into the traffic in leather, which is big business in Mexico. In the period 1944–1946 I often saw stacks of dried, flat hides, sometimes fifty or more, in village stores or trading posts. The legalized trade in buckskin undoubtedly gave encouragement to deer hunting, although I suspect that the meat was of far greater importance to the hunter than the few pesos he obtained for the skin. Nevertheless, it was a very definite advance in Mexican conservation to have the trade in hides declared illegal. This was not easy. In 1936 the Dirección de Caza took such a step, but in 1939 the prohibition had to be withdrawn because it was very unpopular and virtually unenforceable (Zinser, 1936 and 1944). The general Ley de Caza of 1952, however, makes all trade in wildlife products illegal, and this regulation undoubtedly will remain in force.

Javelina leather is tough and durable and was used extensively in the manufacture of work gloves. In Sonora, and doubtless elsewhere, javelinas were hunted with dogs specifically for the market value of their hides. But this free commerce likewise was made illegal by the present law.

Shooting of waterfowl for market is no longer a brisk business, as it formerly was in certain parts of Mexico. The long and finally successful struggle to break the wholesale traffic in ducks deserves full consideration here, for it is one of the major accomplishments of the Game Department. By the terms of the 1936 treaty between Mexico and the United States, the use of migratory birds for commercial purposes was forbidden in both countries. Mexico promptly adopted legislation supporting the terms of the treaty, but enforcement of the new edict proved extremely difficult. In three principal areas—around Mexico City, in Guadalajara, and along the United States border—powerful local groups had built up a substantial trade in dead ducks, and efforts to interrupt this commerce were bitterly resisted.

In the Valley of Mexico and elsewhere within the environs of the capital (upper Lerma Valley, lakes near Apam, Hidalgo) ducks were killed in wholesale lots with an ingenious device known as an *armada*. This apparatus consists of a series of pipes or crude gun barrels buried horizontally in an embankment overlooking the water, the breech ends being connected with a small pipe or trough bearing a powder train. For several days ducks are baited immediately in front of the muzzles, until large numbers are feeding there regularly. Then each barrel is loaded from the muzzle with black powder and crude drop shot, and the powder train is laid connecting the barrels. At a moment when the maximum number of ducks is concentrated in the area of fire, the powder train is lighted, usually with an electric detonator, and all barrels are discharged in a matter of seconds. The one time that I saw an armada fired, the kill was about two hundred ducks, mostly pintails. This is said to be an average take. There is a substantial loss of cripples as well. A period of a week or more must elapse before enough birds will concentrate again on the bait to permit another shot. Localities where illegal armadas are mounted have always been closely guarded by the operators, and it is difficult and even dangerous to undertake an investigation. In 1940 the Game Department, under the directorship of Juan Zinser, attempted to clean up the armadas on Lake Texcoco, in the Valley of Mexico. A shooting scrape ensued in which several men were killed, including two deputies of the department. Help was not forthcoming from other branches of the government, and the department was forced to abandon its effort to enforce the law. Birds continued to be sold to restaurants or retailed "under the counter" in big public markets. A few were peddled openly. The corner of Paseo de la Reforma and Avenida de los Insurgentes in Mexico City was a favorite place to sell game of all kinds, and in the period 1944–1946 I often saw men waving strings of ducks at passing motorists and calling "*Patos!*" Some of this traffic persists even today.

In 1946 the effort to break the duck market was resumed with vigor by the new chief of the Departamento de Caza, Luis Macías Arellano. The pitifully small force of wardens was mobilized into a heavily armed flying squad that raided the armadas and confiscated many truckloads of equipment. The duck business became so risky and unprofitable that most of the big operations were abandoned. The day of the armada is essentially over.

Supplementing the kill by armadas, many ducks were taken with punt guns mounted in boats and with shoulder-fire shotguns. In the other two principal areas of duck marketing in Mexico (Guadalajara and along the United States border), and in numerous additional localities where a few birds are sold, the kill has been made principally with these smaller weapons. I personally observed punt guns being used on the following lakes: Tulancingo in Hidalgo, Pátzcuaro in Michoacán, Papayo in Guerrero, Cuatetelco in Morelos, and Texcoco in the Distrito Federal. Although less spectacular than armadas, these guns may in the aggregate have taken more birds. The relatively few ducks that come into the market today are shot mostly with small arms.

In 1951 evidence was uncovered of a substantial duck marketing operation which had its headquarters in Ciudad Obregón, Sonora. The organizers were Americans, and the birds (mostly pintails) apparently were taken by plane to some market in the western United States, presumably Los Angeles. Law-enforcement officials on both sides of the border applied such close scrutiny that the undertaking was temporarily discontinued, without any arrests being made. However, a sportsman from Hermosillo states that there is still some commercial hunting there.

Although the commercial duck kill in Mexico was rather large at one time, it could never, even in its heyday, have been credited with contributing materially to the total continental kill.

The commercial trade in small upland game has never been organized, like the trade in ducks, as a big business. Quail are sold in small numbers in the border towns, where American tourists pay high prices for quail on toast in the restaurants. Mourning doves and some whitewings are marketed in central and southern Mexico. Hares and rabbits were once important items of commerce in the larger cities.

All of this trade is now illegal, but it still goes on locally on a small scale.

The export of live bobwhites for restocking in the United States was an active business at one time in Tamaulipas and Nuevo León. But the introductions proved to be so unsuccessful that exportation of these birds was discontinued.

The systematic trapping of fur-bearing mammals is, curiously, undeveloped in Mexico. This is probably because furs from this southern latitude have a low commercial value. The southern river otter produces a fairly good pelt. A young man of Tierra Colorada, Guerrero, told me in 1944 that he trapped several otters each winter and that the sale price paid well for the trouble. I saw the pelts of other river otters taken for the market in various rivers of Chihuahua. Beavers and muskrats in small numbers have been marketed along the northern border where they occur. The hides of jaguar, mountain lion, ocelot, margay, bobcat, jaguarundi, bear, coyote, fox, and badger are sold, but most sales are incidental to the capture of the animals for other reasons. The smaller fur bearers such as the opossum, raccoon, ring-tailed cat, skunks, and the small mustelids supply pelts that are put to many home uses. Some of the pelts are taken specifically for sale. According to the 1952 law, the marketing of any of these pelts is now illegal; but it still goes on. Tanned jaguar skins, for example, are offered for rather substantial prices in such places as Mazatlán and Mérida. But whatever the law may be, no counterpart of the big fur industry in the United States, which supplies many a farm boy with spending money, has ever been developed in Mexico.

Alligators and, to a lesser extent, iguanas make up—in the tropics at least—for the low value of furs. So intensive is the hunt for alligator skins that the species has become extremely scarce in much of the lowland. Originally these interesting reptiles were numerous in the coastal swamps, rivers, and *lagunas* as far north as northern Sinaloa on the Pacific side and northern Tamaulipas on the Gulf coast. Commercial alligator hunting was initiated in Mexico by parties of Americans that operated from large boats and systematically worked along the coasts, sending hunting and skinning parties into the swamps in dinghies. Gadow (1908) tells of such a party that entered Huavi Bay in southern Oaxaca and in a few days virtually wiped out the local alligator population, much to the distress of the resident Tehuantepec Indians, to whom the beasts had some religious significance. When all the accessible animals had been taken, the boat moved on, and the local people began systematic hunting of the remaining animals, having discovered by this time the sale value of the hides. Presumably the alligator was crossed from the list of deities.

Continual persecution has virtually exterminated the species on the Pacific coast, and relatively few remain even in the great swamps of the Gulf coast. At Laguna Papayo, Guerrero, I saw skulls of several large alligators along the shores, but our guides stated that they had not seen a live animal in recent years. Discovery of even a single lagarto would be occasion for a special hunt, so great is the commercial value of the hides.

Despite legal restriction of the take under the fishing laws (*Ley de Pesca*) the uncontrolled persecution goes on. Every conceivable device, even dynamite, is used to capture the animals. The present status of the alligator is nearly as precarious as that of the tapir, antelope, or bighorn.

One commercial enterprise that is still permitted to continue by special edict of the Secretary of Agriculture and Livestock is the trade in caged songbirds. Theoretically, the law of 1952 would prohibit such commerce, but it is so important a source of supplemental income to many rural residents that the agricultural unions bring constant pressure upon the Secretary to permit its continuance. The keeping of songbirds is a deep-seated custom in Mexico. I should estimate that at least half of the homes, hotels, and business establishments have caged birds, all—or virtually all—of which were captured in the wild. The humblest dwelling characteristically has a bird cage hanging in the kitchen and potted flowers in the window. Most of the birds are nonmigratory species, some of the favorites being the cardinal, solitaires, parrots and parakeets, the mockingbird, the house finch, and the robin. Doves and quail are taken occasionally. In many a little country hotel I have been awakened at daylight by the clear call of a *clarín* down the hall, or of a Gambel quail in the patio. This expression of love for wild things on the part of the Mexican people strikes a sympathetic chord in me, and I should hate to see the birds taken away by statute, however well intended the law might be. The number of birds confined is probably far less than the normal annual increase in the bird population.

BETTER USE OF THE WILDLIFE RESOURCE

As the foregoing paragraphs imply, the present pattern of wildlife utilization in Mexico is not necessarily the best in terms of the economy of the resource. Let us look at the problem from the standpoint of the rural people of the country who are closest to the wildlife and should profit the most from it.

Wherever possible, wildlife crops should be used for sport hunting, since this brings the highest values to a community. Any village that can create and maintain a mecca for sportsmen will in the end profit handsomely by it. And of course the requisite husbandry of the game by the local people can achieve results in terms of conservation that could never be duplicated by a government agency. The sportsmen, in turn, would have the sport which they so earnestly desire. The basic structure of a future wildlife program, therefore, should have as its primary objective not the curtailment of hunting but the furthering of recreational hunting with parallel encouragement of local game management in the rural communities.

The use of wildlife for food—now its primary use in Mexico—need not be discouraged except as it is excessive and is destroying the resource (ungulates, for example) or as it interferes with the building up of recreational hunting, the higher economic form of use. Certainly no objective observer can minimize the importance of wild animal foods to the rural peoples of Mexico. Nothing should be done to destroy this value. Rather, an attempt should be made to enhance the food value by methods that will give higher yields.

The taking of wildlife for commercial purposes is generally the use least beneficial to the country. The present effort of the government to discourage it is well founded and deserves full support.

This realignment of the pattern of wildlife husbandry will require a strong and well-financed government program, with emphasis upon extension and education. For in the final analysis, the actual conservation of wildlife will be achieved not in the legislative halls of Mexico City but in the pueblos and rancherias of the country.

CHAPTER 4

The Existing Program of Wildlife Conservation

The first protective legislation intended specifically for the conservation of Mexican wildlife was passed in 1894, when the nation was nearly four hundred years old. The forest law of that year included a series of regulations concerning the taking of wild game and established penalties to be incurred for infractions. But no provision was made for their enforcement, and the law was little heeded.

In 1911, López and López pointed out that nearly all civilized countries had reasonably complete game laws but that those of Mexico were singularly inadequate and ineffective. They went on to offer a rather full outline of the manner in which hunting should be regulated, in their opinion; but it was many years before a comprehensive game law was adopted.

However, a Departamento de Caza y Pesca (Department of Game and Fish) was established in 1916, under the Secretaría de Agricultura y Fomento, whose purpose was to administer the game and fish resources under such laws as existed. From time to time new hunting restrictions were added, designed to protect specific kinds of game. For example, in the *Acuerdos de la Secretaría de Agricultura y Fomento,* issued in September,

1918, rules were announced governing the taking of ducks on lakes in the Valley of Mexico. In 1921, President Obregón proclaimed for a period of ten years a complete closed season on antelope and bighorn throughout the country. The actual promoter of the 1921 proclamation was the great Mexican naturalist Alfonso L. Herrera, whose active campaigning for wildlife conservation throughout the Western Hemisphere earned for him the Gold Medal Award from the Permanent Wild Life Protection Fund.

In 1934, under the administration of President Lázaro Cárdenas, the bureaus administering forests, game, and fish were combined into an independent department called the Departamento Autónomo Forestal y de Caza y Pesca. This new branch of government worked very actively for six years and was beginning to develop an effective conservation program when the law was changed again. However, one of the substantial advances during this period was the negotiation in 1936 of the Migratory Bird Treaty with the United States. The treaty became effective in March, 1937, and committed Mexico to a definite program of protection of migratory birds.

PRESENT LEGAL BASIS OF WILDLIFE ADMINISTRATION

Under the new plan of organization, adopted in 1940, the administration of fisheries was transferred to the Navy (Secretaría de Marina) and a Dirección General Forestal y de Caza was created, once more subsidiary to the Secretaría de Agricultura y Ganadería. As now constituted, the organization of forestry and game affairs in the Mexican government is as follows:

    Presidente de la Republica—President of the Republic

        Secretaría de Agricultura y Ganadería—Secretary of Agriculture and Livestock

            Subsecretaría de Recursos Forestales y de Caza—Undersecretary for Forestry and Game

                Dirección General Forestal y de Caza—Bureau of Forestry and Game

                    Departamento Forestal—Forestry Department

                    Departamento de Caza—Game Department

Each of these branches and subbranches of government maintains a central office in Mexico City, and the chiefs are answerable to the next higher authority in the chain of responsibility. Thus, the chief of the Game Department is directly under the head of the Bureau of Forestry and Game, who in turn answers to the Undersecretary for Forestry and Game, and so on. But unlike the system in the United States, each branch does not maintain its own independent field force. In the capital of each state and territory is an office representing the Secretary of Agriculture and Livestock, under the immediate charge of a General Agent for the Secretary. Under this field chief may be one or more representatives of the various bureaus and departments of agriculture; as for example, forestry, game, agronomy, soil conservation, and animal industry. The number of men representing any branch in a local office depends to some extent on the funds allocated to that particular branch in the current year. At times, when the Game Department is relatively well financed, there are assigned to the field offices a number of *vigilantes* (wardens), whose specific duty is to enforce the game laws within the state in which they are stationed. But in years of adversity, which means most years, the game laws as well as the forest laws must be administered by representatives of the Bureau of Forestry and Game, and the Game Department has no wardens of its own. More will be said of this situation later.

Also in 1940, when the present administrative plan was adopted, there came into being the first Ley Federal de Caza (federal game law) establishing a firm legal base for the administration of the wildlife resource. On December 3, 1951, a new and revised Ley Federal de Caza was signed by President Miguel Alemán. It became effective upon its publication in the *Diario Oficial* on January 5, 1952. Since this law is the authority for the conservation and management of wildlife under the Secretary of Agriculture and Livestock, and since it outlines both the objectives and the methods of the present program, it is reproduced in full as Appendix A.

Although the Ley de Caza as here published undoubtedly will undergo modification from time to time, the general legal foundation of wildlife administration will probably remain unaltered. It will be noted that under Article 3 wildlife in Mexico is declared to be the "property of the nation." The Secretary of Agriculture and Livestock is charged with its husbandry. This plan differs materially from that in force in the United States and Canada, where only migratory birds are wards of the federal governments, the individual states and provinces being the legal custodians of all resident wild animals.

One feature of the law, unfamiliar to hunters from the United States, is the specific requirement that, in order to purchase a hunting permit, a hunter who is a resident of Mexico must belong to a recognized hunting club or association (Art. 18). The situation behind this requirement is as follows. The Estado Mayor de la Secretaría de la Defensa has control over the purchase, possession, and use of all types of firearms, including sporting guns. A gun permit must be obtained from the Defense Department before a hunting license may be purchased, and the number of the gun permit is entered directly on the license. A club member may easily obtain a gun permit, since the club itself vouches for the peaceable conduct of its members. Hence, in practice, nearly all Mexican sportsmen belong to clubs to facilitate their obtaining gun permits. It follows logically that club membership becomes a prerequisite for obtaining the hunting permit. A nonresident, however, may purchase a hunting permit at the border by obtaining first a gun permit from an authorized representative of the Defense Department. He need not join a hunting club, although to do so facilitates all matters pertaining to permits.

YEAR-TO-YEAR REGULATIONS GOVERNING HUNTING

The Secretary of Agriculture and Livestock issues periodically a set of specific regulations governing hunting, comparable to the regulations of annual seasons and bag limits issued by game departments in the United States. As an example, the most recent version of the Mexican hunting regulations, published in 1954, is reproduced in Appendix B of this volume. These regulations are not to be construed as currently valid, since they are subject to revision at any time. Anyone preparing to hunt in Mexico should obtain a copy of the current regulations from the Departamento de Caza, Mariscal 3, México, D.F.

ANALYSIS OF THE GAME LAWS

In their objective and intent the existing Ley Federal de Caza and the current hunting regulations must be deemed admirably drawn. What is basically lacking is the financial support of the Game Department to make possible the execution of the program declared in Article 4 as "of public benefit." However, before discussing the problems of administration I must point out one important shortcoming of the law itself.

The whole legal structure of wildlife conservation is based on the premise that regulation of hunting is the one main problem. Indeed, regulation of hunting in Mexico is an important problem, as pointed out in the preceding chapter; but it is not necessarily the only factor—or even the most important one—determining the size and distribution of wildlife populations. On the contrary, the condition of the habitat itself is in many regions of the country the primary determinant of wildlife abundance or scarcity (chap. 2). Although Article 4, d, of the Ley de Caza properly points out that habitat conservation is a desirable objective of wildlife management, no further provision is made in the law to implement this aspect of the conservation program.

Thus, for example, in the management of migratory waterfowl on their wintering grounds in Mexico, the preservation and management of selected lakes and marshes may be far more important than further regulation of the kill, which at present is not really excessive. For preserving some of the endangered big game species, such as antelope and bighorn, the mere passage of protective legislation, or even the setting aside of refuges or special reserves provided for in Article 9, may be less effective than the regulation of livestock grazing on the ranges occupied by these animals.

The possibilities of habitat management, in other words, are not fully acknowledged or adequately spelled out in the law. There is not even any specific authorization for the Secretary of Agriculture and Livestock to assume full administrative authority over such areas as might be set aside as wildlife preserves, although such authorization may be implied under Mexican law.

Granted that the most immediate problem facing the Game Department is the enforcement of its regulations, the law should not be limited to that objective but should be broadened, when opportunity permits, to provide for phases of game management that include environmental conservation.

THE CURRENT WILDLIFE PROGRAM

As administered at present, the wildlife program consists of little more than certain administrative activities conducted in the central office in Mexico City and the operation of a central game farm at San Cayetano and three new branch game farms near the cities of Chihuahua, Durango, and Perote (Veracruz). For lack of funds, the Departamento de Caza is virtually precluded from extending its activities into the country at large. In the central office, hunting permits are issued, recommendations for hunting regulations are drawn, and plans for field operations are prepared and supervised.

The experimental game farm at San Cayetano, Estado de México, established in 1948, is a small but well-run plant. Ring-necked pheasants are raised for possible introduction in suitable places on the central uplands. In an enclosure of 400 hectares, white-tailed deer are propagated with the idea of producing an annual surplus for restocking depleted ranges. To date, some deer have escaped from the enclosure and others have been released to augment the local population; none have been transported elsewhere for liberation. Surplus pheasants have been used to build up breeding stocks in the three supplementary game farms. The program of pheasant and deer propagation is too new to have been tested for effectiveness. But at best it will contribute little to solving the over-all problem of game restoration in the country as a whole.

The most obvious and immediate shortcoming of the wildlife program is the absence of an effective plan of wildlife protection and law enforcement. For lack of financial support the Departamento de Caza has no regular warden force. The forest guards are charged with the duty of enforcing the game laws, and these guards are direct employees of the Departamento

Fig. 39. White-tailed deer in the rearing pen at San Cayetano game farm. Photograph by Bernardo Villa R.

Forestal. They must give so much of their time to administering the forestry laws that they have little or none to give to active enforcement of the game laws. Moreover, the forest guards naturally are assigned to the forested areas, which means that even nominally there is no one on hand to enforce the game regulations in the arid zones or in most waterfowl habitat. The Departamento de Caza, by arrangement, is able to borrow the services of some of the forest guards for special undertakings such as patrolling for armadas around Lake Texcoco. But since there is no regular warden force, the enforcement of game laws is at best rather desultory.

The inadequacy of the present wildlife program stems directly from lack of financial support by the Mexican government. Funds for operation of the wildlife program are drawn from the general appropriation for the Dirección General Forestal y de Caza. But the actual allocation of support from this source is pitifully low. The Game Department does not even get for its own use the equivalent of the hunting license fees. As shown in table 3, total income to the Mexican government from the sale of hunting licenses has varied in recent years from 139,000 pesos to 481,000 pesos. But the sum currently available for use by the Departamento de Caza has been estimated at approximately 100,000 pesos ($8,000, U.S.). A few years ago somewhat more of the license income was allotted to wildlife—160,000

TABLE 3

RECEIPTS FROM SALE OF SPORT HUNTING LICENSES SINCE 1950 AND ESTIMATED FUNDS
AVAILABLE FOR PROGRAM OF THE DEPARTAMENTO DE CAZA

Year	Number of licenses sold	Income from license sales (in pesos)	Estimated amounts allocated for wildlife program (in pesos)
1950	7,996	205,951	. . .
1951	7,419	187,260	. . .
1952	8,524	139,102	. . .
1953	8,307	151,246	. . .
1954	8,162	268,208	160,000
1955	7,208	200,403	. . .
1956	13,680	481,845	100,000

pesos ($13,000, U.S.) in 1954. Manifestly, there can be no wildlife program in Mexico without financial support. From the token funds allotted must be paid the salaries of the director of the department and of his assistants and office help, salaries of personnel on the game farms, and expenses of travel and of operating the game farms themselves. The reason for the lack of a field program in law enforcement, let alone in any other phase of management, is self-evident.

On July 25, 1955, a meeting was called in Mexico City by the Undersecretary for Forestry and Game to attempt to find some more effective way to finance wildlife conservation than dependence on the whims of the Mexican government. All the registered hunting clubs were invited to send delegates, and approximately forty men came, representing clubs from all parts of the Republic. The proposal was made by the Game Department that all licensed hunters be assessed double the normal fee, the additional income (over and above the normal license fees that are paid into the federal treasury) to be deposited in a Game Fund which would be banked entirely apart from the government treasury. Thus, a resident sportsman who normally would pay 30 pesos for a general hunting license would instead pay 60 pesos, of which 30 would go into the Game Fund. A non-resident would pay 480 pesos, 240 for the license and 240 into the Game Fund, and so on. A commission of six members—three from the Game Department and three sportsmen elected by the clubs themselves—would supervise the use of the Game Fund. This plan was accepted by the sportsmen and was to have gone into effect in the autumn of 1955. However, a question of legality arose and the scheme was never implemented.

But even if the Game Fund plan had been adopted it would not have absolved the government from its responsibility to supply more adequate appropriations for the Game Department. Wildlife is a resource of all the people of Mexico. It is used heavily and profitably by the rural peoples for food, and as a tourist attraction it contributes to the general economy of the country. Moreover, the Mexican government in affixing its signature to the Migratory Bird Treaty with the United States in 1936 and to the Inter-American Treaty for the Protection of Nature in 1942 assumed some real responsibility in conservation affairs within its national boundaries. Therefore the sportsmen should not be made to carry the main burden for wildlife conservation and management. In any event, the sportsmen's contributions to the Game Fund would still fall far short of financing the program that is needed.

Certainly the wildlife resource of Mexico is important enough to warrant far more attention and husbandry than the government has seen fit to give it. The passage of nicely worded game laws and of pious resolutions about the protection of wildlife are of themselves empty gestures. Until the government elects to give its Game Department some funds to work with there can be little real progress in wildlife conservation. Self-imposed contributions from the sportsmen would help, but the strong and sustained support of the Mexican government is necessary to ultimate success. Without it the resource will continue to dwindle as it has in the past.

CHAPTER 5

Wildlife in the Future

The people and the government of Mexico have clearly expressed a desire to perpetuate the native wildlife. The present effort to do so is inadequate in some respects, especially in financing, but it denotes a commendable intent. Assuming that the problem of finances will be favorably resolved in the future, it would seem profitable at this time to outline various phases of a more nearly complete and better rounded wildlife program than has been developed in Mexico in the past. First, the primary objectives.

OBJECTIVES OF A WILDLIFE PROGRAM

1. Management and production of wildlife must be fitted into the bigger program of land conservation. Suitable habitat for game can be preserved only within the over-all scheme of land use. Thus, the plans for future agricultural development, for forest utilization, and for livestock grazing all will intimately affect the future of wildlife. This effect should be deliberately planned, not left to chance.

2. Over most of the country the objective of wildlife management should be production of wildlife crops to be used in whatever ways will best serve the people of Mexico. As implied in previous chapters, recreational

hunting is usually the highest form of use for wildlife, both culturally and economically. But utilization of wild animals as food for the people is an equally valid form of *aprovechamiento* that should be purposefully developed. The program of production has many facets—regulation of the harvest, habitat conservation and improvement, and, perhaps most important of all, education of the people concerned.

3. There should be created an integrated system of parks and natural reserves in which examples of all the original biotic types will be preserved intact, without exploitation. For example, at least one and preferably several substantial areas of native rain forest ought to be set aside as permanent natural monuments, free from logging, grazing, hunting, or any other inhibitory use. Similar wilderness preserves are needed in the pine forest zones, the cloud forest, the desert mountains, the interior grasslands, and other vegetation zones. Obviously, the existing system of national parks, administered by the Bureau of Forestry and Game, is the nucleus for such a set of natural reserves. Although these areas would serve primarily recreational, educational, and scientific needs, they would at the same time be important reservoirs of native wildlife some forms of which are largely dependent on undisturbed climax vegetation for their survival.

4. No native animal should be allowed to become extinct. Even the large and sometimes destructive predators such as the wolf and the grizzly bear should be deliberately and carefully preserved in some part of the country so as to keep the native fauna intact. When any species, game or nongame, destructive or beneficial, approaches extinction, vigorous measures should be taken to restore it in at least one or two localities. An immediate problem of this nature, for example, is the Imperial ivory-billed woodpecker (*Campephilus imperialis*), which has been virtually extirpated from its native pine forests in the Sierra Madre Occidental through logging and wanton shooting. I should consider preservation of this species a high-priority task of a wildlife conservation program.

The following paragraphs discuss briefly elements of a wildlife program that would fulfill most or all of the objectives listed above. The points are taken up in order of their immediate practicability, which is not necessarily the order of their importance.

CONTROL OF HUNTING

Effective regulation of the kill is the obvious place to start the program. The game laws of Mexico are good enough on the books; they must be put to work.

A force of full-time game wardens is the most pressing need. Warden positions should be set up, with adequate salary and with provision for advancement so that they will attract the best possible men. Further, they should be continuing positions with professional status, not subject to change of personnel every time a new political group comes into power. The job at hand can be better done by a small force of competent, intelligent, and experienced men than by a much larger number of temporary appointees.

Each warden should be provided with some sort of automotive transportation. Enforcement of the laws must be done in the field, not in some headquarters office.

The wardens should be stationed at points throughout the country where the protection needs seem to be greatest. It is unlikely in the foreseeable future that there will be enough wardens in Mexico to cover all areas equally well. A plan of priorities must therefore be worked out to put each warden in the place where he can do the most good on critical problems. In drawing such a plan, many factors must be weighed.

The distribution of hunting pressure over the country is certainly one factor. The central belt of Mexico, where the human population is densest (see fig. 22), would therefore get high priority. The northern tier of states, although low in population, attracts many American hunters who create special problems of law enforcement. It is disgraceful that many of these visitors come overloaded with ammunition, and with money to bribe

Fig. 40.   Fence construction on the game farm at San Cayetano. Photograph by Bernardo Villa R.

their way into or out of any situation, and that sometimes their conduct is anything but sportsmanlike. Close supervision of this hunting by non-residents is needed.

The status of particular species of wildlife is another factor to consider.

Fig. 41.   Pronghorn antelope. This species, now rare in Mexico, would increase in numbers if given adequate protection from poaching. Photograph by Jim Yoakum.

Antelope, bighorn sheep, and desert mule deer—all in the north—tapirs in the southeast, and white-tailed deer almost everywhere are in special need of protection.

Areas of excessive commercial hunting deserve continuing attention. Some of these are the Valley of Mexico, the environs of Guadalajara, the United States border, and northern Yucatán.

And there may be other factors to consider. The main point is that a small force can do a big job if the group endeavor is critically focused.

The warden should represent the Game Department in all its activities, but particularly in conservation education. Effective enforcement of any law is achieved not merely by throwing violators into jail but by convincing the public at large that the law should be obeyed. The mark of achievement of a good game warden is the occurrence of few violations in his district, not how many convictions he can obtain. In the training of the men at the outset and in later supervision of their work this point should be continually stressed.

The wardens can act as a continuous field survey team, appraising wildlife conditions in various parts of the country and recommending changes in the hunting regulations when needed.

An effective warden force, in other words, is the backbone of the protection program.

NATIONAL PARKS

Additional protection can be extended to endangered wildlife species, or locally to whole faunas, by the establishment of various kinds of parks, preserves, and refuges. Mexico now has a rather extensive system of national parks, which, with some modifications and additions, could become an important part of the wildlife protection program.

The first national parks to be established were Desierto de los Leones, near Mexico City, and El Chico, near Pachuca, in 1856 and 1898, respectively. But most of the present forty-seven parks were set aside in the mid-1930's during the administration of President Lázaro Cárdenas, which was also the period of the very active Departmento Autónomo Forestal y de Caza y Pesca. This same era, it will be recalled, was a time of expansion of national parks, monuments, forests, and wildlife reserves in the United States, being the halcyon days of Franklin Roosevelt's "New Deal." The idea of conservation at that time seems to have been contagious.

In Mexico the national parks have always been administered within the Bureau of Forestry and Game of the Mexican government. The existing park areas are shown on the map in figure 42. Pertinent statistics are included in the legend for this figure. Of the forty-seven areas now

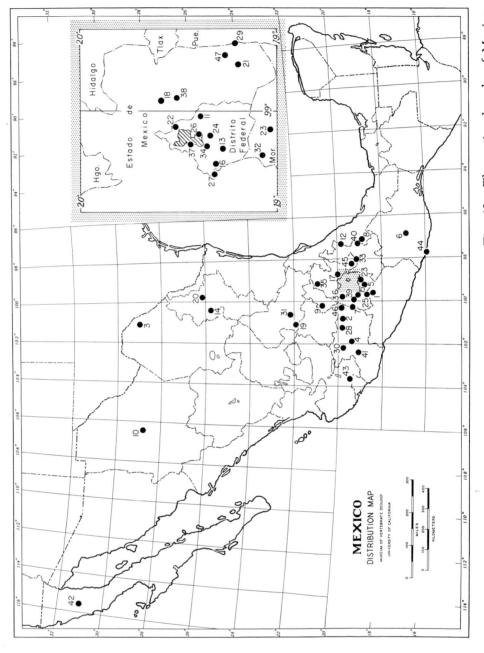

Fig. 42. The national parks of Mexico.

Fig. 42. THE NATIONAL PARKS OF MEXICO

Number on map	Name	Area (in hectares)	Date established	State
1	Alejandro de Humboldt	1,080	1936	Guerrero
2	Cerro de Garnica	1,968	1936	Michoacán
3	Balneario de los Novillos	54	1940	Coahuila
4	Barranca de Cupatitzio	20	1938	Michoacán
5	Barranca de Chapultepec	20	1937	Morelos
6	Benito Juárez	2,700	1937	Oaxaca
7	Bosencheve	15,000	1940	Estado de México
8	Cañon de Rio Blanco	55,690	1938	Veracruz
9	Cerro de las Campanas	58	1937	Querétaro
10	Cumbres de Majalca	4,773	1939	Chihuahua
11	Cerro de la Estrella	1,100	1938	Distrito Federal
12	Cofre de Perote	11,707	1937	Veracruz
13	Cumbres del Ajusco	920	1936	Distrito Federal
14	Cumbres de Monterrey	246,500	1939	Nuevo León
15	Desierto del Carmen	529	1942	Estado de México
16	Desierto de los Leones	1,900	1856 (1917)	Distrito Federal
17	El Chico	1,835	1898	Hidalgo
18	El Cantador	34	1941	Estado de México
19	El Gogorron	25,000	1936	San Luis Potosí
20	El Sabinal	9	1938	Nuevo León
21	El Sacromonte	10	1939	Estado de México
22	El Tepeyac	1,500	1937	Distrito Federal
23	El Tepozteco	24,000	1937	Morelos
24	Fuentes Grotantes de Tlalpan	129	1936	Distrito Federal
25	Grutas de Cacahuamilpa	1,232	1936	Guerrero
26	Histórico Coyoacan	584	1938	Distrito Federal
27	Insurgente Miguel Hidalgo y Costilla	2,100	1936	Estado de México
28	Insurgente José María Morelos	1,813	1939	Michoacán
29	Ixtacihuatl-Popocatepetl	25,679	1935	Puebla, Estado de México
30	Lago de Camecuaro	14	1940	Michoacán
31	El Potosí	2,000	1936	San Luis Potosí
32	Lagunas de Zempoala	4,790	1936	Morelos
33	La Malinche	39,426	1938	Tlaxcala
34	Lomas de Padierna	670	1938	Distrito Federal
35	Los Marmoles	23,500	1936	Hidalgo
36	Los Remedios	358	1938	Estado de México
37	Molino de Belem	96	1952	Distrito Federal
38	Molino de las Flores	78	1937	Estado de México
39	Nevado de Toluca	67,000	1936	Estado de México
40	Pico de Orizaba	19,750	1937	Puebla, Veracruz
41	Pico de Tancítaro	29,316	1940	Michoacán
42	Sierra San Pedro Mártir	63,000	1947	Baja California
43	Volcán de Colima	22,200	1936	Colima, Jalisco
44	Lagunas de Chacahua	14,187	1937	Oaxaca
45	Xicotencatl	800	1937	Tlaxcala
46	Rayon	34	1952	Michoacán
47	Zoquiapan y Anexas	10,000	1937	Estado de México

reserved, about half are historical or archaeological sites, most of them too small to have much significance as wildlife conservation areas. But some of the larger parks, as for example Ixta-Popo, Nevado de Toluca, and Cumbres de Monterrey, are well suited as wildlife sanctuaries if they could be managed and strictly protected.

However, there are some serious difficulties in park administration. In the first place, the budget for park administration is much too meager to permit full protection and proper management. Nowhere are there enough guards to prevent hunting, although nominally the parks are sanctuaries. The areas are not fenced, and it is virtually impossible to exclude livestock. With so few guards it is even difficult to exclude fire. Secondly, most of the parks include substantial areas of private or *ejido* land which have never been purchased by the government. Until these tracts are bought and paid for, the owners have full legal rights to graze, cut timber, and even to clear lands for cultivation. In short, adequate protection and management are impossible, and these dedicated areas cannot serve their declared purpose as natural reserves for lack of government support. The situation has not improved since 1945, when it was deplored by Vogt.

Assuming again, however, that the park system will some day get the backing from the government that it deserves, it can be developed into an exceedingly important part of the total conservation plan. As stated earlier, one phase of the park program should be the preservation in wilderness status of substantial blocks representing all the major biotic associations in Mexico. Two types of country are well represented in the system now— alpine peaks and subjacent coniferous forests. Additions to the system should stress other vegetation zones.

Some new parks already have been formally proposed. In Chiapas, for example, the area near Ocozocoautla known as Selva del Ocote and another tract southeast of Comitán called Lagos de Montebello would both be fine additions to the park system, serving to preserve samples of native rain forest and several other vegetation types with the full quota of native plants and animals. Tapirs, both species of monkeys, brocket deer, and many other interesting mammals and birds still occur in these areas. Both tracts can be made easily accessible to visitors. An informative account of the Selva del Ocote area is to be found in an article by Miranda published in Mexico in 1952 (see Bibliography).

The Sierra del Carmen in northern Coahuila is a spectacular range of pine and oak forest and grama grass mesas, which if preserved could become a haven for white-tailed and mule deer, mountain lions, black bear, antelope, bighorn, and wild turkey. This area has been considered as a prospective companion park to the Big Bend National Park on the Texas side of the Río Grande; but so far, the proposal has not been acted upon. Unless set aside, the Carmens will be logged, grazed, and stripped of their animal life, as have so many of the interior mountains. Logging of the area, in fact, has already started.

Another isolated mountain range in northern Mexico that very much deserves park status is the Sierra del Nido in central Chihuahua. This precipitous outcropping is the last stronghold of the grizzly bear, and I can think of no more worthy cause in conservation than preserving this great mammal through safeguarding its habitat.

The barranca country of northeastern Sinaloa and southwestern Chihuahua should be the site of another big park. In scenery this country

Fig. 43.   Virgin rain forest of Volcán San Martín Tuxtla
in southern Veracruz. This area should be reserved
in a national park or national wildlife refuge.
Photograph by C. W. Schwartz.

rivals the Grand Canyon of Arizona. Here, also, some habitat of the Imperial ivory-billed woodpecker might be maintained, thus saving that interesting bird—the largest woodpecker in the world.

Mexico has the sites with which to create one of the most varied and spectacular park systems in the world. Our immediate interest here concerns the function of the parks in wildlife preservation; but their greatest values to the country will lie in the social and cultural significance to the people of Mexico and in the tremendous attraction which they would have for tourists.

NATIONAL WILDLIFE REFUGES

In addition to the parks there should be created a system of national wildlife refuges. Authority for the Secretary of Agriculture and Livestock to set aside such refuges is established in Article 9 of the Ley Federal de Caza. These can be used to provide special protection for threatened wildlife species, such as antelope and bighorn, or protection for important concentrations of birds, as for example, migratory waterfowl and some of the marsh and swamp birds. Like the parks, however, the refuges must be adequately financed and managed if they are to serve any useful function.

One area now under consideration for establishment as a national wildlife refuge is the remnant of occupied antelope range near Ramos, Chihuahua. Other sites that should be investigated are the mountains in northern Sonora and central Baja California that still retain both antelope and bighorn sheep. If the remaining grizzly bears in central Chihuahua cannot be enclosed in a national park, they certainly should be given the protection of a national refuge.

As part of the program of migratory waterfowl protection, some permanent refuges are very much needed in Mexico, particularly in the central and southern uplands where waterfowl habitat is deteriorating rapidly. The recently completed survey (Arellano and Rojas, 1956) of the interior lakes and marshes and their status as waterfowl habitat will serve as a useful guide to possible refuge sites. Manifestly, any such refuges not only will have to be protected from hunting but should also be managed as waterfowl habitat.

Along the shorelines of Mexico are some exquisite sites for bird refuges. For example, Scammon Lagoon on the west side of Baja California is the winter home of most of the black brant in North America. The birds are so concentrated as to be subject to severe decimation by hunting. This area deserves full protection. The other brant bays along the coast could be left open to hunting. Scammon Lagoon also is a principal calving ground for the Pacific gray whale, which at one time was thought to be extinct. The whales as well as the brant would profit by the exclusion of all disturbance from the lagoon.

On the coastal lagoons of Sinaloa, Guerrero, and Veracruz are many important concentration points for ducks, some of which should be given refuge status. Waterfowl hunting along both coasts of Mexico is becoming more intensive as good highways make accessible the formerly isolated swamps and lagoons. Coastal refuges would also serve to protect many of the interesting swamp birds, such as the roseate spoonbill and various kinds of herons, bitterns, and ibises. The one Mexican colony of nesting flamingos, on the tip of the Yucatán Peninsula, likewise deserves the formal protection of a refuge.

I have not attempted here to plan a full park and refuge program for

Fig. 44.   An interior marsh near Oriental, Puebla.
Marshlands of this kind should be preserved
as winter homes for migratory waterfowl.
Photograph by C. W. Schwartz.

Mexico but only to sketch some of the possibilities. I see no valid reason why this phase of wildlife conservation should not be started in the near future, knowing of course that full development will take much time and money. But like the warden program, the beginning of an effective system of natural reserves would appear to be immediately practicable.

PREDATOR CONTROL

One form of wildlife protection that in past years has been given great emphasis in the United States is the control of predatory animals. Much of this control, of course, is directed toward the protection of domestic live-stock; but I shall not discuss that problem here. The brief remarks and recommendations which follow concern solely the matter of predator control in wildlife management.

It is well established that predators consume large numbers of game birds and mammals. Thus, wolves, mountain lions, and jaguars kill many deer and javelinas; coyotes take some of the fawns of deer and antelope; the smaller cats often live mainly on rabbits; and the accipitrine hawks and horned owls take numerous quail and other game birds. But it does not necessarily follow that the killing of predators will lead to a substantial increase in game. On the contrary, experience in the United States has shown that tremendous sums can be spent on predator control without materially benefiting the game populations, the numbers of which are controlled largely by the condition of the habitat or environment in which they live.

There are several reasons for the general lack of success of predator control as a practical means of management, the most important of which are biological. All wild animals produce far more young than are needed to sustain the natural populations, and it appears that predators live entirely on the surplus. In the same way, a tree produces infinitely more seed than is needed to reproduce the forest, and the excess seeds feed many chipmunks, mice, and small birds. Control of the seed-eating animals will not usually produce any more trees in the forest; by the same token, control of predatory animals does not often produce more game. The surplus animals, like the surplus tree seeds, will be lost in one way or another, since the environment will not support an ever-increasing population of any kind of organism.

Then, too, the populations of flesh-eating animals produce an annual surplus of their own, just as the prey species do, and much effort can be expended in killing predators without cutting deeply, much less per-manently, into the breeding stocks. Unless control is complete or virtually so, the predator populations quickly return to their original levels. The

Grizzly Bear

state of California, for example, has over the years spent more than a quarter of a million dollars on the control of mountain lions; but the kill today is still about two hundred lions a year, as it was in 1916 when the program started. The heavily subsidized lion kill, in other words, is on a sustained-yield basis. And the deer population, which presumably was to be benefited by this endeavor, is still controlled by the forage capacity of the ranges.

Thus, it has often turned out that money spent on indiscriminate predator control is essentially wasted.

However, there are certain critical situations where predator control may be of material benefit, particularly in the initial stages of restoring species that have become rare. For example, when the antelope population is at a very low level, coyotes if abundant may take so many fawns that restoration is retarded. Under such circumstances coyote control might well be adopted as part of the program of antelope management, along with protection from hunting and habitat improvement. After the herds are restored, control of predators can be discontinued.

But predator control is expensive and should be undertaken only when scientific field investigation indicates that it will produce substantial benefits. In making the best use of available funds for wildlife conservation, Mexico can well profit from experience in the United States and not spend money on unnecessary and unproductive lines of endeavor.

HABITAT CONSERVATION AND IMPROVEMENT

Perhaps the most important generalization that has come out of wildlife studies the world over is that game populations are controlled primarily by the habitats in which they live. Good game range supports many animals, poor range supports few. Each species requires certain types and amounts of food, cover, and water; and the arrangement of these necessary elements of the environment determines the number of animals that can exist. Thus, a primary objective of wildlife management is to maintain the game ranges in as nearly optimum condition as possible.

This is easily said but often not easily done. For the economic uses of the land, which affect game habitat, are usually directed toward other objectives than wildlife production. Thus, the patterns of agriculture, grazing, and forest use have profound effects upon local game supplies, but they are dictated by economic needs and are not easily changed to favor wildlife. Nevertheless, with proper planning, the needs of wildlife can often be provided without in any way inhibiting the production of other land crops for human use. On the contrary, proper management of the land from the standpoint of economic production is usually the very best way to maintain good habitat for wildlife.

Chapter 2 elaborated the current misuse of Mexican resources and pointed out how rapidly they are being dissipated. Correction of this situation is perhaps the most profound national problem today. And correction must come through a coördinated program in which agriculture, livestock, soils, forests, water, and wildlife are considered as interrelated facets of one problem—not as separate problems. The complexities and difficulties of overhauling a well-established land economy are staggeringly great, and it is not my place here to consider the economic and sociological aspects of the undertaking. But those of us that are concerned especially

Fig. 45.   Corn culture in northern Puebla. Wildlife
populations are directly affected by land use.
Photograph by C. W. Schwartz.

with wildlife must never lose sight of the fact that total conservation of the land resources is fundamental to us as well as to the farmer, the forester, and the livestock rancher. Without it the environment for wild animals will blow away and wash away with the soil until only a biological desert remains.

When the people and the government of Mexico finally see that the problem of conserving natural resources must be faced, it will be an easy matter to fit wildlife into the new order of things. Any sound plan to conserve soil and water must include the maintenance of soil-binding vegetation; this in turn will produce game coverts of some sort. Each animal has its own requirements, and all will not be equally favored by a given pattern of land use. But with judicious control of vegetation a great many of the Mexican species can be maintained in perpetual abundance. Those that do not adjust to the highly intensive use of land (which certainly will be needed to support Mexico's growing human population) will have to be preserved in parks or refuges.

As a concrete example let us consider a basin somewhere in the central uplands. The farmlands surrounding the village are no longer productive, because of overcropping and erosion. The water that once flowed steadily from forested slopes above now comes in torrents in the summer rainy season and fails completely in winter; for the slopes have been overgrazed, overlogged, and overburned for centuries. The water table is falling steadily. The lake in the basin is dry and wells are failing. Wildlife that once teemed in the area is virtually gone. If the government should choose this basin as a demonstration of how resources might be managed, the upper slopes would be protected from fire and grazing until a new cloak of vegetation could bind the soil. Soon a new forest would form. Water would begin again to percolate into the earth and springs would flow once more. By the use of fertilizer, selected crop varieties, contour farming, and irrigation with dependable water, the valley lands could again be made productive. With reasonable protection, deer would return to the forest, quail and rabbits would frequent the croplands, and ducks would return to the refilled lake. A once destitute village would again be a thriving and happy community.

This is total conservation as it has been envisioned for years by the eminent Mexican conservationist, Enrique Beltrán. The water shortage, the crop failure, the exhaustion of forest products, or the loss of wildlife cannot be effectively dealt with singly. They are part and parcel of a single problem—the problem of land use.

I like the plan, proposed by Beltrán, Gill, and others, of approaching the general conservation program in Mexico through local demonstrations such as the one just described. If even a few such areas were put under good management the basic idea might spread rapidly, since the immediate

Fig. 46. A Mexican hunter. Every hunter should realize the relationship between wildlife and land conservation. Photograph by C. W. Schwartz.

beneficiaries are the living operators of the land, not merely "posterity" or "the nation" or some yet unborn generation.

However Mexico chooses to deal with the problem, she must do something about it and do it soon. Only thus can a comprehensive plan for wildlife conservation be drawn with any prospect of permanency.

On a very limited scale, the Game Department can undertake habitat improvement for wildlife on government lands. Some of the parks and proposed new refuges would lend themselves to various kinds of manipulation without exhorbitant costs. Control of grazing on selected big-game ranges often pays good dividends. Certainly waterfowl reserves will need management—at least the water should be kept at a level high enough to make the reservation attractive to ducks. Water stores created on desert ranges have proved to be highly effective for many kinds of game. Such developments as these are financed by many game departments in the United States to good effect.

But even with generous financing, the management of game ranges by government agencies will never solve the whole problem of wildlife conservation in all parts of Mexico. That must be done by the citizen who owns and operates the land. He alone is in a position to preserve the soil, the vegetation, and the fauna.

EXTENSION AND EDUCATION

Conservation must have its beginnings in the mind of the average *campesino*. And his mind is not easily reached or swayed. In general, the rural Mexican is provincial, illiterate, and rightfully suspicious of outsiders who try to tell him how to handle his land. He lives according to the ageless plan of his ancestors, and only grudgingly accepts innovations. He has no faith in federal laws or governmental edicts, nor in the spoken or printed word. He believes what he was taught at home and what he sees with his own eyes. How is this man to be shown that there is a new way to live and to farm which would greatly improve his lot and that of his beloved community—his *tierra?*

Conservation programs in all countries sooner or later bog down for lack of public understanding. In the United States we have many times launched enthusiastically into a conservation crusade only to find that progress is retarded until the public-education phase catches up with the technical and legal advance. A strong educational effort might as well be initiated at the beginning. This certainly will be necessary in Mexico, for the country as a whole, and the *campesino* in particular, has at present only the dimmest understanding of the critical situation of the country's resources.

Every conceivable method of extension and education should be employed to carry to the Mexican public a clear picture of the significance of conservation. Demonstration watersheds, just discussed, ought to be given heavy emphasis, because they translate ideas from the abstract to the practical level understandable to farmers. Movies, illustrated lectures, printed material, radio, and TV can be used to reach the various strata of Mexican society. The theme throughout should stress the absolute dependence of society on natural resources and the need for managing all resources collectively because of their complete interdependence. All branches of government will have to tell the same story.

One of the greatest hopes is the school system. Already, small beginnings have been made to incorporate conservation teaching into the system of primary education. The Instituto Mexicano de Recursos Naturales Renovables began issuing in 1954 a monthly bulletin entitled *Conservación y Educación,* for the guidance of teachers. This venture is receiving additional sponsorship from the Asociación Mexicana de Protección a la Naturaleza and from the federal Department of Education itself. Some aspects of the problem have been approached through the state and territorial primary schools and the Departamento de Misiones Culturales, which reaches especially the rural areas. The Game Department in 1953 put forth considerable effort to carry the message of wildlife conservation through these channels. Other branches of the government have done likewise from time to time. But a sustained, coördinated program involving all resources has not yet materialized.

The most powerful influence in Mexican life, the Catholic Church, has not yet lent its prestige to this endeavor. The Game Department recently tried to interest the Church in conservation, but negotiations between the Church and the government are difficult indeed, since the Constitution of the Republic specifically and emphatically separates the functions of church and state. Still it would seem that a problem of such significance to the whole country could be attacked jointly by all powers—governmental, ecclesiastical, and, for that matter, private and industrial. This hardly seems an issue in which there are any disinterested parties.

To sum up, wildlife conservation must be considered but one fragment of the total problem of conservation of natural resources in Mexico, and it will only be achieved when the Mexican public is aroused to face the big issue.

RESEARCH AND TECHNICAL TRAINING

Technical knowledge and trained men will be needed to guide conservation efforts in Mexico. Within the wildlife field there is at present no regular research program nor training curriculum whatsoever.

From time to time, as finances permit, the Game Department in coöperation with the Institute of Biology has conducted various surveys and investigations of wildlife problems in the Republic. The most recent and the best of these are represented in the various publications of Bernardo Villa R. (see Bibliography). The Instituto Mexicano de Recursos Naturales Renovables has a varied research program, including, as previously mentioned one project recently completed on waterfowl habitat. The U. S. Fish and Wildlife Service and several American universities are working in Mexico on various problems bearing on wildlife. The work represented in the present volume is itself a research contribution. But all of this together is but a beginning point. Sustained and continuing field investigation will be needed to orient the future wildlife program and to achieve the necessary integration with other facets of conservation.

Wildlife research requires money and trained men, of which Mexico has neither in adequate quantity at the moment. However generous or limited the budgetary support for the Game Department will be in the future, some dependable portion should be allocated for investigative field work. High-priority tasks that come first to mind are surveys of the rare animals such as the bighorn, antelope, and grizzly; continuing appraisal of wintering grounds for waterfowl; and continued investigation of the pheasants and deer which soon will be released from the game farm at San Cayetano. These and a host of other highly practical problems will require extended investigation during the formative years of an active conservation program. Research is the backbone of wildlife management.

The training of technical personnel to carry on the field study and eventually to work into the administrative structure of the department is somewhat of a problem, since educational facilities in field zoölogy and wildlife management are limited. At the National College of Agriculture at Chapingo a course by Beltrán in wildlife and hydrobiology was offered for foresters, starting in 1934. More recently this course has been changed to "Wildlife Administration," given by Luis Macías Arellano. In the Polytechnic Institute (School of Biological Sciences), Beltrán organized a program of teaching in conservation of natural resources which subsequently has been adopted in other institutions, including the University of Nuevo León and the Technological Institute of Monterrey. In the National University a few students of vertebrate zoölogy pursue their studies to the masters level, and some of these elect thesis problems on game species. But on the whole there is no reservoir of trained men from which the Game Department can draw, for the obvious reason, I suppose, that heretofore there have been no positions for wildlife biologists.

Perhaps a nucleus of selected students could be sent to the United States for advanced training. Support for this undertaking very probably could be found in the United States if there were some assurance that the men would find use for their technical skills upon returning to Mexico. Development of one or more training centers for wildlife biologists in Mexico could follow in due time.

Wildlife management is an applied science. Like other branches of land science, its success is contingent upon the ability and training of the men in the ranks.

THE ROLE OF ORGANIZED SPORTSMEN

Sportsmen in Mexico, though few in number, are far better organized than sportsmen in the United States. By law, every licensed hunter must belong to a registered club (Art. 18, Ley Federal de Caza). The 480 clubs in Mexico are federated into a national organization—Federación Nacional de Caza, Tiro, y Pesca—which publishes a magazine and maintains a central office in Mexico City. The basic machinery for active participation of sportsmen in conservation affairs is already functioning.

So far, the influence of organized sportsmen as a supporting force for a strong conservation program has been small. It could be greatly extended to compel the government to provide adequate appropriations and legal support for conservation of resources in general and of wildlife in particular. Democratic governments respond to pressure. It is not my place to say whether this is right or wrong, but it is a fact of political life. Mexican sportsmen have a keen personal interest in conservation. This interest might well be translated into influence.

If the sportsmen of Mexico do enter the arena of conservation politics, they should avoid the temptation of trying to direct technical phases of the field work. In the United States too many hunter-politicians come to think of themselves as wildlife experts, competent to judge any and all phases of wildlife management. Instead of helping conservation they often retard it. The place of organized sportsmen is to support the government program, not to direct it.

THE FUTURE

Mexico faces a gigantic and difficult problem in resource conservation. No palliative measures will solve it. A national effort is called for, and the help of citizens in every walk of life is needed. Nor can the job be done piece-meal. Wildlife conservation is impossible without concomitant attention to the other land resources—the soils, forests, and waters. To be sure, there are some immediate steps that can and should be taken to improve the wildlife situation, but these cannot be looked upon as a final answer. Better law enforcement, establishment and management of parks and refuges, technical surveys and studies, and larger appropriations for the Game Department will all be for nought if the destruction of the natural homes of the wild animals continues.

One organization in Mexico that envisions the broad problem of resource conservation in all its staggering complexity is the Instituto Mexicano de Recursos Naturales Renovables. With limited funds but with great courage this small organization is trying, almost singlehanded, to bring to public attention the need for a vastly improved conservation program. The country will do well to heed this voice crying in the wilderness.

Mexico has established its ability to face national tasks of great magnitude. The recent concerted attack on illiteracy is a case in point. The problem of fostering national resources is admittedly greater in scope, but by the same token it is even more important to national life. The future of wildlife in Mexico will be determined, in the final analysis, by the country's response to the conservation challenge.

PART II

The Game Birds

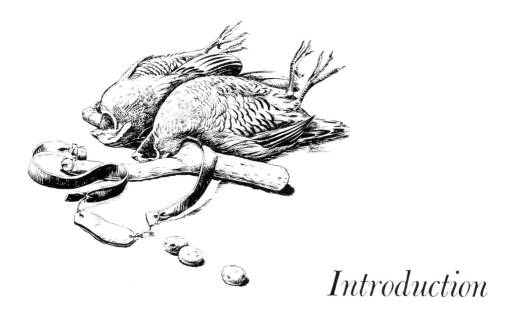

Introduction

As explained in the introduction to this volume, in selecting the species to include under the heading "game birds" I have had to make some rather arbitrary decisions. Some of the criteria used in making the selections were: (1) Resident status: Birds that nest and live throughout the year in Mexico were given high priority. (2) Importance as game: Species widely hunted either for sport or for food were ranked above others—even close relatives in the same family—that are hunted but little. (3) Size: Birds too small to be even potentially important as game were omitted, even though they belonged to a family of game birds.

The net result is as follows. All the tinamous (order Tinamiformes), gallinaceous birds or "fowls" (order Galliformes), and all the larger doves and pigeons (order Columbiformes) are treated fully, with life-history accounts, range maps, and individual plates. All the ducks and geese (order Anseriformes) are considered, but only the four most important resident species are covered fully, the migrants being discussed in terms of their status as winter visitants without reference to the breeding cycle, which occurs outside Mexico. The migrant ducks and geese are not accorded individual plates but are grouped two to four species on a plate. Only a few selected species of cranes, rails, and coots (order Gruiformes) and of shore birds (order Charadriiformes) are included. Most of these species of the marshes and mud flats are of little or no significance as game.

The order of treatment of the birds follows, with only minor exceptions, that of the "Distributional Check-List of the Birds of Mexico: Part I" (Friedmann, Griscom, and Moore, 1950). This document will be referred to hereafter as the "Mexican check-list." As in all such regional faunistic lists, the arrangement is by taxonomic order; that is, groups considered "primitive" in an evolutionary sense come first, the more "advanced" groups later.

Except for the Anatidae, the Mexican check-list is also my authority for the Latin names of the species. Migratory waterfowl of the family Anatidae are named according to the 1957 "Check-List of North American Birds" prepared by a committee of the American Ornithologists' Union.

Vernacular English names were selected according to my own preferences and sense of suitability. I was guided by the two check-lists named above but did not follow either explicitly.

Under the heading "Other names" I have given for each species some of the commonly used vernacular names in Spanish and English, along with obsolete Latin names in certain instances. The first-listed Spanish name is the one which I consider most suitable for general usage in Mexico.

The characters used in identifying birds are the general appearance, color of plumage, and the size and proportions of such parts as the wing, tail, bill, tarsus, and foot. In the accounts that follow I have depended upon the plates to depict the general appearance of a bird. The section entitled "Description" attempts primarily to portray the color of the plumage. After this, some of the measurements useful in illustrating the size and proportions of the species are given. Figure 47 shows the four standard measurements widely used in bird taxonomy. For most species I give the range of these four measurements; that is, the maximum and minimum ordinarily expected. For some species I have omitted from this range measurements of exceptionally large or exceptionally small individuals that might be considered abnormal or out of the ordinary. The tail length of birds having naturally small tails, such as the tinamous, is not given, and this measurement is also omitted where it would not be particularly useful in separating related species, as in the waterfowl. Two measurements of birds often quoted but not really very useful, because of difficulties in taking them uniformly, are total length and wingspread. These are likewise omitted here.

Most game birds molt their feathers once a year, and some male ducks molt twice. This leads to a good deal of seasonal variation in color and appearance. A bird that is rich brown in fresh plumage may be yellowish tawny and tattered at the end of nesting, when the annual molt is due to start again. Or a male duck on the Canadian breeding grounds may molt to an eclipse (postbreeding) plumage that closely resembles that of a female, only to molt back again to a typical male dress in the autumn. I have tried to describe the variations in plumage only so far as it is necessary for identification of the birds as found in Mexico.

The range maps, most of which are inserted in the lower left corners of the plates, I prepared with the vegetation map before me. Knowing the habitat of a species, I could project the range to include all the *probable* habitats occupied in Mexico, even though in some places the established locality records (the black dots) were few and scattered.

One of the great handicaps I encountered in assembling these accounts of Mexican game species was the paucity of records from very large areas, and more particularly the lack of data on life histories of the less familiar species. I hope that this incomplete record will stimulate much more scientific collecting and observation on the part of hunters and amateur naturalists, who can contribute substantially to the work of museums and other scientific institutions. At times this whole volume strikes me as a sort of monument to how much we do *not* know about Mexican wildlife.

Fig. 47.   The measurements of a bird as given in this volume.

Order Tinamiformes

FAMILY TINAMIDAE

TINAMOUS

The tinamous are primitive birds, fairly closely related to the rheas. The four species that occur in Mexico all live in tropical forests and brushlands, but some of their relatives in South America inhabit the altiplano of the Andes, high above timberline. Tinamous characteristically are skulking birds that creep about in heavy cover and fly only when they have to. However, when forced into the air, they fly very much like quail or grouse, and under favorable circumstances they offer good sport shooting.

There are many species of tinamous in Central and South America and some of them have strange customs of breeding. Commonly the female is larger and more brightly colored than the male and she is the aggressive member in courtship. The male usually builds the nest, incubates the eggs, and cares for the young. Beebe (1925) reports that *Crypturellus variegatus* in British Guiana is polyandrous, the female leaving the male with one egg to incubate while she goes courting another male. She or another female may return again to foist a new egg on the male after the first one has hatched. A male may raise as many as three chicks in a season. Carl Koford (personal communication) finds in Peru that tinamous of the genus *Tinamotis* are mated in groups of three—one male and two females. Both females lay eggs in a nest and leave the male to tend it. Pearson and Pearson (1955) report a somewhat more "normal" situation in another Peruvian tinamou, *Nothoprocta ornata,* in which pairs are formed, and although the male incubates and raises the young, the female stays near by and may actually defend the nesting territory. The breeding biology of the Mexican tinamous is not well known, although it appears that the male is invariably the attentive parent.

Great Tinamou. *Tinamus major*

Other names.—Gallina de monte; gran tinamú; perdiz real; robust tinamou.

Description.—Size of a small chicken with a plump body and no visible tail. Head small, neck slender. Nostrils more than half way to tip of bill. Back olive, underparts generally gray but rufous in the belly area. Throat white, crown black. Bill and legs bluish gray, the legs being coarsely scaled. Measurements: folded wing—230 to 238 mm.; bill—30 to 32 mm.; tarsus—71 to 74 mm. Weight: 900 to 1,200 gm. Females slightly larger than males, otherwise similar in appearance.

Range in Mexico.—Wet tropical forests from southern Veracruz and northern Oaxaca eastward through Chiapas and the Yucatán Peninsula.

In the hush of the deep rain forest of northern Chiapas I stepped quietly round the buttressed base of a huge mahogany. With an explosive roar of wings a dark bird burst from the ground and twisted through the underbrush like a ruffed grouse. I missed with both barrels my first chance at the great tinamou. However, there were subsequent opportunities in which I overcame the trauma, and soon I felt well acquainted with this fine game bird.

The great tinamou dwells on the relatively open forest floor of the tropical selva. It does not penetrate the thickets or the second-growth scrub from which flight would be difficult or impossible. On the slopes of Volcán San Martín Tuxtla in southern Veracruz, as well as in Chiapas, I found this bird only in the open glades beneath the tallest forest stands. It follows therefore that the range of the great tinamou is steadily shrinking with the opening up of the rain forest and the intrusion of dense second growth. Within its somber habitat the bird lives inconspicuously, being heard much more often than it is seen. The characteristic call—a long trill ascending slightly in pitch and then dropping again—may be heard at any time of day or, rarely, even at night. One may follow many of these calls and find nothing, for the birds crouch when approached and fly only if the hunter passes very near. After a flight of 50 to 100 yards the great tinamou hides again on the ground. I have never seen one alight in a tree, although Alvarez del Toro (1952a) states that they sometimes roost on limbs.

The breast of a tinamou is surprisingly large for the size of its body, and the flesh is pale and translucent, very much like that of some fishes. This type of muscle in a bird is designed for a sudden, short burst of flight and is incapable apparently of sustained activity. Miller (1943) compares

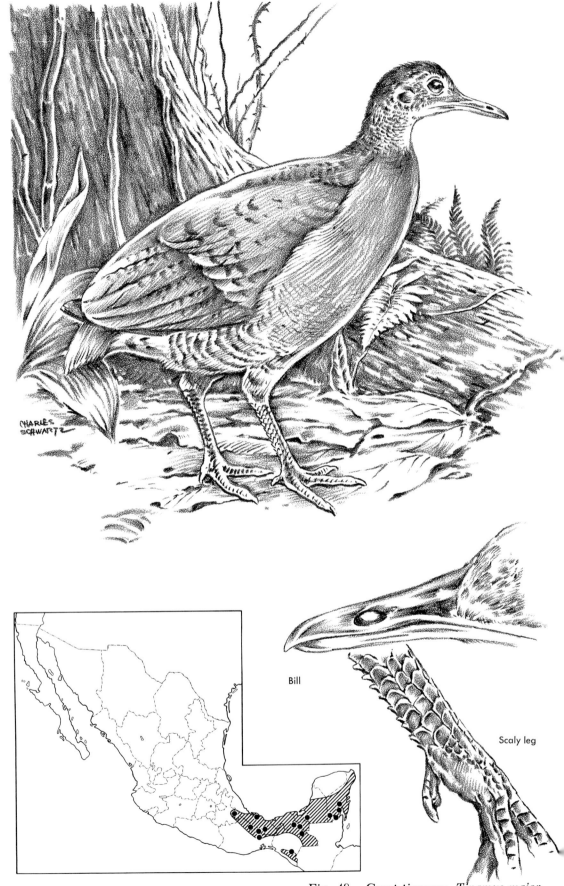

Bill

Scaly leg

Fig. 48.   Great tinamou, *Tinamus major*.

the flesh of the Montezuma quail (*Cyrtonyx*) to that of a tinamou. The flight habits of the two birds are very similar. When cooked, tinamou flesh turns white and is delicious.

The great tinamou nests in the period from April to June, some stragglers breeding even later. Lowery and Dalquest (1951) found a nest with 3 well-incubated eggs on April 14 in southern Veracruz. Van Tyne (1935) reports a nest with 5 eggs found on April 24 in northern Guatemala. Most evidence indicates somewhat later breeding. Clutches range from 3 to 8 eggs, which are almost spheroid, violet, and highly glossed like porcelain. The average egg is 62 by 48 mm. and weighs about 53 gm.; the hatched chick weighs 38 gm. (Beebe, 1925). The nest is a simple depression in the ground, usually in the shelter of a tree, log, or rock. The period of incubation is not known. Presumably the male does the incubating; at least so states Alvarez del Toro (1952*a*), who also postulates polyandry in this species as described by Beebe in the variegated tinamou (discussed above). However, Beebe found the sex ratio of the variegated tinamou heavily weighted in favor of males, whereas Koford found in the Peruvian tinamous that mated in trios (2 ♀ ♀, 1 ♂) an unbalanced sex ratio in favor of females. Adding up all the available records of *Tinamus* collected in Mexico, I find an approximately even sex ratio (10 ♀ ♀, 12 ♂ ♂) which suggests a probable breeding program more nearly allied to normal pairing. Lowery and Dalquest jumped two birds from the nest mentioned above. The young are precocious and follow the parent (male presumably) from the nest as soon as they are dry. Probably only one brood is raised each year. After the young are grown, family ties seem to be broken, for in winter the birds are found singly, never in coveys or organized flocks.

The great tinamou eats a variety of fruits and seeds. Near El Real, Chiapas, I found the large red berry of the *Guatteria* tree to be a dominant food. In the Petén area to the east, according to Van Tyne, the fruits of the "breadnut" (*Brosimum alicastrum*) and of *Pseudolmedia spuria* are the foods commonly found in the crops of these tinamous. The birds have rather weak feet and, as nearly as I can tell, do little scratching but pick up the fallen fruits from the surface of the ground.

These tinamous undoubtedly are preyed upon by many of the smaller predators, such as the cats, the mustelids, and the gray fox. Beebe mentions the margay and ocelot as particular enemies of tinamous in British Guiana.

Because the great tinamou is large and highly edible—"the most perfect of birds for culinary purposes," according to Van Tyne (1935 : 9)—it is heavily hunted, and a good many authors ascribed its disappearance near settlements to overshooting. I am of the opinion that in proper habitat the great tinamou can withstand severe hunting. But the forest near settlements is almost invariably opened up, permitting the growth of dense

Fig. 49. The author with freshly killed specimens of
the great tinamou (right) and the crested guan.
El Real, Chiapas. Photograph by D. L. Spencer.

scrub in which this species will not live. The disappearance of the bird is probably more a function of habitat change than of hunting. The great tinamou is one of a number of rain forest species that require climax forest in order to exist.

Rufescent Tinamou. *Crypturellus cinnamomeus*

Other names.—Perdiz canela; tinamú canelo; perdiz.

Description.—Plump, fowl-like, larger than a quail and having the appearance of being tailless like other tinamous. Head small, neck slender. Nostrils about half way to tip of bill. General tone of the back brown or blackish, finely barred with black, wings barred with tan and black. Underparts bright cinnamon except in western Mexico (Sinaloa, Nayarit), where species has grayish underparts blending to buff on belly. Throat white, crown blackish. Bill black. Feet and legs coral red. Females closely resemble males except for the barred breast, which is more or less uniformly brown or gray in the males. Measurements: folded wing—146 to 165 mm.; bill—23 to 27 mm.; tarsus—45 to 52 mm. Weight: 350 to 500 gm. Birds of the Yucatán Peninsula are smaller than those of Tamaulipas or Nayarit. Sexes about the same size.

Range in Mexico.—Throughout tropical zones from central Sinaloa and central Tamaulipas south along both coasts and east through Chiapas and the Yucatán Peninsula. I heard what sounded like tinamou calls near Generál Terán, Nuevo León; the species may therefore occur that far north on the Gulf side.

One of the most characteristic spring sounds of the Mexican tropics is the mournful whistle of the rufescent tinamou: a monotonous call of three notes, the middle one slightly higher in pitch—sometimes slightly lower— than the first and last. During the breeding period, this plaintive greeting is repeated by singing males at intervals of a few seconds through the morning and evening hours and occasionally even during the day or on clear nights. It is heard infrequently in the fall or winter, however.

The rufescent tinamou is a bird of the dense scrub—the *monte*. It may occupy the forest border but not the deep, wet, rain forest proper. Where the heavy forest has been cut and has grown back to second growth, this species thrives. It follows, therefore, that the rufescent tinamou has profited by man's disturbance of the tropical climax; whereas its larger cousin, the great tinamou, has suffered. Some of the heaviest populations of the rufescent tinamou observed during the survey were in second-growth scrub, as at Sauta, Nayarit (near Santiago Ixcuintla), and near San Juan, Campeche. Elsewhere I found the species equally abundant in naturally stunted, semi-arid scrub like the thorn forest in the Sierra de Tamaulipas. Harrell (personal communication) estimated the population in an oak and sweet gum forest near Gómez Farías to be 7 pairs per 100 acres (in 1949—8 pairs; in 1950—6 pairs); the census was based on the number of whistling males heard in late May.

Living in such dense ground cover, the rufescent tinamou is not very

Male

Female

Head of Male

Fig. 50.   Rufescent tinamou, *Crypturellus cinnamomeus.*

prone to fly. It avoids detection either by hiding motionless in the leaves or by slipping quietly away through the brush. Only when surprised in a very open situation does it take wing, and then it can fly as nimbly as a quail. This species has a plump breast, but Wagner (1949) has shown that the flight muscles are proportionally not as heavy as in the great tinamou, which flies much more frequently (28.5 per cent of body weight, versus 32.8 per cent in *Tinamus*). The flesh is of the same translucent quality as in the larger species but not quite so palatable, in my opinion. The disinclination to fly, impenetrable habitat, small size, and somewhat inferior culinary qualities make this species much less a game bird than *Tinamus*.

The rufescent tinamou is solitary in habit and lives on a small home range, following an orderly and prescribed routine of existence. Dickey and Van Rossem (1938 : 60) state of this bird in El Salvador:

> Perhaps the two most outstanding characteristics which one soon learns to associate with *Crypturellus cinnamomeus* are its solitariness at all times and the fixed routine of its daily life. If a tinamou is found walking along a trail at dawn, or hunting through the leafy ground cover beneath a certain tree, or dust bathing in the road at dusk, it is pretty certain that on the next and succeeding days it will be at the same place at the same time.

Only during the period of mating is the normal pattern disrupted, and even then I found whistling birds in precisely the same places day after day.

The breeding season is long—from late March or early April to the end of July or into August. Paynter (1955 : 19) found little development of the gonads in early March in Yucatán, but "by April all were in breeding condition." Harrell noted a rapid increase in the size of testes of tinamous taken near Gómez Farías, Tamaulipas, between March 23 and April 3. In the same general area but at lower elevation Sutton and Pettingill (1942) found tinamous with the testes already enlarged by March 22. On April 20 a native told them of a nest with three eggs that had recently hatched. In Nayarit I shot a female with ova the size of marbles on April 19. Males collected at the same time were in full breeding condition (testes more than 16 mm. long). There are many records of breeding in early summer. As for evidence of late breeding, Paynter collected a chick on July 5. Harrell mentions an adult seen with small young on August 14. Four males that I collected in the Sierra de Tamaulipas in early August had full-sized testes.

Nests are on the ground, usually sheltered by fallen branches or debris. Clutches consist of 3 to 7 eggs, averaging about 5, which are brightly lustrous and of a "light purplish red," according to Dickey and Van Rossem (1938 : 61), or "of a pale tan shade, faintly purplish," in the words of Sutton and Burleigh (1940 : 259). Eggs measure about 45 by 35 mm. Sutton and Burleigh collected a male from a nest. Presumably the males do the incubating. And yet throughout the breeding season the males are not on nests during the period of active whistling (morning and evening); they can be heard calling for hours on end and will come readily in response to an imitation of their notes. In this manner I called up and collected more than a dozen whistling males and not one female. It would appear that the males on hearing an artificial call come in order to drive out an intruder, hence are defending territory. If this is so, are the eggs left unattended for these long periods? And what are the females doing at this time? There is much still to be learned about the breeding biology of the rufescent tinamou. Certainly there is nothing to suggest the complex system of polyandry described by Beebe (1925) for *C. variegatus*. I have no evidence of a distorted sex ratio. Tinamous collected during the nonbreeding season, when they are come upon by chance and hence should represent a cross section of the population, proved in my experience to be about half females.

The incubation period is not known, but in the closely related *C. variegatus* it is twenty-one days. Chicks of that species are golden yellow in the face and below, with a rich chestnut back and crown. I presume the chicks of *cinnamomeus* would be similar. The young become independent and solitary when about half grown, according to Dickey and Van Rossem.

Rufescent tinamous feed on fallen fruits, berries, and seeds that they gather from the leaf litter. They do little scratching with the feet but deftly sort through and under the duff with the bill. In central Tamaulipas, Sutton and Pettingill found the seeds of *huipilla* (*Bromelia*) in all crops they examined. In El Salvador, Dickey and Van Rossem found insects, seeds, dung beetles, gravel, and corn (trap bait) among the crops of fourteen birds collected. A series of birds which I collected near San Juan, Campeche, contained a wide variety of seeds and fruits, including prominently a small red fig, but no insects.

Little is known of the natural enemies of the species, although presumably it is preyed upon by the full gamut of small carnivores and raptorial birds. Dickey and Van Rossem found the remains of a bird killed on its nest by some unknown mammal that also ate the eggs.

The rufescent tinamou is heavily hunted by the rural peoples of Mexico, yet it continues to thrive literally in the back yards of the houses. This is further evidence that land use in the tropics is generally favorable to the bird, creating more good habitat than is destroyed. The species should be fully utilized, for it is persistent and productive.

Boucard Tinamou. *Crypturellus boucardi*

Other names.—Perdíz de Boucard; tinamú jamuey; perdíz; slaty-breasted tinamou.

Description.—Much the same size and shape as the rufescent tinamou but considerably darker, appearing almost black in poor light. Back deep blackish brown, with narrow brown and black bars on wing and rump of females. Breast slaty gray, blending to buffy brown on belly. Crown and nape blackish; throat

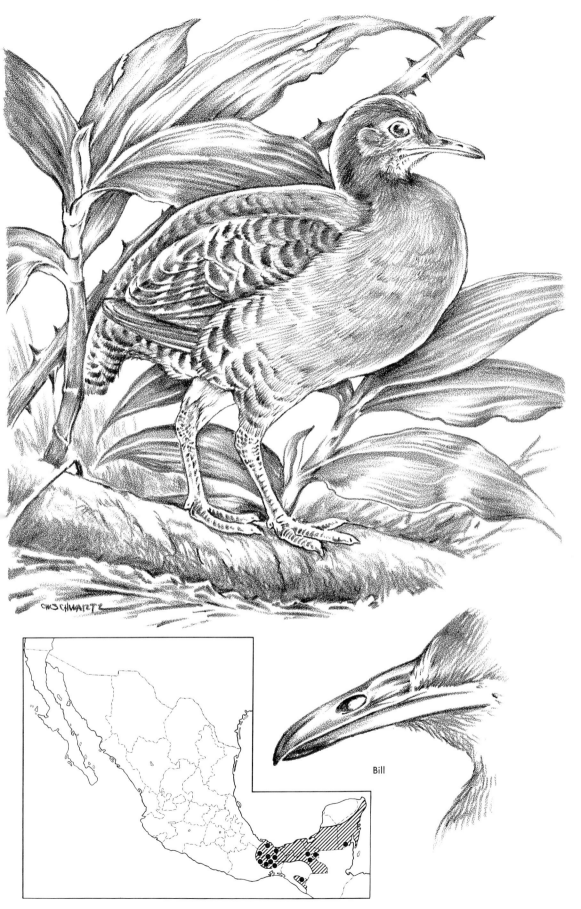

Fig. 51.   Boucard tinamou, *Crypturellus boucardi.*

white; bill black. Legs and feet carrot red. Measurements of two females from Chiapas: folded wing—167 and 161 mm.; bill—25 and 26 mm.; tarsus—53 and 55 mm. Weights: 432 and 485 gm.

Range in Mexico.—Wet tropical forests from southern Veracruz and northern Oaxaca eastward through Chiapas and the Yucatán Peninsula.

The habitat requirements and the range of the Boucard tinamou are essentially the same as those of the great tinamou, *Tinamus major.* The two live together in the twilight of the forest floor under the great tropical selva. Wherever this species occurs, its predilection for the virgin rain forest has been noted. Paynter (1955) found it "extremely common" in the heavy forest bordering the Río Hondo in southern Quintana Roo. Wetmore (1943) calls it "fairly abundant" on the Sierra de Tuxtla in southern Veracruz, and just to the south of there Lowery and Dalquest (1951) found the species in fair numbers; it was not as numerous as the great tinamou, however. My only contact with the Boucard tinamou was near El Real, Chiapas, where I found it moderately abundant. Since it was December, the birds were not calling, and only occasionally was one observed. I collected two females, and others were seen by members of our party. All the areas just mentioned are uncut virgin forest.

Unlike the great tinamou, the Boucard tinamou is loath to fly, preferring to "freeze" or to run away through the forest. It lives quietly in its damp and gloomy home, calling a good deal in the morning and late afternoon. Alvarez del Toro (1952*a*) states that the vernacular name in Chiapas, *jamuey,* is onomatopoetic of its most common call. Since I did not hear this call I am unable to describe it, but it is said to be a low whistle of one or two notes. The bird roosts, feeds, and nests on the ground, rarely if ever going into trees.

Little is known of the breeding biology of the Boucard tinamou. In Veracruz, Lowery and Dalquest found a nest containing 2 rounded (50 by 40 mm.) cream-colored eggs on March 30. The nest was concealed under the branches of a fallen tree. Paynter collected a female containing two well-developed eggs on June 1 in Quintana Roo. Alvarez del Toro says that in Chiapas the species breeds from April to July and lays 2 or 3 eggs. Van Tyne (1935) collected immature (yearling) birds that were breeding in the period from March 31 to May 6 in the Petén region of Guatemala.

I have found nothing on the food habits of the Boucard tinamou but presume that it lives on fruits and seeds, like its relatives.

This species is of little consequence as a game bird, being small and shy and frequenting undisturbed and remote parts of the forest. It undoubtably is decreasing as the rain forest is cut.

Little Tinamou. *Crypturellus soui*

Other names.—Perdíz chica; perdíz de gorro ceniciento; ponchita; pileated tinamou.

Description.—The smallest of the tinamous; a diminutive facsimile of the rufescent tinamou in many respects. Upper parts rich brown, blending to rufous brown posteriorly. Breast grayish brown; belly tawny in male, bright rufous in female; throat white; crown and cheeks gray. Bill gray. Feet and legs olive. Measurements (from Salvin and Godman, 1897–1904): wing—133 mm.; tarsus—36 mm. No weights available. Females are said to be somewhat larger than males.

Range in Mexico.—Wet tropics from southern Veracruz and northern Oaxaca east through the Isthmus area to the Yucatán Peninsula. I know of no Chiapas records, although the species doubtless occurs in the northern part of that state and possibly too in the Sierra Madre de Chiapas.

The little tinamou frequents dense thickets, second-growth forest, and forest border within the zone of the wet tropics. It is more secretive even than the other tinamous and rarely is forced into flight, preferring always to hide in the undergrowth. As a result of this habit the species is scarce in collections, even though in the field it is locally numerous. Wetmore (1943) found it "fairly common" in the wooded lowlands of southern Veracruz, where he heard it calling daily. Griscom (1932 : 98) refers to the little tinamou in Guatemala as "a common bird of the Carribean lowlands, with a marked preference for thickets and bush on the edge of the forest, rather than in the dark forest itself, where only *C. boucardi* occurs." Paynter (1955), however, reports it to be "rare" in the Yucatán Peninsula—"the least common of the tinamous." I did not find the species at all.

The little tinamou is the least known of the four Mexican tinamous in terms of its natural history. The call is described by Friedmann and Smith (1955 : 475) as "dragging the hammer up the upper keys of a xylophone, perhaps seven notes, and then commencing with the same note at which the upward series began, running down the scale about five notes." The effect, according to these authors and others, is very pleasing and bell-like. Paynter (p. 17) adds the following comment regarding the call: "The little tinamou is known to the natives as Kel Nom; the term Nom is applied to any small tinamou, but for this species it is modified by Kel, which means 'cold,' referring to the quivering nature of its call." The breeding season presumably is spring and summer, like that of the other tinamous. Van Tyne (1935) reports a young bird with some down left on the head and back of the neck collected on August 6 in northern Guatemala. Wetmore (p. 229) speaks of a pair taken together in Veracruz on May 8; the female "had just completed laying." The number of eggs in a clutch is said to be two. They are the color of reddish clay and measure approximately 46 by 32 mm.

Schafer (1954) studied this species in Venezuela, along with four other

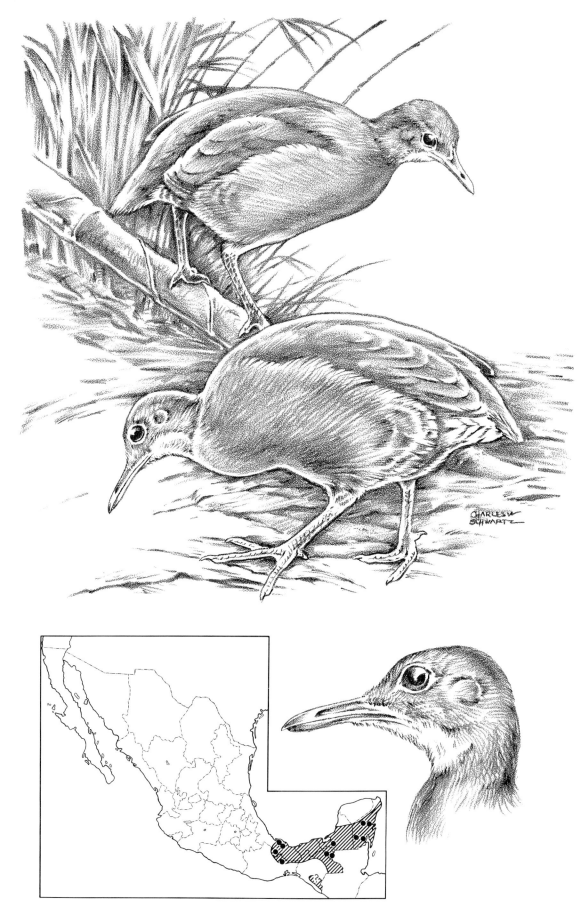

Fig. 52. Little tinamou, *Crypturellus soui.*

tinamous of that country, and adds the following notes. A male was found to have a very circumscribed home range (20 by 50 m.). Both sexes give the long trilling whistle. The birds roost in groups of three to five, except in the breeding season (March to June), when they are found mostly in pairs. The population studied by Schafer contained about as many males as females.

The little tinamou is more of an ornithological curiosity than a game bird in Mexico. Further study of its biology might prove very rewarding. Although it is not an abundant species, its status is safe, apparently, since it responds favorably to secondary stages of succession in the rain forest.

Order Anseriformes

FAMILY ANATIDAE

Ducks, Geese, and Swans

Migratory waterfowl of the family Anatidae constitute much the most important group of game birds in Mexico. Many sport hunters in the country devote at least part of their hunting time to the pursuit of ducks and geese. Local people shoot these birds for food as well as for sport. And in the past there was some local commerce in ducks, although now there is hardly any. No other family of birds even approaches this one in recreational and economic value. For that reason, the status of waterfowl in Mexico and the problems of waterfowl conservation deserve the most careful consideration and scrutiny.

Most of the waterfowl of North America breed in Canada, Alaska, and the northern United States and winter in the southern United States and Mexico (fig. 53). Only a few of the ducks—mostly blue-winged teal, pintail, and lesser scaup—travel beyond Mexico in winter. Hence the three principal nations of North America have it within their power to manage and to regulate the waterfowl resource. As a result of international treaties between Canada and the United States in 1916, and between the United States

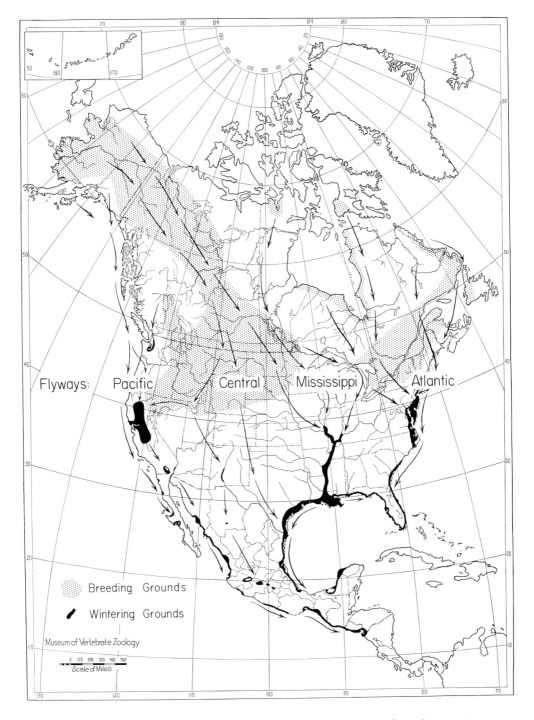

Fig. 53. Principal breeding grounds and wintering
grounds of migratory waterfowl in North America.
The intervening migration routes are grouped
into four recognized "flyways."

and Mexico in 1936, these three nations are, in fact, applying their joint effort to conserving waterfowl for the recreational use of all the people of the continent.

Mexico, being at the southern end of the waterfowl line, is concerned mainly with winter problems. With the exception of four species of ducks that breed principally in Mexico, the species accounts which follow will consider only the status of the various kinds of waterfowl as winter migrants in this country. That is, details of breeding and other events that occur in the main at points far to the north will be omitted. The reader who wishes to follow the individual species through their full yearly cycle is referred to the excellent volume by Kortright entitled *The Ducks, Geese, and Swans of North America* (1942); to two books by Hochbaum, *The Canvasback on a Prairie Marsh* (1944), given over principally to a discussion of biology of ducks, and *Travels and Traditions of Waterfowl* (1955), which treats of their migration; and to *Prairie Ducks,* by Sowls (1955). For a comprehensive report on waterfowl and waterfowl habitat in Mexico I recommend the recent publication by Arellano and Rojas (1956) entitled *Aves Acuáticas Migratorias en México.*

The Mexican hunter is justifiably concerned with the general problems of waterfowl production and with competitive hunting of the birds along the migratory routes before they reach Mexico. These will now be briefly discussed.

Breeding grounds.—Most of the ducks on the continent breed on the Canadian prairies, in the provinces of Alberta, Saskatchewan, and Manitoba. This prairie breeding area laps over slightly into the north-central United States. Lesser numbers of ducks breed in Alaska and in other parts of Canada. Geese, on the contrary, nest chiefly in the remote tundra of Alaska (the Yukon-Kuskokwim delta especially) and in extreme northern Canada.

In the process of land settlement, the Arctic breeding zone of geese and of some of the ducks has been little altered, but the prairie zone, which is the real "duck factory" where most of the game ducks are produced, has been seriously disrupted. Uncounted thousands of the sloughs, marshes, and potholes that once served as duck nesting sites have been drained to make farmland. This process of agricultural drainage has all but eliminated large-scale waterfowl nesting in the northern United States and has curtailed it in varying degree locally in Canada. One of the really difficult problems in waterfowl conservation has been—and still is—to keep the remaining prairie marshes from being drained and to restore some of those previously drained that did not prove to be good farmland. This task has been undertaken jointly by governmental agencies in Canada and the United States and by a private organization named "Ducks Unlimited" that raises funds by private subscription in the United States and Canada for marsh restoration on the Canadian side of the border. Preserving the breeding grounds is still a crucial problem and one that will require continuous attention.

Migration routes.—After breeding is over and the birds have molted into fresh plumage, the great southward trek begins. Some species, such as the blue-winged teal, migrate in August and September; others come later; but all must retreat before the winter ice forms in November.

The principal migration routes are learned by tracing the movements of banded birds, of which more than a million have been marked and released. The movements can be deduced if hunters promptly send in the bands found on birds which they shoot. From data of this nature it has been learned that North American ducks and geese follow four main travel routes. These routes, which are called "flyways," are indicated on the map in figure 53. By and large, individual birds stay in their ancestral flyways without much crossing back and forth. Mexico draws most of its ducks and geese from the two western routes.

Birds of the Pacific flyway that reach Mexico follow the Pacific coastline on the whole, scattering along the wintering marshes from southern Sonora to Chiapas and even beyond. Some of this flight seems to cut inland, perhaps up the Río Santiago, for banded individuals have been recovered at various inland sites and even across the country on the Gulf coast.

Ducks and a few geese of the central flyway travel one of two routes—·down the center of the country between the eastern and the western mountains, or down the Gulf coast from Texas to southern Veracruz and Tabasco. However, since one characteristic species of this flyway, the gadwall, shows up in substantial numbers on the Pacific coast from southern Sinaloa to Guerrero, it is probable that some ducks from the Rocky Mountain region cross Arizona and Sonora and thus mix with the Pacific flight.

Relatively fewer birds from the Mississippi flyway come into Mexico in winter. The blue-winged teal, however, comes in great numbers. This bird, characteristically the earliest migrant, enters Mexico along the Gulf coast. Some of the teal cross the Gulf directly and gather in Yucatán. Some fly round the edge through Tamaulipas and Veracruz. Some cross the mountains to the interior. And a great many go all the way across the country to the Guerrero coast, seemingly ignoring the mountain barriers. However, the main duck of this flyway, the mallard, rarely reaches Mexico but stops on favorable wintering grounds to the north. A few snow geese, with scattered blue geese mixed in, follow the Gulf coast to the Isthmus of Tehuantepec and occasionally cross the isthmus to Chiapas.

As far as we know, virtually none of the birds from the Atlantic flyway come to Mexico.

Problems along the migration routes.—Ducks and geese migrating southward in autumn face two serious problems: they must find adequate marshland habitat where they can rest and feed en route; and they face the danger of being shot by hunters all along the way.

Marshland drainage, which has curtailed the breeding grounds, is even much more severe along the travel routes to the south and on the wintering grounds. Although less than half of the prairie breeding marshes in Canada and the northern United States have been destroyed, probably half or three-quarters of the marshlands in the central and southern United States have been drained. In one sense this is not so serious as it sounds, for ducks in autumn are highly gregarious and will crowd together on small bodies of water in a way that would be impossible when they are breeding. Each nesting pair ordinarily requires a breeding territory which it defends from other birds of the same species. A thinly spread population results. The same ducks with their grown families will concentrate on very small areas in autumn or winter. A widespread network of refuges has been developed in all parts of the United States by federal, state, and private agencies, and these refuges serve well enough as stopping places for the migratory flocks, although their aggregate area is small. However, they do not supply adequate food for the birds. This problem is most severe in the interior of the continent. Along the coastlines the brackish marshes and shallow bays more nearly fulfill the needs of waterfowl for feeding grounds.

Some species have met the food problem by leaving the refuges at night to glean grain in the stubble fields. Outstanding in this regard are two species of ducks—the mallard, which picks the dropped corn, wheat, and barley of the Mississippi Valley; and the pintail, which utilizes in similar fashion the rice and other grain stubbles of the West. Some of the grazing birds, such as the baldpate and certain of the geese, follow the same plan in plucking the green leaves of pastures and winter grainfields. These species that use the refuges as safe resting spots and go elsewhere to feed have become so plentiful that their numbers now dominate the continental population of waterfowl. This system renders most of the birds safe from hunters and keeps them well fed.

Far less successful in meeting their forage needs and in escaping the guns are the compulsory marsh feeders that for one reason or another do not adapt to dry-land foraging. In this category are such ducks as the gadwall, shoveler, teals, redhead, and ringneck. The decrease in numbers of these ducks may be due in part to a loss of breeding grounds, but a heavy kill in the hunting marshes where the birds must go to feed is also an important factor. The redhead, for example, was once one of the most numerous and most important game ducks of the interior. Old shooting-club records from the Central Valley of California show a preponderance of redheads in the bag. The redhead was once a dominant duck also in the marshes near Mexico City. Today it is a rare species in the interior and is by no means common even on the coasts. In other words, the system of refuges along the flyways and on the wintering grounds has not served all species of waterfowl equally well, because some species are much more adaptable in their foraging habits than others.

A second major hazard for the waterfowl as they move south is hunting. This begins in September in Canada, and the birds run a continuous gantlet of shotguns across the whole United States, relief coming only when the season closes in January in the southernmost states. Birds that go on to Mexico face the guns for an additional two months, or until March 15. In Mexico, where hunting pressure is relatively very light, it is difficult for sportsmen to envision the tremendous concentration of firepower that characterizes duck hunting in the United States. Practically every marsh, puddle, pothole, and creek has its quota of eager gunners awaiting the passage of the ducks. As a result, the kill could easily exceed annual production were it not for rigidly enforced laws that limit seasons, bag limits, and methods of hunting. The legal machinery of the United States Fish and Wildlife Service and of the individual states working together has been developed in recent years to allow for annual adjustment of the hunting regulations in accordance with known production on the northern breeding grounds. If a good crop of young ducks and geese is in prospect, the regulations are liberalized. In years of drought, or when the crop fails for some other reason, the laws are more restrictive. The refuges help to protect the migrating birds, but the kill still must be limited by controlling the bag of individual hunters. The Mexican hunting regulations are designed to conform to this continent-wide plan. In this manner, a breeding stock of waterfowl is preserved to return to the breeding grounds for rearing another annual crop.

Winter inventory.—Each year when the shooting is about over and the ducks and geese are settled on their wintering grounds, the survivors are counted. The survey covers all the major concentration points of waterfowl from the central United States to southern Mexico. The more rapidly the count is made, the less is the chance of error from the shifting about of birds. On the Mexican wintering grounds the count is made ordinarily between January 10 and February 10. Although shooting in Mexico is still going on, the kill is so small that the breeding population of the next year can be computed with only a slight chance of error.

The only practical way of taking a rapid inventory of waterfowl in an area as large as the United States and Mexico is by airplane. Numbers are estimated visually by trained observers in airplanes, or large concentrations are photographed and the numbers counted later. Where available, ground observers often are used to tally the birds in many small areas that cannot all be visited by the airplanes. In Mexico the counts in recent years have been made by two crews in airplanes, one covering the Pacific coast and returning north through the interior, the other working the Gulf coast and returning north through the West Indies. Nearly all the figures for Mexico are derived by visual estimate, for there are very few concentrations that lend themselves to photographic coverage; and most of the estimates are made from airplanes, for there is no adequate force of ground observers.

In 1951 and again in 1952 I flew with the survey crew that covered western and central Mexico. As an example of the results of such observations I present here in tables and maps the data of 1952. Our crew consisted of Robert H. Smith of the U. S. Fish and Wildlife Service as pilot and captain, and Wynn G. Freeman of the Montana Fish and Game Department and me as observers. Concurrently on the Gulf coast the count was taken by Edward Wellein and Walter F. Crissey, both of the Fish and Wildlife Service. They kindly gave me their data for inclusion here. The airplanes were both Grumman amphibians. The counts were made from low altitude (150 to 200 ft.), and wherever possible the coverage of marsh areas was complete; that is, by flying a zigzag course an attempt was made to see and estimate the numbers of all the ducks and geese. As the count was in progress, each observer recorded his estimates of numbers of birds seen on

Fig. 54. Amphibious airplane of the U. S. Fish and Wildlife Service used in surveying wintering waterfowl in Mexico. Crew shown covered western Mexico in January, 1951. Left to right: Robert H. Smith, Starker Leopold, and A. Wendell Miller. Photograph by G. B. Saunders.

his side of the airplane and also jotted down the approximate percentage of each species. Later the figures were broken down by species, as shown in the tables. When a good visual estimate of species composition was not obtained, as often happens with respect to mixed flocks of ducks, the aggregate was entered in the column "Unidentified ducks."

In taking such an inventory the pilot also records the percentage of waterfowl habitat covered in each sector of the flight. Although an effort is made to achieve 100 per cent coverage, this is manifestly impossible in some areas; as for example, in the central uplands where thousands of small ponds are scattered over the countryside, or in the Tabasco lowlands—a great region of ramified marshes and meandering rivers. When it is known approximately what part of the habitat has been covered, a rough estimate can be made of the probable percentage of the ducks that have been seen and counted. In 1952, the estimated aggregate coverage, by regions, was:

Pacific coast	90 per cent
Central uplands	60 per cent
Gulf coast	70 per cent

However, in tables 4 and 5 I have chosen to present the actual numbers of ducks and geese seen and counted. The data came directly from the work sheets that were kept in the airplanes. Thus the totals are conservative. Instead of about 2,500,000 migratory ducks as shown, there probably were in Mexico closer to 3,200,000 ducks. Correspondingly, the figure for geese could be adjusted upward from 163,000 to perhaps 200,000. The data on resident ducks and coots are far more incomplete and are not really useful census figures. However, the figures on migratory ducks and geese are useful, and if obtained year after year in the same manner would serve to show up any marked shift in numbers, although minor changes in percentage would not be detectable. The winter inventory figures, from all winter ranges, are given careful consideration in setting annual shooting regulations in the United States.

In recent years the survey figures of waterfowl in North America have indicated that Mexico is the winter home of only about 9 to 17 per cent of the waterfowl, the big majority wintering in the southern United States. A relatively small number pass through Mexico to winter in countries to the south.

Waterfowl habitat in Mexico.—Summarizing the data from the two tables shows the following regional distribution of migratory ducks and geese actually seen and counted in 1952:

Region	Ducks	Geese
Pacific coast	1,440,000	124,000
Central uplands	338,000	32,000
Gulf coast	744,000	7,000
	2,522,000	163,000

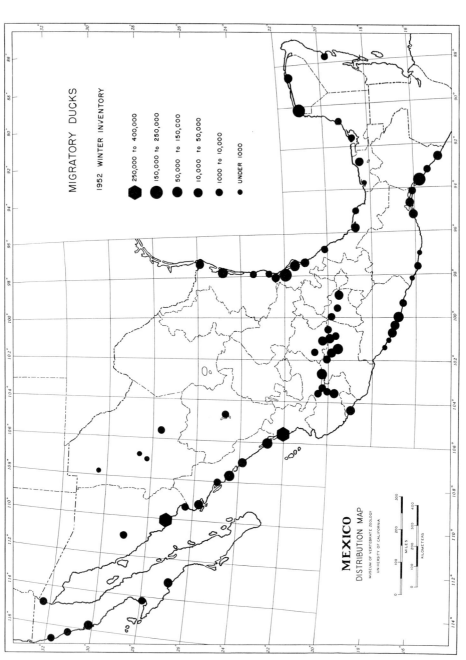

Fig. 55.　Distribution of migratory ducks (left) and geese (right) in Mexico, January, 1952, according to the aerial survey of that year.

	1	2	3	4	5	6	7	8	9	10	11	12	13	14	Total
Lake Mitla	4,680	600	5,385	285	2,900	10,530		5				695		235	25,315
Lake Coyuca	135	125	200	20	1,350	250	100	575	550	400		107,700			108,580
Lake Papagallo	1,930	310	2,170	250	600	300	20		100	1,350		4,930			13,765
San Marcos	510	50	725	835	625	275	20		80	525					3,665
Lake Nexpa	425		260	140						270		100			2,195
Oaxaca															
Lake Alotengo	95	50	130	80	65	25						35			335
Potrero to Río Grande	450		530	70	40	50									1,175
Lake Lagartero	85		60												255
Chiapas															
Laguna Superior	2		595	120	7,050	1,550				36,950					37,667
Laguna Inferior	1,240	310	6,770	1,265		375				7,545					25,730
Mar Muerto	100		1,000							4,050					5,525
Laguna* de Joya	9,160		6,555	1,875	2,050	175,550		700		24,420		1,330			221,640
Buenavista to Río Pijijiapam															
Pijijiapam to Guatemala border	1,525	200	105	325		765									2,920
	6,070	180	9,415	5,425	85	5,440				425					27,040

CENTRAL UPLANDS

	1	2	3	4	5	6	7	8	9	10	11	12	13	14	Total
Chihuahua															
Casas Grandes Lakes		25	100	50	50								300		525
Laguna Bustillos		75	5	200	20										300
Laguna de los Mexicanos															120
Lake Toronto		105	110	25	190	35	1			415	44	160		120	1,085
Durango															
Lake Santiaguillo	215	905	1,465	425	760	1,975	110			60	2			100	6,017
Coahuila, Nuevo León, San Luis Potosí, Zacatecas															(?)
Guanajuato															
Lake Acámbaro	540	425	975	25	25	100									2,090
Lake Yuriria	2,775	430	9,965	600	2,425	3,595				25					19,815
Impoundments S and W of Irapuato	500	720	3,310	1,220	135	135	10	50							6,080
Jalisco															
Lake Atotonilco		400	700	300	50	1,150									2,600
Lake Sayula	130	1,460	195	195		2,670									4,650
Lake Zapotlán		1,500	2,750	1,050	1,050	4,300									10,650
Lake Cajititlán	670	790	1,175	920		8,905				25					12,485
Lakes near Juanacatlán	760		800	1,850	2,200	2,300	380								8,290
Jalisco–Michoacán															
Lake Chapala	910	25,090	25,105	6,950	13,460	27,875	2,840			30				200	102,460
Michoacán															
Lakes near Panindícuaro		500	4,300	200	400	300									5,700
Lake Cuitzeo	2,700	1,245	4,015	775	5,550	7,505		30		340		200		450	22,270
Ponds N of Pátzcuaro	350	3,900	18,685	1,550	5,200	2,225				550		125			32,450
Lake Pátzcuaro	8,010	3,500	8,060	13,400	8,420	3,000	6,500	400							51,965
Lake Morelia			2,900												2,900
Estado de México															
Lower Lerma Valley	100		955		300	100								600	2,055

TABLE 4—Continued

Locality	Blue-winged teals (*Anas cyanoptera* and *A. discors*)	Green-winged teal (*Anas carolinensis*)	Pintail (*Anas acuta*)	Baldpate (*Mareca americana*)	Gadwall (*Anas strepera*)	Shoveler (*Spatula clypeata*)	Canvasback (*Aythya valisineria*)	Redhead (*Aythya americana*)	Ring-necked duck (*Aythya collaris*)	Lesser scaup (*Aythya affinis*)	Bufflehead (*Bucephala albeola*)	Surf scoter (*Melanitta perspicillata*)	Ruddy duck (*Oxyura jamaicensis*)	Red-breasted merganser (*Mergus serrator*)	Unclassified ducks	Total migratory ducks
CENTRAL UPLANDS—Continued																
Estado de México																
Upper Lerma Valley	150	500	4,810	700	3,000	400	...	...	...	...	...	...	...	...	...	9,560
Distrito Federal																
Lake Texcoco	2,550	4,580	15,900	910	460	8,100	580	460	...	...	...	...	...	...	...	33,540
Hidalgo, Puebla, Morelos	...	...	...	...	...	...	...	...	...	...	...	...	...	...	...	(?)
GULF COAST																
Tamaulipas																
Río Grande delta	100	1,500	2,700	550	1,050	800	50	...	...	50	...	...	...	...	7,650	14,450
Laguna Madre	200	...	16,600	1,000	360	100	525	44,750	300	1,700	...	...	50	...	8,600	74,185
Río Soto la Marina to Laguna San Andrés	...	...	...	350	...	...	...	2,500	...	...	...	...	...	...	3,200	6,050
Laguna San Andrés to Tampico	...	...	1,050	...	...	...	...	200	50	...	...	...	...	...	2,500	3,800
Veracruz																
Tamesí River	1,200	500	2,000	100	900	...	1,050	...	100	1,300	...	...	...	...	10,100	17,250
Pánuco River	3,750	14,100	83,300	700	4,700	300	25	...	100	1,800	...	...	800	...	54,800	164,375
Laguna de Tamiahua	200	500	1,500	600	1,200	...	4,200	...	...	100,100	...	...	...	...	9,100	117,400
Laguna de Pueblo Viejo	...	...	...	1,700	10,200	...	...	...	500	...	...	...	...	...	17,500	29,900
Tuxpan to Veracruz	...	100	...	...	100	...	...	...	...	...	...	...	...	...	1,100	1,300
Laguna de Alvarado	6,600	1,000	2,300	100	1,400	...	...	100	1,100	6,600	...	...	...	...	26,500	45,700
Alvarado to Coatzacoalcos	...	...	3,500	...	...	...	...	...	...	1,000	...	...	...	...	...	4,500
Tabasco																
Coatzacoalcos to Laguna Macoacán	200	100	200	...	...	...	...	...	...	...	...	...	...	...	...	500
Marshes N and E of Villa Hermosa	2,000	...	12,500	300	...	...	...	...	...	600	...	...	...	...	3,200	18,600
Campeche																
Laguna de Terminos	1,200	100	3,500	3,000	...	...	...	...	...	300	...	...	...	...	...	8,100
Carmen to Campeche	700	...	500	...	...	...	...	...	...	...	...	...	...	...	...	1,200
Campeche-Yucatán																
Campeche to Progreso	80,100	...	31,200	4,100	1,000	...	...	...	...	56,000	...	...	...	...	32,300	204,700
Yucatán																
Progreso to Cabo Catoche	3,000	...	100	...	...	...	...	...	...	...	...	...	...	...	24,000	27,100
Quintana Roo																
East coast	...	...	...	...	...	...	...	...	...	...	...	...	...	...	(5,000)	(5,000)
TOTAL	160,102	149,975	672,745	77,325	140,995	396,670	16,811	73,910	2,880	442,690	4,831	24,605	127,265	595	230,340	2,521,739

CHARLES W
SCHWARTZ

TABLE 5

Distribution of Geese, Resident Ducks, and Coots in Mexico in January, 1952

Locality	Snow goose (Chen hyperborea)	Blue goose (Chen caerulescens)	White-fronted goose (Anser albifrons)	Black brant (Branta nigricans)	Canada goose (Branta canadensis)	Total geese	Fulvous tree duck (Dendrocygna bicolor)	Black-bellied tree duck (Dendrocygna autumnalis)	Mexican duck (Anas diazi)	Total resident ducks	Coot (Fulica americana)
PACIFIC COAST											
Baja California											
Ensenada Bay				465		465					90
Ensenada to San Quintín				350		350					
San Quintín Bay				13,300		13,300					
Rosario Bay				580		580					
Scammon Lagoon				46,500		46,500					
San Ignacio Bay				41,750		41,750					
Baja California–Sonora											
Rio Colorado delta	(6,500)				(165)	(6,665)					950
Sonora											
Hermosillo Reservoir	700		9,850			10,550					
Rio Yaqui delta											25
Sonora-Sinaloa											
Rio Mayo delta and Agiabampo Bay											
Sinaloa											
Rio Fuerte delta and nearby coast			1,645			1,645		1,125		1,125	70
Santa María Bay			8			8		560		560	600
Rio Culiacán delta and nearby coast			560			560		225		225	4,060
Rio San Lorenzo to Mazatlán											650
Mazatlán to Rio Baluarte											
Sinaloa-Nayarit											
Marismas Nacionales	30		475			505		34,125		34,125	38,550
Jalisco-Colima-Michoacán											
Coastline											(?)
Guerrero											
Lake Potosí to Joluchuca								540		540	630
Coyuquilla to San Luis de la Loma							150			150	200
Lake Nuxco to Rio Atoyac							5	755		760	790

Lake Mitla	...	...	...	...	...	...	95	940	...	1,035	8,150
Lake Coyuca	...	...	...	...	...	...	...	...	...	...	920
Lake Papagallo	...	...	...	...	...	...	625	335	...	960	13,910
San Marcos	...	...	...	...	...	...	20	10	...	30	1,775
Lake Nexpa	...	...	...	...	...	...	20	130	...	150	1,725
Oaxaca											
Lake Alotengo	...	...	...	...	...	...	...	50	...	50	35
Potrero to Río Grande	...	...	...	...	...	...	...	40	...	40	35
Lake Lagartero	...	...	...	...	...	...	30	200	...	230	...
Chiapas											
Laguna Superior	...	...	...	...	...	...	...	...	...	...	...
Laguna Inferior	...	...	...	...	...	...	...	...	...	...	1,925
Mar Muerto	...	...	...	...	...	...	...	...	...	...	100
Laguna de Joya	...	...	...	...	...	...	...	140	...	140	5,275
Buenavista to Río Pijijiapam	...	...	500	...	...	500	...	75	...	75	650
Pijijiapam to Guatemala border	...	...	...	...	...	...	...	565	...	565	1,300
CENTRAL UPLANDS											
Chihuahua											
Casas Grandes Lakes	600	...	...	...	...	600	...	...	...	...	...
Laguna Bustillos	12,000	...	25	...	...	12,025	...	...	...	...	85
Laguna de los Mexicanos	...	...	...	...	...	...	...	...	...	...	...
Lake Toronto	826	...	217	...	...	1,043	...	...	...	...	610
Durango											
Lake Santiaguillo	6,570	...	710	...	...	7,280	...	...	45	45	675
Coahuila, Nuevo León, San Luis Potosí, Zacatecas	...	...	...	...	...	(?)	...	...	...	...	(?)
Guanajuato											
Lake Acámbaro	...	...	30	...	...	30	...	...	...	...	215
Lake Yurirea	...	...	650	...	...	650	...	...	170	170	235
Impoundments S and W of Irapuato	1	...	1,050	...	...	1,051	...	...	850	850	5
Jalisco											
Lake Atotonilco	1,200	...	1,725	...	...	2,925	...	...	...	...	...
Lake Sayula	...	...	250	...	...	250	...	...	...	...	...
Lake Zapotlán	...	...	110	...	...	110	...	...	...	...	...
Lake Cajititlán	...	...	...	...	...	...	...	12	...	12	1,150
Lakes near Juanacatlán	...	...	200	...	...	200	...	...	...	...	800
Jalisco-Michoacán											
Lake Chapala	150	...	1,450	...	...	1,600	95	...	1,350	1,445	...
Michoacán											
Lakes near Panindicuaro	...	...	...	...	...	...	...	...	...	...	400
Lake Cuitzeo	2	...	3,745	...	...	3,747	...	...	640	640	600
Ponds N of Pátzcuaro	...	...	750	...	...	750	...	...	1,200	1,200	350
Lake Pátzcuaro	...	...	...	...	...	...	...	...	400	400	8,670
Lake Morelia	...	...	...	...	...	...	...	...	...	...	...
Estado de México											
Lower Lerma Valley	...	...	...	...	...	...	...	...	...	...	...
Upper Lerma Valley	...	...	...	...	...	...	...	...	50	50	5
Distrito Federal											
Lake Texcoco	...	...	5	...	...	5	...	...	...	...	2,100
Hidalgo, Puebla, Morelos	...	...	...	...	...	(?)	...	...	...	...	(?)

TABLE 5—Continued

Locality	Geese						Resident Ducks				Coot
	Snow goose (Chen hyperborea)	Blue goose (Chen caerulescens)	White-fronted goose (Anser albifrons)	Black brant (Branta nigricans)	Canada goose (Branta canadensis)	Total geese	Fulvous tree duck (Dendrocygna bicolor)	Black-bellied tree duck (Dendrocygna autumnalis)	Mexican duck (Anas diazi)	Total resident ducks	Coot (Fulica americana)
GULF COAST											
Tamaulipas											
Rio Grande delta	1,325	190	...	...	500	2,015	...	...	...	...	700
Laguna Madre	75	...	25	...	200	300	...	...	...	...	47,750
Río Soto la Marina to Laguna San Andrés	...	...	...	...	...	...	...	...	...	...	...
Laguna San Andrés to Tampico	...	...	...	...	...	...	...	...	...	...	...
Veracruz											
Tamesí River	220	50	235	...	10	515	3,350	...	...	3,350	14,000
Pánuco River	...	...	1,135	...	...	1,135	300	...	...	300	213,700
Laguna de Tamiahua	...	...	130	...	...	130	...	...	...	...	1,800
Laguna de Pueblo Viejo	...	...	...	...	...	...	...	...	...	...	7,000
Tuxpan to Veracruz	...	...	100	...	...	100	100	...	...	100	300
Laguna de Alvarado	900	125	2,000	...	...	3,025	500	...	...	500	77,400
Alvarado to Coatzacoalcos	...	...	...	...	...	...	...	...	...	...	...
Tabasco											
Coatzacoalcos to Laguna Macoacán	...	...	...	...	...	...	...	...	...	...	...
Marshes N and E of Villa Hermosa	...	...	50	...	...	50	3,635	...	...	3,635	4,300
Campeche											
Laguna de Terminos	...	...	...	...	...	...	...	...	...	...	6,100
Carmen to Campeche	...	...	...	...	...	...	...	...	...	...	6,000
Campeche-Yucatán											
Campeche to Progreso	...	...	...	...	...	...	...	...	...	...	212,000
Yucatán											
Progreso to Cabo Catoche	...	...	...	...	...	...	...	...	...	...	12,100
Quintana Roo											
East coast	...	...	...	...	...	...	...	...	...	...	...
TOTAL	31,099	365	27,630	102,945	875	162,914	1,040 +7,885 [a]	39,827	4,705	53,457	701,465

[a] On the Gulf coast the two species of tree ducks were not separated in the count.

Historical records indicate that the central uplands were once far more important as a wintering ground than they are today. Accounts written as recently as fifty years ago tell of the "myriads" of waterfowl that wintered in interior marshes from Chihuahua south all the way to the Valley of Mexico. Beebe (1905 : 119) describes thus the waterfowl seen at one point on the shore of Lake Chapala, Jalisco:

The guide pulled up suddenly and pointed ahead, and we saw a misty, dun-colored cloud slowly disentangling itself from the marsh. The glass showed untold numbers of White-fronted Geese drifting slowly off toward the lake. To the left were what appeared like great patches of white sand or snow, and we galloped our horses toward these. Soon the patches enlarged, changing their relative positions, and began to ascend, and we realized that we were looking at enormous flocks of Snow Geese taking to wing.

Ducks were even more numerous—"Scaup, Shovellers, Pintails, Blue-winged and Cinnamon Teal were everywhere."

A few years later, Nordhoff (1922 : 64) described the same scene:

The fresh water marshes of Lake Chapala, in the state of Jalisco, Mexico, form another haven for waterfowl. At one end of the lake there is a great area of flooded land cut by a veritable labyrinth of sluggish channels, 400 square miles, I should say. The far interior of this swampy paradise, reached after three days' travel in a native canoe, is a vast sanctuary for wildfowl, a region of gently-rolling damp prairies, set with small ponds, and traversed by a network of navigable channels leading to the great lake. I saw as many geese, White-fronted (*Anser albifrons*) and Snow (*Chen hyperboreus*), as I have ever seen in the Sacramento Valley, and the number of ducks was past belief, with some interesting species, like the Masked and Florida Black or Dusky, to lend variety. A more thorough investigation of this field would be worth while, for I have reason to believe that several species of northern ducks breed there, and breed at a much later season than in our country. On November 20 [1909] I found a brood of young Shovellers (*Spatula clypeata*) unable to fly, and the natives told me that hundreds of ducks nested there, among them Gadwall, Dusky, Sprig, Shoveller, and Cinnamon Teal.

In 1952 there were only 1,450 white-fronted geese, 150 snow geese, and 102,000 migratory ducks on Lake Chapala, and this is by far the most important unit of waterfowl habitat left in interior Mexico.

Most of the interior marshlands were originally in the countless *bolsones*, or drainage basins, which were fed by runoff from adjoining highlands. The most important such area has always been the Bajío—the great basin lying principally in the states of Jalisco, Michoacán, and Guanajuato. Countless volcanoes interrupted the original pattern of drainage and trapped water in many small or large pockets within the main basin. Other similar basins, containing swamps and lakes, were in Estado de México, Distrito Federal, Puebla, Hidalgo, Zacatecas, Durango, Coahuila, and Chihuahua. As long as runoff waters were permitted to flow without diversion these basins remained swampy and supported many ducks and geese. But in recent years more and more of the feeder streams have been diverted for irrigation, and many of the wet areas have gradually dried up. Some swamps and even large lakes have been deliberately drained to increase the area of cultivated land. Today most of the original wet lands are dry and the water level of the few remaining lakes is steadily lowering. This situation is fully discussed in the excellent report of Arellano and Rojas (1956). It is only a matter of time until nearly all of the upland waterfowl habitat will be destroyed.

The present total of 338,000 ducks and 32,000 geese which we found wintering in the interior can be expected to shrink materially in future years, unless positive steps are taken to reverse the trend and to preserve some of the interior marshlands. To be sure, the loss of natural habitat has been compensated in part by the construction of a great many storage

Fig. 56.   New agricultural land created by shrinkage of Lake Chapala. Most of the value of the lake as a winter home for waterfowl has been lost. Photograph by G. B. Saunders.

reservoirs, most of them small but some very large. In general, these reservoirs support few waterfowl, because of fluctuating water levels and the scarcity of food and cover, but they will always carry at least some birds.

Waterfowl habitat along the coasts consists mostly of salt-water or brackish lagoons, bays, and mangrove swamps, all of which are relatively stable sorts of environment. They cannot be drained or dried up, since the ocean is the water source; nor can they be cultivated, overgrazed, or otherwise materially altered. Most of these bays and lagoons are removed from large cities and hence are not likely to be polluted, filled up, or dredged. In short, there is good prospect that coastal habitats will remain fairly stable well into the future.

In several places along the coast, agricultural development has greatly improved waterfowl habitats. At Obregón, near the mouth of the Río Yaqui, and at other river mouths along the coast of Sinaloa, grain culture has supplied a food source for large numbers of pintails, and even for some white-fronted geese, where formerly there was no food and very few birds. In

Fig. 57.   Juan Zinser standing on the alkali flat left by
receding water in Lake Texcoco, Valley of Mexico.
In the early 1900's this spot was a productive
waterfowl marsh.

these areas, carrying capacity for waterfowl has actually increased. Salt or brackish water areas supply the necessary loafing grounds.

On the other hand, some types of river development—especially the construction of flood control dams—have spoiled waterfowl habitat in delta areas. The delta of the Colorado River, for example, was once an important waterfowl area, but now the long chain of dams has eliminated floods, permitting clearing, drainage, and cultivation of nearly the whole delta area. Only a few thousand ducks and geese stop there today. As various Mexican rivers, such as the Papaloapan, are harnessed behind dams, their delta marshes may shrink. Thus even the coastal areas are not assured waterfowl habitat.

However, in the foreseeable future the coasts appear far more promising than the interior as waterfowl ground, and an increasing percentage of the ducks and geese will probably be found on coastal waters.

Fig. 58.   Extensive waterfowl habitat in the mangrove lagoons of southern Sinaloa. Many ducks winter in this area. Photograph by G. B. Saunders.

The kill of waterfowl in Mexico.—I have already said a good deal about waterfowl hunting in Mexico; it is not necessary to repeat it here. However, an appraisal of the *total* Mexican kill has not yet been offered. Because some commercial duck hunting has persisted in Mexico, certain American sportsmen and newspaper columnists have blamed the continental shortage of waterfowl on the kill in Mexico. Some lurid articles have come to press under such titles as "Mexico Is Slaughtering Our Waterfowl"; most of these were written by authors who have never been farther into the country than Nuevo Laredo or Ciudad Juárez, if indeed they have ever left the Mississippi Valley.

In 1947 an independent appraisal of the Mexican duck kill was made by Hart Stilwell for the American sporting magazine *Field and Stream.* Stilwell traveled to all parts of the country, talking to duck hunters and other informed observers and compiling the estimates of many people. Especially valuable to him was the help of various biologists of the U. S. Fish and Wildlife Service. To the question "Is Mexico killing an unreasonable percentage of the continental supply of ducks?" Stilwell (1948) replies as follows:

The answer is no. And here are the estimates:

Dr. [George B.] Saunders—a total of 460,000 ducks a year, including the commercial kill. He thinks the estimate is high.

Milton J. Lindner, chief of the U. S. Fishery Mission in Mexico, who has lived in Mexico City for a number of years and has studied the duck situation at the request of the U. S. Fish and Wildlife Service—maximum kill, 750,000 ducks a year; minimum kill, 250,000; average, 500,000.

William Vogt, chief of the Conservation Section, Pan American Union, an ornithologist who had visited many parts of Mexico during recent years—"Even with this commercialization, no more than a few hundred thousand ducks are killed in all of Mexico in a year."

Dr. A. Starker Leopold, now at the Museum of Vertebrate Zoology, Berkeley, California, who was in Mexico for several years prior to 1947 making a study of game—"The total annual kill throughout the country from all sources combined is probably less than we shoot in this country on an average week end in autumn. I would say that half a million ducks would be the maximum possible estimate of the total duck kill in Mexico, and this may be too high."

Five veteran hunters in Mexico City—first estimate, 450,000 a year. Second estimate, after further investigation of the armada toll, 310,000.

It is almost phenomenal that from these different sources, and without any comparison of figures, come almost identical estimates of the total kill of ducks: 500,000 or less.

Nothing that I have seen or learned in recent years would cause me to raise these figures. If anything, they are substantially too high. With the duck population on the highlands shrinking and with the sale of ducks greatly curtailed, the total is probably less now than it was in 1948. The Mexican kill, in other words, is modest compared with the annual kill of several millions of ducks in the United States.

However, it does not follow that abuses of the Mexican laws protecting waterfowl should be overlooked. The effort to suppress commercialization of waterfowl in Mexico should be continued and intensified until the last remnants of market hunting have been eliminated. Violations in waterfowl hunting are by no means limited to natives of Mexico. On the contrary, an increasing number of gunners from the United States are entering northern Mexico, and in the absence of adequate game officers these visitors are prone to shoot far more birds than the daily limit of 15. Furthermore, a rather large scale commercial duck ring, run by Californians, has operated in the area of Ciudad Obregón, Sonora, in recent years, the ducks being smuggled to Los Angeles for sale. A full account of the disgraceful situation at Obregón is given in the recent book by Hugh M. Worcester (1955), retired Game Management Agent of the Fish and Wildlife Service. Patrolling the actions of American game hogs along the border has come to be a greater problem than regulating the hunting of native Mexicans.

But, I repeat, even allowing for all known abuses of the law, the aggregate kill of waterfowl in Mexico is low—no more than 10 to 12 per cent of the wintering population of 3,200,000 ducks and 200,000 geese.

Waterfowl refuges in Mexico.—The need for a well-designed system of waterfowl refuges in Mexico already has been discussed. The refuges would serve two purposes. In the interior they could be the means by which some of the dwindling marshes would be preserved and managed in perpetuity. Without such foci of attractive duck lands, duck hunting in central Mexico is, I fear, a dying sport. Second, the refuges could function to protect critical concentrations of ducks and geese from local overhunting, on coastal areas as well as inland. Mexican hunters can well afford to lend their aid in building the refuge system. It is one of the paradoxical facts of managing waterfowl that refuges are good for the ducks and at the same time are good for duck hunting in nearby areas.

To sum up this whole discussion of waterfowl, the continental population is suffering severely from loss of inland habitat—on the Canadian breeding marshes, along the flyways across the United States, and on the wintering grounds in the southern United States and in central Mexico. The greatest task of waterfowl management, from Canada to Mexico, is protecting and restoring whatever part of the marshlands we can preserve from desiccation and drainage.

The hunting kill in Canada is moderate; in the United States it is high but is rigidly regulated; in Mexico it is small, though it is not yet well regulated.

Better law enforcement and a system of managed refuges would extend to Mexico the full benefits of the more mature program of waterfowl conservation that has evolved in the United States and Canada.

Whistling Swan. *Olor columbianus*

Other names.—Cisne chiflador; cisne.

Description.—Slightly smaller than the common mute swan (*Cygnus olor*) of parks and zoos and lacking lump at base of bill. Plumage entirely white, occasionally with a rusty stain. Bill and feet black. Naked skin between eye and base of bill usually marked with a yellow or orange spot; this spot sometimes lacking. Young of the year are ash gray with dull reddish bill and feet. Measurements: folded wing—517 to 572 mm.; bill—91 to 114 mm.; tarsus—96 to 115 mm. Weight: 5,600 to 7,250 gm. Males slightly larger than females.

Range in Mexico.—This swan is a casual winter visitant in northern Baja California and northern Chihuahua.

The whistling swan is a rare bird in Mexico. It has been recorded twice in Baja California—at San Rafael and Laguna Hanson (Grinnell, 1928)— and a group of four was seen near Santa María, Chihuahua, at the time of the winter waterfowl inventory of 1951. This great white bird, with a wing-spread of seven feet, is easily distinguished from the common snow goose by its large size, slow wing beat, and lack of black wing tips. The plaintive and musical "whistling" note, given more or less constantly while the bird is in flight, is also diagnostic.

The trumpeter swan (*Olor buccinator*), an even larger species, was recorded once in Mexico at Matamoros, Tamaulipas, on January 21, 1909. This species no longer migrates even to the southern United States, and thus is not likely to reappear in Mexico.

Swans are completely protected in Canada and the United States. They should be protected in Mexico, even though they rarely go that far south.

Snow Goose. *Chen hyperborea*

Other names.—Ansar blanca; ansar real.

Description.—Size of a common domestic goose. Plumage entirely white except for black wing tips. Head and breast often stained rusty brown. Bill and feet pink to purplish red. Young are pale gray with dusky gray bill and feet. Measurements: folded wing—386 to 435 mm.; bill—51 to 61 mm.; tarsus—76 to 86 mm. Weight: 1,900 to 3,000 gm. Males slightly larger than females.

Range in Mexico.—This goose occurs fairly commonly in the northern tier of states. Small numbers regularly winter in central and southern Mexico.

The snow goose was once an abundant migrant to the central uplands of Mexico, as suggested by the quotation from Beebe given in the section "Waterfowl habitat in Mexico." The bird is now uncommon on those shrinking marshlands and is not overly abundant even in the north. Some of the largest winter concentrations are found on the Colorado delta in Sonora, in the interior *bolsones* of Chihuahua and Durango, and along the coast of northern Tamaulipas. The total population of 31,099 recorded during the

Head of male Ross Goose showing caruncles

WHISTLING SWAN

ROSS GOOSE

BLUE GOOSE

SNOW GOOSE

Fig. 59.   Whistling swan, *Olor columbianus;* Ross goose,
Chen rossii; blue goose, *Chen caerulescens;* and
snow goose, *Chen hyperborea.*

1952 survey (table 5) is a very small fragment of the continental popula-tion. However, the number seems to vary some from year to year, for in 1947 Saunders and Saunders (1949) found 50,000 in Chihuahua alone, and they speak of lesser numbers occurring sometimes in the deltas of the Río Grande and the Colorado and Panuco rivers.

Like some other geese, this species is primarily a grazer, feeding mostly on green grass and various succulent meadow plants. Large flocks com-monly loaf on sterile sandbars or alkaline lake beds, flying out each morn-ing to forage in the green fields that may be many miles away. In late January, 1952, we saw such a foraging flock at Colonia Pacheco, Chihuahua, in a valley high in the pine-covered mountains. Presumably the geese came from the flats near Casas Grandes, far to the east. Leopold (1953) describes how the snow geese of the Colorado delta make equally long flights up-stream to find gravel, which they eat to help grind the food in the gizzard. There is no gravel in the lower delta where the geese roost and loaf.

Blue Goose. *Chen caerulescens*

Other name.—Ansar azul.

Description.—Size of a snow goose, to which it is very closely related; the two occasionally hybridize. Head and neck white, often with a rusty stain. Lower neck, back, breast, and sides dark grayish brown, sometimes almost black in the neck region. Abdomen and under tail coverts whitish gray, frequently stained with rust. The amount of white on the underparts varies greatly. Wings black with upper coverts pale bluish gray. Tail slaty brown, tipped with white. Upper tail coverts whitish gray. Bill dull reddish. Feet pink to purplish red. Juveniles grayish brown all over, but with white chin, bluish-gray wing coverts, and dusky bill and feet. Measurements: folded wing—411 to 437 mm.; bill—54 to 64 mm.; tarsus—77 to 90 mm. Weight: 1,940 to 2,800 gm. Males slightly larger than females.

Range in Mexico.—This goose, an occasional migrant, is found in the com-pany of snow geese along the Gulf coast as far south as the Isthmus of Tehuan-tepec. Recorded once from Cuauhtémoc, Chihuahua.

Blue geese breed in remote areas of northeastern Canada, beyond Hud-son Bay, and migrate down the Mississippi Valley to the coast of Louisiana, where nearly all of them winter. On the wintering grounds they mix freely with snow geese, and apparently a few of the blues follow along with the snows that come down the east coast of Mexico. As shown in table 5, some 365 blue geese were recorded in 1952 along the coasts of Tamaulipas and Veracruz, as far south as the Alvarado marshes. To my knowledge, no museum yet has a specimen of blue goose taken in Mexico.

Ross Goose. *Chen rossii*

Other name.—Ansar de Ross.

Description.—Similar to the snow goose in color and appearance but con-siderably smaller. Plumage white (sometimes with a rusty stain) except for black wing tips. Bill reddish or purplish with warts or bumps near the base. Feet reddish. Young similar to adults but washed with pale brownish gray on the head and back. Feet of young pink. Bill greenish, turning to pink in winter; bill of a young goose lacks warts or caruncles of the adult. Measurements: folded wing—339 to 381 mm.; bill—36 to 42 mm.; tarsus—60 to 72 mm. Weight: 1,040 to 1,600 gm. Males slightly larger than females.

Range in Mexico.—This goose has been recorded only once—from Laguna Bustillos, Chihuahua.

The handsome Ross goose is about the weight of a mallard, although its large wings make it seem much bigger in flight. This species is rare throughout North America and is fully protected from shooting in the United States. From its breeding grounds in the Perry River region of north-central Canada (which were not discovered until 1940), the Ross goose migrates south and west to California, where most of the continental population winters. Lesser numbers have been recorded from other parts of the western United States and, as noted above, from Chihuahua. It would not be surprising if a few Ross geese visited the Colorado delta from time to time. Ross geese often fly with snow geese, in whose company their small size makes them highly conspicuous.

White-fronted Goose. *Anser albifrons*

Other names.—Oca salvaje; ganso frente blanca.

Description.—Very much like the common barnyard goose but trimmer and lighter in body. Head and neck brown, with a white band completely round the base of bill, widest on forehead (hence the name "white-fronted"). Whole back, including wing coverts, brown, feathers tipped with tan. Breast and belly whitish tan heavily splotched with irregular black bars. Tail brown, tipped with white; upper and lower tail coverts pure white. Bill pink. Feet orange. Young resemble the adults but lack the black splotches on the breast and often lack the white face. A young white-front can be recognized from a young blue goose by the pinkish bill and yellowish feet; in the immature blue goose these are dusky gray. Measurements: folded wing—386 to 432 mm.; bill—44 to 51 mm.; tarsus—65 to 79 mm. Weight: 1,800 to 3,000 gm. Males slightly larger than females.

Range in Mexico.—This goose is common in northern and central Mexico. A few white-fronts winter as far south as Tabasco on the Gulf coast, and some cross the Isthmus of Tehuantepec to the Pacific shore of Chiapas.

The white-fronted goose, or "speckle-belly" as it is often known to American hunters, is the most abundant and the most widespread goose in Mexico. Examination of table 5 will disclose that it occurs in many more localities than the snow goose, frequently in small flocks. Years ago, the white-fronts migrated regularly to the Valley of Mexico in numbers sufficient to give good hunting. But since many of the lakes and marshes in the valley have been drained, the bird has virtually ceased to come; only five were seen there in 1952. Now hunters from the capital must travel to the lakes and marshes of Jalisco, Guanajuato, or northern Michoacán to hunt geese, and

WHITE-FRONTED GOOSE

HONKER CANADA GOOSE

CACKLING CANADA GOOSE

BLACK BRANT

Fig. 60. White-fronted goose, *Anser albifrons;* honker
Canada goose and cackling Canada goose—two
races of *Branta canadensis;* and black
brant, *Branta nigricans.*

even there the numbers are few compared with the "clouds" of these birds that could be found until about 1910. White-fronted geese are marsh dwellers. They like to loaf in wet meadows or marshlands, flying out to graze on tender greens or to glean fallen grain from the stubbles. They do not frequent sand bars or alkaline flats as readily as snow geese. Hence the desiccation of the upland marshes has probably led to a greater proportional decrease of white-fronts than of snows. However, the coastal marshlands are still proper habitat for white-fronted geese and fair numbers occur there. At Ciudad Obregón, Sonora, the development of irrigated pastures and grainfields has created a favorable environment where formerly there was desert scrub. The best remaining goose shooting in Mexico is in this region. In fact, the geese are numerous enough to cause some damage to sprouting grain, the birds trampling the plants into the mud. I heard some rather bitter complaints against the geese by ranchers near Obregón.

White-fronted geese are decidedly more wary than snow geese. They fly higher and do not come so readily to artificial decoys. Once in the bag, a white-fronted goose is a more prized trophy—not only because of the difficulties of hunting it but because this species is much the better table bird. Its flesh is tender and sweet in comparison to that of the snow goose, which often is strong-flavored and tough. Young white-fronts in particular are fine eating, and skillful hunters, when they shoot, often select the young, recognizing them by the lack of black splotches on the breast.

In western North America there occurs a subspecies or variety of the white-fronted goose which is known as the "tule goose." It is somewhat larger than the common white-front. Its crown, or "cap," is a much darker brown than the rest of the head, whereas the pattern in the common white-front is a uniformly medium-brown head, including crown. Weights may be as much as 3,400 grams. Most tule geese seem to winter in California, but even there this subspecies is extremely rare. In 1951, Saunders (1953) collected two specimens near Obregón, Sonora, that were identified as tule geese.

Black Brant. *Branta nigricans*

Other name.—Ganso de collar.

Description.—A small goose, scarcely larger than a mallard. Head, neck, and breast black except for a white collar and some white streaks on throat. Back and belly dusky brown. Wings and tail black. Upper and lower tail coverts pure white, the white sometimes extending forward along the sides and flanks. Young similar to adults but paler, the white collar lacking. Bill and feet black in both adults and young. Measurements: folded wing—302 to 340 mm.; bill—31 to 35 mm.; tarsus—54 to 63 mm. Weight: 1,170 to 1,630 gm. Sexes similar in appearance and size.

Range in Mexico.—Salt-water bays along the Pacific side of Baja California.

The brant is strictly a sea goose, rarely if ever leaving salt water more than a few miles. In North America there are two species of brant, one occurring on the Atlantic coast and the other—a much darker bird—on the Pacific coast. Only the latter occurs in Mexico. The discussion that follows is limited to the Pacific population.

The black brant breeds along the coast of Alaska, the point of greatest concentration being the outer fringe (a strip two or three miles wide) of the great Yukon-Kuskokwim delta that juts into the Bering Sea. Some pass Bering Strait and scatter along the Arctic coast as far east as the Anderson River. A few brant breed in Siberia and winter along the coasts of China, Korea, and Japan. There may be some interchange in summer between this population and the much larger group that comes down the Pacific coast of North America to winter.

While the waterfowl inventory was being taken in January, 1952, an opportunity was presented to make a reasonably complete census of the black brant wintering in North America. Our airplane covered the coasts of California and Baja California. Other crews counted the birds in Oregon, Washington, British Columbia, and Alaska. The collective results are shown in table 6. For a complete discussion of this census the reader is referred to the original report, which appeared in *California Fish and Game* (Leopold and Smith, 1953).

Of the 174,740 brant counted, 109,545 (including an estimated 6,600 at Magdalena Bay) were found along the coast of Baja California, most of them in Scammon Lagoon and San Ignacio Bay. The importance of these two estuaries as wintering range for brant was recognized long ago by Nelson (1921), who referred to them as the "main winter home" of the species. Lesser numbers of the birds are scattered along the coast in suitable bays all the way to the tip of the peninsula. Juan García told me he had killed brant near San José del Cabo. However, the species does not enter the Gulf of California, nor is it known to cross to the mainland. The brant frequent the shallow water around the edges of bays off the Pacific Ocean, where they feed on the rootstocks and leaves of eelgrass (*Zostera marina*), a submerged plant characteristic of shallow brackish water. Eelgrass is subject to periodic attack by a fungus disease (*Labyrinthula*), which kills the plants. The disease is known on both the Atlantic and Pacific coasts, but its most devastating effects on eelgrass have been noted off the Atlantic seaboard of the United States. When the eelgrass is killed, the brant population drops markedly, as occurred in recent years in Virginia and the Carolinas. Whether the fungus disease seriously attacks the eelgrass of Baja California is not known, but if it does so, the brant certainly are affected.

Brant are a favorite game species along the Pacific coast, but their oceanic habits render them fairly safe from excessive hunting. Probably no more

TABLE 6

DISTRIBUTION OF BLACK BRANT IN JANUARY, 1952
(From Leopold and Smith, 1953)

Locality	Local numbers of brant	State or provincial totals
Southeastern Alaska	80	80
British Columbia		1,500
Masset, Queen Charlotte Islands	1,000	
Boundary Bay	500	
Washington		16,575
Puget Sound		
Birch and Boundary bays	550	
Samish and Padillo bays	10,000	
Washington Harbor and Dungeness Spit	2,000	
Hood Canal	1,650	
Nisqually Flats	500	
Grays Harbor	640	
Willapa Bay	1,235	
Oregon		3,200
Tillamook and Netarts bays	3,200	
California		43,840
Humboldt Bay	25,000	
Marin County bays		
Bodega Bay	235	
Drakes Bay	2,170	
Tomales Bay	7,900	
Bolinas Bay	535	
Morro Bay	8,000	
Baja California		109,545
Ensenada Bay	465	
San Quintín Bay and nearby coast	13,650	
Rosario Bay	580	
Scammon Lagoon	46,500	
San Ignacio Bay	41,750	
Magdalena Bay and nearby coast (1950 figure)	[6,600]	
Total black brant wintering in western North America		174,740

than 25,000 are killed annually during the southward migration, and practically none are shot in Baja California, because of the isolated situation of most of the wintering bays. Nonetheless, with air travel becoming easier each year, it is only a matter of time until hunters from the north can reach this whole coast. Some forethought should therefore be given to protecting the brant. My suggestion would be to declare Scammon Lagoon a national wildlife refuge to insure at least one spot where the brant will always be able to winter undisturbed.

Canada Goose. *Branta canadensis*

Other names.—Ganso de Canada; ganso gritón; ganso graznador.
Description.—Predominantly brownish gray, with black head and neck and

white cheek patches that usually meet under the head. Wings dusky brown. Tail black, with white upper and lower tail coverts and abdomen. Bill and feet black. Males, females, and young colored essentially the same. Three principal subspecies of Canada goose come into Mexico; these differ markedly in size. Table 7 summarizes weights and measurements of honker Canada goose (the larger one), lesser Canada goose, and little cackling goose. The last-named bird is much darker gray ventrally than the two larger races of this species.

Range in Mexico.—Small numbers of Canada geese enter the northern tier of states, especially in the Colorado and Río Grande deltas. A few stray south in the uplands to Jalisco, Michoacán, and Guanajuato and along the Gulf to the Alvarado marshes in Veracruz or perhaps even farther.

TABLE 7

MEASUREMENTS AND WEIGHTS OF THREE SUBSPECIES OF CANADA GOOSE
(*Branta canadensis*)

	Folded wing (mm.)	Bill (mm.)	Tarsus (mm.)	Weight (gm.)
Honker Canada goose	418–527	48–58	76–98	3,350–5,900
Lesser Canada goose	387–455	35–45	68–86	1,700–3,200
Cackling goose	337–422	26–36	60–80	1,150–1,850

Most of the Canada geese that enter Mexico are the intermediate-sized lesser Canada goose. Saunders and Saunders (1949 : 20), for example, specify this as the form found along the coast of Tamaulipas, and it is the one that has been collected from various localities in the central upland. The big honker winters in considerable numbers along the Colorado River in southern California and Arizona and along the Río Grande in southern New Mexico, and it undoubtedly crosses into Mexico from these points, although in very small numbers, it seems. Honkers are reported to have occurred at Laguna Guzman, Chihuahua, before that marsh dried up. According to Juan Zinser, one was shot on Lake Chapala in 1912. Saunders says that a few are killed in the Obregón area of Sonora.

The cackling goose nests in the far north (beyond the nesting grounds of the larger Canada geese) and winters at various points in the southern and western United States. The largest winter concentration undoubtedly is that in the Sacramento Valley of California. Very few of the birds approach the Mexican border, and fewer yet cross it. I have never seen a cackling goose in Mexico.

I have the distinct impression that the number of Canada geese visiting Mexico is becoming fewer each year. The species was often referred to as common in years past, but the only Canada geese seen in 1952 were 710 in northern Tamaulipas. In 1951 we found 165 in the Colorado delta and 5 in southern Sonora. This is hardly a "common" bird. The desiccation of the uplands doubtless has discouraged migration by this species, as it has many others.

Fulvous Tree Duck. *Dendrocygna bicolor*

Other names.—Pijía; gallarita; serrano; chiquiote; pato silvón; fulvous whistling duck.

Description.—Fairly large, with long legs and very large uniformly dark wings that beat so slowly as to give the impression of a goose. Back dark brown, each feather tipped with russet. A dark streak extends up the hindneck to the brownish crown. Underparts, including face and upper throat area, buffy brown. Flanks and upper and under tail coverts whitish. Speckled white-and-brown band across the throat. Bill, legs, and feet blue-gray. Sexes alike in appearance and size. Measurements: folded wing—203 to 218 mm.; tarsus—51 to 55 mm.; bill—43 to 47 mm. Weight of one male: 766 gm. (1 lb., 11 oz.).

Range in Mexico.—This duck is found principally on the coastal plains but occasionally in the southern highlands. The species has been reported to breed in the deltas of the Río Yaqui and Río Mayo (Sonora), northern Sinaloa, near Tepic (Nayarit), coastal Guerrero, coastal Tamaulipas, and the lowlands of Tabasco. Small populations breed in central and southern California and southern Texas. These northern breeders migrate south along the coasts, mostly in September, and they return in April. The southern breeders are essentially sedentary. In winter the largest numbers are found in coastal Guerrero, but even there the species is not abundant.

The fulvous tree duck has a remarkable world distribution. In addition to the populations in Mexico and the southern United States, there are "colonies" in India, eastern Africa, southeastern South America, and northern South America. Although predominantly tropical in its choice of habitat, this duck often breeds in temperate zones. For example, Chester Lamb has told me that there was a breeding population in the *laguna* near Tepic, Nayarit, before that body of water was drained. Tepic is well up in the pine-oak zone. There is reason to suspect that the east end of Lake Chapala, Jalisco, is a breeding place, for there are a good many summer records of this duck from there. The fulvous tree duck is supposed to have bred originally in the Valley of Mexico.

Tree ducks differ from other members of the family Anatidae in a number of ways. Anatomically they are peculiar in having exceptionally long, slender necks and very long legs which protrude visibly beyond the tail in flight. The tree duck holds its neck at a downward slant when flying, like a wood duck. The voice of this species is a long-drawn, squealing whistle— "pe-cheea." Although the fulvous tree duck occasionally alights in trees, it is found much more commonly in shallow sloughs, where it can walk on the bottom without swimming. It also likes to stand on floating vegetation or on mangrove roots that protrude slightly above the water. Rarely is the bird seen swimming in deep water with other-ducks. The flesh is tender and pale-colored like that of many nonmigratory ducks.

Nests are usually constructed on dry ground or in marsh vegetation such as bulrushes or cattails. This fact was told to Colonel Grayson by the natives

Fig. 61. Fulvous tree duck, *Dendrocygna bicolor*.

of Sinaloa, but Salvin and Godman (1897–1904) and others discounted the information, reasoning that the fulvous tree duck must nest in hollow trees, like its relatives. However, in California, Grinnell *et al.* (1918) did actually find a majority of ground nests, although some of the birds were seen to frequent hollow oaks, apparently nesting there. Nests are said to be well built, lined with grass and feathers, and carefully concealed. Normal clutches are 12 to 17, but this species, like some others, is prone to deposit eggs in communal "dump nests," which may have up to 100 eggs. Such nests are rarely if ever, successfully incubated. The eggs are ivory white and average in size 38 by 53 mm. The incubation period is said to be thirty-two days. The nesting period is apparently June to August (Phillips, 1922–1926, vol. 1).

The fulvous tree duck feeds mostly on the seeds of grasses and weeds that grow in marshy places. Howard Leach of the California Department of Fish and Game analyzed the contents of five crops taken in Imperial Valley and found the seeds of watergrass (*Echinochloa crusgalli*) to predominate, with traces of smartweed (*Polygonum argyrocoleon*) and yellow melilot (*Melilotus indica*). Grinnell found "finely cut up grass and other vegetable matter" in one crop. The fulvous tree duck is said to feed on acorns at times, as well as on corn and rice, which it picks up in the fields at night.

Although the fulvous tree duck is well known over a rather wide range in southern North America, it is a rather uncommon species, as the census figures presented in table 5 attest. Admittedly this census is by no means a complete count, for the tree ducks frequent the marshes, where they are impossible to see unless they take wing. Nevertheless, it seems significant that in 1952 nearly forty times as many black-bellied tree ducks as fulvous tree ducks were seen, although Grayson reported the latter species the more abundant in 1867.

Fulvous tree ducks are decidedly unwary, flying very slowly at low altitude in a manner that makes them easy prey for hunters. At Laguna Papayo, on the coast of Guerrero, our guide, Vicente Leyva, told us that they used to be abundant but in recent years (early 1940's) had become scarce because of overshooting by sport hunters from nearby Acapulco. At the time of our visit we saw only 30 of these ducks mixed in with 3,500 black-bellied tree ducks. In my opinion, the fulvous tree duck should be given special protection, both by legal restrictions on hunting and by the establishment of one or more coastal refuges to serve waterfowl generally but selected especially to protect this species.

Black-bellied Tree Duck. *Dendrocygna autumnalis*

Other names.—Pichichi; pichichil; pichihuile; pijiji (Chiapas); pato maizal.

Description.—Medium size, with disproportionately large wings and long neck and legs. Back uniform brown, with a dark streak extending up the hindneck to the brown cap, or crown. Chest rich reddish brown, belly pure black.

Fig. 62. Black-bellied tree duck, *Dendrocygna autumnalis*.

Under tail coverts white, spotted with black. Head pearl gray, except crown. Wings mostly white, with black secondaries and black tips on primaries. The striking black-and-white wings are the best field mark. Bill pinkish red, orange between nostrils and bluish at tip. Legs and feet pink. Sexes similar. Measurements: folded wing—233 to 246 mm.; tarsus—57 to 66 mm.; bill—48 to 55 mm. Weights of a mated pair: male—838 gm.; female—840 gm.

Range in Mexico.—Tropical coasts of Mexico, from southern Sonora and northern Tamaulipas south through Central America; The central uplands occasionally. Breeding areas specifically reported are southern Sonora; Mazatlán, Sinaloa; Laguna Coyuca, Guerrero; southern Tamaulipas; Tampico and Tres Zapotes, Veracruz; and the Pacific coast of Chiapas.

The black-bellied tree duck is essentially nonmigratory, although A. J. Grayson (1867, unpubl. MS, Bancroft Library, Univ. Calif.) reported some seasonal movement up and down the coast of Sinaloa. Wandering flocks or individuals sometimes appear in unexpected places in winter. Such strays have been recorded in California, Arizona, Texas (regularly), and various points in the Mexican uplands. In the winter inventory of 1952 the largest concentration was found in the great mangrove swamps of Nayarit (Marismas Nacionales). Although we saw only a few hundred along the south coast of Chiapas, Alvarez del Toro (1952a) speaks of the bird as very abundant there also, occurring in flocks of "thousands."

Among the four basically resident ducks of Mexico—fulvous tree duck, black-bellied tree duck, Muscovy duck, and Mexican duck—this species is by far the most abundant today. In flying the coasts while taking the winter inventory, one is repeatedly dazzled by explosions of black-and-white wings from the floating mats of tropical swamp vegetation. I do not recall ever seeing black-bellied tree ducks before they took wing. They have a way of sitting very straight and still, virtually invisible in the leafy cover. But when the wings flash open, one's eye is drawn irresistibly, even at a great distance. I found this phenomenon particularly distracting when I was trying to count the much more numerous migratory ducks that were peeling out from beneath the airplane.

This species is more definitely tropical than the fulvous tree duck, its range extending not so far north and much farther to the south. It breeds principally along the tropical coasts; yet it is known to nest occasionally in the temperate uplands. In the oak groves at the crest of the Sierra de Tamaulipas I found a rather large breeding colony. In the past the species was reported breeding in southern Texas and in the Valley of Mexico (Phillips, 1922–1926, vol. 1); but these are not the customary breeding places.

This bird usually builds its nests in hollow trees. Natives of the Sierra de Tamaulipas told me that they had found many clutches in hollow oaks, and I saw pairs prospecting among the oak trees. However, at least some nests are placed on the ground, for Haverschmidt (1947) reported a clutch of 12 fresh eggs found "in the grass" in Dutch Guiana. Nesting seems to be late. I observed considerable nesting activity in Tamaulipas from August 3 to 11, 1945. On August 4 I collected a pair of birds in which the male had fully developed testes (37 mm.) and the female was laying. My informants in that area told me that young usually are seen in August. Haverschmidt also found the species breeding in August in Dutch Guiana. However, Phillips (p. 161) summarizes records to show that "in Texas and Mexico eggs are deposited in June and July." An average clutch is 12 to 16; the eggs are white and measure about 40 by 54 mm. The incubation period is not known, but it is thought by Phillips to be "probably over thirty days." The pairs are said to stay together through the whole breeding season, and a report from the Tampico area suggested that one male may have been sitting on eggs. Since nest sites are often in hollow trees far from water, the young must tumble to the ground and be led afoot to the nearest pond, in the manner of wood ducks. Grayson presumed, probably without evidence, that the female carried the young from the tree in her bill, but no other tree-nesting duck has been known to do this. The broods are reared in some sheltered lagoon or pond by both parents.

After breeding, the black-bellied tree ducks gather in flocks that frequent tropical lagoons by day and cruise out to feed at night. Their musical whistling note ("pe-che-che-ne") is repeated constantly in flight and can often be heard in the evening as the birds fly to feed. They like grain and often seriously damage standing crops of rice or corn. Colonel Grayson stated in 1867 that the birds perched on cornstalks and stripped the ripe ears. This statement has been repeated in many books, but I doubt that it is true. Where I found black-bellied tree ducks feeding on corn in Nayarit they were plucking the kernels from ears that could be reached from the ground, the stalks having been doubled over in the fashion customary throughout the wet tropics. Nothing is known of the natural foods of this species, but presumably it eats the seeds of many weeds and grasses, as well as some greens.

Although the black-bellied tree duck is heavily hunted in tropical Mexico, and its tender flesh is rightly esteemed as a delicacy, the species seems to be maintaining its numbers far better than the fulvous tree duck. This I do not understand, for the black-bellied tree duck is just as unwary and as easy to shoot as the fulvous. It would be well to watch closely the status of this duck. Special protection should be provided for it at the first sign of serious decrease in numbers, which may be expected as more and more the hitherto inaccessible coastal regions are opened up.

Muscovy Duck. *Cairina moschata*

Other names.—Pato real; pato pinto; pato perulero; solareno.
Description.—Large, the old males crested and as large as a goose. Plumage black, dull below but with a greenish or purplish iridescence on wings and back; wing linings white. Both sexes have a white patch on the wing which may

consist of one or two of the secondary coverts or even the whole wing except the flight feathers. Occasional females have no white. The amount of white is probably proportional to age, the largest and presumably oldest birds having the most white. Feet and legs black. Bill black at base with a blackish band across middle, the rest pinkish white. Males have red caruncles on the bare skin between the base of the bill and the eyes; these excrescences grow with age. Old females may have a few small caruncles. Measurements of male: folded wing— 400 to 450 mm.; tarsus—65 to 75 mm.; bill—68 to 78 mm. Weight: 1,990 to 4,000 gm. Of female: folded wing—315 to 330 mm.; tarsus—50 to 59 mm.; bill—53 to 57 mm. Weight: 1,100 to 1,470 gm. Phillips (1922–1926, vol. 1) gives heavier weights for both sexes, but some of these may be from domestic birds.

Range in Mexico.—Coastal plains from central Sinaloa and central Nuevo León south along both coasts to Guatemala and British Honduras. The species is not found in the highlands, nor in much of the Yucatán Peninsula where suitable rivers and lagoons are lacking.

The wild Muscovy was the progenitor of all the domestic varieties of Muscovy ducks. Phillips (p. 66) states that the Spaniards first met the domesticated bird

at Cartagena, the capital of the State of Bolivar, Colombia, in 1514, where according to Oviedo the Indians kept it in domestication and called it "Quayaiz." He describes the warts about the head and makes the identity clear, showing also that the color had already been affected by domestication. It was extremely abundant in Peru, whence the Spaniards exported it under the name of "Pato perulero" to Central America, Mexico, and Europe.

Presumably, therefore, the domestic bird originated in South America and was not kept by the Mexican Indians until the Spaniards imported it. I find no evidence to contradict this thesis. Although Bernal Díaz in 1518 spoke of "poultry" or "fowls" kept by the natives on Cozumel Island and also near the mouth of the Grijalva River, he probably meant turkeys. In Landa's *Relación de las cosas de Yucatán*, written in 1566, the fowls (i.e., turkeys) are mentioned again, and the natives are said to "raise a certain kind of large white duck, which I think came to them from Peru . . ." (Tozzer, 1941 : 201). Landa was in a position to know. The name *pato perulero*, therefore, is quite properly applied to the domestic Muscovy but not to the wild bird, which has always occurred in the Mexican tropics.

Muscovies are much more inclined to be tree dwellers than the "tree ducks," which spend little time in the timber. I found Muscovies regularly spending the day perched on high limbs of figs and other large riparian trees, coming down only to feed. Near Generál Terán, Nuevo León, the regular loafing spots were in oaks. Salvin and Godman (1897–1904) assert that Muscovies roost in trees at night, using the same trees night after night. On the bottom lands of the lower Río Santiago, in Nayarit, I found the Muscovies feeding every morning at daylight in the cornfields. When driven out, they nearly always took to the timber, although one day a flock that I jumped from the corn alighted in an open pasture and remained

Head of Male

Female

WING—showing white coverts

Fig. 63. Muscovy duck, *Cairina moschata*.

there for a time before flying away to the forest. Because of this habit of tree perching, Muscovies often are difficult to locate during the day, even where they are numerous. On the aerial surveys of 1951 and 1952, for example, we saw not one Muscovy, although other survey parties have seen them. They are best hunted at daylight and dusk when they fly to and from the feeding grounds. Occasionally they can be jumped from small streams and pools in the timber, but I had little success hunting in this way.

When flushed out of the trees, Muscovies drop down with a loud swishing of wings and fly low through the forest until they reach a convenient opening for topping out. It is a thrilling sight to see these great birds twisting through the timber with speed and dexterity, the wind whistling through their pinions.

I have little evidence on the time of breeding in Mexico. Sclater and Salvin (1859) say that nesting occurs in December. However, in South America nests have been found in February and May. In Nuevo León in late July I collected three females that had enlarged ovaries which I took to be regressing following breeding. Saunders saw a hen and three week-old ducklings on the Río Corona near Guemes, Tamaulipas, on July 28. In San Luis Potosí a female collected on October 3 had an enlarged ovary (27 mm. long) that seemed to be almost ready to lay (no burst follicles were visible). Perhaps there is no set breeding time in this species. It is well known that domestic Muscovies are highly promiscuous in their mating, never forming fixed pairs. The wild birds presumably carry on in the same loose manner, the old males doing most of the breeding. A young male, probably a year old, taken in Nayarit in April had very small, undeveloped testes (11 mm.). Nests are usually placed in tree holes, although there are reports from South America of nests in the leaves of palms and one report of a ground nest. Clutches consist of 8 to 14 eggs, about 10 being the average number. The eggs are glossy white with a green sheen and measure approximately 67 by 46 mm. Incubation is thirty-five days. The female tends the nest and raises the young without any help or expression of interest from the male.

Muscovies feed on a wide variety of plant and animal foods, in addition to grain. In eastern San Luis Potosí I found them feeding in fields of *ajonjolí* (sesame) as well as in cornfields. Salvin and Godman mention their eating the roots of the cultivated mandioca plants. Phillips (p. 61) thus summarizes other observations on food habits:

The Penards (1908–10) state that the Muscovy feeds on small fish, insects, small reptiles, and water plants. They seem to like termites (white ants) particularly, and to obtain these the birds have to break open the termite nests with their bills. . . . Beebe (1909) saw them sifting mud for organic material, and running awkwardly after the small mangrove crabs in brackish or salt-water coves, in northeastern Venezuela. . . . Lord William Percy told me that those he collected near Panama were feeding on the seeds of a water-lily. Two stomachs collected by him . . . were found to contain a trace of animal matter (insects), ground-up seeds of a *Pontederiad,* a seed of *Fimbristylus,* and other seeds unidentified.

The Muscovy duck is decreasing in Mexico, apparently as a result of overhunting. Although the bottom-land timber required by this species is being reduced by clearing, many areas so far undisturbed have lost their populations of Muscovies. Hunting is the only logical explanation. At Papayo, Guerrero, Vicente Leyva told us that Muscovies had been abun-

Fig. 64.   Cornfield in Nayarit in which
Muscovy ducks fed daily.

dant up to the early 1930's but by 1944 only a single one was left, to his knowledge. This bird passed his boat landing regularly, flying very high, and he had been trying to find out where it lived so that he could shoot it. He ascribed the disappearance of the species to hunting by both native and visiting (sport) hunters. The bird is large and its flesh is considered excellent; I found the young ones good eating, the old birds somewhat tough and strong-flavored. In any event, unless offered special protection, the Muscovy may disappear from much of tropical Mexico.

Mallard. *Anas platyrhynchos*

Other names.—Pato de collar; pato común; pato galán; *Anas boschas.*

Description.—Male: Head and neck iridescent green with white collar round the base of the neck. Chest rich reddish brown. Breast, belly, and sides white, finely barred with dusky gray. Back dusky brown; overlying scapular feathers of wing grayish white, blending to brown toward wings. Speculum iridescent blue, bordered by black-and-white bands fore and aft. Wing coverts and flight feathers brown. Tail dark gray, bordered with white; upper and lower tail coverts glossy black, some of upper ones curled upward. Bill yellow with a slightly greenish tinge. Legs orange or red. Measurements: folded wing—276 to 293 mm.; bill—54 to 62 mm.; tarsus—41 to 47 mm. Weight: 1,020 to 1,600 gm. Female: A nondescript brown duck, the body feathers bordered with tan, giving a mottled effect. Breast and belly decidedly paler than chest or sides, but breast color varies, ranging from almost white to medium brown. Head pale brown, heavily streaked or mottled with darker brown on crown and in a line through the eye. Wing speculum like that of male; similar to speculum of the Mexican duck (*Anas diazi*), which differs from the female mallard only in being uniformly dark on the breast, belly, sides, and chest. Bill dark orange, splotched with black. Feet orange. Measurements: folded wing—252 to 274 mm.; bill—48 to 58 mm.; tarsus—41 to 45 mm. Weight: 1,000 to 1,400 gm.

Range in Mexico.—The mallard was formerly common in winter as far south as the Valley of Mexico. Now a rare visitant, mostly along the extreme northern border of Mexico.

I know of no species of waterfowl that has so completely changed its migratory habits as the mallard. It is well established that the mallard was once a common migrant over the Mexican uplands and down the coasts at least to southern Sinaloa and central Veracruz. I have record of its having been collected in twenty-four localities, the most southerly being the Valley of Mexico. Beebe (1905 : 118) tells of seeing mallards among the common ducks of the Chapala marshes, and others along the railroad from Guadalajara to Tuxpan (p. 123) and in the Barranca Beltrán near Volcán de Colima (p. 190). López and López (1911) mention the duck as a fine game species and tell how it was hunted in the highlands. There are even Aztec names for the bird—*concanauhtli,* according to López and López; *zolcanauhtli,* as reported by Martín del Campo. But today the mallard is virtually unknown in central Mexico and is a rare vagrant even in the north.

Male

Female

MALLARD

Male

Female

MOTTLED DUCK

Fig. 65.   Mallard, *Anas platyrhynchos,* and mottled
duck, *Anas fulvigula.*

Since 1947, when the aerial waterfowl surveys began, the most mallards that have been seen in any year in Mexico were 490 in 1949, most of which were in northern Tamaulipas. In 1951 we saw 142 mallards in the Colorado delta and 100 near Ciudad Obregón, Sonora. In 1952 a flock of 10 was seen in northern Chihuahua. Occasional strays go farther south. Davis (1952) reports a group of 9 seen near Xilitla, San Luis Potosí. On December 30, 1945, when I was hunting ducks on Lake Tultengo near Apam, Hidalgo, I saw 2 drake mallards with a group of Mexican ducks.

Although the mallard has disappeared from the Mexican migration, the species is not scarce; it is by far the most numerous duck in the Mississippi flyway and is common in the other three flyways. As a gleaner of the grain-fields it is one of the most successful species, along with the pintails, in coping with the changed continental environment for marsh birds. Rather, the bird has become so well accustomed to feeding on grain that the southward flight now stops in the major grain regions of the southern United States—the cornfields of the Mississippi Valley, the wheat and sorghum stubbles of the southern Great Plains, and the rice stubbles of Louisiana and California. In any event, the mallard can be dropped from consideration as a Mexican game species.

Curiously, the mallard breeds in one region of Mexico. Grinnell (1928) cites nesting records from several mountain valleys in northern Baja California—La Grulla, Laguna Hanson, and the San Rafael Valley 25 miles east of Ensenada. The present status of this breeding population is not known.

As a postscript, I cannot refrain from pointing out to the sportsmen of the Mississippi flyway that "their" mallards are *not* being overhunted in Mexico.

Mottled Duck. *Anas fulvigula*

Other names.—Pato tejano; pato chaparro; pato negro.

Description.—Size, conformation, and general color pattern of the Mexican duck but even darker, especially below. Differs from the Mexican duck in the speculum, which is iridescent blue, bordered with a black and a narrow white bar on the trailing edge of the wing and with only a *black bar* on the forward edge. Sexes similar except in bill color: bill of male yellow or yellowish orange with black nail and a black spot at the base; that of female dull orange with irregular black flecks in addition to spot at the base. Feet orange to red. Measurements of male: folded wing—241 to 263 mm.; bill—53 to 59 mm.; tarsus—45 to 48 mm. Of female: folded wing—223 to 242 mm.; bill—49 to 54 mm.; tarsus—41 to 46 mm. No weights available.

Range in Mexico.—This duck breeds along the coast of Tamaulipas from the Río Grande delta south at least to Tampico. It winters in the same area and farther south along the Gulf coast to the Alvarado marshes in Veracruz.

The mottled duck was not known to occur in Mexico, even as a migrant, until the careful work of Saunders (1953) disclosed it to be a regular breeder along the Tamaulipas coast. Phillips (1923) recorded the species as far south as the Río Grande delta, but he had no evidence that it occurred south of the border. The main range of this bird is along the coast of Texas and Louisiana. A separate subspecies lives in Florida.

Since Saunders is the only authority on the mottled duck in Mexico, I quote his report of 1953 in full (p. 85):

The Mottled Duck has been shot by many hunters in coastal marshes and ponds on the Gulf coast near Brownsville, Texas. It is equally common across the Rio Grande in similar marshes and ponds of Tamaulipas. I first observed it in Tamaulipas in 1937, east and southeast of Matamoros on the Arroyo Pita and Arroyo Gomeno.

On a reconnaissance trip from Matamoros southward along the coast to Tamiahua, Veracruz, on February 2 to 4, 1938, I recorded 245. Most were seen in the fresh-water marshes west of Tampico, Tamaulipas.

Since then I have observed the Mottled Duck regularly in that part of Mexico, both during the winter and in the breeding season. No nests were found, but adults with broods of young were recorded occasionally at coastal ponds east of Matamoros from April through June. On a trip to the Rio San Fernando delta, Tamaulipas, July 24 to 26, 1941, I observed two family groups of adults and month-old juveniles. Three other broods of young were seen at Altamira, near Tampico, on July 30, 1941. Localities in Tamaulipas where I have observed this duck during the breeding season are: Matamoros, San Juan (near Laguna San Juan), Tomates, Mogote Largo, Loma Chica, Arroyo de la Pita, Arroyo Gomeno, Anacahuites, a dozen others east and southeast of Matamoros, the vicinity of Barra Jesus Maria, the delta of the Rio San Fernando, Rio Tordo, and Rio Tigre or Cachimbas, the Laguna de San Andres, and near Tampico.

No large numbers have been observed together. To date, the largest flock recorded was one of 16 observed at a fresh-water pond near Anacahuites, a ranch near the north end of Laguna Madre. During the aerial reconnaissance made each January as a part of the Fish and Wildlife Service waterfowl inventory, several hundred Mottled Ducks were seen in the localities listed.

In the state of Veracruz I have recorded this duck in the winter at marshes near the village of Tamiahua, near Tuxpan, near the city of Vera Cruz, and in several places in the vast delta of the Rio Papaloapan, south of Alvarado.

Mexican Duck. *Anas diazi*

Other names.—Pato triguero; criollo; pato cenizo; pato chaparro; sometimes miscalled "black mallard" or "black duck."

Description.—Size and appearance of a hen mallard, but darker. All body feathers dark brown, tipped with light rufous brown, the shading essentially uniform from neck to under tail coverts, along the flanks, and over the back and crown of the head. Upper neck and sides of head tan flecked with dark brown; throat and chin tan. Speculum exactly like that of a mallard: dark blue with white bars above and below. Legs orange. Sexes similar except in details of feather barring (see plate) and in color of bill, which is greenish yellow in males, orange in females (rarely with a few black flecks). Measurements of male: folded wing—270 to 273 mm.; tarsus—41 to 47 mm.; bill—53 to 56 mm. Weight: 960 to 1,060 gm. Of female: folded wing—244 to 264 mm.; tarsus—40 to 45 mm.; bill—49 to 52 mm. Weight: 815 to 990 gm.

Range in Mexico.—Lakes, ponds, and rivers of the central uplands from Jalisco, Morelos, and Puebla north along the eastern base of the Sierra Madre Occidental to northern Chihuahua and up the Río Grande drainage of New Mexico. This is the whole range of the species.

The Mexican duck is one of a number of aberrant offshoots of the mallard tribe, found in warmer regions, in which the sexes look alike. Others are the mottled duck (*Anas fulvigula*), which breeds on the coast of Texas and down into Tamaulipas, and the Hawaiian duck (*Anas wyvilliana*), which was recorded once at Mazatlán, Sinaloa. There are similar species in the South Pacific, Asia, and Africa. In the eastern black duck (*Anas rubripes*), a northern species, the sexes also look alike. This bird winters as far south as Texas but has never been recorded in Mexico.

The Mexican duck is strictly a bird of the temperate uplands, never having been reported from the tropical coasts. Its center of abundance is in the lakes, potholes, and catch basins of the Volcanic Cordillera, but even there it is not particularly numerous. During the 1952 aerial inventory we counted about 4,700 Mexican ducks in the central uplands, most of them in Jalisco, Michoacán, and Guanajuato. This is by no means a complete census, for the species characteristically occurs in little flocks on streams and puddles too small to search out with an airplane. Nevertheless, the figure suggests a rather limited population. I have seen only very small numbers in Durango and Chihuahua. There is a second center of moderate abundance in central New Mexico, however, where the species is called the "New Mexican duck."

Two areas where the Mexican duck lives in small numbers on the fringe of the tropics are Tepic, Nayarit, and the state of Morelos. In Morelos I found the bird breeding and wintering on Lakes Rodeo and Coatetelco, and on a pond near Alpuyeca, all in the upper edge of the tropical deciduous forest but in sight of the pine-oak zone.

This species is essentially nonmigratory. It shifts about some seasonally, but there is no evidence of long movement. In most places where one finds the bird, the natives say it is more or less uniformly abundant throughout the year. Only on Lake Tecocomulco, Hidalgo, did a boatman tell me that there were more *criollos* in summer than in winter, and he presumed they went elsewhere in winter. Virtually all the habitats that I found occupied by Mexican ducks contained some cattail or tule marsh. At least, this seems to be the kind of habitat they prefer.

The Mexican duck pairs in the spring and nests in early summer around the edges of marshes and ponds. Lindsey (1946) has assembled the best

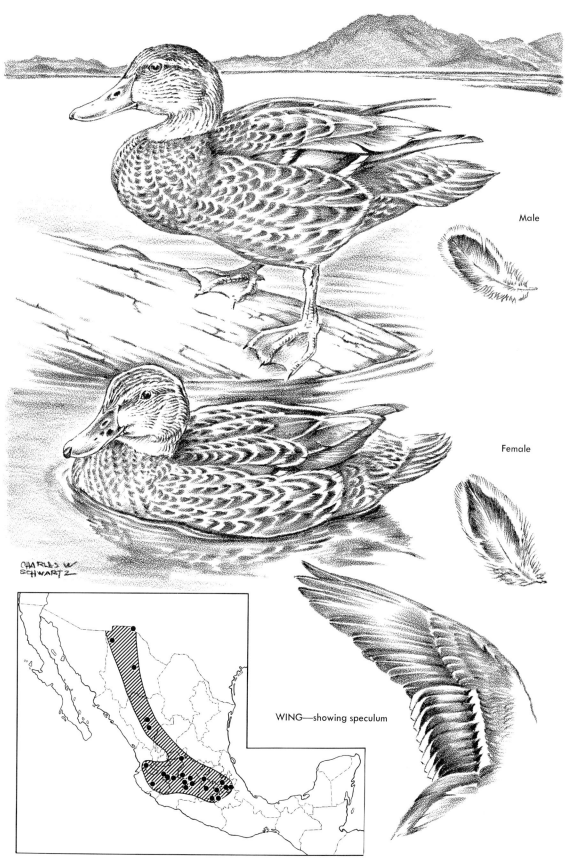

Male

Female

WING—showing speculum

Fig. 66. Mexican duck, *Anas diazi*, showing distinctions
in marking of breast feathers of male and female.

data on nesting in this species. Nests have been found from April 30 to June 25, most of them in May. They are usually in meadows not far from water, often concealed under clumps of grass or sedge. The nest is lined with down, which is used to cover the eggs when the hen is away feeding. The average clutch is 5 to 9. The eggs are whitish, lightly tinged with bluish green, and measure about 57 by 41 mm. The female does all the incubating and cares for the young. In most ducks, and presumably in this species, the male deserts his mate when she starts incubating, but Lindsey found one male still attending a female with eggs that were almost ready to hatch.

Of the food of the Mexican duck, Phillips (1922–1926, vol. 2 : 59) quotes W. Huber:

> The feeding habits of this species are similar to those of the Mallard. They feed along the river-banks, in the drainage-canals, ponds and cat-tail swamps. In the spring the flooded alfalfa-fields are favorite grounds for food. Ever extremely wary, they pass much of the daytime on the mud-flats in the middle of the river. At dusk they seek their favorite feeding grounds, cat-tail swamp or flooded alfalfa-field, even though it lie close to a ranch house or small settlement. The food I found to consist of green shoots of alfalfa and cat-tail, grass roots, corn, wheat, and numerous fresh-water shells together with the larger seeds of weeds and grasses.

I, likewise, found this duck to be primarily a marsh feeder, but at times it goes to the grain stubbles, as the name *pato triguero* (wheat duck) implies. In Morelos it gleans a good deal of rice. In southern Hidalgo, corn was the available and preferred grain. The Mexican duck does not get fat, even when feeding on grain. Being nonmigratory, its physiological processes never call for a large reserve of stored energy.

The Mexican duck is hunted along with the migratory ducks that visit the central uplands. However, there is a period of the year when this is the only species in that part of the country, and then, whatever hunting there is focuses on the relatively sparse breeding population of Mexican ducks. I do not know how serious or detrimental this summer hunting is. In northern Michoacán I talked to some boys who spoke of catching the partly grown young before they could fly. Normal winter hunting, when the northern migratory ducks are present, has little effect on the numbers of Mexican ducks, because they are relatively more wary than other species. However, I saw one hunter successfully approach a flock of these birds at Lake Rodeo, Morelos, with the aid of a stalking horse. With his single shot he killed two birds and lost a cripple, which I later retrieved.

More serious than hunting, in the ecology of the Mexican duck, is the shrinkage of marsh habitat in the central uplands. As described previously, the extensive inland marshes are shrinking rapidly as a result of water diversion and drainage. This loss is only slightly compensated by the construction of *presas*, or artificial lakes and impoundments. I fear that the Mexican duck may become a rare species as a result of loss of habitat.

Cinnamon Teal. *Anas cyanoptera*

Other names.—Cerceta café; zarceta coyota; zarceta colorada; *Querquedula cyanoptera.*

Description.—MALE: A small duck, mostly dark cinnamon red, shading to black on crown, rump, and tail. Back feathers and scapulars edged or streaked with buff and black. Speculum dark green, separated from the powder-blue epaulet by a white band. Primaries and their coverts grayish brown. Bill black, legs dusky yellow. Young males and adults in eclipse plumage resemble females except for the white wing bar and bright green speculum. Measurements: folded wing—184 to 203 mm.; bill—42 to 48 mm.; tarsus—31 to 34 mm. Weight: 340 to 445 gm. (15 birds killed in Hidalgo and Michoacán). FEMALE: A small brownish duck, paler below. Crown and back dusky brown, the feathers edged with buffy brown; sides of head grayish brown, finely streaked with darker brown. Breast and sides buff with darker brown spots and streaks. Chin, belly, and abdomen whitish. Tail and rump brown, the rump feathers edged with buff. Wing like that of male except speculum has more blackish, the white bar reduced or absent. Legs dull yellowish green. The female cinnamon teal is scarcely distinguishable from a female blue-winged teal except for the slightly longer bill, which is more constricted at the base. Measurements: folded wing—175 to 189 mm.; bill—41 to 47 mm.; tarsus—31 to 32 mm. Weight: 335 to 390 gm. (3 birds killed in Hidalgo).

Range in Mexico.—This teal breeds in small numbers in the highlands of Baja California, in central Mexico as far south as Jalisco, and in Tamaulipas. An abundant winter migrant on both coasts and in the interior.

Cinnamon teal breed primarily in the western United States and winter in Mexico. Only a few of the birds stay in Mexico to breed. The species does not occur in central or eastern North America. Like the blue-winged teal, this species is an early migrant, most of the northern breeders moving south in September and October. Points of winter concentration in Mexico where we have found cinnamon teal especially abundant are coastal Sinaloa and Nayarit, the southern uplands from Jalisco to Puebla, and the coast of northern Veracruz.

From an airplane it is virtually impossible to count separately the cinnamon and blue-winged teals, which in many areas flock together. Male cinnamon teal are easily recognized, but the females and both sexes of bluewings look alike from above. Hence in table 4 these two species of teal are recorded together. Of the 160,102 cinnamon and blue-winged teals tallied in 1952, I estimate that three-quarters or more were bluewings. However, in some places cinnamons are more abundant. Most of the 11,000 birds recorded in the table as from Sinaloa and Nayarit were cinnamon teal. On February 4 and 5, 1945, I killed 16 teal on Lake Tultengo, Hidalgo, 12 of which were cinnamon; but in most mixed populations, bluewings strongly predominate.

All teals are necessarily marsh feeders. They dabble in the shallow edges of fresh-water sloughs and ponds, gathering the seeds of such plants as

GREEN-WINGED TEAL

Male

Female

CINNAMON TEAL

Male

Female

BLUE-WINGED TEAL

Male

Fig. 67. Green-winged teal, *Anas carolinensis;*
cinnamon teal (male only), *Anas cyanoptera;*
and blue-winged teal, *Anas discors.*

bulrush, spikerush, and widgeon grass. I have never known teal to fly out to grain in any large numbers. The shrinkage of fresh-water marshes, not merely in Mexico but throughout the continent, is leading to a gradual reduction in teal populations.

Blue-winged Teal. *Anas discors*

Other names.—Cerceta de alas azules; zarceta de verano; zarceta tulera; zarceta de otoño; *Querquedula discors*.

Description.—MALE: Head lead gray, with a white crescent between eye and bill, blackish on crown and face. Back brownish gray with buffy bands on the feathers. Breast, belly, and sides pale cinnamon, heavily marked with round black spots. Tail and tail coverts (upper and lower) black, tail thinly edged in brown. White spots on each flank at base of tail. Speculum dark iridescent green, secondary coverts powder blue, with a clear white band between. Tip of wing including primary coverts brownish gray. The wing is exactly like that of a cinnamon teal. Bill black. Feet dull yellow. In early autumn, males are still in eclipse plumage and resemble females. Measurements: folded wing—184 to 194 mm.; bill—39 to 42 mm.; tarsus—30 to 34 mm. Weight: 313 to 363 gm. (4 birds killed in Hidalgo). FEMALE: Same coloration as in female cinnamon teal. Measurements: folded wing—174 to 182 mm.; bill—38 to 40 mm.; tarsus—29 to 32 mm. Weight: 310 to 360 gm.

Range in Mexico.—This teal is an abundant migrant along the Gulf coast, throughout the interior, and on the Pacific coast from Sinaloa south and east.

The blue-winged teal breeds mostly in the prairie provinces of Canada, lesser numbers nesting in the upper Mississippi Valley of the north-central United States. It is one duck that has persisted as a breeder in heavily developed farmland, for it will rear its young on any little puddle or pothole. An intensive study of the nesting bluewings in Iowa was reported by Bennett in 1938.

A few bluewings nest in marshes of the western and southwestern United States; this breeding population extends into Mexico, apparently, for Stager (1954) collected a breeding pair in the Barranca de Cobre, Chihuahua, on May 29, 1950. This is the only definite breeding record for Mexico known to me.

The blue-winged teal is the earliest of the migrant ducks that come to Mexico. It arrives even before the cinnamon teal. By late August the vanguard has begun to pass through northern Mexico, and for this reason the bird is sometimes called *zarceta de verano*, or "summer teal." The bulk of the flight reaches Mexico in September and early October. Most of the bluewings pass rapidly through and make their way south as far as Panama and northern South America. However, a large proportion of them settle for the winter in Mexican marshes. By far the most important single concentration is that found annually in the *lagunas* of northwestern Yucatán, where 80,100 bluewings were counted in 1952. It is thought that these birds cross the Gulf of Mexico directly from Louisiana. Lesser numbers occur in such places as the Tampico and Alvarado marshes in Veracruz, the coastal marshes of Chiapas and Guerrero, and upland lakes such as Pátzcuaro and Cuitzeo in Michoacán.

The northward drift starts in January. The number of blue-winged teal on the upland marshes increases, the birds coming from the south, apparently. By February most of the teal have left Central and South America, and in March they appear to be well on their way back to the breeding grounds.

Green-winged Teal. *Anas carolinensis*

Other names.—Cerceta de lista verde; cerceta común; zarceta de invierno; salseno; *Nettion carolinense*.

Description.—MALE: Head and neck chestnut brown except for a green area on each side surrounding the eye and sweeping back to the crest. Back and sides gray, with finely vermiculated black and white lines. Chest pinkish brown with round black spots, ending in a white bar on each side. Breast and belly whitish, meeting abruptly a black zone under the tail. Sides of rump creamy buff. Wing grayish brown, the speculum bright green toward body, velvety black toward outer wing, bordered in front with a brown bar and to the rear (trailing edge) with white. Bill black. Feet dark gray. Measurements: folded wing—175 to 190 mm.; bill—36 to 38 mm.; tarsus—28 to 32 mm. Weight: 340 to 370 gm. FEMALE: Head, neck, breast, back, and sides brown, the feathers edged with varying amounts of buff. Breast and belly white. Wing like that of male except that the brown bar in front of the speculum is paler and buffier. Bill black, purplish at the base, with black spots. Feet dull gray. Measurements: folded wing—168 to 178 mm.; bill—34 to 38 mm.; tarsus—27 to 30 mm. Weight: 290 to 340 gm.

Range in Mexico.—Greenwings are common on both coasts and in the interior in winter, being especially numerous in Sinaloa and Nayarit.

The diminutive green-winged teal is one of the fastest flyers among the ducks, although it is the smallest. Or perhaps it should be said that *for its size* the greenwing is remarkably fast, since some of the larger ducks and even the geese move through the air as rapidly as teal. Measured speeds of flying waterfowl show that most species fly at normal rates of 40 to 55 miles an hour and when pursued by an airplane they may exceed 60 miles an hour. The teal flies with the best of them for short distances, but in a long pull a canvasback or even a mallard can outfly a teal. On the take-off, however, the teal is faster, and it can turn and climb much more rapidly than larger ducks; this creates an illusion of greater air speed.

Green-winged teal breed principally in the northwestern United States, western Canada, and Alaska. They start the southward migration early in autumn, but unlike the blue-winged and cinnamon teals, they linger along the way and are rather late in arriving on the wintering grounds; hence the Mexican name *zarceta de invierno*, "winter teal." The great winter concentrations that are found in Mexico—for example, in Sinaloa, Nayarit, northern Veracruz, and Jalisco—assemble usually in December.

Greenwings are marsh feeders. Analysis of the crops of many hundreds of greenwings shows the predominant foods to be the seeds of sedges, pondweeds, and grasses.

Pintail. *Anas acuta*

Other names.—Pato golondrino; zacal; pato de guías; pato floridano; *Dafila acuta tzitzihoa.*

Description.—MALE: Head and neck chocolate brown. Underparts white, a thin line of white extending up each side of the neck. Back and sides finely vermiculated black and white, giving an over-all effect of gray. Wings grayish brown with a coppery green speculum bordered in front with a cinnamon bar, behind with a narrow black and a white bar. Scapulars black, edged with white. Tail black, long, and pointed (central feathers as long as 200 mm.), with black coverts above and below. Bill grayish blue, black along the ridge. Feet grayish blue. Measurements: folded wing—262 to 274 mm.; bill—49 to 55 mm.; tarsus—40 to 44 mm. Weight: 800 to 1,050 gm. FEMALE: A nondescript brown duck, darker above, paler below. Tail somewhat pointed. Speculum of the wing as in the male but much duller copper brown. Bill and feet dark bluish gray. Measurements: folded wing—244 to 265 mm.; bill—47 to 50 mm.; tarsus—40 to 42 mm. Weight: 650 to 900 gm.

Range in Mexico.—The pintail is an abundant migrant along both coasts and in the interior, the greatest concentration being in southern Sonora. Grinnell (1928) suggests that the species may nest in the highlands of northern Baja California.

The pintail is the most numerous duck in Mexico. In January, 1952, a total of 672,745 pintails were found, of which 268,240 were in the delta of the Río Yaqui in Sonora, attracted by the rice stubble. But perusal of table 4 will show that pintails occur in practically any marsh in Mexico. This bird is the most widely distributed species of duck as well as the most numerous.

Although the pintail is capable of living quite well on marsh foods, its success in adjusting to the reduction of marshland stems from its willingness to feed in the grain stubbles at night. Near Ciudad Obregón, Sonora, for example, the vast majority of the pintails loaf all day on the tidal flats, where they are entirely safe from hunters, and come to the rice stubble after dark to gorge and get fat on the waste grain. At daylight they repair again to the safety of salt water. This plan of living is exasperating to hunters but very successful from the standpoint of the duck. Following such a system on all its major winter ranges, the pintail has become the dominant duck throughout western North America.

The first autumn flight of pintails passes through the United States in August, and the earliest arrivals in Mexico are in that month. The southward movement continues until December, by which time some of the birds have traveled to Panama and beyond. The reverse flight northward commences in February. I observed a substantial northward movement of pintails on February 5, 1945, at Lake Tultengo, Hidalgo, when continuous skeins passed over all morning. Curiously, of the 3,500 to 4,000 birds seen, virtually all were males (more than 90 per cent I estimated). Some flocks of 100 birds did not include a single hen but were made up entirely of drakes in full breeding plumage. This suggests some differential movement of the sexes, which, however, has not been noted by others. Banding data seem to indicate that many pintails that migrate down the west coast of Mexico return northward in spring through central and eastern Mexico. In the north the pintails follow the retreating ice closely and are among the first ducks to return to the breeding grounds.

Grain-fed pintails are the fattest and perhaps the best eating of all the ducks. The species is a favorite with hunters everywhere.

Gadwall. *Anas strepera*

Other names.—Pato pinto; pato cabezón; pato pardo de grupo; *Chaulelasmus streperus.*

Description.—MALE: Head and neck dark brown dorsally, buffy brown on face and throat, flecked with dark brown. Back, sides, and flanks vermiculated black and white, giving a gray effect. Rump slaty black. Chest feathers marked with alternate black and white rings, giving an over-all appearance of dusky gray. Underparts white except for black under tail coverts. Wing coverts forward of speculum dark red; speculum black in middle and white on outer and inner edges. Bill dusky gray. Feet dull orange with dark webs. Measurements: folded wing—248 to 277 mm.; bill—41 to 45 mm.; tarsus—39 to 42 mm. Weight: 800 to 1,000 gm. FEMALE: Head and neck like that of male but paler. Chest, back, sides, and rump mottled brown and buff as in female mallard. Breast and abdomen white. Wing like that of male but with less red, duller black. Bill dull orange flecked with black. Feet dull orange with dusky webs. Measurements: folded wing—244 to 257 mm.; bill—39 to 43 mm.; tarsus—36 to 40 mm. Weight: 720 to 900 gm.

Range in Mexico.—The gadwall is an abundant migrant on both coasts and in the interior. The greatest numbers have been seen along the coast of Nayarit.

In the western United States the gadwall is not considered a particularly abundant duck, although it is rather widely distributed. But in Mexico, where the species concentrates in winter, it ranks among the top five or six species. A total of 140,995 were counted in 1952. One-third of these birds were in the Marismas Nacionales of Nayarit. In various small reservoirs of Durango, Chihuahua, and Coahuila I found the gadwall to be the dominant duck. It is easily recognized, even at a great distance, by the handsome white-and-black speculum, to which, I suppose, the Mexican name *pato pinto* has reference.

Female

Male

PINTAIL

Female

Male

BALDPATE

Male

GADWALL

Female

Fig. 68. Pintail, *Anas acuta;* baldpate, *Mareca americana;* and gadwall, *Anas strepera.*

Gadwalls are typical marsh feeders, preferring the seeds and leaves of such plants as the pondweeds, sedges, and widgeon grass. They eat more algae than most ducks, however. This has a very unfortunate effect upon the flavor of the meat, which not infrequently is strong. I have killed fat gadwalls that were scarcely edible; yet at times gadwalls are as sweet as mallards. Presumably the variation in flavor is due to the birds' diet.

Baldpate. *Mareca americana*

Other names.—Pato chalcuán; pato panadero; saradillo; cotorrito; pato calvo; American widgeon.

Description.—MALE: Crown of head white, with adjoining green band on side of head extending back from eye. Lower part of head and the neck buffy gray flecked with black. Back and sides pinkish brown finely vermiculated with black. Chest purplish pink. Underparts white, except for black under tail coverts. Wing coverts clear white, separated from speculum by a black bar. Speculum dark green with one or two white feathers on inner edge. Primaries and primary coverts grayish brown. Bill and feet blue-gray, the bill black tipped. Measurements: folded wing—250 to 263 mm.; bill—35 to 40 mm.; tarsus—36 to 40 mm. Weight: 640 to 900 gm. FEMALE: Head and neck gray, darker above, finely flecked with black. Chest, sides, back, and rump warm brown, back and side feathers edged with buff. Underparts white. Wing similar to that of male but coverts grayish white, speculum duller. Bill and feet bluish gray. Measurements: folded wing—228 to 249 mm.; bill—31 to 39 mm.; tarsus—35 to 39 mm. Weight: 600 to 850 gm.

Range in Mexico.—The baldpate is a numerous winter migrant along the coasts and in the interior, the largest numbers occurring in Sinaloa, Jalisco, and northern Michoacán.

The baldpate, like the pintail, is attracted to irrigated farmlands. However, unlike the pintail, it eats quantities of green food in addition to grain. Tender alfalfa, sprouting grain, and truck crops are eaten by baldpates to the extent that the crops are seriously damaged. In the Imperial Valley of southern California and in adjoining parts of Baja California the baldpate is considered an agricultural pest. However, in marshes well stocked with natural foods—especially pondweeds—baldpates get enough to eat without bothering the farmers. Lake Pátzcuaro in Michoacán, with its heavy growth of pondweed (*Potamogeton*), is an example of fine habitat for baldpates.

Baldpates are among the most talkative of the ducks, frequently emitting a plaintive whistling note as they fly. Flocks moving in tight formation are much given to aerial acrobatics, wheeling and diving with great agility and grace. They come readily to artificial decoys, and many of them are shot along the southward migration. However, the species is still among the most abundant of American ducks.

Its close relative in the Old World, the European widgeon (*Mareca penelope*) is an occasional visitor in North America. There is one record from Descanso in northern Baja California. The European widgeon resembles the American baldpate in most particulars, except that the head of the male is cinnamon brown with dark flecks and the crown is buffy instead of white. There is no green on the face.

Shoveler. *Spatula clypeata*

Other names.—Pato cuaresmeño; pato cucharón; pato bocón; pato cucharudo.

Description.—MALE: Head and neck iridescent green. Chest, foreback, and scapulars white. Back dusky brown. Breast and sides rich reddish chestnut. Belly paler chestnut. Flanks white at base of tail. Tail white, upper and lower tail coverts greenish black. Wing coverts pale blue, separated from green speculum by a white bar. Bill black, much enlarged toward the tip, its shape suggesting a spoon. Feet orange. Measurements: folded wing—243 to 252 mm.; bill—63 to 68 mm.; tarsus—37 to 39 mm. Weight: 600 to 750 gm. FEMALE: A brown duck, distinguishable from other female ducks of like size by the enormous bill, which is greenish gray, and by the wing markings, which are like those of the male but less intense. Feet orange. Measurements: folded wing—223 to 236 mm.; bill—58 to 64 mm.; tarsus—35 to 37 mm. Weight: 500 to 660 gm.

Fig. 69.   Shovelers wintering on coastal lagoons in Oaxaca. Photograph by G. B. Saunders.

Range in Mexico.—The shoveler is an abundant winter visitant on the Pacific coast and in the uplands, the greatest concentration each year being found at Laguna de Joya, southern Chiapas. It is uncommon on the Gulf coast.

The shoveler is a close relative of the blue-winged and cinnamon teals. It carries the same powder-blue epaulet on the wing, and hybrids of these species are known to occur. But the shoveler has digressed in its evolution, to become a specialist in straining the tiny food particles from the surface of the water through the lamellae of its ample bill, retaining the edible matter and discarding the trash. Sometimes it sifts the soft bottom ooze for food—seeds or minute plants and animals. In feeding, the bill is oscillated to maintain the flow of water and materials through the lamellae.

Like the teals mentioned above, the shoveler is an early fall migrant, drifting southward in the autumn to concentrate mainly in shallow waters along the Pacific coast of Mexico well before the winter cold arrives in the north.

Since the shoveler customarily flies low and decoys readily, it makes up a large part of the hunting kill. Because of this and the bird's absolute dependence on shallow marsh habitat, the future of the species in North America looks anything but promising. Special protection may be required in order to maintain its numbers.

Wood Duck. *Aix sponsa*

Other names.—Pato de charreteras; pato de árbol; pato real cimarrón.

Description.—MALE: Head with prominent crest, mostly dark blue-green with narrow white stripes from bill and from eye to tip of crest. White throat and chin, a white bar extending up toward the eye. Back, rump, and tail black with blue or green iridescence. Chest reddish chestnut spotted with white. Sides finely vermiculated with buffy brown and black, the whole side area bordered with bold black and white bars dorsally and forward. Breast and abdomen white. Under tail coverts brown. Wing glossy blue-black at base, dusky at tip, the primary feathers "frosted" with silver at tips. Bill red with a black stripe down middle, black nail, and narrow yellow stripe at base. Feet dusky yellow. Measurements: folded wing—222 to 238 mm.; bill—33 to 38 mm.; tarsus—34 to 37 mm. Weight: 560 to 890 gm. FEMALE: Head with skimpy crest. Crown, back of neck, back, and rump brown glossed with greenish or bronze. Whitish throat and ring around eye extending back toward crest. Chest and sides dull brown marked with buff. Breast and abdomen white. Wing like that of male. Bill bluish gray, darker on ridge, pinkish toward edges. Feet dusky yellow. Measurements: folded wing—212 to 226 mm.; bill—29 to 33 mm.; tarsus—32 to 39 mm. Weight: 450 to 630 gm.

Range in Mexico.—This duck is an occasional winter vagrant mostly in the northern states.

The handsome wood duck, generally conceded to be the most beautiful of American waterfowl, is not a regular migrant to Mexico. It occurs only scatteringly that far south. Salvin and Godman (1897–1904) cite records

Female

Male

WOOD DUCK

Female

Male

SHOVELER

Fig. 70. Shoveler, *Spatula clypeata,* and wood duck, *Aix sponsa.*

from Mazatlán, Sinaloa, and the Valley of Mexico. I find no other accounts of wood ducks in Mexico before 1951, when the species was noted twice in the northeastern region. Evenden (1952) saw a female on a roadside pond 73 miles southwest of Matamoros, Tamaulipas, and Davis (1952) observed another female on the Río Axtla near Xilitla, San Luis Potosí.

Canvasback. *Aythya valisineria*

Other names.—Pato coacoxtle; pato borrado; pato de los bosques; coacostle; *Nyroca valisineria; Marila valisineria.*

Description.—MALE: Head and neck reddish brown, darker on crown and at base of bill. Chest black, the black zone encircling the neck. Back and sides finely vermiculated white and gray. Breast and abdomen white. Tail dusky brown, upper and lower tail coverts black. Wing grayish brown without a distinctively marked speculum. Bill black, tapering from a narrow point to the heavy base in a straight line with the forehead. Feet dusky gray. Measurements: folded wing—228 to 241 mm.; bill—60 to 63 mm.; tarsus—43 to 46 mm. Weight: 1,050 to 1,580 gm. FEMALE: Similar to male, but head, neck, and chest dull brown; back and sides much more buffy than white. Measurements: folded wing—220 to 230 mm.; bill—54 to 60 mm.; tarsus—42 to 44 mm. Weight: 900 to 1,400 gm.

Range in Mexico.—The canvasback is an uncommon migrant along the Pacific coast. It is fairly common in the interior (Jalisco, northern Michoacán) and along the northern Gulf coast.

Of 16,811 canvasbacks found in Mexico in 1952, nearly 10,000 were on Lakes Chapala and Pátzcuaro in the southern uplands, and most of the rest were near Tampico along the Tamaulipas-Veracruz border. This is a very small segment of the continental population, which in the main winters along coastal waters of the United States.

The canvasback is one of the largest of the diving ducks, but like most of this group of waterfowl, it has small wings which beat very rapidly in flight. To get up flying speed the bird must run along the surface of the water with alternate kicks of its feet. Once under way, however, it is one of the fastest of ducks. As a diver it is able to feed in much deeper water than the dabbling ducks, going down twenty feet or more to forage on the bottom for plant seeds, tubers, and leaves, or for invertebrate animals such as shellfish and crustaceans. Ordinarily, canvasbacks are fine eating, but when their diet includes too many shellfish, the flesh takes on a strong, fishy flavor. This happens more often in salt water than in fresh.

Redhead. *Aythya americana*

Other names.—Pato cabeza roja; guayareja; *Nyroca americana; Marila americana.*

Description.—MALE: Head and neck brick red. Chest black. Back and sides vermiculated black and buffy white, giving a dark-gray effect. Breast and abdomen white. Tail brown, upper tail coverts black, lower coverts blackish brown.

Male

REDHEAD

Female

Female

CANVASBACK

Male

Fig. 71.   Redhead, *Aythya americana*, and
canvasback, *Aythya valisineria*.

Wing grayish brown without distinct speculum. Bill blue-gray, with a paler transverse band near tip; the tip is black. Feet bluish gray. Measurements: folded wing—216 to 237 mm.; bill—48 to 52 mm.; tarsus—40 to 42 mm. Weight: 900 to 1,300 gm. FEMALE: Head, neck, back, chest, and sides brown, darker above, paler on chin, throat, and lower sides. Breast and abdomen white. Tail and its coverts brown. Wing grayish brown. Bill and feet like those of male. Measurements: folded wing—210 to 230 mm.; bill—45 to 49 mm.; tarsus—40 to 42 mm. Weight—800 to 1,200 gm.

Range in Mexico.—The redhead is a common migrant along northern coasts, particularly in Sinaloa, Nayarit, and Tamaulipas. It is uncommon in the interior.

The redhead is singularly sensitive to depreciation of inland marshes. Once a common duck on the Mexican uplands, it is now rare as a result apparently of lowered water levels in lakes and marshlands. However, the species is still fairly abundant along the northern coastlines, especially in Tamaulipas, where more than 47,000 redheads were found in 1952. Lesser numbers are to be found each winter in the eelgrass bays and mangrove lagoons of Sinaloa and Nayarit.

Throughout North America the redhead is a favorite game duck, for it is of good size and its flesh is consistently sweet. It is more of a vegetarian than the canvasback and is less likely to have a fishy taste. On Lake Tecocomulco, Hidalgo, sport hunters from Mexico City prized the redhead above any other species, and there in 1945 and 1946 I saw some good strings of these birds taken. Now the lake is partly drained and the redheads are gone. This unfortunately is the situation of most interior lakes and marshes.

Ring-necked Duck. *Aythya collaris*

Other names.—Pato boludo prieto; pato chaparro; *Nyroca collaris; Marila collaris.*

Description.—MALE: Head and neck black with a purplish gloss. Narrow collar round base of neck chestnut brown. Chest, back, rump, and under tail coverts black. Breast white merging to dusky brown on belly and vermiculated gray and white on sides. Wing brown, coverts glossed with green, speculum pearl gray. Bill bluish gray with two whitish rings round the base and near the tip, which is black. Feet yellowish gray with darker webs. Measurements: folded wing—197 to 207 mm.; bill—44 to 47 mm.; tarsus—34 to 36 mm. Weight: 680 to 860 gm. FEMALE: Predominantly brown with a white breast, white eye ring, and whitish face and chin. Bill and wings like those of male. Feet gray. Measurements: folded wing—184 to 193 mm.; bill—44 to 46 mm.; tarsus—32 to 36 mm. Weight: 600 to 760 gm.

Range in Mexico.—This duck is an uncommon migrant along the coasts. It is especially prevalent in fresh-water sloughs along the coastline of Veracruz and occurs occasionally in the interior.

The ring-necked duck is rarely found in great flocks but tends to gather in little groups on fresh or brackish ponds and lagoons. It resembles the scaup ducks at a distance; at close range or in the hand it is easily recognized by the ringed bill. The area in Mexico most consistently frequented by this duck is the Laguna de Alvarado, Veracruz, where the great Papaloapan River meets the sea. Wetmore (1943) speaks of seeing ringnecks there in some numbers, and 1,100 were found there in the 1952 survey—more than at any other point. A scattering was seen farther north along the Gulf in Veracruz and Tamaulipas and on the Pacific side in Guerrero. In earlier years substantial numbers of ringnecks were seen on the coast of Yucatán; 16,000 were observed there in 1947 and 30,800 in 1948. The birds must live in salt water, since there are no fresh-water ponds on this part of the coast.

Greater Scaup. *Aythya marila*

Other names.—Pato bocón; pato boludo; *Nyroca marila; Marila marila.*

Description.—MALE: A large diving duck with black head and neck glossed with green, black chest, gray back of finely vermiculated black and white lines, and white underparts. Tail dusky brown with black rump and brown coverts below. Wing grayish brown with white band across secondaries that fades out across first five primaries. Bill blue with a black nail. Feet bluish gray. Measurements: folded wing—212 to 227 mm.; bill—43 to 48 mm.; tarsus—38 to 40 mm. Weight: 825 to 1,080 gm. FEMALE: Face white all round base of bill. Rest of head and upper parts brown. Breast and abdomen white. Wing, bill, and feet like those of male. Measurements: folded wing—210 to 217 mm.; bill—42 to 46 mm.; tarsus —37 to 39 mm. Weight: 800 to 1,000 gm.

Range in Mexico.—This duck has been recorded only in the delta of the Colorado River, Baja California (once), and along the coast of Sinaloa (twice).

The greater scaup is a sea duck that winters primarily in northern coastal waters. Its occurrence in Mexico is rare indeed. This species can be distinguished from the very abundant lesser scaup by (1) its larger size, (2) the green head gloss on the males, and (3) the extensive band of white in the wing. A lesser scaup is smaller, the male has a purplish gloss on the head, and the white wing band is limited to the secondary feathers, the primaries being more or less uniformly brown.

Lesser Scaup. *Aythya affinis*

Other names.—Pato boludo chico; pato negro; pato boludo; pato del tiempo; pato marino; *Nyroca affinis; Marila affinis.*

Description.—MALE: Head and neck black with a purplish gloss. Chest black. Back and sides vermiculated black and white lines, the effect being gray. Breast white. Tail and under tail coverts brown, rump black. Wing grayish brown with white band across secondaries stopping abruptly at first primary. Bill blue with black nail. Feet bluish gray. Measurements: folded wing—193 to 208 mm.; bill— 39 to 44 mm.; tarsus—34 to 36 mm. Weight: 700 to 925 gm. FEMALE: Face white all round base of bill. Rest of head and upper parts brown. Breast and abdomen

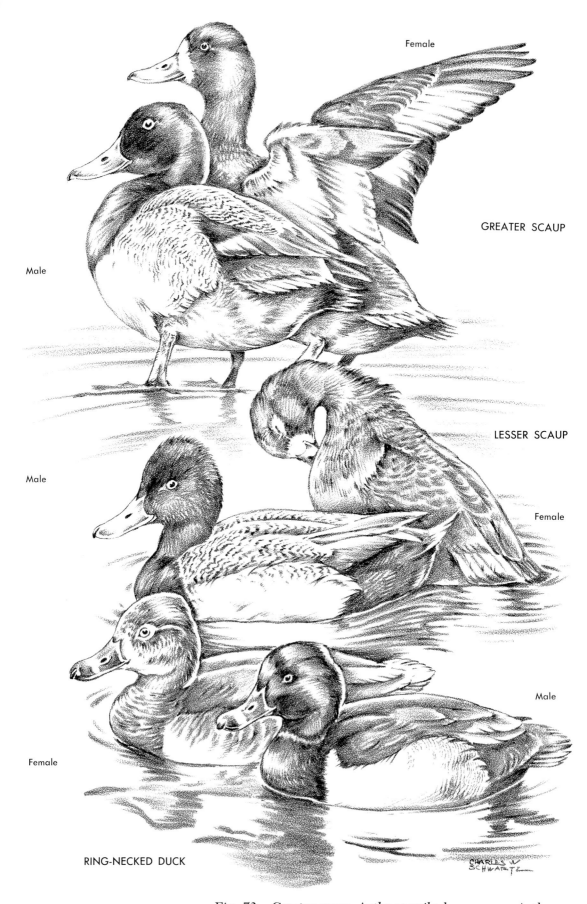

Female

GREATER SCAUP

Male

LESSER SCAUP

Male

Female

Male

Female

RING-NECKED DUCK

CHARLES W.
SCHWARTZ

Fig. 72.   Greater scaup, *Aythya marila;* lesser scaup, *Aythya affinis;* and ring-necked duck, *Aythya collaris.*

white. Wing, bill, and feet like those of male. Measurements: folded wing—188 to 203 mm.; bill—40 to 42 mm.; tarsus—32 to 36 mm. Weight: 680 to 900 gm.

Range in Mexico.—This duck is an abundant migrant along both coasts; small numbers occur in the central upland.

The lesser scaup is second only to the pintail in the numbers that visit Mexico. In 1952 there were recorded 442,690 of these birds, the largest concentrations being along the coasts of Nayarit, Chiapas, Veracruz, and Yucatán. The main flocks are not always found in the same localities, for they seem to shift around from year to year. There are also marked fluctuations in the total number, which suggests that the same birds do not always come to Mexico in winter but large numbers of them stop north of it in some years, or perhaps go beyond Mexico to the south. Wherever the birds are found, however, they are usually on deep coastal lagoons and bays, where their principal food is probably small mollusks.

Saunders and Saunders (1949) gathered information on wholesale losses of scaups and other sea ducks that occurred in past years as a result of oil pollution along the coast of Veracruz. They state (p. 98):

At one time in 1909 and later, blowouts of wells in the fields west of Laguna Tamiahua resulted in that great body of water being completely covered with a heavy film of oil. Pollution was again very bad from 1921–1923. Some of the Tampico lagoons were also covered from nearby wells of the Panuco field. J. L. Friedman of Brownsville, Texas, and a resident of Tampico during the principal years of oil development in the Tampico and Tamiahua districts told me that at the time of the famous Dos Bocas well "blow out" in 1909, it flowed at least 100,000 barrels of oil per day. Other blowouts, plus oil from many broken or defective pipelines, were also sending vast quantities into Laguna Tamiahua. He was an inveterate duck hunter, and working this locality, he was dismayed to see "hundreds of thousands and probably millions of dead ducks" covered with oil, many of which had come or washed ashore and died. He didn't know how many canvasbacks were included among the dead, but both he and Henry Beszlin agreed that most of those that perished were scaup.

No recent losses have been reported around these oil fields.

Despite its abundance, the lesser scaup is hunted very little in Mexico, because of its habit of rafting in the larger coastal lagoons out of reach of shore hunters.

Common Goldeneye. *Bucephala clangula*

Other names.—Pato chillón ojos dorados; *Glaucionetta clangula.*

Description.—MALE: Head black, highly glossed with metallic green, and with a round white spot on each side of the face at the base of the bill. Neck, chest, sides, and underparts white. Back and rump black, scapulars streaked black and white. Wing black with white speculum and with white coverts in front of speculum. Tail dark gray. Bill black. Feet orange or yellow with dark webs. Measurements: folded wing—216 to 232 mm.; bill—33 to 41 mm.; tarsus—35 to 41 mm. Weight: 800 to 1,150 gm. FEMALE: Head chocolate brown. Throat white, neck gray in back. Upper chest, sides, back, rump, and tail gray, the feathers edged in pale gray. Lower chest and underparts white. Wing, bill, and feet like those of male. Measurements: folded wing—190 to 216 mm.; bill—28 to 35 mm.; tarsus—33 to 36 mm. Weight: 700 to 900 gm.

Range in Mexico.—The goldeneye is a rare vagrant in the north, especially along the coasts but occasionally in the interior.

Nearly every year when the waterfowl are being inventoried, goldeneyes are seen in small numbers in salt-water bays off the coasts of Baja California and Tamaulipas. In 1952 we saw a few at San Quintín Bay, Baja California. In 1949 Saunders and Saunders found 50 on Laguna Madre, Tamaulipas, and in previous years they noted 4 on the coast of southern Sonora and 70 in the delta of the Colorado River. Booth (1953) cites another record from Sonora, and the Mexican check-list (1950) reports one occurrence on the coast of Sinaloa. On March 2, 1946, I killed a fat male goldeneye (1,007 gm.) on the Río Nazas west of Ciudad Lerdo, Durango. In a week's stay at that camp we saw a few goldeneyes nearly every day. But, all in all, the goldeneye is a rare duck in Mexico.

Because of their habit of eating mostly animal foods, such as crustaceans, insects, mollusks, and even a few fishes, goldeneyes are usually strong in flavor and scarcely edible. Kortright (1942) cites data on the contents of 395 stomachs showing that about three-quarters of the normal diet consists of animal foods.

Bufflehead. *Bucephala albeola*

Other names.—Pato chillón jorobado; pato monja; *Charitonetta albeola*.

Description.—MALE: A very small duck with black head highly glossed with purple and green. Crown feathers long, making a rounded crest with a wide white band from eye to eye over the top. Neck, chest, sides, and underparts white. Back black. Tail and rump gray. Most of the wing black with a wide white band from the speculum forward to the wrist. Tiny bill bluish gray. Feet flesh color. Measurements: folded wing—165 to 177 mm.; bill—27 to 30 mm.; tarsus—32 to 35 mm. Weight: 420 to 540 gm. FEMALE: Head and neck dusky brown with a roundish white spot back of the eye. Back, rump, and tail dusky brown. Chest, sides, and abdomen ash gray. Breast white. Wing dark brownish gray with white speculum. Bill dusky gray. Feet bluish gray. Measurements: folded wing—151 to 165 mm.; bill—25 to 27 mm.; tarsus—28 to 32 mm. Weight: 300 to 420 gm.

Range in Mexico.—The bufflehead is a fairly common winter visitant in salt-water bays of Baja California, Sonora, and northern Sinaloa. It occurs sparingly in Tamaulipas and in the interior as far south as the Valley of Mexico.

The beautiful little bufflehead is a regular visitor to northwestern Mexico, where in 1952 we counted approximately 4,800 of these ducks, principally in San Quintín Bay, Baja California, and in the lagoons opposite the Río Yaqui delta in southern Sonora.

The species is rare in the interior of Mexico, but according to the

COMMON GOLDENEYE

Female

Male

BUFFLEHEAD

Female

WHITE-WINGED SCOTER

Male

emale

SURF SCOTER

Female

Male

Fig. 73. Common goldeneye, *Bucephala clangula;*
bufflehead, *Bucephala albeola;* white-winged
scoter, *Melanitta deglandi;* and surf scoter,
Melanitta perspicillata.

Mexican check-list (1950) it has been collected in Coahuila, Chihuahua, Durango, Jalisco, Guanajuato, México, and Distrito Federal. Saunders and Saunders (1949) say that buffleheads occur also on Lake Pátzcuaro, Michoacán. A group of five was observed in 1948 along the coast of Yucatán.

In their crisp black-and-white dress these diminutive ducks buzz low over the water with incredible speed. In Baja California they usually are found in association with surf scoters, which on the wing look hulking and awkward by comparison. Buffleheads feed mostly on insects and other animal foods (79 per cent) and are scarcely edible.

White-winged Scoter. *Melanitta deglandi*

Other names.—Negreta de alas blancas; *Melanitta fusca; Oidemia deglandi.*
Description.—Male: A large black sea duck with a small white patch surrounding the eye and a white speculum in the wing. Bill white on ridge, shaded red to orange on side, black at base and along edges of mandible; a prominent black knob at base of bill. Feet purplish red, with dusky webs. Measurements: folded wing—273 to 282 mm.; bill (from edge of feathers to tip)—39 to 42 mm.; tarsus—50 to 52 mm. Weight: 1,360 to 1,800 gm. Female: Whole body dusky brown, except for the white speculum. Bill brownish black with smaller knob than in the male. Feet brownish red, webs dusky. Measurements: folded wing—264 to 273 mm.; bill—36 to 40 mm.; tarsus—45 to 46 mm. Weight: 1,000 to 1,340 gm.
Range in Mexico.—This scoter is a regular winter visitant to northwestern Baja California. It is recorded occasionally from the Gulf of California.

The white-winged scoter is strictly a salt-water species, seen inland only when blown from the sea by storms. Grinnell (1928) cites various records of occurrence, mostly centering around San Quintín Bay, where, it is said, the bird is at times "numerous." In January, 1947, Saunders saw about 175 white-winged scoters scattered along the eastern edge of the Gulf of California in Sinaloa and Sonora. The species feeds almost entirely on mollusks and other sea-bottom invertebrates and is not edible.

Surf Scoter. *Melanitta perspicillata*

Other names.—Negreta de marejada; negreta; *Oidemia perspicillata.*
Description.—Male: A large black sea duck with two white patches on the head—one on the crown between the eyes, the other on the back of the head and upper neck. Bill red, orange, and white, with a roundish black patch on each side near the base. Feet red to orange, webs dusky. Measurements: folded wing—235 to 244 mm.; bill (from edge of feathers to tip)—34 to 39 mm.; tarsus—42 to 46 mm. Weight: 800 to 1,200 gm. Female: Mostly dusky brown, with a whitish breast and pale grayish patches on back of head and on cheeks. Bill blackish, less swollen than in the male. Feet dull brown or reddish, webs dusky. Measurements: folded wing—228 to 231 mm.; bill—38 to 41 mm.; tarsus—41 to 43 mm. Weight: 700 to 1,000 gm.

Range in Mexico.—This scoter is abundant in winter on the outer coast of Baja California and scarce but of regular occurrence in the Gulf of California on the coasts of Sonora and Baja California.

The surf scoter is the common black sea duck of northwestern Mexico. Without making any serious effort to inventory all these birds (since they are not game ducks), we counted 24,605 in 1952, distributed as shown in table 4. The largest population was found in San Ignacio Bay, more than half way down the peninsula. Scattered flocks in the Gulf of California were not recorded.

This species, like the white-winged scoter, is scarcely edible, because of the sea-food diet.

A third species of scoter, the common scoter (*Oidemia nigra*), has been recorded as a very rare summer visitant on the northern coast of Baja California (Hubbs, 1955). The male common scoter is completely black with a yellow lump at the base of the bill. The female is dusky brown with pale cheeks.

Masked Duck. *Oxyura dominica*

Other names.—Pato enmascarado; pato colorado; *Nomonyx dominicus*.

Description.—MALE: Very small, with black face and white chin. Hindhead, neck, and chest cinnamon brown. Back and sides cinnamon, spotted and streaked with black. Breast and abdomen white. Rump and tail blackish, some of the upper tail coverts being thinly marked with white. The tail feathers are long and stiff, like spines. Wing brown with a large white patch in the middle, which serves in all plumages to separate this bird from the ruddy duck. Bill short and wide, bright blue on sides, black on ridge. Feet brown, paler on inner edges, with black spots on the webs. Measurements: folded wing—135 to 140 mm.; bill—33 to 35 mm.; tarsus—26 mm.; tail—95 to 100 mm. No weights available. FEMALE: Head brown-and-white striped, the brown areas being over the crown, through the eye, and across the cheek. Neck, chest, back, rump, and sides brown, feathers edged with buff. Breast white. Abdomen grayish buff. Bill brown with black tip. Wings, tail, and feet as in male. Measurements: folded wing—135 mm.; bill—33 mm.; tarsus—26 to 28 mm. No weights available.

Range in Mexico.—This duck is known from fresh-water marshes of Nayarit, Jalisco, Colima, Tamaulipas, and Veracruz. It probably breeds in Mexico, but records are lacking.

This rare duck is primarily a resident of the West Indies and northern South America, but it is found occasionally in widely separated localities in North America. Most of these scattered records (Vermont, Massachusetts, Maryland, Wisconsin, and various points in the Mexican highlands) represent strays that wandered far from home; but the masked duck is known to breed along the coast of southern Texas. It probably also nests in adjoining Tamaulipas, though records are lacking. According to Salvin and Godman (1897–1904 : 228), "Grayson . . . met with the species in some numbers, frequenting a small lake or lagoon near Tepic in Jalisco [Nayarit],

Female

Male

MASKED DUCK

Male—winte

Female

Male—summe

RUDDY DUCK

Fig. 74.   Masked duck, *Oxyura dominica*, and ruddy
duck, *Oxyura jamaicensis*.

as late as the month of June; the birds were evidently desirous of breeding in that locality, for the ovaries of some of the females shot were enlarged." Grayson's field notes show that he took four specimens of the masked duck in June, 1867, but add nothing more about breeding. He designated this duck "not a common species." Sallé noted the species near Jalapa, Veracruz, and more recently Nordhoff (1922) saw the masked duck in the Chapala marshes; but their records contain no information about breeding.

Perhaps the masked duck is more abundant than the record would indicate, for it lives in dense cattail or tule marshes and is not easily found. Phillips (1922–1926, vol. 4 : 125) states:

This little tropical representative of the Ruddy Duck or stiff-tailed group is one of the most inconspicuous of all ducks. Living, as it does, in waters covered with dense vegetation and seldom trusting to its wings it is scarcely ever noticed, even by the most careful field naturalists. Usually it is collected only by a special effort and by some native who knows its habits and haunts.

Except for being shy and reclusive, the masked duck is much like its relative the ruddy duck in general habits and behavior. It nests in the tules over water. Its eggs are as large as those of the ruddy (63 by 45 mm.). And it feeds mainly on aquatic plants and their seeds.

Ruddy Duck. *Oxyura jamaicensis*

Other names.—Pato tepalcate; pato sonso; pato chiquito; pato bola; yegua; *Erismatura jamaicensis.*

Description.—MALE (summer plumage): Crown of head black. Cheeks white. Neck, chest, back, sides, and rump rich cinnamon red. Tail long, feathers stiff and spinelike, dark brown. Breast and abdomen white, tips of some feathers golden. Wing brown. Bill short, broad, bright blue. Feet bluish gray. In winter plumage the male closely resembles the female except for the pure white cheeks. Measurements: folded wing—144 to 150 mm.; bill—38 to 43 mm.; tarsus—32 to 35 mm. Weight: 500 to 700 gm. FEMALE: Crown of head and back dingy brown. Cheeks whitish with a brown stripe from base of bill to ear region. Throat, neck, chest, and sides brownish gray mottled with buffy brown. Breast and abdomen dull white with some feathers tipped with yellow. Tail and wings brown. Bill dusky blue. Feet bluish gray. Measurements: folded wing—140 to 146 mm.; bill—40 to 43 mm.; tarsus—30 to 33 mm. Weight: 400 to 600 gm.

Range in Mexico.—This duck is resident in fresh-water marshes of Baja California and locally on the central uplands south to the Valley of Mexico. It is an abundant winter migrant along the Pacific coast.

The ruddy ducks that nest in Mexico seem to live in "colonies" and always in interior cattail or tule marshes. Because most of this type of habitat in Mexico has dried up, probably only a small fraction of the nesting colonies that once existed are left. In any event, reproduction of ruddy ducks in Mexico is negligible, most of the birds migrating north to breed on prairie ponds of the northern Great Plains.

In winter, ruddy ducks thrive in brackish coastal marshes and even in salt-water bays. Relatively few of the birds winter in the interior. In 1952 we found an astonishing concentration of ruddies on Lake Coyuca just west of Acapulco, Guerrero. There were estimated to be 107,700 of them on this large lagoon, in practically pure culture—that is, with only a few other ducks in company. No aggregation of like size has ever been seen by the inventory takers in any previous or subsequent year, although in 1947 some 58,000 ruddies were counted, scattered along the coast from Mazatlán to Acapulco.

Ruddy ducks are very tame and can be closely approached without their being startled into flight. When frightened they usually dive. For this reason discriminating hunters do not consider them a good game species. However, under certain conditions—as, for example, when a fresh wind strikes a large lake—ruddies will take wing to reach sheltered water, and then they may offer good pass shooting for sportsmen. They fly low to the water and very fast, like buffleheads. I had a fine shoot of this kind one winter day on Lake Tecocomulco, Hidalgo, which involved the expenditure of a good many shells per bird bagged. Ruddies eat vegetable foods for the most part and are sweet-tasting and palatable. Near Mazatlán, however, Saunders found them eating mostly insect larvae (Chironomidae).

Hooded merganser. *Lophodytes cucullatus*

Other names.—Mergo de caperuza; pato rampla.

Description.—MALE: Head and neck black glossed in green, with a tall fan-shaped crest, the center of which is white (from back of the eye to near the tip, which is fringed in black). Back, rump, and tail black, the outer scapulars longitudinally striped in white. Chest, breast, and abdomen white, with black crescents extending from the back to the white chest area. Sides vermiculated rufous brown and dusky black. Wing mostly brownish black, with gray coverts; secondary feathers white on outer web, black on inner. Black bill narrow and toothed. Feet olive yellow. Measurements: folded wing—190 to 202 mm.; bill—36 to 41 mm.; tarsus—31 to 35 mm. Weight: 600 to 950 gm. FEMALE: Head and neck brown with a sparse, reddish-brown crest. Chin white. Back, sides, rump, and tail brown, the side feathers edged with buff. Chest pearl gray. Breast and abdomen white. Wing like that of male. Bill dusky with dull orange along the edges. Feet yellowish green. Measurements: folded wing—174 to 188 mm.; bill—37 to 41 mm.; tarsus—31 to 33 mm. Weight: 450 to 675 gm.

Range in Mexico.—This rare vagrant has been recorded several times in Baja California and one or more times in Tamaulipas (Matamoros), Veracruz, Michoacán (Pátzcuaro), and the Valley of Mexico.

The handsome hooded merganser is not a regular visitor in Mexico. Usually it winters along both the Pacific and Atlantic coasts well to the north of Mexico, but even there it is not abundant. The occasional birds that stray this far south must be considered vagrants.

Like other mergansers, this species feeds mainly on small fishes, frogs,

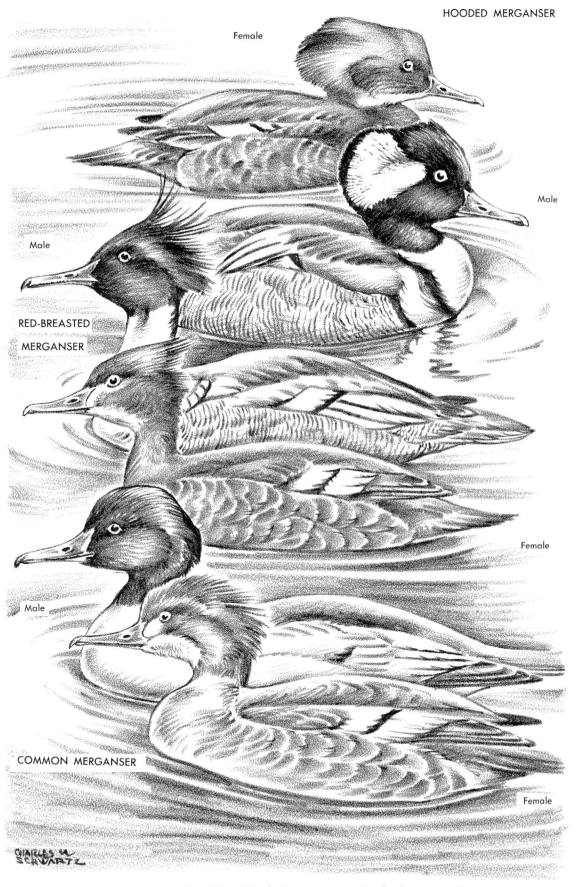

HOODED MERGANSER

Female

Male

Male

RED-BREASTED
MERGANSER

Female

Male

COMMON MERGANSER

Female

CHARLES W.
SCHWARTZ

Fig. 75. Hooded merganser, *Lophodytes cucullatus;*
red-breasted merganser, *Mergus serrator;* and
common merganser, *Mergus merganser.*

and invertebrate animals. It is not generally considered edible. So rare and beautiful a bird should not be shot.

Common merganser. *Mergus merganser*

Other names.—Mergo Americano; *Mergus americanus;* American merganser.
Description.—MALE: Head iridescent greenish black without noticeable crest. Chest, sides, and underparts white tinged with salmon pink that fades soon after death. Back black. Rump and tail slate gray. Wings brownish black except for coverts and secondaries, most of which are white, the secondaries narrowly edged with black. Bill bright red, dark along ridge, narrow and toothed. Feet red. Measurements: folded wing—258 to 273 mm.; bill—52 to 58 mm.; tarsus—47 to 53 mm. Weight: 1,300 to 1,800 gm. FEMALE: Head and neck reddish brown, with elongated crest. Chin and throat white except for a broad band of brown which extends round the lower neck and is sharply defined from the pale-gray chest. Back, sides, rump, and tail ashy gray, the side feathers tipped with whitish. Underparts white. Wing coverts ash gray, secondaries and outer scapulars black except for about five central secondaries and their coverts, which are white. Bill dusky on the ridge, dull red on the sides. Feet red. Measurements: folded wing—234 to 257 mm.; bill—44 to 53 mm.; tarsus—46 to 50 mm. Weight: 900 to 1,300 gm.
Range in Mexico.—This uncommon winter visitant in northern Mexico has been recorded one or more times in each of the following states: Baja California, Sonora, Chihuahua, Coahuila, Nuevo León, Tamaulipas, and Estado de México.

The large common merganser or "goosander" occurs in Mexico more frequently than the little hooded merganser, but it still must be considered a rare migrant. Usually it is seen in small flocks on open waters of the seacoast or interior reservoirs, where it feeds upon small fishes and, to a lesser extent, on mollusks, crustaceans, and other invertebrate animals. The bird can swallow fishes up to seven inches in length, but most of its victims are fingerlings and fry.

Red-breasted Merganser. *Mergus serrator*

Other names.—Mergo copetón; pato de copete; mergo de pecho obscuro.
Description.—MALE: Head with prominent crest of long, scraggly feathers, whole head and back of neck black with a metallic green gloss. Front and sides of neck white. Chest reddish brown spotted with black. An area on each side back of chest black with large white spots. Rest of sides vermiculated black and white, appearing gray. Breast and abdomen white with faint tinge of salmon pink that fades after death. Back black, blending to vermiculated black and gray on the rump. Wings mostly brownish black, but most of coverts and secondaries white, the latter narrowly edged with black (the wing is much like that of an American merganser). Bill carmine, dark along the ridge, narrow, and toothed. Feet red. Measurements: folded wing—222 to 242 mm.; bill—54 to 59 mm.; tarsus—44 to 46 mm. Weight: 1,080 to 1,270 gm. FEMALE: Much like the female common merganser except that it is smaller and the lower neck and chest feathers blend imperceptibly from brown to whitish gray (in the female common merganser

the rich brown neck contrasts sharply with the whitish chest); also, the feathers at the base of the upper mandible extend farther forward than the feathers on the lower mandible in this species. By contrast, in the common merganser the feathers are of the same length on upper and lower mandibles. Measurements: folded wing—209 to 224 mm.; bill—49 to 54 mm.; tarsus—41 to 43 mm. Weight: 730 to 900 gm.

Range in Mexico.—This merganser is a fairly common migrant along the northern coasts and in the interior reservoirs of the northern states.

In 1952 we recorded 595 red-breasted mergansers in Mexico, at various points in Baja California, Sinaloa, and Chihuahua (see table 4). Van Rossem (1945) calls the species a "common winter visitant" on the coast of Sonora, and Saunders and Saunders (1949) list it as of regular occurrence along the coast of Tamaulipas. It is much the most common merganser found in Mexico.

Like its saw-billed cousins, the red-breasted merganser is primarily a fisheater. As such it is not edible; hence it is not a game duck.

Order Galliformes

FAMILY CRACIDAE

Curassows, Guans, and Chachalacas

The six species of cracids that occur in Mexico are all long-tailed, fowl-like birds, mostly arboreal in habit and tropical in distribution. These species or their relatives occur on south through Central America and the tropical parts of South America. Only the horned guan (*Oreophasis derbianus*) of Chiapas and Guatemala is typically a resident of the temperate uplands.

Curassow. *Crax rubra*

Other names.—Hocofaisán; faisán real; faisán.

Description.—Size of a turkey, with a crest of curly feathers. Male all black except for white abdomen and crissum. Bill horn-colored at tip, yellow at base, with a yellow cere or casque on top. Feet and legs dark gray. Most females have body predominantly cinnamon brown, shading to black on neck and tail. The degree of blackness varies, and some females have white bars on the back. Wings brown, finely marked with black and buff, sometimes with white. Head black-and-white barred. Abdomen and crissum buffy. Bill horn-colored at tip, black at base, without yellow cere. Feet and legs brown. Measurements: folded wing— 355 to 445 mm.; tail—305 to 362 mm.; bill, including cere—44 to 58 mm.; tarsus

Female

Male

Head of Male showing casque

Fig. 76.　Curassow, *Crax rubra*.

—108 to 127 mm. Males slightly larger than females in all measurements. Weights: males—3,600 to 4,630 gm.; females—3,100 to 4,270 gm.

Range in Mexico.—Wet tropical forests of eastern Mexico, from southern Tamaulipas south along the eastern escarpment to the Isthmus of Tehuantepec, thence eastward through the forests of the Yucatán Peninsula. Although Martín del Campo (1948) has a specimen labeled "Estado de Guerrero," and Hellmayr and Conover (1942) cite Tschudi in giving the range as "western Mexico," there is no real evidence that *Crax* occurs west of the isthmus.

The great curassow is one of the finest native game birds of Mexico. Living exclusively in the tall tropical forests, it spends much of its time on the ground and when disturbed runs away like a turkey. However, sometimes it makes its escape by half flying, half hopping to the top stratum of the forest, and from there it launches into the air in a long, gliding, downhill flight to safety. The normal social unit is the family—the male and female and one or two offspring. Only occasionally did I see a curassow by itself. Aggregations of families sometimes occupy favored fruit trees, but these scatter readily and are not organized flocks. Curassows shift about seasonally, following the fruit and mast crops. Byron Harrell comments on the vertical movement of the birds near Gómez Farías, Tamaulipas, where in winters of good acorn fall they are found high in the oak–sweet gum forest, well above their normal breeding range.

Pairing and nesting occur in the spring. Alvarez del Toro (1952a) describes the elaborate courtship display of the male, who struts with tail raised and body feathers fluffed out, displaying prominently the white under tail coverts. The male also does much calling at this season, emitting a deep booming "oomp" from some perch high in a tree. Sutton and Pettingill (1942) heard this call daily from March 15 to April 14 near Gómez Farías. They also found two nests, on March 17, 15 to 20 feet above the ground—one in a tree fork, the other in a vine. The nests were constructed of twigs and leaves. Two eggs are a normal clutch. The eggs are surprisingly large (about 87 by 65 mm.) and are dull white. The incubation period is not known. The chicks, which resemble baby turkeys, apparently fall from the nest to the ground and are reared by both parents, the female usually being in attendance. Sutton and Pettingill found two separate females (March 21 and April 14) that seemed to have young concealed, for they flopped about, acting crippled and emitting squeals and groans. Young chicks have been found as late as July (Lowery and Dalquest, 1951; Paynter, 1955). Presumably these represent second nesting attempts after loss of earlier nests.

At an early age the young are able to fly to safety in the trees. In juvenal plumage the young of both sexes somewhat resemble adult females, although young males are darker. In the postjuvenal plumage of the first winter, the young have almost the same coloration as adults but are much smaller. In February, 1946, I collected a young male in San Luis Potosí along with an adult; the two looked alike but the immature bird weighed only 2,760 gm., the adult 4,630 gm. The small bird lacked the cere on the bill. I doubt that it would have been ready to breed as a yearling. Wagner (1953a) asserts that most cracids start to breed as two-year-olds.

According to various accounts, curassows seem to feed primarily on fruits of many kinds, picked up on the ground or occasionally taken directly from trees or vines. Specimens taken in eastern San Luis Potosí in autumn had crops filled with the red berries of *Chione mexicana*. Acorns, another food, have already been mentioned. In scratching up the leaves for food, the birds uncover many insects and eat them. Curassows eat some green leaves as well. I have never heard of any feeding on cultivated grains.

Curassows are preyed upon by the tropical cats and doubtless by foxes and some of the mustelids. One of the nests observed by Sutton and Pettingill in Tamaulipas was broken up by a predator, presumed to be a kinkajou (Sutton, 1944). The birds are also beset by ectoparasites, especially ticks, which I found literally in thousands on some specimens.

The range of this fine bird is shrinking and the population has been greatly reduced as a result of both overhunting and habitat destruction. The bird is a great favorite of local hunters, not only because it is large, but also because the light-colored flesh is very good eating—it is far better than the meat of the crested guan and the common chachalaca. At various camps I found curassows scarce or even locally extinct in good habitat as a direct result of shooting. Of the situation in Veracruz, Lowery and Dalquest state (p. 558):

North of the Tuxtla Mountains, in the northern three-fourths of the state, [the curassow] has been almost exterminated. Even in southern Veracruz, wherever roads have been built into the previously inaccessible forests, for hauling out mahogany logs, this fine game bird is rapidly disappearing. It forms one of the principal game species wherever found. In the Rincón area, west of Jimba, great piles of feathers of Curassows and Guans were seen along the newly built roads where previously few hunters had even been able to penetrate.

Timber-cutting operations not only open the wilderness for hunters but often so change the forest that it no longer is a suitable home for the curassow, which is very much of a "climax" species. Again I call attention to the desirability of preserving in wilderness status some samples of the rain forest. Much immediate good would also accrue from more strict enforcement of the laws protecting this species.

Crested Guan. *Penelope purpurascens*

Other names.—Cojolite; pava cojolita; ajol; faisán gritón; faisán; "guajalote silvestre" (Guerrero).

Description.—Size of a small turkey, with large wings, very long tail, and rather small body. Over-all color dusky olive brown with a faint greenish or purplish iridescence. Feathers of breast and belly edged with white. Throat sparsely covered with bristles, the loose skin hanging in a small red wattle. Crown feathers normally erected as a crest. Bill blackish. Feet and legs magenta. Measurements: folded wing—362 to 415 mm.; tail—350 to 408 mm.; bill—32 to 44 mm.; tarsus—81 to 90 mm. Weight: 1,620 to 2,430 gm. Sexes similar in size as well as in appearance.

Range in Mexico.—Tropical forests from northern Sinaloa and central Tamaulipas south along both coasts to the Isthmus of Tehuantepec and east through Chiapas and the forested parts of the Yucatán Peninsula. The crested guan penetrates cloud forest and some types of montane hardwoods; for example, in the highlands of Michoacán, Guerrero, Oaxaca, and Chiapas. Its range, therefore, often reaches to higher elevations than that of the curassow.

The crested guan occurs throughout the range of the curassow (except, curiously, in the Sierra de Tamaulipas), and the two are often found together. In addition, the crested guan has a wide range in the somewhat drier and less luxurious tropical forests of western Mexico. It is more tolerant than the curassow of second-growth forest; hence it is considerably more persistent under the present pattern of land use. However, the highest populations of crested guans found during the survey were in undisturbed tropical forest—east of El Real, Chiapas, and west of the Río Salto in San Luis Potosí, for example. Harrell estimated a density of one bird per 100 acres in the tropical forest and oak–sweet gum forest near Gómez Farías, Tamaulipas. He did not find the species in adjoining pine-oak woods. I found a sparse population in the cloud forest near Omilteme, Guerrero, and was told that guans had occupied the very similar forest of Mount Tancítaro, Michoacán, until the ash fall from Volcán Parícutin blanketed the area and apparently wiped them out. Heavy cutting of the forest has led to local extermination of this bird in a number of places, just as it has of the curassow.

Guans occur in loose flocks, but because the sexes and ages of individuals cannot readily be recognized in the field I am uncertain whether the basic social unit is the family, as in *Crax*. Wagner (1953a) thinks so. In any event, the groups are primarily arboreal, rarely being found on the ground. Usually they are high in the trees. They escape by leaping or half flying from limb to limb with incredible speed and agility. They are not as shy as curassows, however, and often walk along the limbs cackling and peering down at the source of disturbance. In this situation they are easily shot. Guans can often be located by their plaintive calling, especially when they leave the roost in the early morning.

Courtship was observed by Sutton and Pettingill (1942 : 11):

From March 21 to the end of the month courtship antics were observed, especially in the deep woods half way up the mountain. Here the males sparred, threatening their rivals with harsh, throaty cackles; pursued each other through

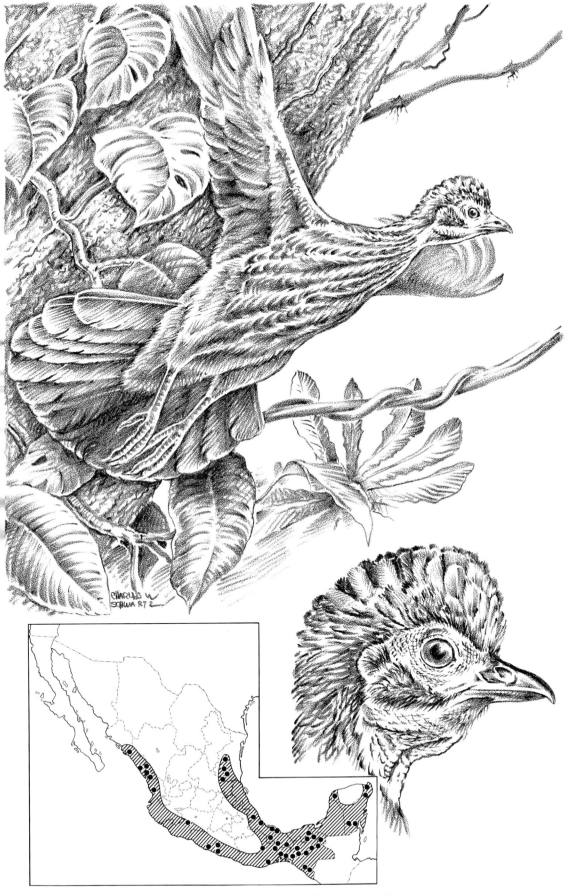

Fig. 77. Crested guan, *Penelope purpurascens.*

the tops of the big trees; and *drummed* by flying from perch to perch with wings beating rapidly. They were surprisingly nimble.

Wagner states that courtship and breeding begin at the age of two years. He collected yearlings in April and May that were sexually quiescent and molting.

The guan nests in trees, like the curassow, building bulky nests of twigs and leaves, well up in the branches. Egg laying apparently starts in April. Harrell reports a female taken on March 27 in Tamaulipas in which the oviduct and ovary were enlarging. I collected a laying female in Nayarit on April 19. Alvarez del Toro (1952a) states that guans breed from April to August. J. H. Batty reported breeding in Sinaloa in June (Miller, 1905). Young chicks have been collected on April 26 by Sutton and Pettingill, on April 23 by Van Tyne (1935), and on June 6 by Paynter (1955). The normal clutch is 2 eggs, according to Wagner; these are dull white and measure approximately 75 by 51 mm. Natives of Sinaloa told Batty that a clutch was 4 to 6 eggs, but this seems unlikely. The extent of the incubation period is not known. The chicks are attended by both parents, at first on the ground, but very soon in the trees.

The guan, like the curassow, is primarily a fruit eater. Among the fruits which I found most prevalent in crops were the "capulin selvaje," *Bumelia peninsularis,* a common tree near Santiago, Nayarit; *Guatteria,* one of the dominant trees in the rain forest of northern Chiapas; *Chione mexicana,* a small tree of the tropical evergreen forest of eastern San Luis Potosí. Two of the birds from San Luis Potosí contained only soil in their crops—a reddish clay, traces of which were sticking to their bills. The significance of this dietary supplement escapes me. Sutton and Pettingill name the plums of "xoxotl" (probably *Spondias mombin*) as a dominant spring food in Tamaulipas, and Harrell found acorns in the crops of two birds taken in the same locality in winter. Wagner lists figs and other fruits; Alvarez del Toro adds green leaves and insects. The birds often concentrate in groves of desirable food trees. I once flushed five guans from one very small capulin tree that was loaded with fruit. They seem to prefer to pick fruit directly from the twigs rather than gather the windfalls from the ground as curassows are inclined to do. The much greater weight of the curassow may hinder its movement among the terminal branches.

In spite of its inferior table qualities, the guan is hunted heavily in all parts of its range. Although guans are less wary than curassows, they seem to withstand hunting better, for what reasons I do not know. I observed, as have several others, that on hunted range occupied jointly by the two birds, the guan is always the more abundant. But in isolated virgin forest the two are often equally numerous.

There is a limit to the amount of persecution that even the guan can stand. At San Juan, Campeche, both species have been exterminated,

Fig. 78.   Specimen of crested guan, collected at Tapalapan, Veracruz. Photograph by C. W. Schwartz.

apparently by hunting, for there is still plenty of good habitat. Paynter in 1955 noted the extreme scarcity of guans in northwestern Yucatán, where Gaumer recorded prodigious numbers seventy-five years earlier. However, in that area, as in many others where guans have decreased, there has been a good deal of logging; it is therefore difficult to distinguish between the effects of hunting and those of habitat deterioration. Near Batel, Sinaloa, we found the guan virtually extinct in 1946 as a result of combined logging and hunting. The problems of conserving this species are essentially the same as for the curassow, though the situation is somewhat less critical.

Chachalacas. *Ortalis vetula* and Related Species

Other name.—Chachalaca.
Species included here.—*Ortalis vetula* and *O. poliocephala.*
Description.—Long-legged, long-tailed, fowl-like birds about the size of bantam chickens, with a small crest. Exposed bare skin in front of eye and on throat. General color of whole body olive drab, except abdomen, under tail coverts, and tip of tail, which are rufous in *O. poliocephala* of the northwest coast, whitish buff in the southern form of that species from Jalisco to Oaxaca, and varying shades of pale olive buff in members of the species *O. vetula* from eastern Mexico. Chachalacas vary greatly in size, the *poliocephala* group from the west coast being much larger than members of the species *vetula* from eastern Mexico (see table 8). The sexes are similar in both appearance and size, males being only slightly larger than females.

TABLE 8

MEASUREMENTS AND WEIGHTS OF CHACHALACAS FROM VARIOUS PARTS OF MEXICO

Locality	Folded wing (mm.)	Tail (mm.)	Bill (mm.)	Tarsus (mm.)	Weight (gm.)
Ortalis poliocephala					
Sonora, Sinaloa, Nayarit	238–272	265–307	23–28	67–80	700–880
Jalisco, Colima, Michoacán, Guerrero, Morelos, southern Oaxaca, southern Puebla	229–282	247–310	25–33	66–77	713–861
Ortalis vetula					
Tamaulipas, Nuevo León, San Luis Potosí, northern Veracruz	185–219	205–264	19–27	49–63	470–685
Southern Veracruz, northern Oaxaca, Tabasco, Chiapas	177–214	197–252	22–28	54–65	318–410
Campeche, Yucatán, Quintana Roo .	172–204	197–258	22–28	55–66	397–527

Range in Mexico.—Throughout the tropical zones and into the adjoining temperate uplands in most canyons. Ranges of the large western species (*poliocephala*) and the small eastern species (*vetula*) overlap in Puebla, Oaxaca, and southwestern Chiapas. There is no indication of interbreeding.

The chachalacas of Mexico are commonly listed under the specific names *Ortalis wagleri,* which refers to the birds of Sonora, Sinaloa, and Nayarit,

Fig. 79. Chachalaca, *Ortalis vetula*. Lower figures on the plate
compare the size and shading of the common chachalaca of
the Gulf coast, *O. vetula*, with two subspecies of the
larger western chachalaca, *O. poliocephala*.

O. poliocephala

O. vetula

and *Ortalis vetula,* which includes chachalacas from other parts of Mexico. However, it has been pointed out by Wagner (1953*a*) that the chachalacas of southwestern Mexico, originally named *Ortalis poliocephala,* do not hybridize with the members of the eastern species, *O. vetula,* where the two populations meet in Chiapas; hence they should be considered specifically distinct. More recently Moore and Medina (1957) have verified this observation and have shown further that the *poliocephala* population does intergrade with the *wagleri* group along the Jalisco-Nayarit border. Therefore the specific name *poliocephala* (which antedates the name *wagleri*) is applied to all the large western chachalacas. The ranges of the two species, as presently constituted, are shown on the map.

Chachalacas of extreme southeastern Chiapas have been considered by some taxonomists to represent a third species, *Ortalis leucogastra,* which ranges into southern Guatemala and southward. However, the relationship of the birds of southeastern Chiapas is not at all understood, and pending study of the matter I shall follow the Mexican check-list and group the chachalacas of that area with the species *vetula.*

During the mating season chachalacas are among the most noisy and conspicuous birds in Mexico. Driving along the Pan-American Highway in early summer through the dense scrublands of southern Nuevo León or Tamaulipas one passes pair after pair of these gangling fowls sitting close together high in a tree and cackling in unison at the top of their lungs. The name "chachalaca" is obviously onomatopoetic of the four-noted cackle, which is repeated rapidly at intervals of a few seconds. Although both sexes call, the voice of the male is noticeably deeper and coarser, no doubt because of the peculiar elongation of the windpipe that loops down over the breast almost to the posterior tip of the sternum. The female's windpipe goes directly to the lungs, as in other birds. She calls much less than the male. I found no evidence of the "threesomes" (one male with two females) described by Bent (1932); nor did Wagner (1953*a*) find any. The pair is the normal social unit, even in winter.

Although calling is most noticeable during the mating season, the chachalacas cackle at daylight and dusk at other times. In late November in the arid tropics of northwestern Guerrero the chachalacas in every thicket serenaded us exactly at 7:15 every morning and less regularly about 7:00 in the evening. In winter the males do most of the calling. When not calling, the birds skulk in the thickets and are hard to find. When flushed, they fly laboriously between trees or gracefully skip and glide from limb to limb within a grove, making difficult targets.

Unlike any of the other cracids of Mexico, chachalacas thrive best in the thickets and tangles that follow clearing of the tropical forest. Hence, where the other species have decreased with land use, chachalacas have held their own and perhaps even increased despite much hunting. They are well adapted to exist in settled communities.

Nests are usually constructed in dense trees or tall shrubs, although Al-varez del Toro (1952*a*) says that chachalacas sometimes nest on the ground. I found the adult birds of Nayarit partly developed sexually in mid-April (yearlings apparently do not breed). J. H. Batty reported June as the peak nesting period in southern Sinaloa, and he found a chick on July 3 (Miller, 1905). I have found conflicting evidence concerning the time of nesting along the northern Gulf coast. In Tamaulipas I collected several females that were in the process of laying on July 7, and Jordi Julia Zertuche found a nest with 3 eggs on July 6 in eastern Nuevo León. Yet Davie (1889) re-ports collecting fresh sets in the Río Grande delta between April 10 and 20. After April 20, he says, the eggs contain embryos. Helmut Wagner tells me that in southern Veracruz young begin to appear by May 15, and in southern Chiapas by June 1. Paynter (1955) gives the nesting period in Yucatán as March and April. A clutch of eggs is usually 2, rarely 3 or 4. The individual eggs measure about 58 by 40 mm. (they are possibly larger along the Pacific coast) and are buffy white. Bent (1932) gives the incuba-tion period as twenty-two days. It is common in Mexico for chachalaca eggs to be hatched under hens and the young raised as pets. When eggs in wild nests hatch, the female takes almost complete charge of the chicks, and within a few days the chicks are skipping and gliding through the trees. The families apparently scatter after the young are partly grown, for even in October and November, pairs, rather than family groups, are the normal social unit. Wagner also comments on the desertion of half-grown young by the parents. I have seen loose aggregations of adults and young in a grove of figs that were in full fruit, but such flocks do not stay intact.

Like their larger relatives, the chachalacas are fruit-eaters primarily. In various parts of Mexico I have found them eating the fruits of the palmetto, persimmons, wild grapes, various kinds of figs, *capulin* (*Bumelia*), and zapotes (*Achras*). The crop of one bird taken near Valles, San Luis Potosí, was full of the leaves of lantana, and another from the Balsas Valley of Guerrero contained twigs and buds of an unidentified tree. The birds scratch on the ground to some extent and presumably get some insects, but I did not find any in crops that I examined.

There is a frequently repeated rumor that tame chachalacas cross readily with domestic poultry. In my travels I never saw such a cross, and I doubt that it could occur. Bent likewise discounts this tale.

Because of its wide range and abundance (and in spite of its small size and tough, strong meat), the chachalaca is an important game bird. Hunt-ing usually takes the form of "following the noise" and attempting to stalk the cackling birds. But in Veracruz, plans are more elaborate, as described by Lowery and Dalquest (1951 : 559):

In the thorny woods of the coastal plain, the resident peoples hunt this bird by driving. Two or three hunters are stationed in comparatively open woods, while others circle out and away to a distance of a kilometer, and then return slowly to their starting point, driving the birds ahead of them. The hunters stop at intervals, to chop on trees with machetes. The Chachalacas move ahead of the hunters by flying from tree to tree, but do not become frightened. The birds pause in almost every tree along the way, and when they pass the concealed hunters they are shot. Several drives were observed, and one to three birds were killed on each drive.

In southern Veracruz, Chachalacas are usually hunted from canoes, the birds being shot from trees and bushes along the bank. In the state of Veracruz as a whole, this bird is probably the most important single game species. Like the cottontail rabbit, it seems to hold its own in spite of steady, around-the-year, hunting. The birds are not sold to any great extent. The meat brings about one-half the price of a chicken, or three times the cost of a shotgun shell.

Like the above authors, I see no cause for concern over the status of chachalacas. Every encouragement should be given to hunters to take full advantage of the productivity of the populations. Wildlife management must differentiate sharply and clearly between species that need protection, such as the curassow and guan, and those that thrive without it and hence should be heavily hunted to supply the food and recreational needs of the community. The chachalaca is one of these.

Black Chachalaca. *Penelopina nigra*

Other names.—Pajuil; pachita.
Description.—Size of a chicken, with the long tail typical of cracids, a naked throat wattle, and a low compact crest. Males jet black with orange legs, feet, wattle, and bill. Females and young males sooty brown, heavily marked with black; legs, feet, wattle, and bill red. Measurements (both sexes): folded wing—223 to 266 mm.; tail—265 to 312 mm.; bill—23 to 26 mm.; tarsus—67 to 81 mm. Weight of one male from Chiapas—820 gm.
Range in Mexico.—Cloud forest and humid canyons in the pine-oak forest of Chiapas and the adjoining highlands of extreme eastern Oaxaca (north of Niltepec). Wagner (1953a) gives the vertical range as about 1,200 to 2,100 meters.

The black chachalaca is a bird of the moist upland forest (cloud forest), which I have classified as a tropical vegetation type but which frequently is designated as subtropical. There in the lofty stands of pine, oak, and liquidambar, heavily draped with orchids, bromeliads, and other epiphytes, this handsome game bird lives in relative seclusion. It is in no sense secretive, however, for in the manner of all its near relatives it cackles with vigor and enthusiasm during the mating season and to some extent throughout the year. The call is similar to that of the common chachalaca, *Ortalis vetula,* but, according to Frank Pitelka, who heard the two together, it is "deeper, more hollow, and less rasping." Alvarez del Toro (1952a) says that the black chachalaca spends much time on the ground scratching in the leaf litter for fruits, insects, and tender green plants, which constitute its diet. However, when disturbed it usually flies into the trees and makes its

Male

Fig. 80.　Black chachalaca, *Penelopina nigra*.

escape by alternately flying and hopping through the limbs like the common chachalaca.

Salvin and Godman (1897–1904 : 278) thus describe the courtship drumming of the black chachalaca: "When shooting in one of the ravines of the Volcan de Agua we observed that the male bird had a curious habit of 'drumming.' As it flew in a downward direction, it emitted a sort of crashing or rushing noise, like that produced by a falling tree." This habit is reminiscent of the drumming of the crested guan, already described. Alvarez del Toro states that courtship calling is first heard in February in Chiapas, and he thinks that nesting follows soon afterward.

Wagner (1953a) found a nest on the ground under the dense cloud forest. It was dug into the leaf mold and was lined with feathers. It contained two eggs, which he states is a normal clutch for the species. Apparently the black chachalaca and the horned guan are the only cracids that nest regularly on the ground. The young are tended by the female alone until they are well grown. Wagner believes that in this species, as in *Crax, Penelope,* and *Ortalis,* the young do not breed as yearlings but begin to do so when they are two years old. He found yearlings that were clearly undeveloped sexually.

The black chachalaca is a fruit eater like its near relatives. Berries and fleshy fruits are listed by various observers as the principal fare.

The black chachalaca is not heavily hunted, because of its isolation in the mountain forests. But its flesh is said to be excellent—more like that of the curassow than like that of its nearer relative the common chachalaca. As long as there remain undisturbed areas of cloud forest this bird will probably be secure. But clearing of its habitat will inevitably eliminate it locally.

Horned Guan. *Oreophasis derbianus*

Other names.—Guan cornudo; pavón.

Description.—Size of a turkey, with a long tail and other points of conformation typical of guans, but with a bright red "horn," or casque, extending vertically from the forehead. Head, back, and flight feathers black except for a broad white band across middle of tail. Underparts white, the feathers streaked longitudinally with brownish black. Feet and legs red. Bill yellowish. Measurements: folded wing—332 to 394 mm.; tail—300 to 368 mm.; bill—19 to 23 mm.; tarsus—80 to 92 mm. Weight of one male—2,300 gm. Sexes alike in coloration; females slightly smaller than males and with a smaller casque.

Range in Mexico.—Mountain forests above 1,800 meters elevation in Chiapas, on Volcán de Tacaná and the higher peaks of the Sierra Madre de Chiapas.

This interesting and bizarre guan is one of the rarest and least-known game birds in the Americas. It was first collected by Skinner from Volcán de Fuego in Guatemala, and for many years it was known only from that

Male

Head of Male showing horn

Fig. 81. Horned guan, *Oreophasis derbianus*.

mountain. The species was named by Gray in 1844 after the Earl of Derby, a dilettante collector of bird skins (in the best English tradition) who purchased the type specimen from Skinner. Later Oswald Salvin made a number of ascents of Volcán de Fuego and other nearby volcanoes in search of more specimens. His brief account of the bird, which appeared in the *Ibis* in 1860, is still the basic source of information. A few additional notes were added in the Salvin and Godman compendium (1897–1904). Wagner's classic paper on the Cracidae (1953a) includes the only new and original observations published in the ensuing half century.

The horned guan inhabits the wind-beaten mountaintops on the upper fringe of the cloud forest. Most of the year, the birds frequent the forest border, roosting in the trees and often feeding on tree fruits. In the breeding season, however, they stay on the open slopes above timberline. They are perhaps the most terrestrial of all the cracids. The birds group in small flocks during the nonbreeding period; presumably these are family groups.

Pairing occurs in the dry winter season. Wagner describes the noisy calling of the males in late February, accompanied often by loud clicking of the bill. The horn and wattle are an intense coral red at that season. Pairs establish themselves in territories on streams, running water apparently being a requisite of a breeding territory. In the upper Paval Valley above Mapastepec, Wagner found the pairs distributed along the streams well above timberline, each defending a segment of watercourse. Natives told him that the birds nested on the ground in February and March and laid two eggs. The color and size of eggs, and the time of incubation, are not known. Both parents attend the young, which are half grown by the time the rainy season begins in summer. Wagner believes that the young horned guans, unlike other cracids, mature and breed as yearlings. His data on this matter, however, were not clear to me.

Not much is known of the feeding habits of horned guans. Salvin (1860) found the birds often in groves of "palo careta" (*Prunus*) eating the ripe plums. He also noted that they did much scratching on the ground, which presumably would yield insects as well as seeds and fallen fruits. Wagner lists the contents of three crops as "leaves, buds, and vine tendrils."

Practically nothing is known of the natural enemies of the horned guan, although Wagner states a belief that the tayra may destroy some nests.

Rare as this species is, it inhabits a region that is fairly secure from the ordinary disturbances of man. I foresee no danger of upset in its habitat, but there may be need for control of hunting in the more accessible parts of the range.

FAMILY PHASIANIDAE

QUAILS, PHEASANTS, AND PARTRIDGES

One or another native species of quail occurs in virtually every part of Mexico. There are species adapted to live on the highest peaks, in the steaming rain forest, on the barest desert, and in all intermediate zones. Two nonnative species—the ring-necked pheasant (*Phasianus colchicus*) and the chukar partridge (*Alectoris graeca*) have spread into northern Mexico in recent years from points of introduction in the United States.

Tree Quails. *Dendrortyx macroura* and Related Species

Other names.—Gallina de monte; gallinita; charando; cordorniz coluda; long-tailed partridge; wood-partridge.

Species included here.—Dendrortyx macroura, D. barbatus, and D. leucophrys.

Description.—Tree quails are the largest of Mexican quails. With their long and conspicuous tails they look like bantam chickens; hence the name *gallina de monte*, or "chicken of the forest." The sexes are similar in all three species.

D. macroura: Most of head and throat black, with faint white lines above and below the ear. Chest and upper back reddish brown, the feathers broadly edged with gray. Lower back, wings, and tail mottled olive brown, black, and tawny. Breast gray streaked with reddish brown, blending to olive on sides and abdomen. Bill large and bright red. Feet and legs red. Naked skin around eye red.

D. barbatus: Crown of head buffy brown. Throat and chest gray. Breast and abdomen cinnamon brown. Otherwise colored like *D. macroura*.

D. leucophrys: Forehead pale buff. Back of head and sides of neck chestnut streaked with white. Chin and throat white. Breast, sides, and upper back chestnut, the feathers broadly edged with gray. Lower back, wings, and tail finely vermiculated olive brown, black, and tan. Breast gray, heavily spotted with pale cinnamon, blending to olive on the abdomen and flanks. Bill blackish, horn-colored at tip. Feet and legs orange red. Naked skin around eye red.

Measurements and weights are given in table 9.

Range in Mexico.—The tree quails are all residents of high mountain forests, mostly cloud forest, but extend into the upper pine-oak zone in the volcanic belt from the Valley of Mexico westward. (See map for individual ranges.)

TABLE 9

MEASUREMENTS AND WEIGHTS OF TREE QUAILS FROM MEXICO

Species	Folded wing (mm.)	Tail (mm.)	Bill (mm.)	Tarsus (mm.)	Weight (gm.)
Dendrortyx macroura	141–167	122–175	19–22	45–54	350–465
Dendrortyx barbatus	147–166	110–121	20–23	45–54	. . .
Dendrortyx leucophrys	139–146	124–128	18–19	49–53	. . .

Much the most common and widespread of the Mexican tree quails is *Dendrortyx macroura,* often called the "long-tailed partridge." It occurs on most or all the bigger volcanoes and higher ridges across the southern uplands from Oaxaca and central Veracruz to western Jalisco. The very distinct "bearded partridge," *Dendrortyx barbatus,* overlaps this range in central Veracruz (both species occur, for example, on Pico de Orizaba and Cofre de Perote), but only *barbatus* occurs to the northward along the escarpment to eastern San Luis Potosí. The bearded partridge is rare indeed in collections. The third species, *Dendrortyx leucophrys,* given the vernacular name "buffy-crowned wood-partridge" by Blake (1953), is primarily a Central American species, its range extending northward only to the highlands of southern Chiapas. Helmut Wagner found this quail to be quite common in the oak forests east of Motozintla, Chiapas, at an elevation of 2,000 meters. Although these three species are entirely distinct and are not known to hybridize, they are very similar in their habitat requirements and, as far as we know, in their general biology. For that reason I discuss them together.

In my experience, the tree quails are the shiest and most elusive of Mexican game birds, not even excepting the small tinamous. Judging from their calls, they are fairly abundant in the dense underbrush of many southern mountain forests, but they are difficult to see and to collect. At Apo on the slopes of Mount Tancítaro, Michoacán, the vigorous clear calls of *D. macroura* rang out each morning in the canyons around camp, sometimes six to eight calling birds (males?) being audible at once. Yet in a week of hunting I obtained only one specimen, and that was with the aid of a local hunter and his dogs. In other places where the tree quails were heard, we failed to get even one shot. Their habit of skulking on the ground under the very thickest cover is guarantee enough that these birds will never be overhunted.

Dickey and Van Rossem (1938) found *D. leucophrys* in small coveys of a few birds each in the mountains of El Salvador, and I suppose that the Mexican species occur in similar groups. The birds roost in trees and feed and loaf during the day on the ground. In foraging, they scratch up the forest floor rather like little turkeys, and their sign is distinctive and easily recognized.

The general appearance of a tree quail is thus described by Dickey and Van Rossem (p. 157):

In handling skins one fails utterly to gain a correct idea of this bird in life. It has a "long-legged" appearance with erect posture when unobserved, but on the least alarm will flatten out and dart away through the brush with rapidity and silence. The body is compressed laterally to a point equalled only by some of the rails, and is thus well adapted for slipping through the close growing stems of its usual habitat.

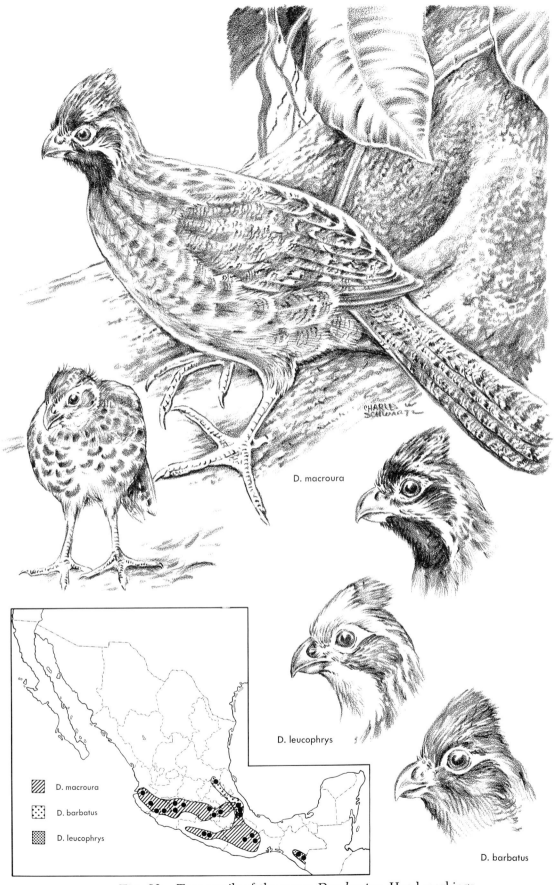

D. macroura

D. leucophrys

D. barbatus

D. macroura
D. barbatus
D. leucophrys

Fig. 82. Tree quails of the genus *Dendrortyx*. Head markings of the three Mexican species are compared.

The tree quails pair in early spring and nest on the ground, laying four to six eggs. Dwain Warner found a nest of *D. macroura* near Huitzilac, Morelos (2,900 meters elevation), on July 1, 1954, tucked under a loose mat of brush and pine needles in a pine-fir forest. One of the birds was sitting on the six fresh eggs. Warner took two of the eggs and found them to measure 49.2 by 33.5 mm. and weigh 28.3 gm. each. They were "pale cream in color, rather lightly and evenly spotted with light brown." An egg of *D. leucophrys* in the British Museum is "of a reddish-buff color, spotted and blotched with reddish brown. It measures 1.75 by 1.22 inches [44 by 30 mm.]." (Oates, 1901 : 65.)

The female of *macroura* collected on June 9, 1945, on the slope of Mount Tancítaro was well past laying. Lowery and Newman (1951) collected a female of *barbatus* with three downy chicks on June 12 in eastern San Luis Potosí. A quarter-grown chick of *macroura* now in the University of California Museum of Vertebrate Zoölogy was captured on September 27 near Cuapongo, Guerrero. However, two older juveniles (both three-quarters grown) were taken in Guerrero on August 29 and December 1, respectively. This suggests that young may come off the nest at widely different times. Although I have no definite information on the tenacity of the pair bond, I should suppose that tree quails, like their near relatives, remain paired through the whole breeding season, both members helping attend the young.

Of the food habits of these birds I have little information. The one specimen that I handled had a crop full of the seeds of various legumes, mostly of the genus *Desmodium* (tick trefoils).

Tree quails are hunted but little in Mexico, because of the difficulty of their capture. When hunted with the aid of dogs, the birds are taken more easily, for they tend to fly into the trees when a dog comes near, and in this exposed situation they can be shot. The next problem is to recover the bird from the dog—which is not easy when dealing with underfed curs.

As long as the high mountain forests remain intact, tree quails will be found in the thickets.

Mountain Quail. *Oreortyx picta*

Other name.—Codorniz de montaña.

Description.—A large quail distinguished by a tall, straight, black topknot (70 to 100 mm.) composed of two narrow feathers. Top of head, nape of neck, and breast steel gray. Throat chestnut, separated from the gray by a white line which passes under base of bill, through each eye, and down sides of neck. Back, wings, rump, and tail olive. Abdomen and sides chestnut, with a row of wide white and black bars on each side. Under tail coverts black. Bill black. Feet and legs dusky. Sexes similar in both appearance and size. Measurements: folded wing—129 to 139 mm.; tail—76 to 92 mm.; bill—14 to 16 mm.; tarsus—32 to 37 mm. Weight: 200 to 290 gm.

Fig. 83. Mountain quail, *Oreortyx picta*.

Range in Mexico.—Mountains of northern Baja California, principally in the pine-oak and boreal zones.

The mountain quail in its simple but strikingly arranged dress, with tall plume erect, is one of the most handsome of gallinaceous birds. Primarily a resident of the mountains of Oregon and California, it reaches southward only to the Sierra Juárez and San Pedro Mártir ranges in northern Baja California. There it summers on the high crests, in conifer forests, and around the edges of mountain meadows, dropping down in winter to the oak and chaparral zone on the western slope. Winter coveys are usually small, six to a dozen birds being the normal size range of coveys. These social units form in late summer on the breeding range and retain their identity during the downhill migration, through the winter, and on the return trip to the crest again. Then the coveys disintegrate and breeding pairs are formed.

The migration of mountain quail is performed for the most part on foot, although the birds take wing occasionally to cross canyons. Each segment of the population seems to have a traditional migration route, passed on from parents to offspring. Thus survivors of a winter covey will return to their familiar breeding area by the route they used coming down, and in the following fall they will bring their young that way again. Studies of this bird in California have shown that new impoundments of water, interrupting established migration lanes, cause great confusion among the quail. Coveys have been seen to attempt flight across new reservoirs rather than seek a logical route around them.

On both summer and winter ranges, mountain quail show a decided preference for thick brush. They never venture far from dense cover, and when disturbed they run away through the thickets rather than fly or hide. For this reason the bird is not a favorite game species. I have hunted mountain quail where they were abundant and found that, even when hunting with a dog, two or three birds is a fair day's bag. There is little shooting but much running up and down canyon slopes of nearly impenetrable oak and manzanita in pursuit of running coveys.

Pairing in Baja California occurs in March and early April and nesting from March 29 to May 28, according to records compiled by Bent (1932). The mating call of the male is a single clear whistle that falls slightly in pitch toward the end. After finding a mate, the male calls very little. Pairs remain together throughout the whole breeding period. Nests are placed on the ground, usually concealed in low vegetation and often tucked under the edge of a protecting rock or fallen log. Eight to twelve eggs constitute a normal clutch. The eggs are pale reddish buff and measure about 34 by 27 mm. The incubation period is twenty-one days (Bent). As is true of most game birds, mountain quail raise only one brood a year. If the first nest is destroyed, the birds may make a second or even a third attempt—which accounts for young hatched late in the summer. At first the young

Fig. 84.　Portrait of a mountain quail, by P. J. Fair.

feed principally on insects, which they catch themselves. As they mature, the diet shifts to include more plant materials. The parent birds are constantly on hand to guard the young, warn them when to scatter and hide, and brood them at night. They roost on the ground, as the coveys of adults do ordinarily. If a large brood is raised to adulthood, the single family probably becomes a winter covey. Unsuccessful pairs combine with small broods.

In very dry years the winter coveys of mountain quail may stay together through the summer without any pairing or attempts to nest. Helmut Buechner observed this phenomenon on the crest of the Sierra San Pedro Mártir, near La Grulla. He wrote in his notes on June 7, 1955: "Enroute back to Encantada we saw 50 to 60 adult Mountain Quail, some of them in large coveys of ten or more, indicating that little if any breeding and nesting was taking place during this exceptionally dry year." This behavior pattern is known in all the desert quails and even in bobwhites. It relates seemingly to inadequate diet and loss of vigor during dry periods.

Mountain quail feed on the seeds and fruits of a wide variety of plants, such as manzanita, service berry (*Amelanchier*), and wild grape (*Vitis*), and on many forbs and weeds. A series of twenty-three crops collected in the "arid regions of California" (the southern mountains, I presume) were said by Sylvester Judd (Bent, p. 48) to have contained

animal matter, 3 per cent, and vegetable matter, 97 per cent. The animal matter was made up of grasshoppers, 0.05 per cent; beetles, 0.23 per cent; miscellaneous insects, including ants and lepidopterous pupae, 1.90 per cent; and centipedes and harvest spiders (Phalangidae), 0.82 per cent. The vegetable food consisted of grain, 18.20 per cent; seeds, practically all of weeds or other worthless plants, 46.61 per cent; fruit, 8.11 per cent; and miscellaneous vegetable matter, 24.08 per cent.

More recent food-habits studies, conducted for the most part in the Sierra Nevada of California, show more fruit and greens than are indicated in the data given above. Mountain quail scratch and dig as they feed and sometimes uncover and eat many plant bulbs and tubers. I have found them eating quantities of acorns in some situations. These birds drink daily and rarely are found far from surface water.

Although the mountain quail is a charming addition to the avifauna of Baja California, it is hunted very little and cannot rightly be called an important game species. It doubtless is less abundant now than formerly, because of the severe overgrazing of the Juárez and San Pedro Mártir highlands.

Scaled Quail. *Callipepla squamata*

Other names.—Codorniz escamosa; zollín; codorniz azul.
Description.—Pale gray with a tufted whitish crest. Head and neck brownish

gray, paler on throat. Foreback, sides, and chest steel gray, each feather bordered with black, giving a scaled effect. Underparts buffy gray, the breast feathers scaled, all ventral body feathers with a brown streak along the shaft. Scaled quail of northern Tamaulipas, Nuevo León, and northeastern Coahuila have a wash of chestnut brown on the abdomen. Back, wings, rump, and tail brownish gray. Bill blackish. Feet and legs gray. Measurements: folded wing—111 to 121 mm.; tail—75 to 90 mm.; bill—15 to 17 mm.; tarsus—28 to 33 mm. Weight: 150 to 200 gm. Sexes similar except for white topknot, which is larger in male, and color of the throat, which is clear buff in males, grayish with faint brown streaks in females.

Range in Mexico.—Central desert and mesquite-grassland, from northern Sonora and Tamaulipas south to the Valley of Mexico.

In the great arid interior of Mexico the scaled quail is the only native gallinaceous bird. It thrives along the desert washes wherever there is water and a bare minimum of shrub or cactus cover. It penetrates the grasslands where the grama sod has given way to mesquite and weeds as a result of past grazing. By the same token, the species now occurs in areas that were once pine-oak forest but that have been reduced to secondary desert by clearing, agriculture, and grazing. The extension of range from central Hidalgo—the southernmost tongue of natural mesquite-grassland— southward to the Valley of Mexico is of this nature, in my opinion. The scaled quail, in other words, requires a habitat where the ground is mostly bare, where there are annual weeds to supply the seeds which are its food, where there is some shrubby or spiny ground cover, and where there is some surface water. These requirements are best met in certain of the more lush parts of the natural desert, and there quail densities are highest. Relatively low populations inhabit the secondary desert areas and the sterile creosote-bush flats of the extreme desert.

Curiously, the scaled quail has never jumped the highland barrier between southern Hidalgo and the isolated unit of natural mesquite-grassland in central Puebla, in the rain shadow of Volcán Orizaba. The latter area looks to be excellent habitat for scaled quail, and it is scarcely 50 miles from occupied range to the north. I am sure that this vacant niche could be filled by introducing live-trapped birds, and this would supply some nearby quail shooting for the sportsmen of Puebla.

Scaled quail live most of the year in coveys of 10 to 40 birds, although groups of 100 to 200 are found occasionally. Each covey has its own home range, which may overlap the home ranges of other coveys at water sources but is likely to be discrete away from water. An average covey range is large in comparison to that of many other quails. This I suppose is due to the open character of the habitat and the willingness of the birds to cruise widely in search of food. I have tracked scaled quail a mile or more from water to feeding grounds, and they may well go even farther in a single foraging expedition. Under these circumstances, the number of

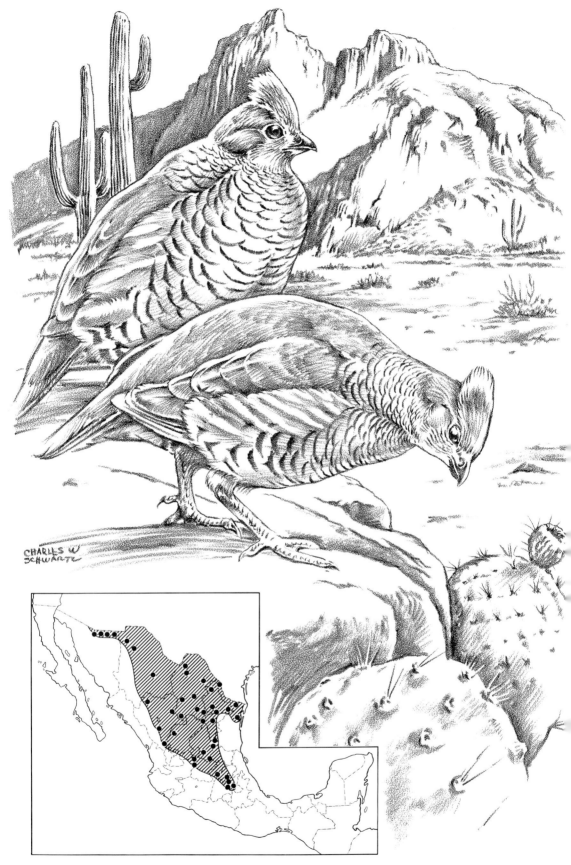

Fig. 85. Scaled quail, *Callipepla squamata*.

birds to a square mile may be quite low, although an illusion of great density of population is created at the water source, where birds from a wide radius congregate daily to drink. In highly favorable range, coveys may live comfortably in much smaller areas—less than a hundred acres sometimes.

Often a few scaled quail are found many miles from water, obtaining moisture apparently from greens and succulent fruit. However, I have never seen large numbers of these birds living away from water, nor do I know of any evidence that scaled quail can raise young where there is no water. It is therefore false to assume that water is not necessary for scaled quail just because a few adults can survive without it. Nor should that assumption be made about the Gambel quail and the California quail of the northwestern deserts.

The coveys break into pairs in early summer, and nesting occurs principally in June, July, and August over much of the interior of Mexico. The hatching and rearing period thus comes at the time of summer rains, when water, insects, and succulent foods are normally abundant. I collected laying females on July 13 at Galeana, Nuevo León, and chicks from the downy stage to nearly full grown in the first week of September at Ramos, Chihuahua. However, near Piedra Blanca in northern Coahuila we collected calling males with fully developed testes (10 and 11 mm.) in late April, 1953, which suggests a somewhat earlier breeding schedule in that region. Nests are on the ground, carefully concealed in tufts of grass or weeds. A clutch consists usually of 9 to 16 eggs, averaging about 12. The eggs are dull white, more or less speckled with tiny brown or buff dots. They measure about 33 by 25 mm. Incubation requires twenty-one days.

In very dry summers, scaled quail may reproduce scantily or not at all. Such a year was 1945. In various camps in northern Jalisco, Coahuila, Nuevo León, and Durango I found scaled quail extremely scarce; the small coveys included no young birds whatsoever. Chester Lamb had visited some of these areas in 1943 and 1944 and reported scaled quail abundant. Apparently, inadequate summer rainfall inhibits nesting and results in a total loss of eggs or chicks, so that in the subsequent winter the only birds of this species are adults. Since quail populations regularly undergo rapid "turnover"—that is, a large proportion (50 to 80 per cent) of the population dies and is replaced each year—failure to replace the losses leads naturally to a sharp drop in numbers. Lack of moisture may inhibit reproductive success by (1) weakening the adults because of poor diet; (2) inhibiting the hatch of eggs, which require moisture to develop; or (3) reducing the number of insects, seeds, greens, and drinking water needed to rear the chicks. In any event, the result is that few or no young are reared.

Scaled quail feed primarily upon seeds, secondarily upon insects and greens. In Mexico I have found the seeds of many weeds in the crops, including *Bidens*, corn cockle, dove weeds (*Croton*), and annual grasses

Fig. 86. Portrait of a scaled quail, by P. J. Fair.

such as foxtails, panic grasses (*Panicum*), and Johnson grass. The fruits of cacti and of shrubs such as *Atriplex* and *Mahonia* are eaten in season. I noted also many insects in the crops, including grasshoppers, ants, beetles, caterpillars, crickets, and millipedes. Some crops contained green leaves of clovers, and various forbs. The stomachs of two birds shot in February in southern Coahuila were stuffed with the leaves of a sagelike shrub. Where cultivated grains, such as wheat, are available, the quail make full use of the fallen seeds, but grainfields are scarce in most scaled quail range. In general, food conditions are optimum along watercourses and alluvial flats that are not excessively grazed by livestock. Unfortunately, however, livestock tend to congregate near water, so that even in the great central deserts of Mexico, hundreds of miles in extent, the critical areas for quail are often overgrazed by a relatively small number of livestock.

Scaled quail are preyed upon by various predators, especially horned owls and accipitrine hawks. Coyotes and bobcats pursue them, but with relatively little success. Usually the shrubby cover is adequate to protect these birds from excessive predation, and I found no place in Mexico where in my opinion predators were a serious limiting factor. Food and water supplies are far more crucial.

The scaled quail is a fine game species, although hunters find it rather exasperating at times when trying to run down a covey and force it to fly and scatter. Once the covey is properly scattered, the singles will hold well for jump shooting, coming out one at a time from their hiding places in the rocks or brush. The birds do not stay put well enough for handling with a pointing dog, however. López and López (1911) lament the difficulties of hunting this species with dogs. In spite of this, many Mexican sportsmen hunt the scaled quail avidly. It is shot and trapped by local people for food, but not to any great extent. Hunting, no matter how heavy, seems to have little effect on the populations of this bird.

California Quail. *Lophortyx californica*

Other name.—Codorniz californiana.

Description.—MALE: Forehead straw yellow. Crown chocolate brown edged with a black line and that in turn by a white line. Black topknot composed of six feathers. Sides of head and throat black with a white collar. Back and sides of neck gray scaled with black. Chest gray. Back, wings, rump, and tail gray washed with olive on the wings. Underparts buff with a central area of rich chestnut, all the feathers of breast and forebelly edged with black, giving a scaled effect. Side feathers brownish gray with shaft streaks of white. Bill black. Feet and legs dusky. FEMALE: Crown and ear patches dull brown, the blackish crest smaller than that of male. Throat and sides of head streaked brown and buff. Chest gray; back, wings, rump, and tail brownish gray, the nape feathers edged with brown. Breast and abdomen buffy white, the breast feathers edged with black, belly and side feathers mottled and streaked with brown and gray.

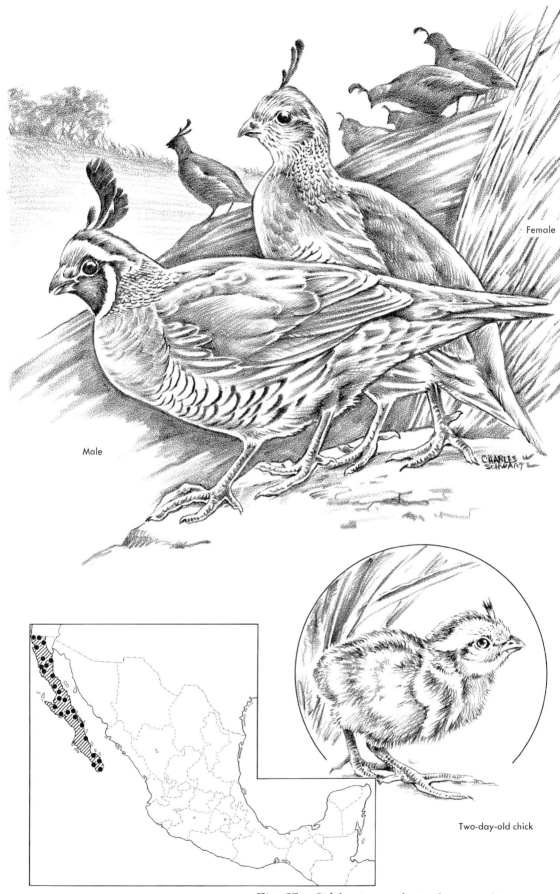

Male

Female

Two-day-old chick

Fig. 87. California quail, *Lophortyx californica*.

Bill brownish black. Feet and legs dusky. Measurements: folded wing—105 to
114 mm.; tail—81 to 100 mm.; bill—14 to 17 mm.; tarsus—29 to 33 mm. Weight:
130 to 160 gm. Males slightly larger than females.

Range in Mexico.—Peninsula of Baja California.

Over most of its range in the western United States, the California quail
occupies woodland, chaparral, and valleys, but not desert. However, in

Fig. 88.   Portrait of three California quail, by
P. J. Fair. Two males above, female below.

Baja California the species is adapted to desert conditions and occurs along washes, like a true desert quail. To be sure, the highest populations are found in chaparral, as along the northwestern coast and foothills, and in the scrubby tropical forest and brushland of the cape. But throughout the peninsula this quail occurs in fair numbers wherever there is brushy cover and water, often in areas that receive far less rainfall than the central desert of Mexico.

California quail are highly gregarious. During the breeding season the social unit is, of course, the family; but as families meet daily at the drinking places, social barriers break down and large coveys are formed, which may include hundreds of individuals. The higher the population, the larger the coveys tend to be. In dense populations of one or more birds per acre I have seen coveys of 500 and even 600 quail. Normally coveys are from 25 to 60 birds. Each covey has its own fixed range within which it lives. These home areas are from a quarter of a mile to a mile or more in diameter, depending on the proximity of food, water, and suitable cover. The birds roost in thick trees or tall shrubs. In the morning they set out to gather breakfast, flying or running to the feeding ground, which may be some distance from the roost. After the crops are filled, the group heads for the water hole, where all drink. The day is spent loafing and preening in the shelter of some thicket. Late in the afternoon there is another foraging expedition. When the evening meal is over, the birds return to the roost, where they fly up and arrange themselves for the night with much small talk and chatter. Such is a typical day in the life of a covey of California quail.

After the winter rains, the covey bonds weaken and the birds begin to form pairs. The pairs split off from the bunches and go about nesting, leaving always some unmated cocks, since males usually outnumber females in a ratio of about 113 to 100. The unmatched males continue to give the mating call (a single note descending at the end), and they try to capture females from established pairs. This earns them many beatings but rarely a mate. Nests are concealed in grass or weeds or under protective shrubs and are usually very difficult to find. There are 9 to 17 eggs (the average is 13). These are creamy white with pale brown blotches and measure about 32 by 24 mm. The period of incubation is twenty-one days. Normally only one clutch is hatched and reared by a pair, but there is recent evidence that in very favorable years on arid ranges—that is, rainy years—some pairs may bring off a second brood. Both parents are active in the care and rearing of the young. If the female is killed, the male may carry on the work alone, sometimes even incubating the eggs. The chicks grow rapidly and by the age of two weeks can make short flights. When the young are almost grown, the families combine into winter coveys.

As stated above, spring is the normal period of breeding in Baja California, the young hatching in late May or June. But unusual rainfall distribution may bring on nesting much earlier or later than normal. Hill and Wiggins (1948) found California quail approaching breeding condition in northern Baja California in late October in 1946, after heavy autumn rains. In southern California, nesting is sometimes delayed until the end of summer or may be missed entirely if winter or spring rainfall is inadequate. The control is probably nutritional, the breeding birds requiring green food in order to develop sexually. Even when nesting occurs, drought may preclude a successful hatch of California quail, as it does of the other desert

Fig. 89.   California quail at a watering device. Rain falling on apron (center) is stored in an underground tank. Quail readily enter tunnels (lower right) and descend a ramp to the water. Photograph by California Department of Fish and Game.

quails. As a result of this dependence of reproduction on capricious rainfall, populations are subject to violent fluctuations.

California quail eat mostly seeds in dry periods and a mixture of seeds and greens in the rainy season. Many detailed studies have been conducted of the feeding habits of this bird in California. As one would expect, the particular foods utilized vary from place to place and from season to season according to availability. Among the many kinds of seeds taken are such common weeds as filaree (*Erodium*), trefoils (*Lotus*), lupines (*Lupinus*), clovers (*Trifolium*), various grasses, shrubs like saltbush (*Atriplex*), and berries of one kind or another. Acorns and cultivated grains and fruits also are eaten. Tender green leaves of many forbs and grasses comprise an important part of the diet and may in fact be crucial in preparing the birds physiologically for breeding. The birds eat some insects at all times of the year—more in the period of insect abundance accompanying seasonal rainfall than at other times.

Like scaled quail, California quail live at times without drinking water, but not many of them do so, nor do they breed in the absence of water. Water is essential to the well-being of this bird, and in the dry parts of California very good success has been achieved in increasing the quail population by supplying water where food and cover are adequate. Wells, windmills, or artificial ponds may be installed for this purpose, or a device developed by Ben Glading of the California Department of Fish and Game—an underground tank of concrete or plastic that stores about seven hundred gallons of rain water caught on an asphalt apron. A ramp permits the quail to reach the water in the tank (see fig. 89). The tank is replenished by each rain and requires little maintenance. Such devices when properly placed may attract and support several hundred quail in places where none could exist before for lack of water.

The California quail is much the most important game bird in Baja California. It is abundant enough to supply fine shooting for the local hunters and to attract many American sportsmen from California, who enter northern Baja California specifically for quail hunting. Although many thousands of birds have been killed annually in the foothills back of Tijuana and Ensenada, the numbers have not diminished. Actually this quail is highly prolific and can withstand an annual harvest of half or perhaps more of the fall population without prejudicing the next year's crop. Hunting of this bird should be encouraged.

Gambel Quail. *Lophortyx gambelii*

Other name.—Codorniz de Gambel.

Description.—MALE: Face and throat black. Crown reddish brown, separated from black forehead by a black and a white line. Crest black. Narrow white collar separating black of throat from gray chest. Sides of neck and foreback gray, each feather with a shaft streak of brown. Back, wings, rump, and tail olive gray. Breast clear buff in front, black beneath, with flanks and abdomen mottled buff and brown. Side feathers rich chestnut with pale shaft streaks. Bill, feet, and legs black. FEMALE: Like a female California quail in head, neck, chest, and upper parts, but with buffy underparts lightly streaked with brown but not scaled. Side feathers chestnut with white shaft streaks. Bill, feet, and legs dusky. Measurements: folded wing—105 to 118 mm.; tail—85 to 101 mm.; bill—15 to 17 mm.; tarsus—29 to 33 mm. Weight: 160 to 175 gm.

Range in Mexico.—Desert and mesquite-grassland of northeastern Baja California, Sonora, northern Sinaloa, and a fringe of northern Chihuahua. A male specimen in the Instituto de Biología, México, D.F. (collected Jan. 15, 1923, prepared by A. W. Anthony), taken at Tijuana, Baja California, seems to be a stray far out of the normal range.

This species, which resembles the California quail in many ways, is strictly and wholly a bird of arid regions. It is the dominant galliform of the Sonoran desert, where it frequents the mesquite and hackberry thickets along washes and on the flats. Like the California quail, it is gregarious and often forms large coveys including hundreds of birds in areas of great abundance. Coveys of 20 to 50 are more usual, however.

The Gambel quail is perhaps the strongest runner of the desert quails. When a hunter finds a covey, he often must run at full speed to force the birds to fly. Even after one flight, the birds may continue running if the group alights together. If the birds can be scattered, however, they hide individually and can then be flushed one at a time to give good shooting. The problems of hunting Gambel quail are set forth by Leopold (1953), who explored the delta of the Colorado River in 1922. At that time the delta was virgin wilderness and quail were unbelievably abundant. The combination of mesquite and such weeds as wild hemp, tornillo, and arrowweed, all growing on rich alluvial soil, produced ideal habitat for the quail. There are few such concentrations left today, since most of the fertile river bottoms (including that of the Colorado) have been drained and cleared for agriculture. Nevertheless, Gambel quail are still relatively abundant in many parts of Sonora where mesquite stands are interspersed with open patches of grama grass and seed-bearing annuals. For example, on the flats near Pitahaya, Sonora, we easily found several large coveys a day in late October, 1946, and that area was not exceptionally good quail range.

Since the Gambel quail is a major game bird in the southwestern United States, its natural history and ecology have been carefully studied. The account that follows has drawn on various publications, particularly those by Gorsuch (1934), who studied the bird in southern Arizona, very near the Mexican border, and by Gullion (1956a), who worked in southern Nevada.

The winter coveys begin to break up in February and March, when

Female

Male

Fig. 90.   Gambel quail, *Lophortyx gambelii*.

pairs are formed. There is much fighting among the males for mates, since there usually are not enough females to go round. Some unmated cocks are left over and call hopefully but in vain throughout the spring for a female. The mated pairs normally are nesting by the end of March. Nests are concealed in grass, weeds, or occasionally in thorny bushes. They contain 10 to 17 eggs (the average is 12), which are white more or less heavily splotched with purplish brown. The average size of the egg is 32 by 24 mm. Incubation usually requires twenty-one to twenty-three days, but Gorsuch noted a few nests in which it took much longer, the maximum time being thirty-one days. The young leave the nest after they are dry and follow the parents from then on until maturity. The full nesting cycle requires about four and one-half months—ten days to select the nest site and build the nest, twelve to twenty days to lay the eggs, twenty-two days of incubation, and two and one-half to three months to rear the brood. Hence two successful nestings in one season are ordinarily impossible. Nevertheless, in highly favorable (wet) years two nestings may be accomplished by abandonment of the chicks to the care of a few adults while many pairs start new nests. This apparently happens on rare occasions, as Gullion (1956b) noted in southern Nevada. Conversely, in unfavorable (dry) years the birds may not nest at all.

Predators destroy many—ordinarily at least half—of the nests of the Gambel quail, as they do those of other quails that nest on or near the ground. The bereaved parents usually try again, and yet a third time if necessary, until by the end of the season most of the pairs have raised young. The heavy loss of eggs to coyotes, ground squirrels, snakes, and other animals is a normal phenomenon to which the quails are well adapted by virtue of large egg clutches and willingness to renest. Rarely if ever is this sort of predation a primary cause of quail shortage. Quantity and quality of food is much more important in determining nesting success, by regulating the vigor and the determination of the nesting adults.

In feeding habits, the Gambel quail is much like the California quail. The chicks start on an insect diet, ingesting more and more seeds and other plant foods as they grow up. By August they are feeding like adults. Among the plant foods which Gorsuch and Gullion found to make up most of the diet of Gambel quail in Arizona and Nevada are legumes of the subfamilies Mimosaceae and Fabaceae; the flowers and seeds of mesquite (*Prosopis*) alone make up nearly a fifth of the annual forage. The seeds of the common honey mesquite (*P. juliflora*) cannot be obtained by the quail direct from the tough pods but must be eaten by some other animal, such as a cow, and passed out again; then the quail can use them. Other important leguminous seeds are those of deer vetch (*Lotus*) and locoweed (*Astragalus*). A great variety of other weeds, such as mustard (*Sophia*), morning glory (*Evolvulus*), and panic grass (*Panicum*), supply supplementary seeds and greens. The green foods apparently are needed to condition the birds for nesting by supplying qualitative elements in the diet (vitamins especially) and succulence. Also, green vegetation supports an abundance of insects needed in rearing the quail chicks.

The water needs of Gambel quail are about the same as those of the scaled and California quails. Except when succulent foods are easily available, the birds drink frequently, although not necessarily every day. Large populations are not usually found where there is no drinking water.

In Sonora, Gambel quail are widely hunted near highways, and in the back country they are trapped and shot by local people for food. But great areas of Sonora are so isolated that the quail are left undisturbed; there are no more quail there than in places where hunting and trapping are heaviest. This is further evidence that hunting usually has little effect on quail abundance. Overgrazing of the range by livestock and shortage of water are important influences locally. Year-to-year rainfall is the most important and the most variable factor of all in determining abundance.

Douglas Quail. *Lophortyx douglasii*

Other names.—Codorniz de Douglas; codorniz gris; chole; chacuaca; pascuala; *Lophortyx bensoni.*

Description.—MALE: Head gray, streaked with black on forehead and sides, speckled or dotted with black on the throat. Bushy, pale reddish crest. Sides and back of neck reddish brown flecked with gray. Back, rump, and tail gray. Wings brown, heavily mottled with russet and a little white on the coverts. Chest gray. Breast and abdomen gray with round white spots, larger toward the rear. Sides streaked reddish brown and gray with elongated white spots. Under tail coverts dusky brown edged with tawny. Bill and feet blackish. FEMALE: Plumage mostly mottled grays and browns dorsally, with small dusky crest sometimes streaked with brown. Underparts gray with round white spots, as in the male. Bill and feet blackish. Measurements: folded wing—106 to 115 mm.; tail—66 to 94 mm.; bill—13 to 16 mm.; tarsus—29 to 33 mm. Weight: 160 to 190 gm. Males slightly larger than females.

Range in Mexico.—Pacific slope from central Sonora south to Colima. The species has been introduced on María Madre Island.

Along the tropical foothills of west-central Mexico the Douglas quail is the only species of quail found. Its range overlaps that of the Gambel quail to the north and of the barred quail to the south. The center of the range, and the region of greatest abundance, is the dense brush of southern Sinaloa and Nayarit. In a camp near Santiago Ixcuintla, Nayarit, we found ourselves in a virtual metropolis for this species, which, although closely related to the other *Lophortyx* quails, is quite different in habit.

The Douglas quail thrives best in the dense second growth of cutover tropical forest. We found few birds in the forest itself (only near the forest edge) and none whatsoever in the open fields or pastures. But in the

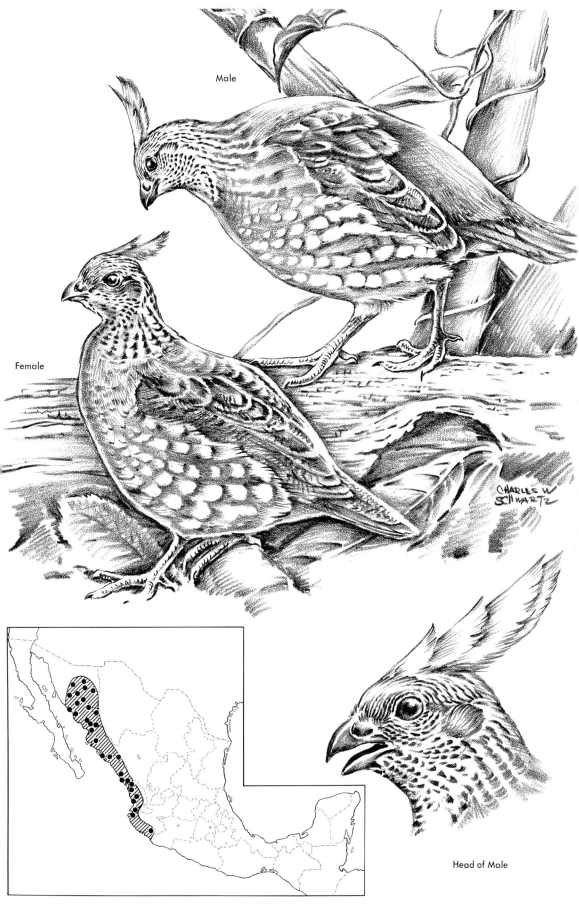

Fig. 91. Douglas quail, *Lophortyx douglasii*.

almost impenetrable *monte* the quail were abundant. Coveys seemed to be small (6 to 20) and closely spaced. Along the narrow roads and trails through the brush one would often come across coveys every hundred yards or so when the birds were actively feeding. I am sure that near our Nayarit camp there were pockets with a density of more than a bird to the acre.

These quail we found roosting in vines or thick brush a few feet above the ground. A covey I watched as they went to bed one night hopped and scrambled up to their sleeping places with continous throaty chatter, sounding much like California quail. In the morning they hopped back down again and fed under the brush or along the edges of clearings. When frightened, as for example by shooting, the birds would flutter or hop up into the dense *monte* and "freeze" there, coming back to the ground only after the disturbance was long over. It was many days before I forced a covey to fly into the open.

When we were in Nayarit, in mid-April, the winter coveys were just starting to break up and pair formation seemed to be under way. Some of the males were "crowing" from low perches. The gonads of twenty birds I collected were starting to develop. It appeared to me that laying would begin in early May. Batty, who knew this quail well in southern Sinaloa, said of its breeding habits: "Breeds in April and May. Lays eight to twelve eggs; nest on the ground. Sometimes has as many as twenty eggs at one sitting. Roosts in bushes and trees, and not on ground." (Miller, 1905 : 342.) I have no data on the size or appearance of the eggs.

The foods of the Douglas quail seemed to be the expected assortment of weed seeds, fruits, and insects. A large proportion of the seeds found in crops were of legumes, which, however, I failed to identify. The birds scratch vigorously when feeding, and when their crops are full, they frequently are found loafing and dusting along the roads and trails.

Because the Douglas quail thrives in cutover forest, it has increased its range and numbers with the extension of settlement and clearing. Hunting is negligible, since the brush is so dense and the birds are so difficult to obtain. There is no problem of conservation of this species.

Barred Quail. *Philortyx fasciatus*

Other names.—Codorniz listada; chorrunda.

Description.—A small quail in which male and female are identical in appearance and size. Adult: Head grayish brown with chin and throat dull white and a straight black-and-brown crest 25 to 30 mm. high. Back and chest grayish brown, each feather edged with rufous. Wing coverts brown, barred and mottled with blackish brown and tan. Tail gray, finely vermiculated with white and black. Sides and breast boldly barred black and white. Abdomen and mid-line of breast white. Under tail coverts pale tan with blackish spots. Bill black. Feet and legs brown. Immature in autumn: Like adult but with shorter crest and black chin, throat, and face; during the winter and early spring this plumage molts to that

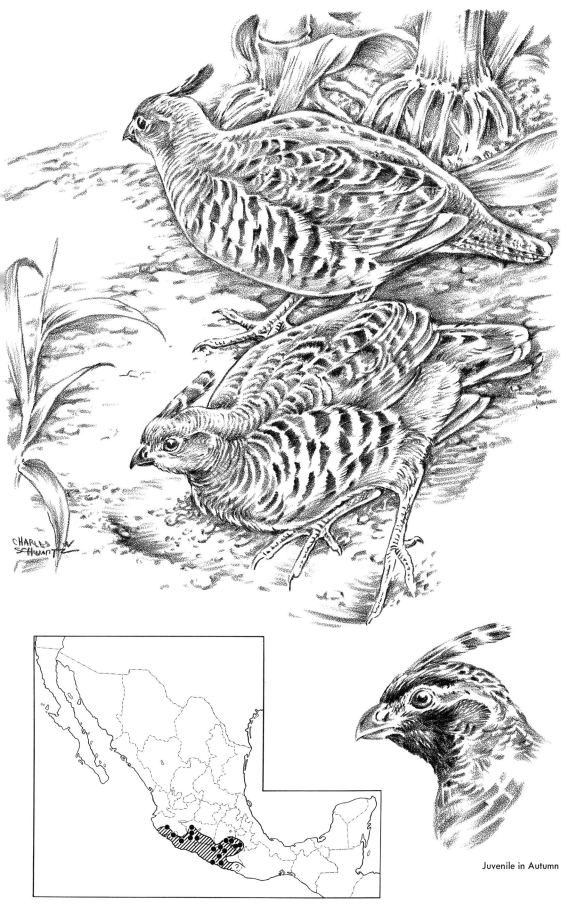

Juvenile in Autumn

Fig. 92. Barred quail, *Philortyx fasciatus*.

of adult birds. Measurements of adults: folded wing—94 to 104 mm.; tail—58 to 68 mm.; bill—14 to 16 mm.; tarsus—27 to 30 mm. Weight: of adults—115 to 160 gm.; of fall immatures—93 to 120 gm.

Range in Mexico.—Semiarid tropical scrub of the Pacific slope from southwestern Jalisco to southeastern Guerrero, Morelos, and Puebla.

The beautiful barred quail is closely related to the *Lophortyx* quails, but in many of its habits it is much more like a bobwhite. Its preferred habitat is the dense weed patches that border the milpas. Coveys are relatively small —5 to 20 birds, rarely 25, averaging 12 (based on 18 coveys). The birds roost on the ground in open low grass or weeds. They crouch when approached, instead of running away. When scattered, they hide in ground cover or in thick vines or shrubs and reflush only if they are nearly stepped on. These attributes and behaviorisms are shared with the bobwhite. But the barred quail and some of the *Lophortyx* quails "squeal" when flushed, whereas the bobwhite does not.

I found the barred quail most abundant in the valleys and alluvial flats of the lower Río Balsas Basin in Guerrero. There in favorable weed-bordered agricultural areas, protected by fences from grazing, this quail is very numerous indeed. Hunting without a dog, as I was, one finds only a small fraction of the birds; but from scratching and other sign I gathered that coveys were spaced only 150 to 200 yards apart, which would suggest a density greater than one bird per acre. Populations as high as this occur only where there is no grazing. Few, if any, barred quail live on badly overgrazed hillsides or in abandoned fields (see fig. 30). The bird follows agricultural valleys up to elevations of 5,000 feet or more above sea level (e.g., at Teloloapan, Guerrero), but densities are greater at lower altitudes.

The breeding season of the barred quail seems to be late summer. Alberto Navarro, a native of Poliutla, Guerrero, stated emphatically that nests are found in August and September, never earlier. In Michoacán, Blake and Hanson (1942) collected a female with a hard-shelled egg in the oviduct and males with enlarged testes in August. Likewise Davis (1944a) took a series of specimens near Acapulco, Guerrero, all in breeding condition, in early August. R. W. Storer found the birds of northern Michoacán still in coveys early in August but developing sexually. I saw small young (quarter-grown) in Guerrero early in December, although most young were two-thirds grown by then. I have no information on nests or eggs.

A curious and unique character of the barred quail is the striking black face and throat in the juvenal plumage. The natal plumage of these parts is buffy yellow. When the chick is about half grown, the black juvenal feathers grow in; the young birds are then recognizable from adults, even on the wing, for a period of about two months (late November to late January). After that, the black face and throat are lost in postjuvenal molt, and the bird assumes the appearance of an adult. Young can still be recognized, however, by the juvenal primary coverts when the bird is in the hand (see bob-white account).

Of 31 specimens of *Philortyx* I handled in Guerrero and Morelos, 9 were adult males, 8 were adult females, and the rest were young—7 of each sex. From this limited sample it appears that adults outnumbered young in fall and winter populations of 1944–1945 and that juvenal survival and rate of turnover were both low at that time. However, breeding success may vary greatly from year to year.

Among the foods identified in the crops of these quail were a wide variety of weed seeds, especially legumes such as *Desmodium* and *Crotalaria*. Others were the seeds of sunflower, thistles, corn cockle, dove weed (*Croton*), and cultivated plants like beans and *ajonjolí* (sesame). Blake and Hanson found some insects in their five specimens. In Guerrero I found the barred quail watering regularly after both the morning and evening feedings; this was in the dry season.

Many predators undoubtedly prey on the barred quail, for I found scattered remains in several places. Along the Río Balsas sharp-shinned hawks were quite numerous in December, and they are perhaps a principal enemy.

There is some sport hunting for barred quail in Morelos and near Acapulco, but over most of its range the species is hunted lightly. I feel sure that this bird would hold well for pointing dogs and could be a fine game bird. Its pursuit should be encouraged.

Bobwhite. *Colinus virginianus*

Other names.—Codorniz común; cuiche.

Description.—MALE: Highly variable in appearance in various parts of Mexico (see fig. 94). Crown brown to brownish black, without crest. White stripe from top of bill passing above eye and down side of the neck; stripe shrinks to a faint line in bobwhites from Chiapas. Black stripe from base of bill passing below eye and under white throat, forming a collar. The black collar expands to include the whole chest in Puebla and Morelos; in specimens from Sonora and southern Mexico the throat too is black, hence the collar effect is lost. Breast and abdomen barred black and white in northeastern Mexico, the barring giving way to bright reddish brown in the south and west. Back and wing coverts mottled browns, black, and white. Tail bluish gray, the central feathers finely vermiculated with black and white. Bill black. Feet and legs brown. FEMALE: Crown and ear area chocolate brown. Eye stripe and throat buffy tan. Back, wings, and sides mottled browns and buff. Underparts buff, the chest barred with dusky brown; barring extends to whole undersurface in southern populations. Measurements and weights are given in table 10.

Range in Mexico.—Gulf coast, from the Río Grande valley to Tabasco and Chiapas, and the central uplands from San Luis Potosí and Jalisco south and east to Puebla and Oaxaca. There is a disjunct or isolated population in the valleys and foothills of central Sonora.

Female

Male

Fig. 93. Bobwhite. *Colinus virginianus*.

TABLE 10

MEASUREMENTS AND WEIGHTS OF BOBWHITES FROM VARIOUS PARTS OF MEXICO
(Both sexes included in the figures)

Locality	Folded wing (mm.)	Tail (mm.)	Bill (mm.)	Tarsus (mm.)	Weight (gm.)
Sonora	109 (101–115)	63 (59–69)	15 (14–17)	30 (28–31)	...
Central uplands of San Luis Potosí, Jalisco, Queretaro ..	108 (101–115)	61 (55–67)	16 (15–17)	30 (28–33)	159 (149–178)
Tamaulipas, Nuevo León .	107 (99–112)	61 (51–64)	14 (13–15)	30 (28–31)	152 (132–186)
Morelos, Puebla	105 (101–109)	56 (52–63)	16 (15–18)	30 (28–32)	149 (133–170)
Gulf coast of eastern San Luis Potosí, Veracruz ...	103 (100–107)	54 (51–60)	15 (15–16)	30 (28–32)	133 (124–137)
Chiapas	94 (91–97)	47 (45–51)	14 (14–15)	26 (25–28)	129 (122–139)

The bobwhite is probably the most variable game species in Mexico in size and in appearance. A male bobwhite from Chiapas, for example, would hardly be recognized as belonging to the same species as a specimen from Tamaulipas. Yet all the variant forms shown in figure 94 interbreed with one another and are clearly conspecific. Presumably each segment of the population is in some way adapted to the particular environment in which it lives. Birds of the tropical lowlands are smaller than those of the uplands (table 10) and in general they are darker. They differ also in timing of the breeding cycle and perhaps in other physiological traits.

The bobwhite is a quail of the farmlands. Its preferred habitat is the border of weeds and brush around grainfields. Bobwhites do occupy pastureland and even open woodland, but they reach maximum abundance in the vicinity of tilled fields because food is usually more plentiful there. Winter coveys consist of 8 to 20 birds averaging about 12. Each covey has its own home area, which is usually a quarter mile or less in radius. Within this home range there must be weed patches or grain stubble for feeding, and cover for protection from predators. Water is necessary in dry periods. Bobwhites roost on the ground in low grass or weeds, the covey arranged in a circle, tails together. If disturbed at night, the roosting birds explode into the air, each one aimed in a different direction so that there is no interference in flight.

Bobwhite coveys apparently try to defend their home areas from other coveys, for there is little or no overlap in the territories of adjoining groups. In very good range the coveys are close together and their territories are small. However, on even the best range, one bird per acre is about maximum density. Seemingly the birds will not stand crowding beyond that point, no matter how much food and cover there is. In country that is overgrazed, or

Fig. 94.   Male bobwhites from various parts of Mexico.
A, Jalisco; B, southern Puebla; C, southeastern
San Luis Potosí; D, northern Nuevo León;
E, Sonora; F, uplands of central Chiapas.

in terrain that is inferior for other reasons, each covey occupies a larger area and the density is correspondingly lower.

In spring or early summer the coveys break up into pairs. There is always a small surplus of unmated males that hopefully keep giving the "bobwhite" call through the whole breeding season, trying to find an unattached female. The mated cocks do very little calling. In most parts of Mexico nesting occurs in April, May, and June, and a few pairs that have lost their early nests persist even into the autumn. Late broods are a result of destruction of nests; they are not second broods. Nests are concealed in grass or weeds and are amazingly difficult to find. Clutches of 10 to 15 eggs are normal; the eggs are dull white and measure 30 by 24 mm. The period of incubation is twenty-three to twenty-four days. Male bobwhites share in the tasks of incubating the eggs and caring for the young. If the female is killed, the male will bring up the young alone.

In most bobwhite populations the rate of death and replacement is rapid. Fall coveys are composed usually of 60 to 85 per cent young. This means that

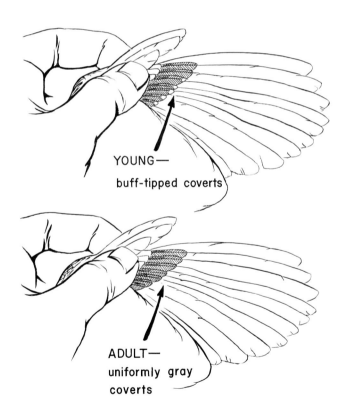

YOUNG— buff-tipped coverts

ADULT— uniformly gray coverts

from one autumn to the next about three-quarters (more or less) of the birds die and are replaced by young ones. The young birds are very similar to adults in appearance but can be recognized by the presence of juvenal upper primary coverts, which are mottled in contrast to the steel gray coverts of adults (see illustration).

Bobwhites are seedeaters primarily, although greens and insects contribute to the diet seasonally. In the crops of birds collected in various parts of Mexico I have found seeds of sunflowers, foxtails, panic grass, thistles, many wild legumes (especially tick trefoils of the genus *Desmodium*), and such cultivated crops as frijoles, corn, wheat, and tomatoes. In oak woods the birds often eat many acorns. Fleshy fruits of various kinds are relished. During the dry season, Mexican bobwhites drink water daily, but they get along on dew and raindrops in wet periods.

In most parts of its range in Mexico the bobwhite is thriving where cover and food plants are not overgrazed. In good habitat the population can withstand a heavy annual harvest; there are few places indeed where it could be said that bobwhites are overhunted. But where domestic animals are permitted to eat or beat down the weeds and grasses, the bobwhite cannot survive, even if fully protected from hunting. The interesting masked bobwhite of Sonora, for example, is disappearing because of overgrazing of its river-bottom and foothill ranges. In Morelos I found bobwhites abundant in fenced milpas, but there were few or none on grazed lands outside the milpa fences. In 1938 Sr. Juan Zinser, then chief of the Game Department in Mexico, tried to overcome the bobwhite shortage in Morelos by importing and releasing 5,000 bobwhites from Ciudad Victoria, Tamaulipas. This accomplished nothing, for the basic cause of scarcity, overgrazing, was not corrected. The only effective way of increasing bobwhites is by improving their habitat. For this purpose the barbed-wire fence will do what no game law or restocking program can accomplish.

Yucatán Bobwhite. *Colinus nigrogularis*

Other names.—Codorniz de Yucatán; codorniz garganta negra; bech'.

Description.—MALE: Crown mottled brown, black, and tan bordered with whitish. Face and throat black with a whitish line passing below eye and ear to neck. Feathers of chest and breast white heavily bordered with black, giving a scaled effect. Sides and foreback rich reddish brown, mottled with white. Back and wing coverts olive brown, streaked and vermiculated with buff, brown, and black. Tail gray. Abdomen dull reddish brown. Bill black. Feet dusky brown. FEMALE: Crown and ear area dark brown streaked with buff. Throat and superciliary line buffy tan. Back, wings, and sides mottled brown, black, and tan. Chest reddish brown heavily mottled with dusky brown. Underparts barred white, black, and brown. Bill dark brown. Feet dusky. Measurements: folded wing—95 to 104 mm.; tail—50 to 59 mm.; bill—15 to 16 mm.; tarsus—27 to 32 mm. Weight: 126 to 144 gm. The sexes are essentially the same size.

Range in Mexico.—Comparatively arid northwestern part of the Yucatán Peninsula. The species occurs also in Guatemala and British Honduras, but these populations are separated from the Yucatán range by uninhabitable rain forest.

The Yucatán bobwhite is much like the common bobwhite in behavior and in choice of habitat. Most of the year the birds are in coveys of 7 to 15 individuals, which live around fields or clearings in the forest. They cannot exist in the unbroken heavy forest itself. Although in the Mayan cornfields the bobwhite population is fairly high, it is in the henequen plantations that ideal habitat conditions are found. There the quail population is very high indeed. Paynter (1955 : 81) states:

> Because of the extensive cultivation of *henequén* in the vicinity of Mérida, and the presence of Indians who practice *milpa* agriculture in the outlying districts, the present area of habitats suitable for quail is vastly greater than at any time during the history of the Peninsula. Without doubt, the existing population of quail is at least several times greater than that during even the height of the Mayan culture, when much of the Peninsula was inhabited and under cultivation. To be convinced of this, one has merely to walk through the *henequén* fields where the quail occur in almost unbelievable numbers within the thick grass which has developed after repeated burning.

As clearings are penetrating the rain forest, the Yucatán bobwhite is extending its range. Nelson (1932) reported quail near Lake Petén, Guatemala, where none had been found by earlier collectors; he felt that new clearing had made a niche for the bird. Paynter noted similar range extension in Campeche. In southeastern Yucatán I found this bird in all open, weedy fields, no matter how remote they seemed to be from other clearings. The species, in other words, takes full advantage of improvements in its range.

The call notes of the Yucatán bobwhite are virtually indistinguishable from those of the common bobwhite. Chapman (1896 : 289) remarked on this: "It was exceedingly interesting to hear bobwhites so unlike our *virginianus* in appearance singing and calling in a manner so nearly like our northern species that the casual listener would appreciate no difference in the voice of the two birds." I found that the three-note assembly call of the northern bobwhite served admirably to call up scattered coveys near Chichén Itzá. Although I did not hear the male "bobwhite" call, Chapman apparently did.

Nesting in Yucatán occurs in spring and throughout the summer. Paynter found evidence of breeding from mid-April to late June and noted half-grown "squealers" in December. Traylor (1941) collected young chicks in early November. But these late records undoubtedly represent repeat nesting. Early summer would seem to be the peak period of normal reproduction. I have no data on eggs or incubation.

Such crops of the Yucatán bobwhite as I examined were filled with assorted

Fig. 95. Yucatán bobwhite, *Colinus nigrogularis*.

weed seeds, a dominant one being the common tick trefoil (*Desmodium*) of the newly cleared fields.

The bobwhites of Yucatán are hunted regularly by sportsmen from Mérida and to a limited extent by native people shooting for food. Since this quail holds very well for pointing dogs, it is an ideal game bird, except for the fact that the henequen fields, where quail are most numerous, are difficult and even dangerous to hunt through. The needle-sharp leaves of henequen are waiting to impale dog or hunter at every turn. There is no serious problem of conservation or management of this species, which thrives with agricultural development.

Spotted Wood Quail. *Odontophorus guttatus*

Other names.—Bolonchaco; golonchaco; cobán chaco; bulu'tok'; totoloschóco.

Description.—As big as a domestic pigeon. Crown blackish brown, terminating in a broad crest, which is black in females, flaming orange in males. Throat black, streaked with white. Underparts rich olive brown to reddish brown, flecked with white spots 2 to 6 mm. long. Back, wings, and tail dark brown mottled with velvety black and a little buff. Bill and feet black. Except for the crest, the sexes look alike. Measurements: folded wing—134 to 154 mm.; tail—61 to 77 mm.; bill—18 to 23 mm.; tarsus—42 to 49 mm. Weight: 260 to 360 gm. Males slightly larger than females.

Range in Mexico.—Wet tropical forests from central Veracruz and northern Oaxaca east through Chiapas and the Yucatán Peninsula.

The home of the spotted wood quail is under the deep rain forest, where the canopy is so dense as to shade out ground vegetation. There in the half-light they live in company with such other jungle dwellers as the great tinamou, the Boucard tinamou, and the Cassin dove. My single experience with the wood quail was at a camp near Monte Líbano in northeastern Chiapas. The birds were quite abundant there, and we collected 9 adults and 3 well-grown young between December 1 and 6, 1945. The coveys we saw consisted of 5 to 10 birds each. These evidently were not family units, because most of the birds were adults. Lowery and Dalquest (1951) found the species in groups of only 1 to 4 birds in southern Veracruz, but that was in late April, when the winter coveys may have been separating prior to breeding. Alvarez del Toro (1952a) says that coveys range from 6 to 20.

Every group that I saw was on the ground. The birds would usually run when discovered, or crouch in the forest litter. Only when I fired would they fly. The flight is rapid, like that of other quail, but short—usually not more than a hundred yards. Birds thus scattered would hide in the leaves until all was quiet, and then the covey would reassemble, with much calling back and forth. The call is loud and strong, consisting of six notes, repeated at frequent intervals.

Nesting is reported to occur in May and June (Paynter, 1955). Van Tyne

Female

Male

CHARLES W. SCHWARTZ

Head of Male

Fig. 96. Spotted wood quail, *Odontophorus guttatus*.

(1935) collected in Guatemala on May 5 a chick which he estimated to be less than a week old. An equally young chick in the collection of the Museum of Vertebrate Zoölogy was taken on May 22 near Villa Allende, Chiapas. I have no information on nests or eggs.

Wood quail scratch in the duff and litter, and wherever they live their scratchings may be seen. In the crops I examined were small bulbs and soft rootlets, insects and their pupae and larvae (mostly Diptera and Coleoptera), miscellaneous seeds, and the white meat of a large nut or seed. These foods all seemed to have been dug from the forest litter.

Lowery and Dalquest report a quaint method of hunting wood quail by natives of southern Veracruz (p. 561):

This species . . . was always located by dogs. On every occasion the birds flew to low perches, ten to fifteen feet from the ground, and blinked their eyes stupidly. The natives captured our specimens by making a small vine into a noose and, with the aid of a slim pole, slipping the loop over the birds' heads. On some occasions, the quail ducked their heads out of the noose. If this occurred, and the birds seemed about to fly, the Indians barked like dogs, and the quail again settled down. The natives seemed more anxious to obtain the birds for pets than for food.

The future status of the wood quail will depend entirely upon whether some of the dense rain forest is preserved. The bird disappears when the canopy is broken and a brushy understory springs up.

Singing Quail. *Dactylortyx thoracicus*

Other names.—Chivizcoyo; chibilúb; codorniz dedilarga; long-toed quail.

Description.—Medium-sized, with very short tail and astonishingly large feet and claws (up to 20 mm.). Sexes similar dorsally: upper parts chestnut brown, mottled and streaked with black, olive, and buff. Male has tawny orange on throat, cheeks, and in a line above the eye; underparts pale olive brown (palest in the center of the breast) with prominent whitish shaft streaks, especially in the chest area. Female is dull gray in the face and throat, rather bright reddish buff below, palest in center of breast; shaft streaks dimmer than in the male. Measurements: folded wing—125 to 137 mm.; tail—46 to 57 mm.; bill—16 to 18 mm.; tarsus—31 to 37 mm. Weight: 170 to 266 gm. Males slightly larger than females. Birds from Yucatán Peninsula 20 per cent smaller than those from mainland of Mexico.

Range in Mexico.—The range is strangely discontinuous. This quail is known from the highlands near San Sebastián, Jalisco; the mountains of central Guerrero; the eastern escarpment from southern Tamaulipas to central Veracruz; the highlands of Chiapas; and the lowland tropical forests of the Yucatán Peninsula.

The singing quail is one of the more interesting but least known of the Mexican quails. Over most of its range it is found in upland cloud forest, oak–sweet gum forest, or humid canyons in the richer parts of the pine-oak forest. But on the Yucatán Peninsula, curiously, it inhabits the lowland deciduous

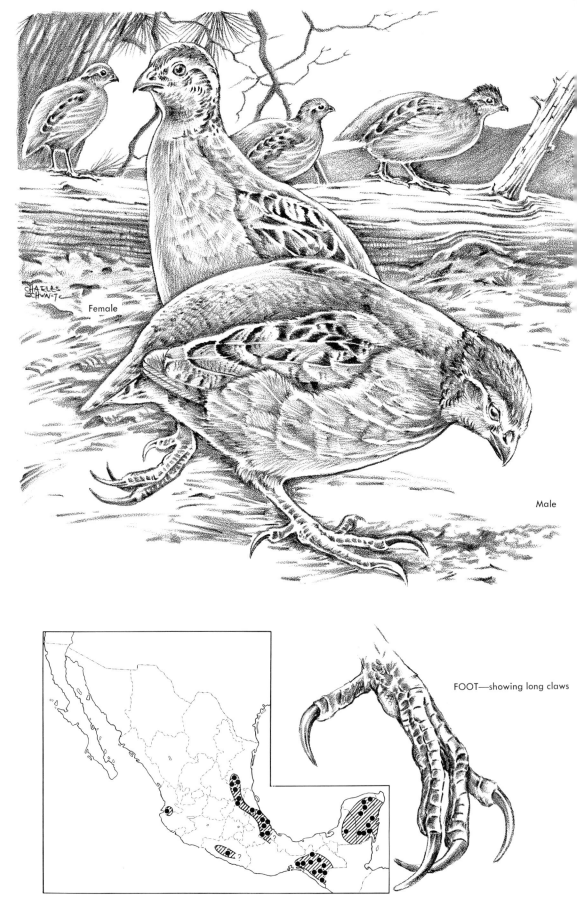

Female

Male

FOOT—showing long claws

Fig. 97. Singing quail, *Dactylortyx thoracicus*.

scrub that has developed as a result of cutting and burning of the original rich selva. It is found ordinarily in small coveys of 5 to 10 birds, living always in the forest and, as a rule, in thick undergrowth. The bird is shy and elusive, preferring to run away stealthily when disturbed but capable of rapid and deft flight if the issue is forced. The flight is short (50 to 75 yards), but the birds run and then hide after a flight, and they are virtually impossible to reflush without the aid of a dog. Consequently they are not satisfactory game birds; in fact, experienced collectors have great difficulty in obtaining specimens. Near Omilteme, Guerrero, I hunted for ten days in forest thoroughly scratched up by these birds before I finally flushed a covey and killed two.

I know of only one estimate of population density of *Dactylortyx*. Warner and Harrell (1957) report approximately 3.5 pairs per 100 acres in climax oak–sweet gum forest, at 3,600 feet elevation, near Rancho del Cielo, Tamaulipas. Their paper contains more information on the biology of the singing quail than any other publication, and in this account I have drawn heavily upon it.

An outstanding characteristic of the singing quail is its song, which is more melodious and complicated than that of any other gallinaceous bird known to me. It is described thus by Warner and Harrell (p. 130):

The first part of the song is a series of about four loud, penetrating whistles, which increase in frequency and pitch . . . The last of these notes is followed immediately by the second part of the song, a series of three to six rapid phrases, each made up of notes of differing pitch, the middle ones higher and more definitely accented. . . . These phrases are followed by a low twittering which is often not audible or may be absent. There is no evidence that the female sings.

The breeding season is long, extending at least from March to August in all parts of the range and perhaps longer in some places. Warner and Harrell report evidence of breeding in March and April in southern Tamaulipas, and Sutton and Pettingill (1942) found a brood of young on April 16 in the same region. Dickey and Van Rossem (1938) collected birds approaching breeding condition in late March in El Salvador. Paynter (1955) found a female incubating five eggs on May 7 in Yucatán and took partly feathered chicks on July 24 and August 10. Few nests have been found, and the average, or "normal," clutch is not known. The eggs are described by Nehrkorn (in Warner and Harrell) as white with "yellow clouds" and measuring 31 by 25 mm. Presumably these quail remain paired in summer and both parents attend the young, but I cannot find positive evidence of this.

The singing quail is equipped with powerful digging feet, and obtains much of its food by scratching in the forest litter. Specimens that we collected in the mountains of Guerrero contained bulbs that looked like tiny onions, some small unidentified seeds, and larvae and pupae of several kinds of insects. All food items seemed to have been dug from the ground. Warner and Harrell cite other observations of crop contents, most of which included insects, centipedes, crickets, grubs, and various kinds of seeds. The scratching of this quail is not limited to specific narrow holes, as is that of the Montezuma quail, but is more diffuse, upturning wide areas of forest duff. It reminded me of the scratching of wild turkeys but was on a smaller scale.

The best habitat for singing quail is cool, moist forest that has been neither grazed nor burned. This perhaps is because of their preference for feeding in deep, rich litter, which would be compacted or destroyed by either grazing or burning. As the Mexican forests are further opened up and exploited, the range of this handsome quail will probably shrink.

Montezuma Quail. *Cyrtonyx montezumae* and Related Species

Other names.—Codorniz pinto; cincoreál; *Cyrtonyx massena;* harlequin quail; Mearns quail.

Species included here.—*Cyrtonyx montezumae* and *C. ocellatus.*

Description.—MALE: Face and throat boldly marked with black and white (see plate). Crown feathers elongated and spread into a broad hood, tan, streaked above with darker hues. Back and wings mottled browns, grays, and black, with elongate buff streaks. Center line of breast chestnut brown. Sides of *C. montezumae* bluish black with round white spots: these spots are rich purplish brown in southern Mexico. In *C. ocellatus* the chest is buff, the breast and flanks are chestnut brown barred with black and gray. Abdomen and under tail coverts black. Bill black at base, horn-colored at tip. Feet bluish gray with long claws. FEMALE: Head and neck mottled brown and buff with whitish chin and with a hood like that of male but smaller. Back and wings mottled browns and grays with elongate buff shaft streaks. Chest and sides pinkish brown, lightly streaked with brown. Underparts buff, with some black barring on breast. Bill and feet like those of male. Measurements: folded wing—111 to 131 mm.; tail—48 to 63 mm.; bill—15 to 17 mm.; tarsus—28 to 33 mm. Females slightly smaller than males. Average weight of males: 195 gm.; of females: 176 gm.

Range in Mexico.—Of *C. montezumae:* all the pine-oak upland from Sonora and Coahuila south to Oaxaca. Of *C. ocellatus:* the same vegetation zone in eastern Oaxaca and Chiapas. A narrow strip of tropical forest breaks the continuity of range in the Isthmus of Tehuantepec.

The Montezuma quail is perhaps the most beautiful of the gallinaceous birds of Mexico. It lives in small coveys (5 to 10 birds) in the temperate pine-oak upland, ordinarily in rather sparse populations. A covey seems to be a family unit—a pair of adults with their offspring of the previous year and perhaps an additional adult or two. On their winter ranges the coveys are very sedentary, often living on a few acres of favorable ground. Optimum habitat consists of pine-oak woodland with an understory of coarse bunch grasses and occasional clumps of brush. But the species can tolerate a wide range of cover conditions from timberline to the desert edge, always however in the pine-oak zone. In the highlands east of the Valley of Mexico the Montezuma quail persists even in fenced croplands of corn or maguey so long as there are grassy or brushy draws and fencerows with patches of forest.

Fig. 98.   Montezuma quail, *Cyrtonyx montezumae*. Inserted
figures show differences in marking between males of
C. montezumae from northern and from southern
Mexico and *C. ocellatus* from Chiapas.

This quail is strictly a ground dweller, rarely if ever going into trees. It lives inconspicuously in the thick ground cover and is not easily seen even when one is searching for it. The birds hide when approached and take flight only if nearly stepped on. Flight is explosive and very rapid but short —50 to 100 yards usually. Montezuma quail do little calling except during the breeding season, when some males (probably the unmated ones) give a high-pitched, ascending "buzz" note, which sounds more like that of an insect than a bird. This presumably is the mating call. Scattered birds of either sex, and even juveniles, use a low tremulous whistle descending in scale, to assemble the family or covey. Imitating the whistle, I have successfully called "buzzing" males during the summer.

Nesting occurs in midsummer, about when the rains begin. Nests, eggs, and even young have been recorded in June, but most records of active nesting are in July and August. Nests are carefully concealed in deep grass and are even roofed over, which makes them very difficult to find. Clutches range from 6 to 16, averaging 11 eggs. The eggs are chalky white and about 32 by 25 mm. Incubation requires twenty-five to twenty-six days. The female normally incubates, but the male is in close attendance and has been recorded by at least one observer (F. C. Willard, in Bent, 1932) as assisting in the incubation. Floyd Johnson of Colonia Pacheco, Chihuahua, however, has flushed many hens from nests but never a cock, though he once found a cock sitting close beside an incubating hen. The cock helps brood the young after they are hatched. Robert McCabe and I found a pair and their eight young chicks settled on a night roost near the Río Gavilán, Chihuahua. All the chicks were under the cock, who was fluffed out to twice his normal size. The hen was a few feet away. In our observations of many pairs and their broods, we have found the cock fully as solicitous as the hen in diverting attention from the young. As the family matures it becomes the nucleus of the winter covey.

The principal winter foods of the Montezuma quail are bulbs and fleshy tubers that are dug from the ground. Morphologically *Cyrtonyx* is well equipped for digging, with its stout legs and long toes and claws (Miller, 1943). In various parts of Mexico I have collected samples of the bulbs unearthed by these quail and have identified a few of them. The most common are "nut grasses" of the genus *Carex*. Others are lilies (*Brodiaea*, *Echeandia*, etc.), buttercup (*Ranunculus*), and sorrel (*Oxalis*), and there are many that could not be identified. Acorns and the fruits of such other trees and shrubs as manzanita, juniper, pines, sumac, and mountain laurel are important winter foods. Smaller quantities of weed seeds and cultivated crops (wheat, corn) have been found in the crops. In summer, insects and other animal foods comprise most of the diet. The availability of insects is a direct result of summer rains that bring on green growth and flowers. Young Montezuma quail eat virtually nothing but insects. A dry summer, which inhibits plant growth and hence insect populations, therefore prejudices the welfare of the quail.

Within the pine-oak zone, the highest populations of Montezuma quail are found where there is no grazing by domestic livestock. Grazing seemingly reduces or eliminates the herbaceous perennials that produce bulbs, and in their place come up stands of annual weeds and grasses that reproduce by seed. Without bulbs the Montezuma quail disappears, for from them the bird obtains not only food but water. On the waterless cinder cones of Michoacán this quail thrives in areas too rough and too dry for livestock. It is not found on the lower reaches of the mountains which are accessible to stock. The forest may be slashed, burned, or even cleared to a large extent without eliminating the quail, and the population can withstand heavy hunting without being seriously depleted. But grazing is extremely prejudicial to this bird. Within the pine-oak zone the population of Montezuma quail therefore is more or less inversely proportional to the population of livestock, and grazing control is the most effective measure of management.

For a fuller account of the life history and ecology of Montezuma quail, the reader is referred to a recent review paper by Leopold and McCabe (1957).

Ring-necked Pheasant. *Phasianus colchicus*

Other names.—Faisán chino de collar; *Phasianus torquatus*.

Description.—Size of a chicken, both sexes with a pointed tail. MALE: Head bluish green with a gray-green crown and fleshy red area round the eye. White collar. Back rich browns and yellows spotted with black and white. Rump bluish green. Wings brown with pale-blue coverts. Underparts mostly purplish brown flecked and streaked with black. Sides straw yellow spotted with black. Abdomen black. Tail brown, purplish on the edges, barred with black. Legs spurred. Measurements: folded wing—213 to 246 mm.; tail—408 to 513 mm.; bill—38 to 43 mm.; tarsus—68 to 76 mm. Weight: 1,100 to 1,400 gm. FEMALE: Generally buffy brown, flecked and streaked with darker browns, especially on dorsal surface and chest. Chin and breast clear buff. The pointed tail is barred irregularly with dusky brown. Measurements: folded wing—194 to 216 mm.; tail—236 to 273 mm.; bill—32 to 38 mm.; tarsus—61 to 68 mm. Weight: 850 to 1,100 gm.

Range in Mexico.—This pheasant has been introduced into the Mexicali Valley of northern Baja California. Further introductions in the Mexican uplands are contemplated.

The ring-necked pheasant is a native of China and adjoining parts of Asia. The bird was introduced into Europe soon after Marco Polo's travels to Asia, and more recently it has been successfully acclimatized in North America and New Zealand. In North America the pheasant has thrived best in the central grain belt, but throughout the West some thrifty local populations have developed in irrigated valleys. Such a colony was created in the Mexicali Valley by private introduction of stock from China, beginning in

1912. According to Hart *et al.* (1956), pheasants were established in the Mexicali Valley by 1922. Soon afterward, in 1926, some were liberated in the adjoining Imperial Valley by the California Division of Fish and Game. Today these two valleys, which together comprise an irrigated lowland (mostly below sea level) of 800,000 acres, support a pheasant population of moderate density, averaging perhaps 50 birds per square mile. Because of less intensive farming methods, the habitat is better in the Mexicali Valley than across the border in the Imperial Valley; the pheasant population is therefore higher in the Mexicali Valley even though there is no program of protection or management.

Nominally the Mexicali Valley is open to pheasant hunting only during the month of November, with a daily bag limit of two cocks (see Appendix B). Hart *et al.* report that actually both sport hunting and some market hunting are pursued with little regard for the law. The aggregate kill in the Mexicali Valley is estimated to exceed 1,000 birds a year.

The pheasant is almost exclusively a bird of the farmlands. It feeds upon waste grain and weed seeds and finds shelter in crop stubbles or along ditch-banks and fencerows. In the arid west, a critical factor controlling pheasant distribution and numbers seems to be ground moisture during the nesting period. The species thrives only on irrigated lands or in places where natural rainfall or fog keeps the ground moist. Presumably the moisture is required to hatch the eggs. After a dry spring the ratio of young to adults drops far below that found in wet years, which suggests that rainfall stimulates a good hatch. Irrigation water serves the same purpose. But many nests are on dry banks not affected by irrigation, and others, in low spots, are drowned out by the water. Spring or summer rains are the best assurance of a hatch.

Pheasants are gregarious in that they gather in loose flocks, but they do not form fixed coveys like quail. In winter there is a tendency for the cocks and hens to run in separate flocks, but segregation is never complete—there are always some mixed groups. In spring the cocks establish individual breeding territories, and they fight vigorously in defense of their respective holdings. It is then that they may be heard crowing, especially in the morning and evening hours but often at other times during the day. The noisy crowing call, accompanied by a whirring of wings, is an invitation to hens to come join the harem and a warning to other cocks to stay away. Pheasants are polygamous. The hens in each harem establish nests and raise their young without assistance from the cock. Only the most vigorous cocks have territories and harems; the weaker ones go mateless. Because of this habit of mating, it has become customary in many parts of the world to shoot cocks only, preserving the hens as breeders. One cock can serve as many as 20 hens in the field (even more in confinement), and rarely if ever is there a shortage of males for breeding, even in the most intensively hunted areas.

In California the nesting season extends from April to July, and in Baja

Male

Female

Fig. 99. Ring-necked pheasant, *Phasianus colchicus*.

California it presumably is the same. The hens make their nests in the cover of weeds or grass and deposit one egg each day until the clutch is complete (8 to 16 eggs, averaging about a dozen). Incubation then begins. The eggs are dull green and measure about 41 by 33 mm. The chicks hatch twenty-two to twenty-three days later, and as soon as they are dry start following the hen. Many nests are broken up by such predators as skunks or raccoons, by domestic animals, or by farm machinery. These hens often renest and try again. When the young are two-thirds grown they become independent, and the family units break up and lose their identity.

The feeding habits of pheasants vary somewhat, depending on the availability of different kinds of foods. First and foremost in importance are cultivated grains, such as wheat, corn, and rice. Where these are abundant the birds eat little else. At times they eat large quantities of various kinds of weed seeds and also greens, such as the tender leaves of clover, alfalfa, and various wild forbs. The chicks start on a diet of pure insects and shift to plant foods as they grow up; adults, too, eat some insects.

Pheasants are now being raised on the game farm at San Cayetano for release in the highland valleys of central Mexico. It is difficult to prognosticate the possibilities of successful acclimatization. There are extensive areas of cropland that appear to be suitable habitat. The summer rains, coming as they do during the nesting season, would probably be beneficial. Yet the pheasant has failed in areas seemingly as favorable, as for example in the rice-lands of Texas or, for that matter, in the whole southeastern quarter of the United States. Various theories have been advanced to explain the failures, —that the weather was too hot for the eggs and there was not enough calcium in the diet on leached, unglaciated soils, for example. Perhaps these problems will be avoided in the Mexican uplands, for the climate is cool and many of the soils are enriched with volcanic ash.

In any event, the ring-necked pheasant is a fine game bird and well worth trying to establish in central Mexico, where most of the native game species, adapted to natural environments, have been crowded from the richest soils by land cultivation.

Chukar Partridge. *Alectoris graeca*

Other name.—Chukár.

Description.—Black line crosses forehead, passing through both eyes and down around throat area, forming a black collar. Small black patches on chin and at gape of bill. Ear coverts chestnut. Dorsal area and chest ashy with slight pinkish tinge. Throat buffy white. Breast, abdomen, and sides rich buff with bold black bars on the sides, fringed with chestnut. Bill crimson. Feet and legs coral red. Sexes alike in appearance and size. Measurements: folded wing—146 to 180 mm.; tail—78 to 105 mm.; bill—19 to 21 mm.; tarsus—41 to 52 mm. Weight: males about 800 gm., females 680 gm.

Fig. 100. Chukar partridge, *Alectoris graeca*.

Range in Mexico.—This partridge is fairly numerous along the border of California and Baja California east of Jacumba. Donald D. McLean of the California Department of Fish and Game states that chukars have been seen on the east slope of the Sierra Juárez 60 miles south of the border. Presumably the population is spreading southward.

The chukar is another Old World fowl that has been introduced successfully in North America. It is thriving in the arid foothills and desert mountains of the Far West, from the state of Washington to southern California. Recently the bird has spread into northern Baja California. Its chosen home seems to be the most forbidding dry rocky ridges and breaks, similar to its ancestral habitat in the Middle East. To date, the principal success with chukars has been achieved in Nevada and eastern California. This abbreviated account is drawn in large part from the reports of the bird in Nevada by Christensen (1954) and in California by Harper, Harry, and Bailey (1958).

Chukars live in coveys of 10 to 40 or more birds. They are strong runners and cover a good deal of ground afoot in their daily foraging and trips to water. They also may shift their range seasonally. Marked birds in Nevada have been found as much as 20 miles from the site where they were initially caught and marked. Chukars rarely take wing unless disturbed, but they are good flyers when forced to take to the air. The most essential type of cover required by chukars for shelter from the weather and for escape from natural enemies is rocks. In their arid home (average rainfall 5 to 20 inches) vegetation is sparse and rocks are abundant. When pursued, the birds will run uphill, dodging through the rock piles or outcroppings, fly down the other side into the canyon beyond, and then either hide or run up the next hill. This type of behavior leaves most hunters far behind and renders the chukar population virtually immune from overshooting. When the disturbance subsides, the scattered members of a covey call to each other and reassemble. Christensen (p. 32) describes the call as follows:

The birds begin with a slow "chuck-chuck-chuck" and increase the volume and tempo until the "chucks" merge as a "chuckle." They seem to prefer to call from rocky outcrops, where they have a good view of the surroundings. The throaty chucking is very resonant and will carry for great distances. Both sexes use this call. However, during the nesting season it is heard less frequently, and appears to be confined mainly to the males.

In Nevada pairing takes place in late March and nesting in late April. The birds are monogamous and the male helps raise the brood. Nests are in the shelter of rocks, usually close to water, and are lined with dry grass and breast feathers. The size of the clutch is not accurately known, but nests have been found with as many as 19 eggs. These are pale brown or creamy, thickly speckled with purplish, reddish, or brown flecks, and measure about 45 by 31 mm. The period of incubation is twenty-one to twenty-two days. After the young are a few weeks old, the families often combine into packs, or bands, and individual broods lose their identity.

Studies of the food habits of chukars indicate that during dry periods the birds feed mostly on seeds of such annual plants as cheat grass (*Bromus tectorum*), fiddle-neck (*Amsinckia*), and filaree (*Erodium*). In time of rain they shift to green leaves and insects, especially grasshoppers. Coveys will widely shift their ranges in following seasonal food supplies. Grain stubbles and irrigated farmlands in the valleys attract the birds when conditions are adverse in the hills, as in time of drought or severe cold. In very dry years, when food of all kinds is scarce, the chukars may not breed, or if they do, few young are produced. This was the situation in Nevada in 1953.

Although the chukar lives in some of the driest country in North America, it requires drinking water. The birds drink daily in hot, dry weather. Only in the rainy season, when succulent greens and insects supply moisture, do the birds get along without water. Lack of water is a principal factor limiting the spread of chukars in the desert mountains; it follows, therefore, that supplying water is a primary method of improving habitat for chukars. This can be done in various ways, as described in the account of the California quail (see p. 236).

The chukar partridge in western North America is filling a niche occupied

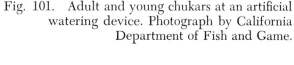

Fig. 101.   Adult and young chukars at an artificial watering device. Photograph by California Department of Fish and Game.

by no other game bird. The range overlaps that of the Gambel quail somewhat, but there is little direct conflict or competition. The bird may well
spread through the desert areas of Baja California and central Mexico, supplying shooting in types of country that are now virtually gameless.

FAMILY MELEAGRIDIDAE

TURKEYS

The turkey family, Meleagrididae, consists of but two species, both of which
occur in Mexico. One is the common wild turkey, from which the domestic
bird was derived. Its native range includes northern Mexico and most of the
United States. The other, the ocellated turkey, occurs only in southeastern
Mexico and adjoining parts of Guatemala and British Honduras. The family,
then, is strictly North American.

Wild Turkey. *Meleagris gallopavo*

Other names.—Guajalote silvestre; cócono.

Description.—Size and general appearance of the common "bronze" turkey
of the barnyard. MALE: Head naked, with extensible fleshy cere on forehead,
blue dorsally, red on throat, except in summer, when the throat wattle becomes
extended and the whole head may be red. Body plumage dusky brown with a
bright, bronze iridescence of red, green, and gold. Body feathers edged in velvety black. Beard of hairlike feathers projecting from chest elongates with age
up to about 12 inches. Wing primaries barred black and white, secondaries
barred brown and white, greater wing coverts iridescent purplish. Tail vermiculated dusky and light brown, with subterminal black band. Tips of tail feathers
and of upper and lower tail coverts white in western and central Mexico, buffy
brown in northeast. Bill horn-colored at tip, blackish red at base. Legs coral
red with stout spurs. Measurements: folded wing—465 to 545 mm.; tail—345 to
437 mm.; bill—34 to 41 mm.; tarsus—162 to 182 mm. Weight: 4,800 to 7,500
gm. FEMALE: Like the male but head blue with very small cere and no wattle;
no beard or spurs. Body plumage much less iridescent and each feather tipped
with dull white. Measurements: folded wing—396 to 436 mm.; tail—311 to 362
mm.; bill—33 to 36 mm.; tarsus—130 to 140 mm. Weight: 2,800 to 4,400 gm.

Range in Mexico.—Originally, pine-oak uplands of western Mexico from
Sonora and Chihuahua south to Michoacán; pine-oak uplands of eastern Mexico
and adjoining coastal plain, from Coahuila and Tamaulipas south to central
Veracruz. Present reduced range shown on map.

In order to understand recent regressions in the range occupied by wild
turkeys, it is important to ascertain accurately the original range of the
species. The following observations are taken from a previous paper on the
subject (Leopold, 1948 : 393).

Published statements about turkey distribution in Mexico frequently mention Oaxaca as the most southerly point of original occurrence (Ridgway

Male

Female

FORMER RANGE

PRESENT RANGE

Head of Female

Fig. 102.   Wild turkey, *Meleagris gallopavo*.

and Friedmann, 1946; Friedmann *et al.*, 1950). I had every confidence that turkeys once lived in the pine-oak uplands of both Guerrero and Oaxaca until I actually plotted on a map all the established points of occurrence and found not a single defensible record of any south of the Río Balsas valley.

Reports of turkeys in the southern uplands are based without exception on word-of-mouth evidence, the validity of which hinges on the use of vernacular names. As nearly as I can tell, all referred either to curassows or to escaped domestic turkeys.

E. W. Nelson (unpubl. field notes) contributed three such doubtful records. Near El Rincón, Guerrero, Nelson was told of the existence of wild turkeys in 1903, but he did not see them. In the same general area in 1944 (Omilteme, Guerrero) a local man named Juan Cámara informed me that "guajalote silvestre" occurred on Cerro Picacho de Oro; but careful inquiry revealed that the bird referred to was the guan (*Penelope purpurascens*), well represented by specimens from that locality. Nelson's report may have stemmed from the same misapplication of the common name for wild turkey. Other questionable turkey localities mentioned by Nelson are Tlalpancingo and Tequisistlán, Oaxaca. Nelson did not obtain specimens from any of these localities, nor did he see the birds.

Early historical documents from southern Mexico offer no more reliable records than those given above. Dr. Carl Sauer permitted me to examine photostatic copies of the "Relaciones de Oaxaca," longhand accounts by members of the clergy describing the people, agriculture, commerce, natural history, and so forth, in numerous localities throughout Oaxaca in 1777. Frequent references are made to wild fowls under such names as *pavo montes*, *guajalote silvestre*, and *pavo real*, but all of these probably were cracids, either *Crax* or *Penelope*. Wright (1914) notes that Oviedo in his classic *Natural History of the Indies* (1535) used the name *pavo* indiscriminately for curassows and turkeys. Domestic turkeys are mentioned frequently in the *relaciones* of southern Mexico and also in the writings of Alexander von Humboldt in 1811. But Humboldt states clearly that "one only meets the wild [turkeys] in the northern provinces" (Wright, 1914). I conclude that wild turkeys have not occurred in southern Mexico in historic times.

Even north of the Río Balsas there apparently were no turkeys in some parts of the pine-oak uplands. The *Relación de Mechoacán*, written by a Franciscan friar in 1538–1539, describes the many types of game found in the Pátzcuaro region and the hunting methods of the Tarascan Indians but does not mention wild turkeys. León (1887) likewise describes the fauna of the Pátzcuaro basin without including the turkey. I know of no reference to wild turkeys in the vicinity of the Valley of Mexico. It appears to me that, around the original centers of Indian population, turkeys must have been exterminated even before the Spanish Conquest.

The "original" range of the turkey (meaning the post-Conquest range) must have been limited to two principal blocks—the western mountains from northern Sonora to western Michoacán, and the northeastern mountains and plains from Coahuila and Tamaulipas to northern Veracruz and Hidalgo. There may have been population "islands" in the central uplands from Jalisco to Hidalgo, such as the one persisting even today in northern Guanajuato, but I doubt that the range was continuous across this zone, even in 1500. It probably was so in prehistoric times before the growth of the great Indian populations.

Most of the recent turkey records shown on the map were gathered during my field survey or were supplied by Chester C. Lamb, who has collected birds in most parts of Mexico over the past twenty years. A few were taken from the literature.

The main blocks of range still occupied are the Sierra Madre Occidental, and the Sierra Madre Oriental and adjoining coastal plains. "Island" populations remain in southern Jalisco, southwestern Michoacán, northern Guanajuato, the Sierra del Nido of Chihuahua, and the Sierra del Carmen of Coahuila. In 1945 a Señor Islas of San Bartolo, Hidalgo, reported to Aaron J. Sharp of the University of Tennessee that there still were wild turkeys a few miles northeast of San Bartolo. Since the record is uncertain, it is shown on the map with a question mark. Another unestablished record is the reported occurrence of turkeys, up to the early 1940's at least, in the pinelands along the Michoacán–Estado de México line. This also is shown with a question mark, since no specimen has ever been obtained there.

In some areas, turkey populations are still high. Near Acuña in the Sierra de Tamaulipas I estimated a density of one turkey per 15 acres in a limited tract of oak woodland. At Maitínez, eastern San Luis Potosí, our observations, together with accounts offered by a local rancher, Dallas Blagg, indicate that winter concentrations along the Río Salto might be almost that dense. West of Colonia Pacheco, Chihuahua, in virgin pine-oak–juniper woodland the population in 1937 was about one bird per 60 acres, but when I revisited this area in 1948 I found it had so increased that it more nearly approximated a bird per 20 acres.

Around the fringes of the range most populations are sparse and there is a slow but steady shrinkage of occupied area. Marginal localities where turkeys have been exterminated in the past fifty years are listed in Table 11.

TABLE 11

LOCALITIES IN WHICH WILD TURKEYS HAVE BEEN EXTERMINATED IN THE PAST FIFTY YEARS

Locality	Last record of turkeys
San Luis Springs (Chihuahua)	Mearns (1907)
Rancho Batél (Sinaloa)	Moore (1938)
Los Reyes and Mt. Tancítaro (Michoacán)	
Camargo, Matamoros, Soto la Marina (Tamaulipas)	E. W. Nelson, field notes
Cerro de la Silla (Nuevo León)	
Sabinas (Coahuila)	

Some turkey populations, particularly in northeastern Mexico, lived along rivers which traverse semiarid scrub country. These have been almost eliminated by clearing of the alluvial bottoms for agriculture. In 1902 Nelson found turkeys rather common in the palo blanco and cypress timber near Camargo, Tamaulipas, and reported them also "a few miles" from Matamoros farther down the Río Grande. These bottom lands are now all in cultivation and the turkeys are gone. The same situation exists at Sabinas, Coahuila, where Nelson reported turkeys "sparingly along the river" in 1902, but where there is no cover for the birds now.

At La Unión (near Generál Terán), Nuevo León, we found a few turkeys in oak timber along the small streams in 1945. But the bottoms are currently being cleared for orange orchards, and the birds will not outlast the disappearing timber.

Turkeys were found by Nelson frequenting tropical deciduous timber in the narrow valleys of southwestern Michoacán. A few remain in that region, according to Juan Zinser, but they seem to be decreasing with the increased intensity of cultivation.

In the pine-oak uplands, where most of the turkeys survive today, the tenable range is being reduced by a combination of lumbering, expanded agriculture, grazing, and burning. To cite a specific example of recent extermination, there were turkeys at Rancho Batél, Sinaloa, until a few years ago. Moore (1938) mentions their feeding in the cornfields near the settlement. In 1941 a sawmill was installed near Batél and roads were built for transporting the logs and lumber. Ground fires were incident to the logging operation. Mill hands and loggers cleared new fields through the forest and turned their livestock loose on the range. Likewise they hunted deer, turkeys, and other game throughout the year. The combination of shooting and habitat destruction killed off the turkeys in that area. When I was there in 1946 the birds were only a pleasant memory to the local hunters. Because logging in the pinelands of western Mexico has been greatly accelerated in recent years, the peripheral retreat of the turkeys must be occurring in many localities.

The clearing of turkey woods along river bottoms is lamentable but inevitable, since bottom lands are the best agricultural lands in this arid and rocky country. But the mountain pine forests could and should be managed for watershed protection and timber production, and this would also preserve the habitat for turkeys and other game. If, in addition, a reasonable degree of legal protection for the turkeys could be offered, there would be no further shrinkage of occupied range.

Wild turkeys occur in flocks at all times of year except during the nesting season. The sexes segregate, male flocks averaging 5 to 10, females and young 10 to 25. Each group has its established range, usually not more than a mile in radius. The flocks roost at night in trees, preferably big oaks or pines. In the morning they fly to the ground and start feeding, sometimes moving rapidly along, pecking here and there as they go, at other times stopping to scratch at length in a favorable spot where the ground is well littered with acorns or some fruit. Usually the birds go to water after the morning feeding. The middle of the day is spent loafing in some secluded patch of brush or grove of trees. In the late afternoon they venture forth to fill their crops again before going to roost. Unless disturbed, they do little flying, except of course to roost.

In spring the flocks break up as gobbling and mating get under way. Adult males select individual gobbling territories and compete in calling the hens to them for mating. Mating is polygamous. Young gobblers are not sexually mature at the age of one year, so they take no part in the proceedings. They are often found in small bands, abandoned by the hens, who are busy with their nests and with their daily visits to the old gobblers. Occasionally a young male will attach himself to an old "tom" as an apprentice or, more accurately, an observer. He is not driven off unless he starts to gobble or to show signs of wanting to enter the game. Young hens, however, breed and nest as yearlings.

The time of gobbling varies. In northeastern Mexico it starts in early March and lasts until late April. Floyd Johnson states that in Chihuahua the gobbling period is from April 10 to May 20. Nests are built and incubation begins during the gobbling period. Most nests are well concealed in brush or grass and are surprisingly difficult to find, considering the large size of the hen and of the eggs. Nests are usually within 200 yards of water. Clutches range from 8 to 18, averaging about 11. The eggs are creamy white, sprinkled with brownish spots, and measure approximately 61 by 47 mm. The period of incubation is twenty-seven to twenty-eight days. The young leave the nest soon after hatching and stay with the mother through the first year. Broods combine to form the winter flocks of hens and young.

The foods of the wild turkey are many and varied. In fall and winter, acorns are perhaps the most important single food item. The majority of the turkeys of Mexico live in the pine-oak zone, and they take full advantage of the oak mast. Other mast and fruit-bearing trees and shrubs contribute to the diet; for example, juniper, pines, madrone, wild cherry, manzanita, and blackberry in the highlands; palms, palmettos, figs, capulin, acacia, roses, and various others in the northeastern lowlands. Seasonally, wild turkeys eat quantities of insects and tender green leaves. A favorite food is grasshoppers when they are numerous. The turkeys also scratch out and eat some types of small bulbs, and with the bill they strip off the seed heads of grasses. They find domestic grains very attractive, and they visit cornfields and wheat stubbles when seeds are available. I personally have examined the crop contents of about twenty-five wild turkeys taken in various parts of Mexico and found most of the foods mentioned above in one or another of the crops. Virtually all foods eaten are picked up from the ground or are plucked or stripped from low-growing plants. Unlike the curassows, the wild turkeys rarely feed in trees.

The wild turkey is the king of North American game birds. It is exceedingly wary and shy and will test the skill of the finest hunter. There are many

Fig. 103.　A wild turkey gobbler—one of the finest trophies sought by hunters in Mexico.

ways of hunting turkeys; probably the most common is by simple stalking —approaching to shooting distance under cover of brush or by taking advantage of the topography. When a flock has been scattered, the birds can sometimes be called back by a person skilled in imitating the assembly note. During the gobbling season the males can be called by an imitation of the hen's voice. This, however, is illegal since the season closes February 1 and gobbling begins later in the spring. Some hunters use dogs to scatter the birds or drive them into trees. Both rifles and shotguns are used in turkey hunting. Turkeys are so large and their flesh is so esteemed that they are more or less severely overhunted wherever they occur in Mexico. Only in remote country, or on some private ranches where hunting is prevented by the owner, are turkeys still abundant.

The turkey was domesticated in Mexico some time before the Conquest. It is the one and only important domestic animal of North American origin. When the Spanish arrived, they found barnyard turkeys in the possession of Indians in all parts of Mexico and even in Central America. However, the Aztecs and the Tarascans, originating in west-central Mexico, seemed to have achieved the highest development of turkey culture, and it is probable that turkeys were domesticated in the western highlands, perhaps in Michoacán. Nelson (1904) was of this opinion and I concur with it. Wild turkeys of that region are morphologically very similar to the primitive domestic bronze type. Both the Aztecs and Tarascans kept great numbers of the birds, including even white ones. They paid royal tribute to their respective kings in turkeys, according to the *Relación de Mechoacán*. The Tarascan king fed turkeys to the hawks and eagles in his zoo. The whole economy of these highland tribes was based on the cultivation of corn and the raising of turkeys. The Spanish exported the domestic turkey to Europe and from there it has spread over the world.

Ocellated Turkey. *Agriocharis ocellata*

Other names.—Pavo de monte; guajalote de Yucatán; guajalote brilliante; cūt; *Meleagris ocellata*.

Description.—MALE: Head naked, bright blue, with scattered orange warts or excrescences clustered especially on the crown, where they surround a large, fleshy orange knob. A pendant fleshy cere hangs from the forehead, as in *Meleagris*. Plumage generally dusky, body feathers tipped with iridescent green or bronze. Flight feathers barred black and white, the secondaries broadly edged with white. Wing coverts iridescent bronze. Tail finely vermiculated black and white, each feather tipped with subterminal bands of velvety black and iridescent blue and a terminal band of bronze; tail coverts similarly tipped. Legs bright red with long sharp spurs. Measurements: folded wing—348 to 413 mm.; tail—284 to 347 mm.; bill—25 to 32 mm.; tarsus—131 to 139 mm.; spur—25 to 40 mm. Weight: 4,300 to 5,000 gm., rarely heavier (Van Tyne, 1935, cites one record of 5.3 kilos.). FEMALE: Similar to male but duller, less fiery iridescent, lacking warts and pendant cere on head and spurs on tarsus. Measurements: folded wing—313 to 357 mm.; tail—244 to 282 mm.; bill—21 to 30 mm.; tarsus—109 to 115 mm. Weight: 2,600 to 3,100 gm.

Range in Mexico.—Yucatán Peninsula, as far west as southern Tabasco. This turkey has been exterminated in western Yucatán and northern Campeche.

The ocellated turkey is one of the finest game birds of Mexico, and for that matter, of North America. Strong of wing, wary in behavior, and highly adaptable in its living habits, it is thriving despite persistent hunting and severe alteration of its habitat. The comments which follow are repeated from an earlier report (Leopold, 1948).

On the Yucatán Peninsula, ocellated turkeys frequent savannas or the edges of cleared fields. We did not find any in extensive, dense jungle. The original range, before the Mayans came up from Honduras and began clearing the forest, probably was limited to savannas, semiopen swamps, and the arid scrub of northern Yucatán. Mayan corn culture presumably opened up vast areas of climax rain forest for occupancy by the birds.

Turkeys are abundant in southern Quintana Roo and southeastern Campeche. The sparse Indian population maintains enough scattered cornfields to create a highly favorable environment for the species. David B. Legters of Xocempich, Yucatán, who has walked over most of Quintana Roo in recent years, speaks of seeing turkeys in considerable numbers throughout that territory. David Amram, a mahogany buyer whom we met in Tabasco, stated that he had found turkeys "as abundant as quail" along the rivers of northwestern Guatemala. Even in northern Campeche near San Juan, they were quite common when we were there—we saw birds every day. Frans Blom reports one record of this species in Chiapas—a bird killed near the ruins of Yaxchilán, along the Río Usumacinta.

Along the arid northwestern border of the peninsula where the forest has been replaced with extensive sisal plantations, turkeys were eliminated some time ago. Sisal culture requires permanent clearing of the land, which leaves no cover for turkeys. Only a narrow belt has been cleared, however, and further expansion into the humid interior is not possible.

We found only a sparse turkey population between Dzitás and Chichén Itzá, in the corn belt of Yucatán. Here cornfields revert to jungle after three years of cultivation, and the scrub is permitted to grow until it is about twenty-five years old before it is cleared again. This recurrent clearing gradually impoverishes the flora and seems eventually to reduce the carrying capacity of the country for game. A few turkeys persist, however, even around Chichén Itzá, where the system of rotating milpas has been practiced by the Mayans and turkeys have been hunted for almost a thousand years. In view of this fact, I feel that the future of the ocellated turkey in southern Mexico is much more promising than that of *Meleagris* in the northern pine forests.

Female

Male

CHARLES
SCHWARTZ

Fig. 104. Ocellated turkey, *Agriocharis ocellata*.

Unless some major changes in land use occur, ocellated turkeys should hold up without any significant loss of range far into the future.

Twelve flocks which we observed in November, 1945, near Xocempich, Yucatán, and San Juan, Campeche, ranged from 3 to 10 birds. All were mixed flocks of hens and gobblers. In addition, we saw two single adult males and a pair of adult males. Segregation of hens and young from old males does not occur in winter populations of ocellated turkeys. David B. Legters verified our observations in this regard. A few old gobblers run alone, but most of them are found in mixed flocks with hens and young. In this respect the behavior of *Agriocharis* is decidedly different from that of wild *Meleagris*, in which marked segregation is almost universal.

Gobbling starts in April, according to Legters, reaches a peak about May 1, and tapers off in May. The gobble is utterly unlike that of *Meleagris* and may be written phonetically as "ting-ting-ting—co-on-cot-zitl-glung," the last note having a bell-like quality. Some Mayan hunters stalk the gobbling males, but this is said to be a difficult feat in the tinder-dry forest of spring. The trick of calling gobblers with a hen call apparently is not known.

Nests are found in May and early June. The normal clutch is 8 to 15 eggs. These are buff, speckled and blotched with brown, and measure about 61 by 45 mm. Legters has set eggs under chickens many times, and although they usually hatch, he has raised only one female to maturity. Repeated attempts to induce this hen to mate with a domestic turkey gobbler failed—she was completely disinterested. The ocellated turkey has, however, been successfully bred in captivity at the San Diego Zoo, as reported by Lint (1952). The period of incubation was twenty-eight days, as in the common turkey. The chicks would eat only insects until they were four weeks old; thereafter they shifted to mash and plant foods. Lint gives a good summary of the growth and molts of the young.

The wild population stays in heavy jungle through the summer and early fall, but about October 1 the birds begin visiting isolated cornfields to feed in the early morning and late afternoon. The flocks slip quietly out of the *monte* and eat the corn closest to the edge of cover. Later in the winter, as the fallen corn around the borders of the fields is consumed (by squirrels, agoutis, etc., as well as by turkeys), the birds venture farther into the fields. When disturbed, a feeding flock almost invariably takes wing, even though the source of disturbance is 200 yards away. The birds fly several hundred yards into the forest and alight on the ground running. Recommended hunting procedure in winter is to stalk quietly around the edges of cornfields most remote from human habitation and jump shoot the feeding birds at dawn or dusk. Ocellated turkeys are surprisingly fast on the wing, and I recommend hunting them as one of the finest sports to be had in North America.

Agriocharis, which has a noteworthy flying ability, has a plump, well-

rounded breast, much like that of a quail. The high sternum and poorly developed pectoral muscles of the wild *Meleagris* are indicative of its comparatively inferior capabilities on the wing. Poultry breeders are attempting to
take advantage of the fine breast conformation of *Agriocharis* by crossing
it with the domestic turkey. So far, the experiments have come to naught because the hybrids are not completely fertile.

In their native habitat ocellated turkeys eat a wide variety of seeds, fruits,
and greens. Besides corn, we found a good many green leaves in the crops
of the four birds we killed. Two contained also corollas of squash blossoms.
One of the four, shot in an abandoned field where no corn was available,
had eaten, besides green leaves, the fruits of a nightshade, *Solanum hirtum*,
many small cucumbers (Cucurbitaceae), and a few berries identified by
Wagner (1953*b*) as fruits of *Orbignya cohune*. Legters told us that this was
only a small sample of the many types of foods eaten by *Agriocharis*.

The ocellated turkey is another species of the rain forest zone which thrives
in the secondary growth that emerges when the virgin forest is removed. It,
too, is holding its own today, and its future looks reasonably secure.

Fig. 105.   Hunting ocellated turkeys along the border
of a weedy cornfield in Yucatán. Photograph by
D. L. Spencer.

Order Gruiformes

FAMILY GRUIDAE

Cranes

In Mexico there occur members of two families of the order Gruiformes that are popularly considered to be game birds. These are the cranes of the family Gruidae, and the coots, gallinules, and rails of the family Rallidae.

Only one crane regularly visits Mexico today, and that is the sandhill crane, which is treated in the following account. A second species formerly migrated to Mexico—the rare whooping crane (*Grus americana*)—but it is now only a casual vagrant. The whooping crane is considerably larger than the sandhill crane and is mostly white, with black wing tips. The surviving remnant of these birds nests each year in northwestern Canada and winters on the Aransas National Wildlife Refuge in southern Texas. The flock consisted of only 28 individuals in 1955, and great concern is felt for the survival of the species. Occasional whooping cranes still make forays into northeastern Mexico from the wintering grounds in Texas. Evenden (1952) saw two of these birds 58 miles southwest of Matamoros, Tamaulipas, in February, 1951. It is essential that they be protected from shooting, for every individual is important. A special effort should be made to warn hunters of northern Tamaulipas of the existence of these rare birds.

Sandhill Crane. *Grus canadensis*

Other names.—Grulla; grulla cenicienta; brown crane.

Description.—Size and build of a large heron but with a bald face and fore-head of reddish skin. Plumage ash gray, often with rusty stains. Wings slate gray. Legs and feet dusky. Sexes similar in appearance. In flight these birds fully extend the head and neck, whereas herons crook the neck. There are two subspecies in North America, which are alike in coloration but which differ in size. Both occur in Mexico. Average measurements are summarized in table 12.

Range in Mexico.—This crane is a common migrant in the northern states, south to Jalisco and Puebla in the interior. It is occasionally found on the Yucatán Peninsula.

TABLE 12

MEASUREMENTS AND WEIGHTS OF THE TWO SUBSPECIES OF CRANES

Subspecies	Folded wing (mm.)	Tarsus (mm.)	Bill (mm.)	Weight (kg.)
Sandhill crane	460–598	222–265	113–159	3.6–6 (8–13 lbs.)
Little brown crane	418–510	156–228	69–110	3.2–5 (7–11 lbs.)

Sandhill cranes nest in the northern United States, Canada, and Alaska and migrate in winter to the southern United States and Mexico. At one time the species apparently bred far to the south, for Martín del Campo (1944) reports subfossilized eggs found in the marshes of the Valley of Mexico. But no nesting has been known in Mexico in historical times.

Cranes leave the north in October, arrive in Mexico usually in November, and stay until March or early April. The points of winter concentration are widely scattered. The Colorado delta is one such spot, mentioned by Grinnell (1928) and Van Rossem (1945); most or all of the cranes of this area seem to be the small form—the "little brown crane." Another area of concentration is in San Luis Potosí, where from an airplane in 1952 we saw numerous flocks in the arid basins and valleys north and west of the capital. Perhaps the greatest gathering of cranes in Mexico occurs each winter on the llanos near El Carmen, Puebla. Sportsmen from Mexico City go regularly to El Carmen for crane hunting, and I am told that there are usually 5,000 to 7,000 of the birds in that region. Scattered flocks, however, are found in all parts of northern Mexico, and it is very difficult to assess the number of wintering birds. At various desert camps I found a bunch or two of cranes regularly spending the night at a nearby *presa* and flying away at daylight to feed in some distant grainfield. It would be virtually impossible to count these thinly dispersed flocks, but the aggregate number must be great.

Cranes are gregarious, in the manner of geese. In winter they occur almost always in flocks of 10 to 50 birds; only rarely is one seen alone. They are

Fig. 106. Sandhill crane, *Grus canadensis*.

highly mobile and often fly long distances to forage. Moreover, the cranes fly high, usually far above gun range. A commercial airplane pilot told me of passing a flock of cranes at 19,000 feet elevation over Chihuahua. Sandhill cranes, in approaching the ground for a landing, are extremely wary, circling the area and looking for possible danger before dropping down to low level. A hunter must be well concealed to escape the sharp scrutiny of a crane flock.

Although cranes superficially resemble herons, and often frequent the same types of marshy terrain, they are very different in their food habits. Herons eat mostly animal foods; cranes are essentially vegetarian. They prefer the seeds of domestic grains such as corn, wheat, rice, sorghum, and oats. Lacking these, they take as second choice the seeds, roots, tubers, or even green foliage of various marsh and prairie plants, especially some of the wild grasses, sedges, and bulrushes. And they take incidentally small amounts of animal food (mostly insects).

The cranes are fully protected from hunting in Canada and the United States, but in Mexico they are listed as game birds and are subject to hunting from November 1 to January 30, with a bag limit of five birds per day. Very few cranes are actually killed, however, because of their extreme wariness. I know many Mexican sportsmen who consider one crane an adequate reward for a week-end hunt. The flesh of this bird is highly palatable—much superior to that of geese.

Although the crane is a fine game bird, its highest values are esthetic. A migrating wedge of these birds, high in the sky, serenading the earth below with clarion calls, is one of the most elegant expressions of wild America.

A good book on the natural history of the crane is that of Walkinshaw (1949).

FAMILY RALLIDAE

Coots, Gallinules, and Rails

There occur in Mexico eleven species of rails, two gallinules, and the common coot, or mud hen—all members of the family Rallidae. The coot is an important game bird, as will be brought out in the next account. The other members of the family are far less significant economically. Some of the larger species, such as the clapper rail (*Rallus longirostris*) and the gallinules (*Gallinula chloropus* and *Porphyrula martinica*), may occasionally be taken for food in rural Mexico, but of this I have no record.

American Coot. *Fulica americana*

Other names.—Gallareta; gallina de agua; garreta; mud hen.

Description.—The size of a small chicken. Dusky gray, with black head and neck. White coverts under each edge of tail appear as two vertical white bars when tail is raised. Bill white with dark spots near tip and with a reddish brown "shield" overlaying the forehead and upper base of bill. Feet large, each toe broadly lobed, greenish in young birds, turning to yellowish green in adults and eventually to dull orange in very old birds. Sexes similar in size and appearance. Measurements: folded wing—170 to 200 mm.; bill (to top of shield)—39 to 47 mm.; tarsus—47 to 60 mm. Weight: 380 to 830 gm. Males slightly larger than females.

Range in Mexico.—A few coots breed in fresh-water marshes of Mexico, particularly in Baja California and the Volcanic Cordillera. The species is an abundant winter migrant along both coasts and in interior marshes and lakes throughout Mexico.

The lowly coot is an aberrant rail that has left the dense marshland vegetation, the home of most of its relatives, and moved out into open water to join the ducks. With its lobed feet, it is a fairly competent swimmer and diver; but its short, rounded wings and weak breast muscles do not permit good performance on the wing. A coot kicks along the water to gain flying speed, and even when launched and proceeding under full steam it is a slow flyer.

However, millions of these birds fly from the breeding grounds in Canada to Mexico and far beyond in winter. Coots migrate entirely at night, never being seen in transit in daylight hours. They start arriving in northern Mexico in September, and the numbers are augmented steadily by new arrivals until December, when the full population has reached winter quarters. Table 5 presents a partial census of the coots in Mexico in January, 1952. This record, totaling 701,465 birds, is far from a complete tally, for coots were recorded only incidentally in the duck count. But it does show that the greatest concentrations are in lagoons along the tropical coasts, especially of Veracruz, Yucatán, and Nayarit. Coots prefer fresh or slightly brackish water and do not usually concentrate on heavily saline bays. In March and April the coots drift back to the breeding grounds in the north, in order to arrive by nesting time.

A few of the birds remain to nest in some interior marshes of Mexico. I have found small breeding colonies in many scattered localities of central and northern Mexico, but never large numbers of coots. Breeding coots often are associated with breeding ruddy ducks.

The nesting habits of coots in Mexico have not been studied, but those in the north are well known, particularly as a result of the work of Gullion (1953; 1954) in California. Pairs form in early spring and adopt territories in suitable habitat. These areas they rigorously defend from other coots, and at times even from ducks and unrelated birds. A territory normally includes some open water and adjacent cattails, or bulrushes, which serve as cover and support for the nests. Coots build several types of structures—display platforms, egg nests, and brood nests—making them of floating vegetation, such as cattail leaves. Copulation takes place on a display platform. The eggs are laid one a day in an egg nest, and the two parents share incubation, the

Fig. 107. American coot, *Fulica americana*.

male actually doing most of it. Early clutches average 9 eggs, later ones 6 or 7. The eggs are buff or cream-colored, finely speckled with brown, and measure about 50 by 36 mm. Since incubation often begins before the full clutch is laid, the hatch is staggered over several days. The parents raise the young to about half adult size and then desert them to start a new nesting cycle. A pair of coots may raise two or three families in one season.

Coots feed mostly on aquatic vegetation, eating both the seeds and the leaves of a wide variety of water plants. Saunders (1949) found them eating *Heteranthera dubia* in the Tampico area, and the leaves of water hyacinth in Lake Chapala. On Lake Pátzcuaro the birds seemed to be living mostly on pondweeds (*Potamogeton luceus* and *P. foliosus*), which are also favorite duck foods. In winter, coots sometimes forage far from water in meadows or even in agricultural fields. They may damage such crops as alfalfa or winter grains by their grazing.

The coot is widely hunted in Mexico. Rural peoples hunting waterfowl for food kill far more coots than ducks. Much of the pothunting that goes on in dugout canoes on hundreds of Mexican lakes and marshes is directed at coots, and the aggregate kill is considerable. At Pátzcuaro, and perhaps in other places, a few coots are sold in the markets, but most of the birds are taken for home consumption. This use should be encouraged, for the prolific coot is increasing in North America, causing agricultural damage in some places and competing with ducks for food and breeding sites. In the United States, hunters are being widely encouraged to shoot more coots. The high kill in Mexico helps to maintain proper balance in the waterfowl population of the continent.

Order Charadriiformes

This large order of birds is composed of ten families, four of which include species that are considered game birds, or have been so considered in the past. They are the Charadriidae (plovers), Scolopacidae (snipe and sandpipers), Recurvirostridae (avocets and stilts), and the Phalaropodidae (phalaropes). Collectively the members of these four families are referred to as *shore birds*. In North America as a whole these birds are no longer important as game, only the jacksnipe and woodcock being hunted legally in the United States and Canada. Mexican law permits the shooting of all types of shore birds under the following restrictions (1954 regulations):

Species	*Open Season*
Plovers and phalaropes (chichicui-lotes) of the families CHARADRIIDAE and PHALAROPODIDAE	Aug. 15 to Sept. 30, inclusive Limit, 25 per day or in possession
Snipe (Agachona) and others of the family SCOLOPACIDAE, except upland plover (ganga), which is protected	Oct. 15 to Feb. 15, inclusive Limit, 10 per day or in possession
Avocet (avoceta) and stilt (zancuda) of the family RECURVIROSTRIDAE	Nov. 15 to Feb. 15, inclusive Limit, 15 per day or in possession

In spite of the liberal seasons and bag limits there is little shore-bird hunting in Mexico, either for sport or for food. Near Mexico City I found a few sport hunters going out after *chichicuilotes* in September, I think mainly for the purpose of burning some gunpowder while waiting for the duck season to begin. The kill was low, and no one seemed to take the sport very seriously. Later in the autumn there is a small kill of shore birds in connection with duck hunting. The *agachona,* or jacksnipe (*Capella gallinago*), may be sought by a few of the more ambitious waterfowl hunters after the morning duck flight has subsided. And some hunters regularly shoot any of the larger shore birds that happen to pass the duck blinds. But all in all, the sporting kill of these birds is negligible. Nowhere in Mexico did I find any regular hunting of shore birds for food, probably because most of them are small and are difficult to shoot or to capture.

In past years the hunting of shore birds was a popular sport in Mexico, as indeed it was in the United States. López and López (1911 : 484–502) include in their classic book on Mexican hunting rather long accounts of the upland plover (*Bartramia longicauda*) and the jacksnipe and how they were hunted at that time. They mention some of the other shore birds also. The upland plover became scarce in North America and was given full legal protection, in Mexico as well as in other countries. Most of the other shore birds, however, remain fairly abundant, but they have fallen from favor as game birds—for reasons not clear to me. In any event, I have given none of this group detailed treatment in this volume.

Order Columbiformes

FAMILY COLUMBIDAE

Pigeons and Doves

Mexico is richly endowed with pigeons and doves. In all, 24 species are known from this country, of which 12 are treated in the accounts that follow. Of the rest some brief comment will be made here.

The largest and most dramatic of the native pigeons of Mexico—the passenger pigeon (*Ectopistes canadensis*)—has been extinct for nearly half a century. Although the original hordes of these birds stayed mostly in the United States and Canada, lesser numbers occasionally visited eastern Mexico. There are records from the Distrito Federal, Puebla, Veracruz, and Tabasco. Two mounted specimens in the Museo Nacional de Historia Natural in Mexico City are labeled "México."

Five species are casual vagrants in Mexico or are so limited in range as to be ornithological curiosities. These are: (1) the white-crowned pigeon (*Columba leucocephala*) of the West Indies, known from Cozumel Island and recorded twice on the mainland; (2) the rufous pigeon (*Columba cayennensis*), which occurs sparsely in the wet tropical forests of southeastern Mexico but is widely distributed in Central and South America; (3) the Socorro mourning dove (*Zenaidura graysoni*) of Socorro Island in the Revilla

Gigedos in the Pacific; (4) the Zenaida dove (*Zenaida aurita*) of the West Indies, which occurs casually on the Yucatán Peninsula; and (5) the quail-dove (*Oreopelia lawrencii*), another West Indian species, which is known in Mexico only from the Sierra de Tuxtla in southern Veracruz.

Six species, including some of the most abundant of Mexican doves, are too small to be seriously considered game birds: (1) the Inca dove (*Scardafella inca*), which is almost ubiquitous in the cities and ranch yards; (2) the ground dove (*Columbigallina passerina*), which is nearly as widespread as the Inca dove; (3) the Talpacoti dove (*Columbigallina talpacoti*), occurring principally along the tropical coasts; (4) the plain-breasted ground dove (*Columbigallina minuta*) of the southern coastal zones; (5) the blue ground dove (*Claravis pretiosa*) of the Gulf coast; and (6) the rare Mondetoura dove (*Claravis mondetoura*), known only from six localities in the mountains of Veracruz and Chiapas.

But most of the twelve species described below are large enough and abundant enough to be hunted—some of them heavily.

Red-billed Pigeon. *Columba flavirostris*

Other names.—Paloma morada; pepencha; patagona; patagonia; tecaco; torcaza; paloma mora.

Description.—Size and general appearance of common barnyard pigeon. Head, neck, foreback, chest, and lesser wing coverts grayish maroon, paler under the chin. Back, wings, and tail dark gray. Abdomen and tail coverts steel gray. Bill pale brown at tip, red at base. Feet and legs red. Sexes similar in size and appearance. Measurements: folded wing—185 to 198 mm.; tail—110 to 125 mm.; bill—13 to 16 mm.; tarsus—23 to 27 mm. Weight: 241 to 336 gm.

Range in Mexico.—Coastal plains and foothills from central Sonora and northern Tamaulipas south to Chiapas and the Yucatán Peninsula. Inland there is a very sparse population in the lower Río Balsas valley of Guerrero.

Of the several tropical pigeons in the genus *Columba,* the red-billed pigeon is much the most widely distributed in Mexico. Locally it is abundant. I have seen hundreds or perhaps thousands in a few localities along the Gulf coast, such as Rancho Maitínez, San Luis Potosí, and La Unión, Nuevo León. But usually the bird is found in modest populations—as a rule only a few individuals, perhaps a dozen, are seen in a day's hunt. This pigeon is a high, strong flyer in the manner of the band-tailed pigeon. It does not skulk in the timber but cruises in the open where it is easily seen. In winter the birds flock in groups of 5 or 10, or even as many as 50. During the breeding season they are more often seen singly or in pairs.

Breeding begins in Mexico in March and April. Near Gómez Farías, Tamaulipas, Sutton and Pettingill (1942) noted a bird carrying twigs as early as March 18 and found the testes of males enlarging in April. I observed much courtship flight and heard constant cooing among the pigeons near

Fig. 108.   Red-billed pigeon, *Columba flavirostris*.

Sauta, Nayarit, in mid-April. The coo is described by Sutton and Pettingill (p. 13) as "a long-drawn-out *ooooooh*, followed by the syllables *up-cup-a-coo*"; the latter phrase was repeated usually three times in my observation. Grown young begin to show up in June, but breeding continues well into July and perhaps later. At La Unión, Nuevo León, I still heard cooing in late July but concluded that breeding was tapering off. Nests are flimsy platforms of sticks, built in the dense trees and thickets. The single egg, which is a normal clutch, is white and measures about 39 by 28 mm. Occasional clutches of two eggs are reported; in fact, Alvarez del Toro (1952*a*) indicates that two is the common number. How long the period of incubation is I do not know; it is probably about eighteen days, like that of the band-tailed pigeon. Each pair presumably goes through several nesting cycles, or so I would surmise from the length of the breeding season. Fledged young closely resemble adults but are smaller and grayer—not so richly colored. By August the birds are re-forming into winter flocks. There is considerable local shifting about at that time, but I have no evidence of long seasonal migrations.

Red-billed pigeons feed mostly on fleshy fruits and berries but may take rather large quantities of seeds in winter. In northeastern Mexico I found the summer diet dominated by such fruits as the purplish berry of the thorny tree *Condalia obovata* and wild grapes (*Vitis cinerea*). At Poliutla, Guerrero, the sparse population of pigeons came reguarly to a grove of *corongorro* trees (*Zizyphus sonorensis*) to eat the shriveled berries in December. It was there that I ambushed two specimens which had in their crops other fruits, never identified. Wetmore (1943) found palm seeds and figs in the crops of birds from southern Veracruz, and Lowery and Dalquest (1951) in the same region noted hundreds of the birds gathered in groves of the *nanchi* when fruits were ripe. Yet in Nuevo León I have found the seeds of corn and of Johnson grass in specimens killed in winter, and in eastern San Luis Potosí I have noted hundreds of pigeons feeding in cornfields. Grayson reported these birds eating acorns in Sinaloa (Salvin and Godman, 1897–1904), but there are not many places where red-billed pigeons invade the temperate oak forests.

In Mexico this pigeon is hunted some for sport and occasionally for meat. Lowery and Dalquest (p. 566) state: "The *paloma mora* is shot for food whenever a hunter can be reasonably sure of killing several birds with a single shell. For the most part, however, single birds are not shot, for the value of the meat of one bird is less than the cost of the ammunition to kill it." This principle governs the hunting of all the doves and pigeons for food. Sport hunters, however, are willing to expend ammunition if the birds are abundant enough to offer fast shooting without much walking or waiting. There is some such hunting of red-billed pigeons in Veracruz, but not a great deal. The species could withstand a much heavier harvest.

Band-tailed Pigeon. *Columba fasciata*

Other names.—Paloma de collar; pichón grande; yaz; cuauhpaloma.

Description.—Similar to the common barnyard pigeon in size and appearance. Head, throat, chest, and underparts purplish drab, paling to white on the lower tail coverts. White crescent across the back of neck. Foreback and hindneck iridescent bronze. Back, wing coverts, rump, and tail gray; the tail broadly tipped with pale brownish gray. Primaries blackish, edged with white. Bill yellow tipped with black. Feet and legs yellow. Sexes similar in size and appearance. Young birds more grayish below, without white crescent or iridescence on back of neck. Measurements: folded wing—198 to 216 mm.; tail—129 to 145 mm.; bill—17 to 19 mm.; tarsus—25 to 28 mm. Weight: Adults—280 to 350 gm.; young—260 to 300 gm.

Range in Mexico.—Pine-oak highlands throughout the country.

The band-tailed pigeon is nearly as dependable an indicator of pine-oak forest in Mexico as the Montezuma quail. Flocks of these handsome birds may be seen anywhere in the higher mountains, from Baja California to Chiapas. Band-tails breed throughout most or all of this range in local colonies, but they are not uniformly distributed. I personally found breeding colonies in Chihuahua, Michoacán, Nuevo León, Guerrero, and Oaxaca, and nests have been reported from many other states. In winter the birds gather into groups of 10 to 100 and shift about widely, going wherever acorns, manzanita berries, and other winter foods become available. There is a definite southward influx of birds from the western United States into northern Baja California and probably into Sonora and Chihuahua at that season. But in most parts of Mexico seasonal movements are local and in no particular direction. In spring the flocks drift back to their breeding areas.

The nesting season is long, extending at least from May to August. On June 2, near Los Reyes, Michoacán, I collected a male band-tail in full breeding condition, and six days later I found two nests high in oak trees on the slopes of Mount Tancítaro. At the same time in this locality we collected well-grown young that had left the nest, a sign that breeding had been in progress for well over a month. The latest nest found during the survey was seen on August 18 near Pacheco, Chihuahua; but on September 10 on the Cerro San Felipe, Oaxaca, I collected two adults with gonads indicating recent cessation of breeding. Each pair of pigeons may complete several nesting cycles during the summer; this was recently proved with marked birds under study in California.

The courtship display of a male band-tailed pigeon includes loud and persistent cooing and a nuptial flight repeated frequently for the edification of the female. The flight consists of a high circle, usually 200 yards or more in diameter, made with the wings extended horizontally, the tips making short, fast, fluttering strokes. This is quite unlike the nuptial flight of the red-billed pigeon, which makes its circle with deep, slow wing strokes, slapping the

Fig. 109. Band-tailed pigeon, *Columba fasciata*.

wings together above and below as it flies. In both species the male returns to alight near the female at the end of the flight.

The normal clutch is a single white egg, measuring 40 by 28 mm. However, clutches of two eggs are not uncommon. Neff (1947) summarizes the literature on this point. Incubation requires eighteen days or slightly more. Both sexes share in incubation and in later brooding of the young. After three to four weeks of care in the nest, the young pigeon leaves its home platform of twigs and flies away; and the adults may begin over again with a new nest.

Like other doves and pigeons, band-tails feed their young through the early developmental period on "pigeon milk," secreted in the crops of the parent birds by a thick yellow tissue that develops during the nesting period and disappears in autumn. Each parent pumps its supply of milk into the squab twice or three times daily when it is young, once a day after it is three weeks old. When the squab is fledged, it is also weaned and must seek its own food.

Band-tailed pigeons eat mostly fruit in the summer and mast (acorns especially) in the winter. In Michoacán in June I found various fruits and berries in the birds' crops, particularly pokeberries (*Phytolacca rugosa*) on the slopes of Mount Tancítaro. This weed had invaded the ash fields caused by the eruption of nearby Volcán Parícutin, and the birds came by the hundreds to eat the purple berries. In central Nuevo León, pigeons were eating wild cherries (*Prunus serotina*) and elderberries (*Sambucus*) in July, although the crop of one bird contained also some grains of wheat, picked up no doubt in a stubble field. Near Pacheco, Chihuahua, most of the pigeons were feeding on manzanita berries in July and August. But the majority of the specimens taken from September to April in various parts of Mexico had acorns in their crops. It would be safe to say that acorns are the principal winter food. In winter, which is the dry season, band-tailed pigeons also come daily to water, usually in midmorning after having gathered a breakfast of acorns.

Band-tailed pigeons are not heavily hunted in Mexico, and most of the hunting that takes place is for food. Locally I found evidence of a substantial kill at water holes, as for example at various places in the mountains of Michoacán. Local hunters would wait at the water and mow through the flocks that alighted to drink, killing several birds with each shot. But this practice is not widespread. There is relatively little sport hunting, which is too bad, for band-tails are difficult targets. Often in the mountains there are low passes through which the flocks travel at high speed on their way to feeding, watering, or roosting areas. Overhead shooting at the passing flocks is an exacting sport that deserves the attention of Mexican sportsmen.

Scaled Pigeon. *Columba speciosa*

Other names.—Paloma escamosa; paloma del breñal; paloma real; chukib.
Description.—Top and sides of head maroon. Foreback, neck, and chest heavily scaled, feathers iridescent blue-black at tips, rufous in the central and

Fig. 110.   Portrait of two band-tailed pigeons, by P. J. Fair.

basal parts. Back rich reddish brown, darkening to brown on the wings. Under-parts grayish, paling to white on the under tail coverts, the feathers edged with vinaceous brown. Tail black. Bill red. Feet and legs lavender. Females and young similar to males but duller. Measurements: folded wing—174 to 188 mm.; tail—97 to 108 mm.; bill—18 to 21 mm.; tarsus—24 to 26 mm. Weight: of one adult male—287 gm.; of a young female—254 gm.

Range in Mexico.—Rain forest and tropical evergreen forest of southeastern Mexico, as far north as Córdoba, Veracruz.

The scaled pigeon is one of the least-known game birds of Mexico. It lives in the dense tropical forest and is highly retiring in habit, spending much of the time sitting quietly in the treetops, where its scaled pattern renders it vir-tually invisible. In late November, 1945, we found occasional pairs of these birds in tall trees along the river by San Juan, Campeche. Never did we see them flying in the open or being obvious in any way. Lowery and Dalquest (1951) and also Paynter (1955) agree with my observation that the bird may be considerably more abundant than the relatively few museum speci-mens would indicate. Its habits make it difficult to find and to collect. Typical is the experience of Lowery and Dalquest (p. 566) here repeated in full:

The two specimens were taken almost by accident. The one from near Minatitlán was in a tall tree, fully seventy-five feet from the ground. A Chachalaca had been heard in the vicinity, and was being hunted. A small branch was seen to move in the leafy crown of the tree, and a shot, supposedly at a Chachalaca, brought down the pigeon that had been hitherto unseen and unsuspected. An-other pigeon flew from the same tree. The specimen from near Jesús Carranza was in the lower part of a dense tree, perched about fifty feet from the ground. Attention was called to the tree by slight movements of twigs and leaves, but no bird was seen, even after considerable peering. When the motion again started, a shot was fired into the branch and one of these pigeons fell to the ground. Again, another flew from the same tree.

Practically nothing is known of the life history of this bird. Alvarez del Toro (1952*b* : 113) found the species "more or less common from March to August at El Ocote, Ocozocoautla (Chiapas), for many years; recorded breeding there in May." Cole, quoted by Paynter (1955), suggests that scaled pigeons are found in Yucatán only in summer, implying a migration. Salvin and God-man (1897–1904 : 234), however, state that the species "doubtless breeds throughout its range, as Mr. Richmond records the capture of a young bird in first plumage on the Escondido River, and near Petén, Leyland found it domesticated and very tame." One of the specimens that we took on Novem-ber 22 in Campeche also was young, still molting into its winter plumage.

I have found no data on the nest or on clutch size. One egg in the British Museum is described by Oates (1901) as "glossy" and as measuring 1.48 by 1.05 inches (about 38 by 26 mm.).

Little, too, is known about the food of the scaled pigeon. Alvarez del Toro (1952*a*) states that it eats "fruits and seeds."

Female

Male

Fig. 111.   Scaled pigeon, *Columba speciosa*.

The bird is probably shot very little, because of its retiring nature. However, its range undoubtedly is shrinking with clearing of the tropical forest, which is its habitat.

Short-billed Pigeon. *Columba nigrirostris*

Other names.—Paloma piquinegra; limonera; bust-a-huei.

Description.—Small. More or less uniformly vinaceous brown; darker and more purplish on head and foreback, blending to brownish drab on back, wings, and tail. Bill black and noticeably short. Feet and legs red. Measurements: folded wing—157 to 167 mm.; tail—111 to 119 mm.; bill—13 to 15 mm.; tarsus—21 to 22 mm. Weight of one female from Chiapas: 186 gm.

Range in Mexico.—Rain forest and tropical evergreen forest from southern Veracruz and northern Oaxaca eastward along the Gulf coast to northern Chiapas and Tabasco. One record from southern Quintana Roo. One autumn record (Sept. 16) from Mount Zempoaltepec, Oaxaca, which probably represents a stray.

The distribution of this beautiful pigeon is spotty and irregular. It is abundant in parts of the rain forest. We heard many short-billed pigeons cooing at Monte Líbano near El Real, Chiapas, and on the slopes of Volcán San Martín Tuxtla, Veracruz. Lowery and Dalquest (1951) found them plentiful in extreme southern Veracruz. But in similar forests of the Yucatán Peninsula the bird is rare, in fact, virtually unknown. It is abundant, however, along the Caribbean coast of Guatemala (Griscom, 1932).

In our camp at Monte Líbano I tried for days before I succeeded in collecting a specimen, for the birds were living so high in the great mahogany trees that a shotgun could scarcely reach them. We could see them often in the mornings and late afternoons flying back and forth in the highest stratum of the forest. And their beautiful, tantalizing calls floated down to us on the dark forest floor below—"Coooo-coo-coo-coo," as I put it in my notes. The first and last syllables are accented, and the calls are repeated several times at intervals of about twenty seconds. Finally, on December 5, the last day in camp, I located a bird barely within gun range and brought it down with a lucky shot (one pellet in the head). It fell so far that it burst upon striking the ground, an experience reported previously by both Wetmore (1943) and Lowery and Dalquest. On Volcán San Martín Tuxtla the timber was lower and there was less difficulty in taking specimens.

Presumably short-billed pigeons feed on fruits plucked from the treetops; but I have no record of crop contents, nor can I find any notes by others on food habits. However, Lowery and Dalquest (p. 567) observed some of these pigeons drinking:

In the late morning and afternoon, the Short-billed Pigeons are seen along the shores of rivers, where they probably go to drink. At such times they are seen perched on low branches or in low trees beside the water. They choose places where the rivers are deep and still, where the low, fringing vegetation grows

Fig. 112. Short-billed pigeon, *Columba nigrirostris*.

down to the water level and permits them to drink without alighting on the ground. None was ever seen on a sand or gravel bar.

Salvin and Godman (1897–1904) likewise note that short-billed pigeons often concentrate in the timber along streams, especially in the trumpet tree (*Cecropia*).

Seemingly nothing is known of the nest or eggs of this bird.

The short-billed pigeon is shot occasionally by local people where it is abundant. At Tapalapan, Veracruz, our guide, Epileme Tegoma, spoke of the *limonera* as a common bird for the pot, but since it is rather small and difficult to hunt I imagine the actual kill is negligible. Like the scaled pigeon, this rain forest species is doubtless affected adversely by the continued clearing away of the trees.

Mourning Dove. *Zenaidura macroura*

Other names.—Huilota; tórtola; tiuta; kuikipu.

Description.—Medium-sized, with a long, pointed tail. Top of head, back, rump, wing coverts, and central tail feathers brownish gray. Flight feathers of wing dark gray, innermost secondaries prominently spotted with black. Forehead, sides of head and neck, and underparts rich fawn color, darkest on the chest, paling toward the under tail coverts. Lateral tail feathers graduated in length, longest toward the center, shortest on the sides, all broadly tipped with white (30 to 40 mm.), gray at base, with a medial black band. Bill black. Feet and legs red. Measurements: folded wing—136 to 157 mm.; tail—117 to 158 mm.; bill—12 to 15 mm.; tarsus—18 to 21 mm. Weight: 96 to 130 gm. Females slightly smaller and duller than males.

Range in Mexico.—This dove breeds abundantly in the northern and central regions, south in Baja California to latitude 26° and in the interior to Jalisco and Hidalgo, sparingly to Oaxaca (Tamazulapan and Tlacolula). It is much more numerous in winter, along the coasts as well as inland, and south to the arid central valley of Chiapas. There are two records from the Yucatán Peninsula.

Of all the doves and pigeons that occur in Mexico, the mourning dove and the white-winged dove (*Zenaida asiatica*) are much the most important game species. The substantial breeding population of mourning doves in northern and central Mexico is augmented in winter by a considerable migration from the United States, and this bird is hunted in that season. The greatest concentrations occur in the arid, temperate uplands, the numbers diminishing toward the tropical coasts. The converse is true of white-winged doves, which are most numerous along the coasts and are sparsely present in the interior. The Río Balsas valley of Guerrero and Morelos is a sort of middle ground; there the two species are present in roughly equal numbers in winter. On a typical November morning hunt near Poliutla, Guerrero, I would see 300 to 400 of each species. The mourning doves start migrating into northern Mexico in September, but it is November before they reach Guerrero in any large numbers. The northward exodus occurs mostly in March.

Fig. 113.   Mourning dove, *Zenaidura macroura*.

In observing the doves in southern Mexico I found that the mourning doves and whitewings tended to segregate even where both were locally abundant. They would roost and loaf apart, each species'in loose aggregations. From a given grove of trees one might flush a hundred mourning doves, from the next grove a like number of whitewings. Both species fly out into the fields to feed morning and evening, coming to water after each feeding. The birds do not mix freely even on the feeding grounds or when drinking. I could not detect any signs of hostility between the species—merely an apparent lack of mutual attraction. However, along the Guerrero coast where whitewings outnumbered mourning doves 50 to 1, the few mourning doves were skulking in the timber and feeding in small openings rather than going to the big fields that swarmed with whitewings. There was a suggestion of social intolerance that was keeping the mourning doves from their preferred type of habitat.

Mourning doves pair early and have a long nesting season, raising several broods a year. In California, Cowan (1952) found old birds nesting from mid-March to mid-September, young birds (yearlings) pairing and starting to nest somewhat later. Each nesting cycle requires about thirty days to complete—two or three days for nest building and laying the two white eggs (29 by 20 mm.), fourteen to fifteen days for incubation, and twelve days for brooding of the young until they are ready to fly from the nest. After a successful cycle the pair usually straightway starts to work on a new nest and a new family. In the six-month period of reproduction a pair could raise six broods of 2 young each, or 12 young altogether. Cowan, in fact, observed one pair that did so. Usually, however, some of the flimsy twig nests blow from the trees, or the eggs or young are taken by a predator, so that average production is much lower—nearer 6 young per pair. Occasionally mourning doves build their nests on the ground, and in some localities this habit is more common than tree nesting. Presumably the nests thus saved from wind losses are balanced in number by those destroyed by ground predators, so that ground nesting probably does not increase the total number of young.

In selecting nesting sites, mourning doves are not noticeably colonial but tend to scatter out and use whatever sites are available. Often nests are several miles from water, the parents having to fly that distance at least once a day to drink. The doves will go equally far to good feeding areas. Breeding doves are easily located, not only by their conspicuous movements to and from the nesting area but by the persistent cooing of the male: a long, accented "cooo" followed by two or three shorter notes at a lower pitch. The courtship flight of the male is distinctive also—a high circle, started with deep wing strokes that slap the primaries together above and below, followed by a stately glide on fixed wings back to the lady dove.

Young doves in the nest are fed "pigeon milk" as are other young birds of this family. Both parents secrete the "milk" in their crops. Seeds and other adult foods are added to the diet as the squabs grow. When the young fly from the nest, they are entirely on their own and must learn quickly to forage for themselves. The new fledglings tend to gather in loose groups apart from the breeding adults. In late summer it is common to find 30 or 40 young sitting about in some well-situated grove of trees, loafing and preening during the day while their busy parents are still tending new nests and other babies.

Mourning doves feed almost entirely on plant seeds which they pick up from the surface of the ground. They prefer small seeds, but often take kernels of corn and, rarely, even acorns. In many of the dove crops that I examined in Mexico I found a wide variety of seeds, some of the dominant ones being pigweed, sunflower, turkey mullein (*Eremocarpus*), doveweed (*Croton*), rattlebox (*Crotalaria pumila*), beans of the genus *Desmodium*, various large-seeded grasses, and cultivated crops such as corn, wheat, beans, and sesame (*ajonjolí*). Doves have such small, weak legs and feet that they cannot scramble through thick weeds or grass but must move about on essentially bare ground. Perhaps for this reason they favor arid regions where the ground cover is sparse and such seeds as fall to the surface are easily gathered.

The mourning dove is a remarkably fast flyer. It is this attribute of speed that makes it a favorite game bird with sportsmen. The usual method of sport hunting is to take a stand near a water hole, feeding area, or other site used by a good many doves and shoot the birds as they pass overhead in the late afternoon flight to feed or drink. López and López (1911) speak of this sport as "difficult enough to be worthy of the most presumptious sportsman." Throughout Mexico there are many devotees. Considerable numbers of mourning doves are also taken for food. I saw many local people hunting doves with single-barrel shotguns (sometimes muzzle-loaders) by waiting for the birds to alight—often in groups—along the banks of a water hole or stream. Near Poliutla, Guerrero, an ingenious clap net was in use for capturing flocks of doves flying through low passes in the hills on their way to roost. The net was held upright on tall poles by two men. When an unsuspecting group of doves hit the mesh, which was nearly invisible in the poor evening light, the men pushed the poles down to the ground, with the whole flock trapped. Elsewhere I heard of the use of box traps baited with grain to capture the birds. But all in all, the kill of mourning doves in Mexico is minor in view of the abundance of the species.

White-winged Dove. *Zenaida asiatica*

Other names.—Paloma con alas blancas; torcáz; torcaza; tortola; huilota costeña; *Melopelia asiatica*.

Description.—Medium-sized, somewhat larger than the mourning dove and with a square tail like that of a pigeon. Top of head and foreback purplish gray, blending to drab brown on the back, middle wing coverts, and two central tail feathers. Flight feathers dark gray finely edged with white. Distal wing coverts white, forming an elongate white patch on spread wing. Rump gray. Tail (except central feathers) dark gray at base, with a subterminal band of black, broadly white at the tip. Sides of neck iridescent bronze, with a black spot on each side. Underparts tawny brown blending posteriorly to pale gray on abdomen and on under tail coverts. Bill black. Legs and feet red. Measurements: folded wing—147 to 166 mm.; tail—95 to 113 mm.; bill—19 to 24 mm.; tarsus— 23 to 26 mm. Weight: 130 to 196 gm. Males slightly larger than females.

Range in Mexico.—This dove is an abundant resident along both coasts, especially in thorn forest and tropical deciduous forest. It occurs sparingly in the arid interior zones of Mexico. The resident population is augmented in winter by a relatively small migratory population from the southwestern United States (especially southern Arizona and southern Texas).

Whereas the mourning dove is essentially a bird of the temperate interior of Mexico, the whitewing is primarily tropical and coastal in its distribution. Highest populations observed during the survey were in thorn forest and tropical deciduous forest, in such places as the tip of Baja California, coastal Sinaloa, Nayarit, Guerrero, and Tamaulipas, and the lower Río Balsas valley. Lesser numbers were observed in the Tehuantepec region, along the dry tip of the Yucatán Peninsula, and in the upper Río Balsas basin, although these areas would appear to be quite suitable range.

White-winged doves are noticeably more gregarious than mourning doves at all times of year. In winter they tend to fly about in definite flocks, and during the breeding season they are decidedly colonial in habit. Arnold (1943) who studied the nesting of this species in Arizona, concluded that the formation of nesting colonies was a function of limited habitat, which forces the birds to congregate in the best areas; but with this view I cannot agree. Along the Mexican coasts I repeatedly found whitewings nesting close together in colonies when suitable habitat seemed almost limitless. Even in the active nesting period, when individual pairs are busy with their own domestic duties, the whitewings often fly to and from feeding grounds or water in flocks of 5 to 25. They seem to like each others' company.

Nesting white-winged doves are conspicuous by virtue of their numbers in and around a large colony (hundreds or even thousands of pairs) and the loud and persistent cooing of the males. Saunders (1951) has recorded the songs of these doves and transcribed them on a musical staff. The usual popular description of the song is the phrase "Who cooks for you?"—a four-note melody strongly accented on the last syllable. The males also indulge frequently in nuptial flights much like those of the mourning dove.

Nests are usually in groves of low dense trees such as mesquite or acacia, but they may be in clumps of cactus or in vine tangles. I have not often found whitewings nesting in tall timber and have never seen them nesting on the ground. The nest platform is built of twigs or straw, usually 6 to 20 feet from the ground. Two eggs constitute the usual clutch. The eggs are buffy white and measure about 31 by 23 mm. Incubation—carried on mostly or entirely by the female—is normally fifteen to seventeen days, but periods of as many as

Fig. 114. White-winged dove, *Zenaida asiatica*.

nineteen days have been reported (Neff, 1940). The young are fledged and leave the nest when fifteen to eighteen days old, by which time they have been "weaned" from the diet of pigeon milk to the fruits and seeds eaten by the adults. Thereafter the young forage for themselves and the adults go about renesting, as the mourning doves do. How many broods of young a pair of whitewings may produce in a season is not known, but the nesting season is long enough (March to August or September) for birds to produce several families. Neff concluded that in Arizona, only one brood was raised in unfavorable years, two broods in good years. I should expect two or more broods to be reared annually on the better ranges of Mexico. Some of the fall age ratios recorded in Arizona show that as high as 85 per cent of the whitewings killed by hunters were young ones; this indicates that there these doves are highly productive.

The diet of white-winged doves includes many kinds of seeds and also a wide variety of fleshy fruits not often taken by mourning doves. I have found most of the common cultivated plants in the crops of whitewings—corn, wheat, beans, sesame, melon seeds—as well as a long list of weed seeds and fruits of such woody plants as palms, figs, mesquite, hackberry, *Condalia*, and the larger cacti. In Arizona and Sonora and at the tip of Baja California cactus fruits seem to be the favorite summer food as long as they are available. Wetmore, as quoted by Bent (1932), noted some damage by whitewings to shocked wheat; but generally speaking, the birds eat waste seeds in the fields, along with wild foods, and thus only rarely constitute an agricultural problem.

Little is known of predation on white-winged doves. Neff mentions dogs and coyotes as predators of young that have fallen to the ground. Nests may be robbed by such mammals as opossums and other climbing carnivores, and perhaps by snakes, jays, road-runners, or predatory birds. Near Acapulco I found the remains of several whitewings, which apparently had been taken by accipitrine hawks.

There are no estimates of numbers of white-winged doves, except of some local nesting colonies, but in places the bird clearly is enormously abundant. In areas of concentration it is not unusual to see thousands of these doves milling about over croplands or streaming in to water. Shooting in these circumstances can be fast and furious, resulting in heated gun barrels and large bags. For this reason and because the birds are plump and tasty, the whitewing is a highly popular game species with sportsmen. It is also customarily hunted for food locally in many parts of Mexico. I have seen the flocks ground-sluiced at watering holes, trapped with nets, and peppered with slingshots or even hand-thrown rocks. But since the breeding stock, like that of the mourning dove, is large and production high, heavy hunting of this bird should be encouraged.

White-fronted Doves. *Leptotila verreauxi* and Related Species

Other names.—Paloma suelero; cuizula; alcabús; tsutsuy; arroyera.

Species included here.—*Leptotila verreauxi, L. plumbeiceps, L. cassinii,* and *L. jamaicensis.*

Description.—The four species of *Leptotila* that occur in Mexico are quite similar in appearance and in habit. The ranges of all four overlap, yet the species remain distinct without interbreeding. These doves are olive brown on the back, buff or fulvous on the underparts paling to white on the abdomen, and have pale throats and foreheads. Both wings and tails are relatively short and rounded, the tails always white-tipped except for the central feathers. The outside primary on each wing is noticeably attenuated or narrowed at the tip. Bills are black, feet and legs red. The species can be told apart by the following characters:

L. verreauxi: Forehead pale buff. Top of head olive brown. Back of head and hindneck iridescent with red, blue, and green lights.

L. plumbeiceps: Forehead whitish gray, blending to lead gray on top of head. Barely perceptible purplish sheen on foreback, none on head or neck.

L. cassinii: Forehead pale buff, blending to rich brown on top of head. No iridescence on neck or back. Chest purplish gray shading to fulvous on breast. Flanks olive brown. Under tail coverts partly brown (pure white or cream in other species).

L. jamaicensis: Largest and palest of the species, with a pure white forehead blending to gray on crown. Neck and foreback brightly iridescent. Tail gray, dorsally broadly tipped with white (10–20 mm.) except two central feathers that are brown like the back. Outer tail feathers narrowly edged with white.

Weights and measurements are given in table 13.

In all the species, females are very slightly duller in color than males and are a little smaller.

Range in Mexico.—The species *L. verreauxi* is widely distributed in tropical zones, as far north as Sonora and Tamaulipas, penetrating the southern temperate uplands (Guerrero, Oaxaca, Chiapas) in canyons. It is most abundant in semiarid zones broken by clearings. *L. plumbeiceps* is limited to wetter and denser tropical forests of the Gulf coast and the base of the Yucatán Peninsula (fig. 116). The other two species occur only in very circumscribed areas of unbroken rain forest in extreme southeastern Mexico, as shown in figure 117.

The white-fronted doves all live on the ground or in the lower stratum of the forest vegetation. They are fast runners and have better-developed legs and feet than any of their relatives except the quail-doves. They are likewise deft flyers, dodging through the undergrowth with speed and remarkable control. They never fly high, and do not often fly in the open except to dart across some clearing.

The rounded wings and tail are clearly adaptations to brush dodging. A special feature of the *Leptotila* wing is the attenuated outer primary, which is reminiscent of the corresponding feather of the woodcock (*Philohela minor*), a brush-dwelling shorebird of northeastern North America. The woodcock has three such narrowed primaries. Repeatedly I have been struck with the similarity in flight habits of these two birds and the remarkable way they both can change direction and change pace in negotiating passage through a thicket. I suspect that the "slotting" of the wing tip is a structural feature for this type of flight.

Although the various kinds of white-fronted doves in Mexico have individual habitat preferences, they seemed to me much the same in general behavior. I have collected all four species at one time or another and will discuss them together here. Most of my observations, however, pertain to the commonest and most widespread species, *L. verreauxi*.

TABLE 13

Measurements and Weights of Four Species of Doves of the Genus *Leptotila*

Species	Folded wing (mm.)	Tail (mm.)	Bill (mm.)	Tarsus (mm.)	Weight (gm.)
Leptotila verreauxi	135–150	95–110	15–17	28–31	145–205
Leptotila plumbeiceps ...	136–144	89–96	16–18	30–31	150–160
Leptotila cassinii	129–135	85–89	14–16	30–31	155–168
Leptotila jamaicensis	153–157	106–111	16–17	29–31	197 (one)

In moving along a trail through dense woodland anywhere in tropical Mexico, one is likely to flush a white-fronted dove. A flutter of wings in the brush, a flash of brown and white, and the bird is gone, darting low to the ground. Flight is short—often only a hundred feet or so. With good luck the bird may be marked down where it can be stalked and observed. If seen again it will likely be scurrying rapidly along the bare ground, pecking nervously here and there as it feeds. Or it might be in a low tree or shrub, sitting quite motionless and nearly invisible in the broken light. Chances are, however, that the first flash would prove to be your last view of this individual—the birds have a way of disappearing after even the shortest flight. But if this is good habitat for *Leptotila*, others will fly out farther along the trail, especially near an opening or clearing. White-fronted doves are found thus scattered through the thickets, in singles or pairs, never in flocks. On a morning or evening walk one might flush as many as a dozen. Harrell estimated three pairs per 100 acres in timberland near Gómez Farías, Tamaulipas. Occasionally the birds will be seen flying to some favorite feeding ground or to water, but usually one must go into the brush to find them.

During the breeding season one is much more conscious of their numbers, for then the males are cooing—a low, soft, three-noted call: "Who're you?" There is also a courtship flight rather like that of other doves but small in diameter (50 ft. or so), executed in some break in the timber or even through and under it. A courting male frequents low perches, the female often feeding on the ground below, looking very unconcerned. The breeding season is long. Paynter (1955) noted signs of breeding in Quintana Roo as early as

Fig. 115.   Four species of Mexican doves of the genus
Leptotila, showing range of the most widely
distributed species, *L. verreauxi.*

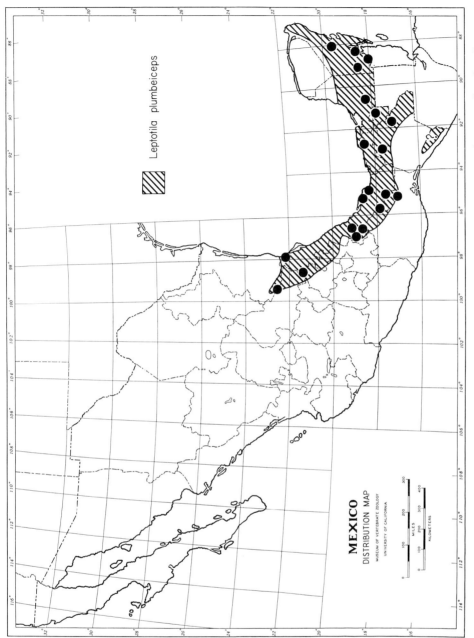

Leptotila plumbeiceps

Fig. 116. Range of *Leptotila plumbeiceps*.

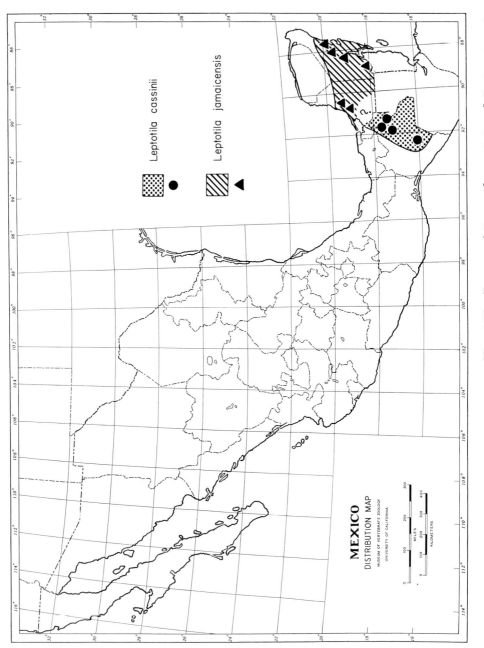

Fig. 117. Ranges of *Leptotila cassinii* and *L. jamaicensis*.

January in *verreauxi* and February in *jamaicensis* and *plumbeiceps.* Sutton and Pettingill (1942) found two nests of *verreauxi,* with eggs well incubated, on March 29 in Tamaulipas. The eggs in one of these hatched on March 30. I collected adults with "milk" in the crops in mid-April in Nayarit. There are breeding records on through the summer and well into autumn. I took birds that seemed recently to have finished nesting in mid-October in Sinaloa and mid-November in Guerrero. A half-grown bird (108 gm.) was collected on December 11 near Acapulco. From this evidence I presume that white-fronted doves are repeat-nesters like so many of their relatives.

Nests are usually in low, dense shrubs or vines, and are constructed of twigs or dry weeds. Sutton and Pettingill found nests on the ground ("among boulders") on steep hillsides. The number of eggs laid ordinarily is two. They are creamy white and measure about 31 by 23 mm. (*verreauxi*). The period of incubation is not known, but Skutch (1945) has recorded the time of care in the nest as fourteen to fifteen days. Lawrence (1874) quotes Grayson to the effect that ". . . the young soon follow the mother, before being able to fly, like some of the gallinaceous birds." Of this I have no personal knowledge; but it would not be surprising if partly grown young were running around freely, especially if they came from nests on the ground, where Grayson seemingly found most whitefronts nesting near Mazatlán.

White-fronted doves forage normally on the ground, picking up seeds and fruits from bare areas such as trails, clearings, and open patches on the forest floor. I found a wide variety of weed seeds in the crops, especially thistle seeds and various wild beans. These doves glean cultivated grains from the edges of open fields, but I have never seen any go far into open country to forage. Corn and sesame are two agricultural plants that are widely used for food by these doves. Various fruits are found in the birds' crops, too; I presume these are picked up from the ground, although it is possible that some are gathered in the trees. Along the Santiago River in Nayarit the purple fruits of *capulín del monte* (*Bumelia peninsularis*) were often found in the dove crops. In Nuevo León, I found the berries of *Condalia obovata* and two other fruits in the crop of a bird jumped from the edge of a small cornfield, and in the deep rain forest of Chiapas I saw doves (*cassinii*) taking fallen fruits of zapote and various other trees.

The white-fronted doves have great potential value as game birds. For sportsmen who enjoy difficult brush shooting, the hunting of whitefronts offers all the features of woodcock hunting and, in addition, the chance for pass shooting along river banks or on the edges of feeding grounds. I found it a distinct challenge and pleasure to collect these birds on the wing with a 20-gauge scatter-gun. To my knowledge the white-fronted doves are scarcely hunted at all by Mexican sportsmen, nor are they used to any appreciable extent for food, being much too difficult to obtain in large numbers. The common species (*verreauxi*) is not only holding its own but doubtless is increasing, since it thrives in cutover forests broken with trails and openings. The other three species, however, may be suffering, since they are all types that live in the forest.

Ruddy Quail-dove. *Oreopelia montana*

Other names.—Paloma montañes; paloma montañera; k'ankab tsutsuy.

Description.—Small, plump, with short tail, rounded wings, and well-developed legs and feet. MALE: Bright reddish brown dorsally, including wings and tail, with a purplish iridescent gloss on nape, foreback, and shoulders. Chest vinaceous fawn, fading to pale buff both anteriorly on throat and chin and posteriorly on the abdomen. FEMALE: Dark olive brown dorsally, including wings and tail. Chest dull brown, lightly washed with cinnamon, fading to buff both forward and aft, as in the male. In both sexes the bill, feet, legs, and bare area round eye are red. Measurements: folded wing—136 to 146 mm.; tail—73 to 82 mm.; bill—10 to 13 mm.; tarsus—26 to 29 mm. Weight: 110 to 145 gm. Males slightly larger than females.

Range in Mexico.—Wet tropical forests or canyons in the deciduous forest, from southern Sinaloa and eastern San Luis Potosí southward along both coasts to Chiapas and the base of the Yucatán Peninsula. There is a gap along the Pacific slope between the Río Santiago and the Río Balsas where the species has not been recorded, although it probably occurs. A record in the dry zone of northern Yucatán (Temax) is considered by Paynter (1955) to be accidental and outside the normal range.

The ruddy quail-dove is unusual among the North American Columbidae in possessing a marked degree of sexual dimorphism, the males and females being utterly unlike in color. Only among ground doves of the genus *Columbigallina* is there a like contrast in the plumage of the sexes.

Quail-doves are solitary in habit, frequenting the dark floor of the tropical forests, where they may be found running about as nimbly as quail but bobbing their heads in the typical fashion of pigeons and doves. The ruddy quail-dove is not a particularly abundant species in most of its Mexican range. Although Paynter (1955) speaks of it as "common" at the base of the Yucatán Peninsula, he had only four skins. In the main the species is represented in collections by an odd specimen or two from each of the localities shown on the range map. The scarcity of specimens no doubt is in part due to the shyness of the birds and their elusiveness in the dense forest.

Virtually nothing was known of the life history of this handsome dove until Skutch (1949) published his careful paper on the nesting habits of the species in Costa Rica. Most of the account that follows, including direct quotations, stems from this source.

The presence of ruddy quail-doves in the forest is most obvious during the mating period when the males are calling with "a soft deep *coo,* usually delivered while the bird rests upon the ground—a mournful sound often heard amidst the forests . . ." Nesting in Costa Rica begins in April, "after the forest has been soaked and refreshed by the returning rains," and extends to July or

Male

Short rounded tail

Fig. 118. Ruddy quail-dove, *Oreopelia montana*.

even early August. The time of nesting in Mexico is not precisely known. Paynter noted slightly enlarged gonads in a specimen collected February 9 in Campeche, and two June specimens from Quintana Roo were in full breeding condition. Brodkorb (1943) records a juvenile taken July 12 in northern Chiapas. Alvarez del Toro (1952a) gives the breeding season in Chiapas as May to August.

Nests are on stumps or in vines, epiphytes, or tangles of fallen vegetation, and usually are 2 to 8 feet above the ground. According to Skutch, they are built mostly of green leaves that turn brown during the period of use. Two eggs are laid. These are creamy buff and measure about 28 by 20 mm. The period of incubation is astonishingly short for so large an egg—ten to eleven days. Both sexes incubate, the male during the day, the female in the evening and through the night. Skutch observes that this regimen is normal for pigeons and doves. After hatching, the young are tended in the nest for about ten days, by which time they are well grown and able to fly; they grow rapidly on a diet of pigeon milk. The adults may start a new clutch of eggs after the first young are fledged and on their own. In the one instance of renesting that Skutch observed, there was an interval of one month between the departure of the first brood and the laying of the second set of eggs.

Of the food habits of this dove, Skutch states (p. 4):

The Ruddy Quail-Dove picks most if not all of its food from the ground. Gosse (1947: 321–323) mentions that in Jamaica it eats the fallen berries of the pimento, the physic-nut and other oily seeds, berries of the sweet-wood, and small slugs, and that in captivity it thrives upon maize.

I have no record of the ruddy quail-dove's being hunted in Mexico, either for sport or for food. So retiring a thicket dweller is difficult to shoot.

White-faced Quail-dove. *Oreopelia albifacies*

Other name.—Paloma codorniz.

Description.—Size of a domestic pigeon but with shorter tail and rounded wings. Top of head lead gray, paling to grayish white on the forehead. Upper parts, including wings and tail, rich chestnut brown, glossed with purple iridescence on the back. Underparts pale cinnamon brown, fading to buff under the chin and around the vent. Bill black. Legs and feet red. Measurements: folded wing—149 to 156 mm.; tail—90 to 106 mm.; bill—14 to 16 mm.; tarsus—40 to 42 mm. No weights available. Sexes alike in plumage and size.

Range in Mexico.—Humid mountain forests (cloud forest principally) along the eastern escarpment from southern San Luis Potosí to the Isthmus of Tehuantepec, in the Chiapas highlands, and in the Sierra Madre del Sur of central Guerrero. One might expect to find the species in the uplands of eastern Guerrero and southern and western Oaxaca, but it has never been recorded there.

This large and handsome quail-dove is a resident of the highland cloud forests of Central America, from southern Mexico to Nicaragua. Its home is

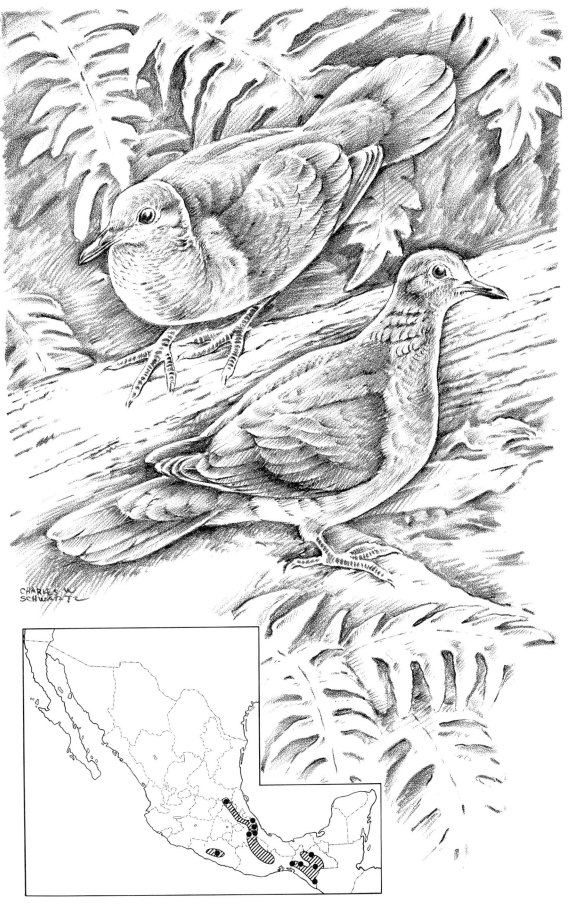

Fig. 119.   White-faced quail-dove, *Oreopelia albifacies*.

on the ground beneath the great stands of pine, oak, liquidambar, beech, and tree ferns, the larger trees draped with tropical vines and epiphytes such as bromeliads and orchids. In spite of the heavy canopy, the ground cover is often dense, making it difficult to see the shy quail-doves as they run along the ground or dodge in erratic flight low through the shrubs. In Mexico, white-faced quail-doves share their range with tree quails of the genus *Dendrortyx*.

I have found scarely any information on the life history of this bird. The best account, incomplete as it is, comes from the report on the birds of El Salvador by Dickey and Van Rossem (1938).

Of the call note, these authors state (p. 199): "Certain deep and very loud notes, which were heard at rare intervals in the cloud forest, were positively ascribed . . . to this species."

Nesting.—Possibly, like *Leptotila*, this species is a year-round breeder. On Cerro de los Naranjos on May 7, 1927, a female and a nearly grown juvenile were flushed from a well-concealed nest in a tangle of vines hanging from a tree in a steep-walled ravine in the forest. The young bird and the female were on the nest together, and there can be no question but that the older bird was the parent. On skinning her it was evident that an egg would have been laid within a few hours at most; in fact she was probably on the nest for that purpose at the time she was shot. The egg, which was creamy buff, was broken and there-fore not saved. This nest was about twenty feet from the ground and seemed to be supported only by looped and crossing vines. It was well concealed and was discovered only by accident. (*Ibid.*, p. 200.)

A series of 11 white-faced quail-doves collected by W. W. Brown near Omilteme, Guerrero, sheds some light on the breeding period in Mexico. A female taken February 18 had eggs in the oviduct, and a male taken July 16 had fully enlarged testes. A juvenile not long out of the nest was taken August 12. Breeding in this area therefore probably lasts at least from February to the end of July. Four males and four females taken between August 3 and December 20 were noted by Brown as having quiescent gonads or slight de-velopment. None of these were breeding; thus there seems to be a five-month period of sexual inactivity. I would suppose that courtship and pairing take place in January, leading up to February nesting.

The cloud forest near Omilteme was being actively logged when I camped there in 1944, and neither quail-doves nor tree quails were in the new slash. To find them one had to go some distance to undisturbed forest. I imagine that the status of these climax forest birds is being adversely affected by the continued penetration of the highland forest by logging operations. Hunting of quail-doves is too light to affect their numbers.

PART III

The Game and Fur-bearing Mammals

Introduction

Of the various kinds of mammals which occur on the mainland of Mexico, according to the *List of North American Recent Mammals* compiled by Miller and Kellogg (1955), I have treated, in the accounts that follow, 83 species under 51 headings. These include practically all the mammals larger than a cottontail and a few of the smaller ones—the tree squirrels and the weasel. Some of the species are clearly game animals, widely hunted for sport or food, such as the deer, armadillo, and bear. Others are strictly fur bearers, without much food or sport value, as for example the skunks and the beaver. Then there are some that have no apparent utility at all, such as the collared ant-eater and the porcupines. When I look back over my own selection of mammals to include in this book, I can see that the principal criterion was size. Because there are not many medium-sized to large mammals in Mexico, it is practicable to include them all. The volume therefore is a guide to all the Mexican mammals of any appreciable size, although it certainly is not a guide to all the birds.

Among the smaller mammals that I had to leave out are many important agricultural pests and some species that are taken in quantity for eating. In the list of pests excluded are many kinds of rats and mice and the vampire bats. Some of the rodents that locally are captured for eating are the ground squirrels, prairie dogs, gophers, and wood rats. Much as I regret omitting these groups, it seems a practical necessity of publication to do so.

In organizing the mammal accounts, it was deemed best to follow almost to the letter the taxonomic arrangement put forth in the new list of Miller and Kellogg. With a few minor exceptions, the sequence of presentation and the actual scientific names of orders, families, genera, and species conforms to that work. Although a great deal remains to be done in the classification of Mexican mammals, the Miller-Kellogg treatment comes nearer than any other to being definitive.

As stated in the Introduction, I have taken certain liberties in grouping species for simplicity of treatment, but this arrangement is not intended to have any taxonomic significance. When I discuss cottontails or tree squirrels or skunks as a group it does not mean that I think the animals making up the group are any more closely related than the cats or the mustelids that I discuss and figure individually. The criterion is merely one of convenience.

The characters used in identifying mammals are not the same as those used for birds; hence the treatment in both text and plates is a little different. The important criteria used in museums for mammal identification are not only the external appearance of the skin but also characters of the skull and certain measurements of the fresh animal taken before preservation. Thus a complete mammal specimen consists of the preserved skin (either stuffed or flat), the skull, and four standard measurements taken when the animal is freshly killed: *total length, length of tail, length of hind foot,* and *length of ear* measured from the notch (see fig. 120). The artist has depicted skulls on the plates, along with a view of the live animal. For present purposes I have recorded, instead of all four measurements, only average figures for length—

Fig. 120.   Measurements of a mammal.

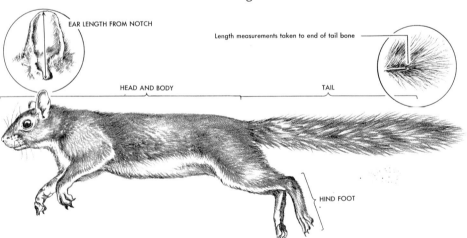

EAR LENGTH FROM NOTCH

Length measurements taken to end of tail bone

HEAD AND BODY

TAIL

HIND FOOT

head-and-body and tail length—which added together give the total length. Both sexes are included in these average figures for animals in which the sexual dimorphism is not very great. For the few species in which males are considerably larger than females, a range of measurements for each sex is given. The skull dimensions shown in the figures are taken from the particular skulls depicted by the artist and do not show any range of variation. These simplified measurements are usually enough to convey a general idea of size. Weights of the animals are given when available.

As for skulls, there are many diagnostic characters in shape, size, and proportions; foremost in importance perhaps are the teeth. Most mammals have four kinds of teeth: (1) incisors, which are the front cutting teeth; (2) canines, which tend to be long and sharp for piercing; (3) premolars; and (4) molars, which are the grinding teeth. The numbers and shapes of the individual teeth are highly diagnostic characters of identification; these are shown, in general silhouette at least, in the lateral views of the skulls. For some animals, additional details are given in enlarged drawings. In figure 121, a coyote skull, the teeth are labeled. It must be remembered that some young animals have milk teeth that are not quite the same as adults' teeth, and when they are in the midst of replacing their teeth the dental pattern is

Fig. 121.   Skull of a coyote, with teeth labeled.

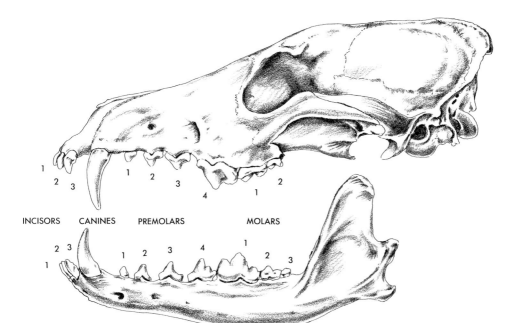

often odd. As the coyote grows up, all its teeth except the molars are replaced. Very old individuals often have badly worn or broken teeth. The condition of the teeth is actually the best criterion of age in most mammals, so a good deal of variation in appearance is to be expected.

The range maps, like the maps showing the ranges of birds, I drew with a knowledge of the animal's habitat requirements and with the map of vegetation types before me. If, for example, a species is known to frequent the pine-oak forest, I drew the lines of its probable range to conform roughly to this vegetation zone, even though my total number of known records of occurrence was limited. In other words, the range maps are based on more than merely the plotted specimen records.

Order Marsupialia

FAMILY DIDELPHIDAE

OPOSSUMS

The common opossum of Mexico and the principal marsupial of any consequence as a game animal is *Didelphis marsupialis*, a wide-ranging species that occurs from the northern United States southward to Peru. Formerly several specific names were applied to different segments of the population. In the United States the animal was called the Virginia opossum, *Didelphis virginiana;* in most parts of Mexico it was the Mexican opossum, *Didelphis mesamericana;* and farther south other names were applied. Now these populations are all recognized as being of a single species, *marsupialis,* the name first applied by Linnaeus in 1758.

Other opossums found in Mexico are *Caluromys derbianus*, the "woolly opossum," and *Philander opossum*, the "four-eyed opossum." These smaller animals, scarcely larger than a common rat, are of infrequent occurrence in the wet tropics and are not treated in this volume.

Common Opossum. *Didelphis marsupialis*

Other names.—Tlacuache; zorro; *Didelphis mesamericana; Didelphis virginiana; Didelphis yucatanensis.*

Description.—Size of a house cat, with a long, pointed nose and relatively short legs. Measurements: head and body—350 to 450 mm.; tail—325 to 400 mm. Ears short, rounded, and almost naked. Prehensile tail round and scaly, with only a scattering of fine hairs. General coloration grizzled, ranging almost to black in some specimens. Feet and legs and basal half of tail black. Females have a ventral pouch for carrying young.

Range in Mexico.—Tropical lowlands and foothills from northern Sonora and northeastern Coahuila south along both coasts to central and southern Mexico, where it includes valleys in the temperate uplands as well as the lowlands. The species has been recorded in river bottoms of southwestern Coahuila and may occur elsewhere in the central desert along watercourses. It has been introduced in California and by now may have spread into northern Baja California, but no actual specimens have been recorded there to date.

The Mexican opossum is a slow-witted, sluggish animal of unattractive appearance and uninspiring habit. It is in the main nocturnal and frequently may be seen at night shuffling across the highway or standing on the road shoulder, a picture of indecision, slowly turning its head and blinking beady eyes at the light. An occasional individual may venture abroad in daylight hours, and unless the animal escapes by climbing a tree it is an easy matter to overtake and capture it by the tail. Sometimes an opossum will feign resistance by snarling and hissing when caught, but at best it is a poor fighter. Often when captured it curls up and opens its mouth as though dead or asleep, and from this action is derived the common English expression "to play possum."

Opossums occupy dens in hollow trees, rock piles, or cliffs, or under stumps, logs, or buildings. They may even utilize ground holes dug by rabbits or armadillos, so long as these are dry. Each den usually is occupied by only one animal or by a female with her young. Opossums are unsociable among themselves, and adults are not often found together, except during the breeding season. Dens are lined with dry leaves or grass gathered and transported in the owner's prehensile tail. Apparently the feet and mouth are not used in carrying nest material.

The breeding season of the Mexican opossum is not well known, but it probably varies in different areas according to the timing of the rainy season. Villa (1953a) notes the possibility that Mexican opossums may bear two litters a year—one in early spring, the other in late summer. He found young in the pouch of a female on April 9, 1947, in the Valley of Mexico. There would have been time after weaning for this female to bear again the same summer. At El Batel, Sinaloa, in mid-October, 1946, we took two juvenile opossums estimated to be approximately three months old, which would place the breeding time in late June or early July, at the beginning of the summer rains.

The gestation period is only about thirteen days, and the young when born are little more than a centimeter in length and a tenth of a gram in weight.

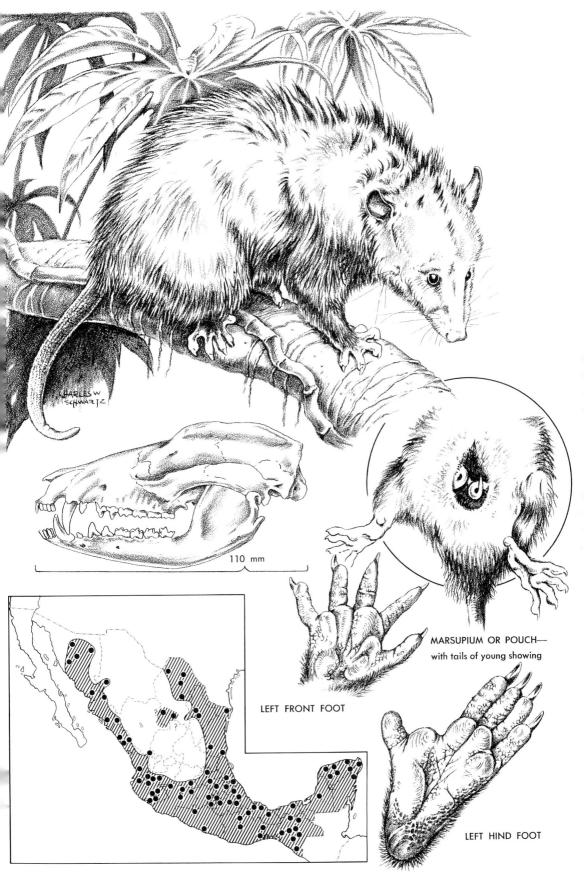

MARSUPIUM OR POUCH—
with tails of young showing

LEFT FRONT FOOT

LEFT HIND FOOT

Fig. 122. Opossum, *Didelphis marsupialis*.

They make their own way into the marsupial pouch, where each grasps a nipple and remains attached to it for about two months. Litters are usually 5 to 10 young but may consist of as many as 21. The maximum number of young that can be raised ordinarily is 13, which is the usual number of nipples in the pouch of the female. Litters of 14 have been recorded, but very rarely. After two months the young begin to venture from the pouch, and by three months they are weaned and leave the mother, to adopt the solitary habits which are characteristic of adults.

No figures on population density of Mexican opossums are available. The density reported by Lay (1942) for Texas is one opossum to four acres, which is undoubtedly higher than on most of the Mexican range. In only a few localities in Mexico did I see enough sign of opossums to make me consider the animals abundant as compared with populations in the southern part of the United States.

Opossums are omnivorous. Perhaps the bulk of their diet consists of insects and other invertebrates (Reynolds, 1945). They readily eat carrion and garbage when these are available. Sutton (1944) speaks of opossums paying nightly visits to his camp in southern Tamaulipas for the purpose of picking over the discarded scraps of food. The opossum is also well known as an egg thief, robbing the nests of wild birds as well as taking chicken eggs from the hen house. There is little evidence that the slow-moving opossum regularly captures wild vertebrates, but in a chicken house it sometimes does away with young poultry. Damage of this sort has given the species a reputation as a pest wherever it occurs near human habitations in Mexico.

Fruits and berries make up a large part of the diet. Gaumer (1917 : 14) mentions bananas, avocados, papayas, cherimoyas, annonas, and melons among the cultivated fruits taken by opossums in Yucatán. Figs and many other wild fruits are eaten as well.

In Mexico the opossum is little hunted for sport, but it often is killed for food by rural peoples. It is best taken with dogs and a flashlight at night. The fatty flesh is not particularly relished even by those who subsist mainly on beans and tortillas; but because it is easy to capture, the *tlacuache* is a readily available source of edible meat for those who have none better.

The fur of the opossum is used locally but has never had much commercial value. Yet the northern opossum is one of the most important fur bearers in the United States. Opossum fur from Mexico, coming mainly from tropical climates, is sparse and of poor quality as compared with that from the north.

Native peoples of various parts of Mexico have great faith in the medicinal properties of the opossum, particularly of the fat or grease and the tail. From the time of the Aztecs to the present day, ointments and potions have been concocted of these ingredients for the treatment of assorted ills.

Order Primates

FAMILY CEBIDAE

MONKEYS

There are two kinds of monkeys in Mexico—the large, heavy-bodied howler and the gay, slender little spider monkey. Both live in the heavy tropical forests and both are important game animals. Despite nominal legal protection, the monkeys are almost universally overhunted and their numbers are shrinking steadily. Clearing of the lowland forests does even more to decrease the population than hunting.

Howler Monkey. *Alouatta palliata*

Other names.—Saraguato; aullador; *Alouatta villosa; Mycetes villosus.*

Description.—Easily distinguished from the spider monkey by the larger head, long silky beard of adult males, a somewhat heavier and more compact build, and in the forest by the voice, which is so strong and loud that Gaumer (1917) compares it to that of a jaguar. Some individuals are glossy black, both dorsally and ventrally; others are dark reddish brown. Thumbs are present on forepaws. (Spider monkeys normally have only the four fingers.) Measurements: head and body—515 to 570 mm.; tail—560 to 630 mm.

Range in Mexico.—Rain forest and cloud forest from southern Veracruz and Chiapas eastward through the Yucatán Peninsula.

A traveler in the rain forest whose good fortune it is to meet a band of howler monkeys will not soon forget the experience. The sight of these agile fellows swinging through the tops of lofty mahoganies or zapotes is a true glimpse of the deep tropics, but even more impressive is the vocal accompaniment supplied by the monkeys themselves. A disturbance frequently will cause a band of howlers to begin their strenuous chorus, which Gaumer (1917 : 311) describes as follows. The old male who is leader of the band begins slowly a series of chesty roars, which gradually come with increased frequency and volume until the sound is almost continuous, without audible pause, and of astonishing power. Soon all other members of the band join in, and the sound is multiplied manyfold. The bedlam may last for several minutes. To conclude, the old leader slows down gradually to a series of shorter roars, and the other members follow suit. The echoes finally die away among the trees, leaving once more the characteristic silence of the rain forest.

The best general accounts of the home life of howler monkeys are those written by Gaumer, Carpenter (1934), and Alvarez del Toro (1952a). The following paragraphs are based in large part upon their reports.

Howlers are fairly common in the chicle forests of southeastern Mexico, although their range has been considerably restricted in recent years by clearing and settlement. They are found only in tall, virgin stands of forest, where they live virtually their whole lives in the treetops. A howler comes to the ground to drink only in the dry season, when succulent fruits are scarce. Normally these monkeys can find in the trees all the necessities of life. Water ordinarily is supplied in succulent food or by rain.

An average band is composed of from five to twenty-five individuals, of which about a quarter are adult males, about a half are adult females, and the rest are young individuals. The manner in which the sex ratio among adults becomes distorted is not known. Some adult males range alone, but they join small, organized bands from time to time. Within a band there is no strongly developed social hierarchy, according to Carpenter. The adult males, however, tend to lead the band in travel, in play, in flight from danger, and in the chorus.

Each band occupies a home range that may be as small as five hundred meters in diameter or as large as four kilometers. Carpenter found that bands in tall, dense forest had smaller ranges than those in less luxuriant vegetation. He further noted that the ranges of individual bands were more or less constant from year to year, changing very little. The home ranges of some bands were found to overlap, indicating that ranges are not necessarily defended from encroachment by adjoining groups (although Gaumer thought that they were).

The fruit of the chicle tree (Achras zapota) is a mainstay of diet, but the fruits, flowers, buds, and even leaves of many other trees are eaten seasonally. Carpenter lists fifty-six kinds of plants—nearly all trees—that provide food

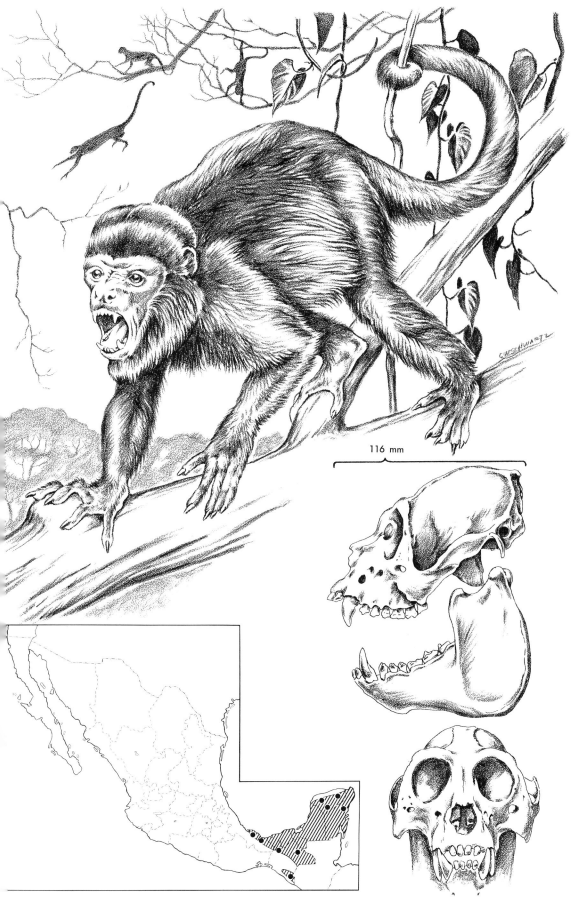

Fig. 123. Howler monkey, *Alouatta palliata*.

for the howlers of Barro Colorado Island, Panama. When the food supply diminishes or fails, a home range doubtless is abandoned.

Howlers sleep in the treetops, clinging to limbs with their feet and powerful tails. On cold nights a band may huddle together for warmth into an almost solid mass, high in the limbs of a tree. After the sun has warmed them they separate and set out foraging for the morning meal. When their hunger is satisfied, they loaf comfortably in the branches or play simple taglike games through the hot hours of the day. Another meal is eaten in the late afternoon. Frequently the howlers join in an evening "chorus" just before dark.

When disturbed during the day, howlers sometimes "freeze" in the branches and become virtually invisible among the leaves and epiphytic plants. When one member of a band is shot, the others usually scatter and hide. A wounded animal may hang by the tail for hours without dropping, even long after it is dead.

Adult females have one young, which clings to the mother through its period of infancy until it is strong enough to follow the band. The gestation period in this species is 139 days. Breeding presumably takes place at any time of year, for Alvarez del Toro speaks of seeing very young animals "from April to August and December."

As natural enemies, in addition to men, the howlers have the larger cats and the monkey-eating eagles such as the harpy. This great bird is rare in southern Mexico but it is said to live principally on monkeys.

Howlers are widely hunted by the native people of southern Mexico for the fine pelts and for the meat, which is considered quite palatable. The spider monkey is said to be superior in flavor, and for that reason it is subjected to even more persecution than the howler. In the conservation of both species, preservation of some of the native rain forest is fully as important as hunting control. Lumber interests will sooner or later find means of logging the mahogany and red cedar, and more of the forest is being cleared each year for agriculture. Although these trends are inevitable over much of the low tropics, it is nonetheless desirable to preserve some parts of the wilderness so that the fascinating virgin tropical flora and fauna will not disappear entirely. The howlers and tapirs are two game species that persist only in true wilderness. Even in 1917, Gaumer noted that forest clearing had eliminated howlers from the state of Yucatán, and since then a great area of the peninsula has been cleared.

Spider Monkey. *Ateles geoffroyi*

Other names.—Chango; mono; mono araña; *Ateles vellerosus.*

Description.—Slender of build, with long, gangling limbs, a relatively small head, and no beard on the males. Measurements: head and body—350 to 480 mm.; tail—750 to 830 mm. Reddish brown on back and sides, buff to almost

108 mm

Fig. 124. Spider Monkey, *Ateles geoffroyi*.

white on underparts. Thumbs on forepaws rudimentary or absent. Normal voice a noisy chattering or discordant screaming.

Range in Mexico.—Tropical evergreen forest, rain forest, and cloud forest, from southern Tamaulipas south along the Gulf coast to southeastern Mexico; an isolated colony along the coast of Jalisco recently reported by Villa.

The spider monkey is a familiar and interesting part of the fauna of wet tropical forests in eastern Mexico, but its existence on the west coast was unknown until in 1955 Bernardo Villa R. saw a group of eight to ten near the Bahía de Navidad in southwestern Jalisco. The extent of this western colony, at present or in the past, is not known.

Spider monkeys require a habitat of more or less continuous tropical forest, but they are much more tolerant of logging and partial clearing than the howlers. Howlers seem to disappear as soon as pristine conditions are disturbed; yet the spider monkeys persist even today in parts of Veracruz, Oaxaca, and Yucatán that have been inhabited by agricultural Indian populations for centuries. Second-growth timber, although not so desirable as virgin stands, will still sustain populations of this species.

The habits of the *chango*, as set forth by Gaumer (1917) and Wagner (1956) are not unlike those of the howler. Only in the treetops are the animals really at home. Their gait is clumsy on the ground, and they come down only for food or drink. When frightened, spider monkeys swing through the trees as rapidly as a man can run (Kellogg and Goldman, 1944), or, like the howlers, upon scattering they may hide in the leaves. A normal band is composed of 10 to 50 individuals. According to Wagner, small bands are family units; larger bands are aggregates of families. Each band has a definite home range (which Wagner calls a "territory"), but evidence of defense of the area is lacking. Wagner states that adjoining bands live in harmony. Although Gaumer refers to frequent fights and altercations that go on among these monkeys, he does not specify whether the fighting is among members of a band or between bands. Among the members of a band of spider monkeys, as in bands of howlers, there seems to be no well-defined social hierarchy. Adult males, however, tend to lead the band in most activities. When a group grows too large for the facilities offered by a given range, some of the individuals break off and form a new band, which must find its own range. Shortage of food is the usual cause of segmentation and migration of bands.

The females bear one young. Alvarez del Toro (1952a) states that young are born in February or March, but Gaumer and others express the opinion that they may be born at any time of year. Wagner noted more young in autumn than in other seasons. There probably is no set breeding period. Breeding among the adults is seemingly promiscuous. The gestation period is 139 days. The young monkey is carried by its mother during the period of infancy, clinging at first to her front as she moves about through the trees. After a few weeks the young one shifts to the mother's back.

Among the foods of spider monkeys in Mexico, Gaumer and Wagner list a variety of fruits, nuts, roots, grains, tender leaves, insects, eggs, and small vertebrates. Probably fruits are the most important foods in the normal diet. A band may form the habit of regularly visiting orchards or cornfields, which results in some damage to crops. Usually, however, there is so much hunting near farming communities that the monkeys are driven far back from the clearings.

Spider monkeys are considered highly palatable by most natives of southern Mexico, and hunting goes on almost the year round despite a nominally closed season from March 1 to October 31. In 1917 Gaumer expressed astonishment that a species hunted so heavily and seemingly so exposed to rifle shooting could persist in such large numbers. It seems likewise surprising today. Under persecution these monkeys become adept at fleeing or hiding at the slightest alarm, and shooting them is no longer a simple matter. However, as was true of the howlers, it is not hunting so much as clearing of the forest that brings permanent reduction in the range and numbers of spider monkeys. Although the spider monkeys are more tolerant of disturbance and partial cutting of the forest than the howlers, they still must have tall continuous forest in which to live. The constant clearing of tropical forests and overshooting may soon cause this interesting mammal to become rare.

Order Edentata

FAMILY MYRMECOPHAGIDAE

ANTEATERS

Two kinds of anteaters are found in Mexico—the large collared anteater and the squirrel-sized, two-toed anteater, *Cyclopes mexicanus.* Both are limited in distribution to the wet tropical forests of the southeast. Only the collared anteater is treated here. The small *Cyclopes* lives almost exclusively in the trees of the rain forest and is rarely seen. It is much too small and too scarce to have any significance as a game animal. If one is found it can be recognized readily by the golden-orange color with faint brown streaks on back and belly, and by the sharp, curved claws—two on the front feet, four on the rear. All records of *Cyclopes* in Mexico have come from the isthmus area, Tehuantepec to eastern Tabasco.

Collared Anteater. *Tamandua tetradactyla*

Other names.—Hormiguero; oso hormiguero; brazo fuerte; chupa miel; *Myrmecophaga tetradactyla.*

Description.—Size of a fox, with much elongated head, minute ears, and short, stubby legs. Measurements: head and body—575 to 630 mm.; tail—525 to 600 mm. Prehensile tail strong-muscled. Head, legs, and tail white. Body, including

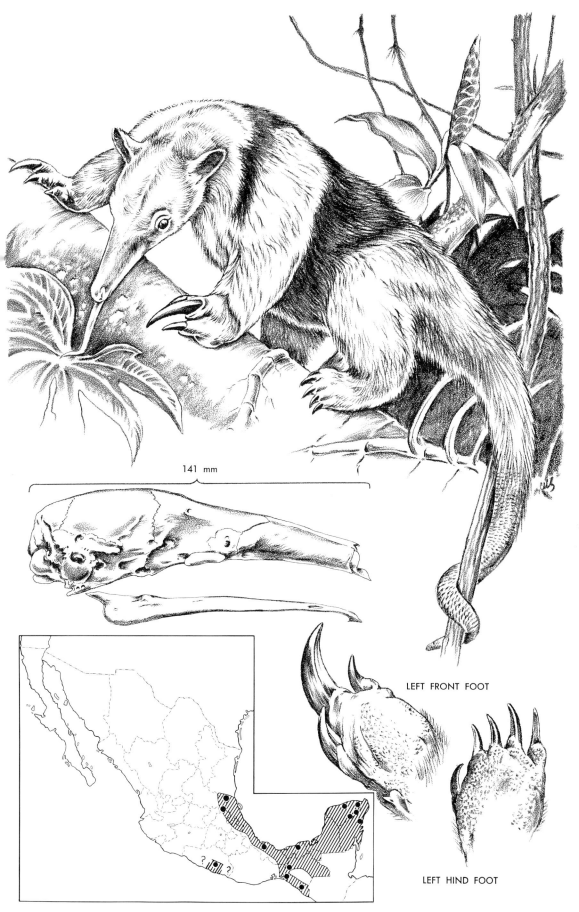

141 mm

LEFT FRONT FOOT

LEFT HIND FOOT

Fig. 125. Collared anteater, *Tamandua tetradactyla*.

collar round the base of the neck, black. Juveniles yellowish white all over, acquiring adult coloration when about three years of age.

Range in Mexico.—Rain forest and tropical evergreen forest from eastern San Luis Potosí and probably southern Tamaulipas south and east through the Isthmus of Tehuantepec and the Yucatán Peninsula. Davis and Lukens (1958) recently found this animal in the mountains of Guerrero. The extent of the western range is not known.

The striking, black-and-white, collared anteater is somewhat more common and more widely distributed in Mexico than the small two-toed anteater. Alvarez del Toro (1952a) states that it occurs in all parts of Chiapas except in the temperate uplands and that it is most often found in the mangrove swamps near the Mar Muerto. But being mainly arboreal, the collared anteater is not often seen. Its prehensile tail and sharp claws permit it to navigate through the high branches, slowly but with perfect sureness. The animal does come to the ground occasionally, but not often. Perhaps the difficulty of detecting anteaters in the dense foliage of the tropical forests makes them seem more scarce than they really are. When not feeding, they rest in the trees. Asleep on a high limb, the anteater is supported by the tail and hind feet, while the head is inclined on the chest and covered with the forefeet (Gaumer, 1917).

As the name implies, anteaters feed mostly on colonial insects, particularly termites and ants that live in the trees. They obtain the insects by tearing open nest chambers with the powerful forefeet and then licking up the swarms that rush out to defend the colony. The name *chupa miel* (honeysucker) is a misnomer, derived possibly from the tubelike appearance of the mouth. The collared anteater is not known to feed on honey regularly, although at times it may do so. Insects are its main fare. Because of the specialized diet, these toothless animals are difficult to keep alive in captivity. Apparently nothing is known of their breeding biology.

Ordinarily, the collared anteater is a shy and peaceful animal, but if attacked it is quite capable of protecting itself. When cornered on the ground, it rears on its hind legs like a bear and fights with its powerful forefeet and claws. In such a situation it can seriously injure a dog or even a man.

The animal has a strong odor, which apparently affects the flavor of the flesh, for it is said to be completely unpalatable. The fur is coarse and of little value.

FAMILY DASYPODIDAE

ARMADILLOS

Armadillos are primitive, armored mammals without incisor, premolar, or canine teeth. Their dentition consists of simple, peg-shaped molars which lack roots or enamel. The armadillos are related to the anteaters and sloths. Several species occur in South America; but the only North American species is the nine-banded armadillo (*Dasypus novemcinctus*), which is widely distributed in Mexico and is an important game animal.

Nine-banded Armadillo. *Dasypus novemcinctus*

Other names.—Armadillo; armado; mulita, ayotochtli.

Description.—Size of a house cat or a small dog. Enclosed in a tough coat of armor plate which is flexible by reason of nine joints, or rings, round the midsection. (The species derives its name from these rings.) Armor over shoulders and foreparts, and over rump, fused into solid, scarcely flexible plates. A small plate covers the forehead. Even the tapering tail is enclosed in armored rings. Armor blackish dorsally, with dull white spots on sides where individual scales are worn down; dull white ventrally. Measurements: head and body—260 to 490 mm.; tail—240 to 380 mm. Weight: 3 to 7 kg.

Range in Mexico.—Tropical zones from southern Sonora and eastern Coahuila south along both coasts to Michoacán and Puebla, from which point south the species occurs in the uplands as well as on coastal plains.

Armadillos are insect-eating ground dwellers, whose peculiar attributes are external armor and an ability to dig. They occur in greatest density in fairly dry regions of warm climate and soft, diggable soil. Since they have no fur they cannot withstand freezing temperatures and so do not penetrate far into the temperate uplands. Drinking water seems to be requisite; the desert proper therefore is not armadillo habitat; but too much water in the burrows will drown out the animals. In view of these several limitations, the best areas of armadillo range in Mexico are the well-drained coastal plains and the tip of the Yucatán Peninsula. The highest populations found during the survey were in Sinaloa, Nayarit, and southern Veracruz.

A good general account of armadillo ecology and life history is that of Taber (1945), who studied the animal in southern Texas. The following paragraphs are based in large part on his work.

Armadillos live in underground dens, which they excavate with their powerful front feet. Each animal may have four or more dens, in one of which is the home nest. The others are used as escape burrows, or perhaps as food traps. The nest consists of a bushel or so of dry grass or leaves, which the animal carries, with a "jackknife" hold under the belly, into the previously constructed chamber. The armadillo backs down the burrow, retaining its load of vegetation tucked up under the arched ventral surface between fore and hind feet. In this nest the animal rests during daylight hours in warm weather, and at night in cold weather. The young are born and reared in such a nest until they are old enough to venture forth into the world.

The movements and gait of the armadillo are generally slow, as a result, I suppose, of the inhibiting and unyielding armor carried on the back. In the open a man can easily run down and capture one, but in underbrush these

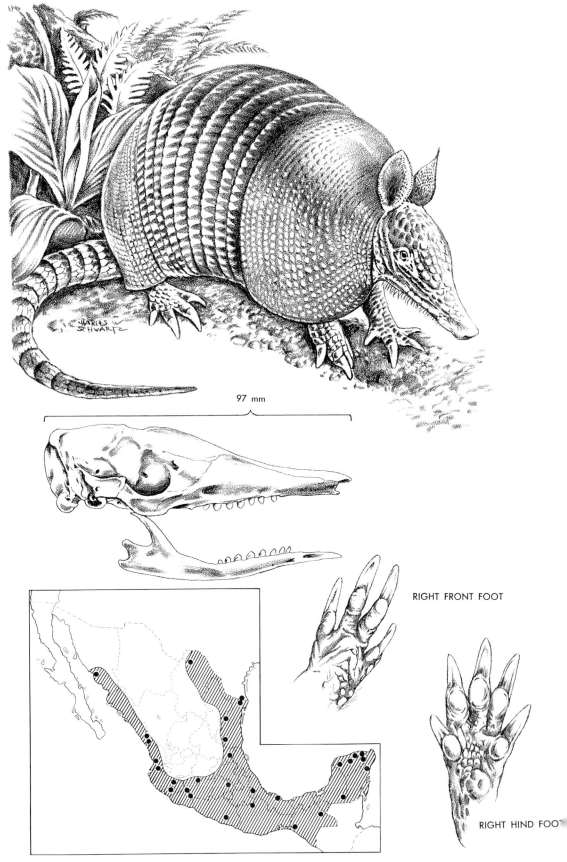

97 mm

RIGHT FRONT FOOT

RIGHT HIND FOOT

Fig. 126.   Armadillo, *Dasypus novemcinctus*.

animals are not readily overtaken. One night in our camp near El Batel, Sinaloa, an adult armadillo wandered into our tent where we were writing notes by lamplight. Two of us lunged after it with flashlights, but the animal scampered through the brush with such agility that it soon outdistanced us.

Taber estimates that 90 per cent of the normal diet of armadillos consists of insects. In captivity he taught several animals to eat mash, dead chickens, and some plant foods, but they required several days to learn. In foraging for insects, armadillos root through the leaf litter or under clumps of grass or herbs, locating their prey chiefly by smell. Their eyesight is poor, and their

Fig. 127.   Portrait of an armadillo, by Paul J. Fair.

hearing is not much better. Taber (p. 223) describes the method of foraging as follows:

> In soil of average diggability the nose is pushed into the surface litter as far as possible and when an insect is detected, a conical hole is quickly dug by short, alternate strokes of the forefeet. With each thrust of the feet, the nose is pushed deeper into the soil, not once being lifted from the probe while digging is in progress. . . .
> Their ability to locate insects beneath 5 or 6 inches of soil is uncanny. I have watched an armadillo shuffle quickly across the forest floor with its nose ploughing a furrow through the litter down to mineral soil. A sudden halt and sniff initiated a probe resulting in the capture of a beetle larva. Hesitating only sufficiently long to crush and swallow the grub, the animal continued its ploughing.

The feces are spherical, about the size of a marble, and consist of mud encrusted with the chitinous parts of insects. The mud probably is ingested unintentionally along with the ground-dwelling insects.

In Texas, breeding occurs in late summer or early fall, the young being born in February, March, or April. Villa (1953a) reports approximately the same breeding period in the Valley of Mexico. The fertilized egg starts to develop 14 weeks after mating, and subsequent development of the young requires about 120 days before they are born. A litter normally consists of 4 identical young of the same sex. This peculiar situation results from the fact that a single egg divides into 4 cells, each of which becomes an embryo. Young armadillos are suckled by the mother for some weeks before they learn to capture and eat insects. After weaning, the young become solitary in habit like their parents.

Estimates of population density are given by Taber. He calculated that in several counties of the best armadillo range in Texas there was one armadillo to 3 acres. In one small area he found 2 animals per acre, but such high populations are localized. Over most of the Texas range the density was one animal per 10 to 50 acres, which is perhaps the degree of abundance that would be found over most of the Mexican range.

When attacked by a predator an armadillo will try to reach the safety of a burrow. It cannot depend on its armor plating. This protection probably suffices against small predators and raptorial birds, but coyotes, dogs, and the larger cats can easily tear away the plates and reach the tender flesh. Besides limitations imposed by the environment (food, places for burrows, and water), predation perhaps is a factor in holding down populations.

The flesh of the armadillo is delicious, and the animal is hunted everywhere throughout its range. In Mexico most armadillo hunting is done at night with flashlight and shotgun, but the animals are sometimes hunted with dogs or are dug out of their burrows with a shovel and machete. It is virtually impossible to cut the armor with ordinary tools, but the animal can be dressed from the ventral side by cutting away the flesh from the shell, just as must be done in dressing a turtle. The meat is white and tastes much like tender pork. The shell, or carapace, occasionally is made into a basket, a tray, or a woman's handbag.

Overhunting may be an important limitation on populations in some areas because of the low breeding potential of the species, but since capturing an armadillo involves a good deal of work, hunting is not usually an important cause of scarcity. Conservation is chiefly a matter of preserving the environment from overgrazing, erosion, or inundation by floods.

Order Lagomorpha

FAMILY LEPORIDAE

Hares and Rabbits

Hares and rabbits are the most abundant game mammals in Mexico. Under some conditions they may even become so numerous as to inflict severe damage on cultivated crops and range forage. However, they are widely hunted all over Mexico for food and sport, and their importance as food alone generally outweighs the damage done to crops.

Jackrabbits (hares) of the genus *Lepus* occur mostly in the arid temperate zones of northern and central Mexico where the ground vegetation is sparse. All forms of *Lepus* are commonly called *liebres,* an appropriate and distinctive name which differentiates them from the cottontails of the genus *Sylvilagus,* which are known as *conejos.* One or another species of cottontail occupies every part of Mexico, and in places the ranges of two and even three species overlap.

There are several essential differences in habit between jackrabbits and cottontails. Jackrabbits live in "forms" on the surface of the ground, and the young are born fully furred and with their eyes open. Cottontails live in underground burrows and bring forth their young naked with eyes still closed. Although some species of cottontails use surface forms, or "hides," all make use of burrows to some extent for escape from their natural enemies. Jack-rabbits rarely if ever enter burrows.

The little volcano rabbit, *Romerolagus diazi*, is an aberrant form, closely related to the cottontails but still quite distinct. It is confined to stands of coarse grass on the volcanoes surrounding the Valley of Mexico.

Figure 128 shows on one plate the various hares and rabbits of Mexico.

White-sided Jackrabbits. *Lepus callotis* and Related Species

Other names.—Liebre torda; liebre.

Species included here.—*Lepus callotis, L. alleni, L. gaillardi,* and *L. flavigularis.*

Description.—Large hares, dorsally light gray or grayish buff, with whitish underparts and large white patches on flanks. Ear tips edged with white. (Black-tailed jackrabbits have black-tipped ears.) Tail shorter than that of black-tailed jack. Measurements: head and body—470 to 525 mm.; tail—60 to 75 mm.

In the field the white-sided jackrabbits have a habit of "flashing" the white flanks, as will be described later.

Range in Mexico.—Along both sides of the Sierra Madre Occidental, from Sonora and Chihuahua to Jalisco, thence across the southern reaches of the central uplands to Puebla and northern Oaxaca. There is an isolated population on the Isthmus of Tehuantepec.

Mexican hares of the genus *Lepus* are divided into two main types, or species groups, by Nelson (1909) in his monograph on the American Leporidae. I shall discuss black-tailed jackrabbits in the next chapter. The white-sided jackrabbits under consideration here include the four closely related species listed above. Since the ranges of these species are geographically complementary, without any overlap of occurrence, it is possible that additional collecting may demonstrate intergradation between the "species," in which case they would become subspecies or geographic races of *Lepus callotis,* the earliest named of the four "species." Nelson calls these jackrabbits collectively the *Lepus callotis* group. Whether the various segments of the population are called distinct species or merely subspecies is relatively unimportant to us here.

White-sided jackrabbits range for the most part in semiarid zones supporting a fairly dense ground vegetation—particularly mesquite-grassland and thorn forest. Only in western Sonora does *L. callotis* occur on true desert, and even there it frequents brushy watercourses rather than the bare desert plains. Through the pine-oak belt from Jalisco to Puebla, this animal lives in the grass and brush of open valleys and basins, not in the forest proper. In contrast, the black-tailed jackrabbits prefer the sparse vegetation of open desert or heavily grazed plains.

White-sided jacks are common in the mesquite-grassland of Sonora and the thorn forest of Sinaloa. Along the highway from Nogales to Hermosillo, Sonora, we saw dozens of these handsome hares in the fall of 1946, in the

EASTERN COTTONTAIL

AUDUBON COTTONTAIL

BRUSH RABBIT

MEXICAN COTTONTAIL

VOLCANO RABBIT

TROPICAL FOREST RABBIT

BLACK-TAILED JACKRABBIT

WHITE-SIDED JACKRABBIT

Fig. 128.   The hares and rabbits of Mexico.

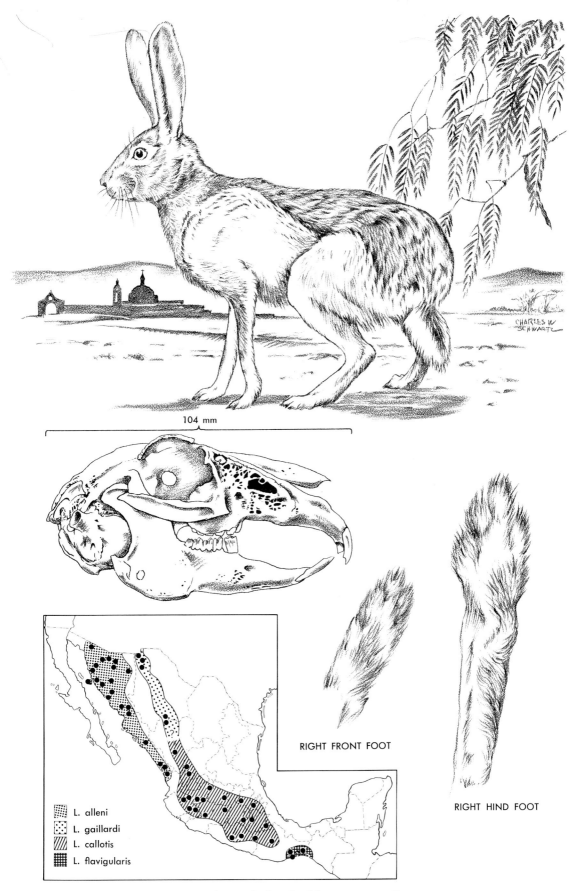

104 mm

L. alleni
L. gaillardi
L. callotis
L. flavigularis

RIGHT FRONT FOOT

RIGHT HIND FOOT

Fig. 129. White-sided jackrabbit, *Lepus callotis*. Range map
shows distribution of this and other species of
white-sided jackrabbits in Mexico.

late afternoon and early evening when they came out to feed. They are less numerous in the uplands of central Mexico.

During the heat of the day, white-sided jackrabbits rest in "forms," which are no more than pockets in the grass shaped to fit the body of the animal in its hunched resting position. The vegetation offers concealment and some-times shade. Each rabbit has several forms, some facing the sun for use in cold weather, others in the shade for summer use. During the day, the animal will crouch in the hiding place until closely approached, whereupon it darts forth and makes its escape by running away over the plains. Speed is the jack-rabbit's only protection against pursuit by predators.

Jackrabbits have many natural enemies. Coyotes, foxes, bobcats, and the larger hawks and owls are perhaps the main ones in Mexico. In a straight chase, jackrabbits can outrun any of the mammalian carnivores named above; but many rabbits are surprised and pounced upon before a chase can develop. Also, coyotes are said to wear down jackrabbits by relay pursuit; that is, by taking turns in the chase. The breeding potential of rabbits is so high, how-ever, that populations can withstand heavy predation—and likewise heavy hunting—without reduction in actual density.

Jackrabbits have 2 to 4 young in a litter. They may have several litters a year, since the gestation period is only six weeks and the young are weaned a few weeks after birth. The number of young per litter and the number of litters per year probably are correlated with the food supply, reproduction being most successful when the parent rabbits are getting plenty of succulent food. The young are born in a nest hollowed out of the ground under a pro-tective bush or grass clump, and the mother covers them with a blanket of fur plucked from her own coat. Young jackrabbits have short ears like those of cottontails, but in a few weeks the ears grow to the proper size for hares.

One of the most distinctive actions of this animal is the "flashing" of the white side patches, described as follows by Nelson (1909 : 115).

By means of muscles the skin of either side can be drawn over the back at will. In this manner the buffy or brown dorsal area is shifted more or less completely to one side and the white on the opposite side is drawn nearly or quite to the median line. This habit has been observed when the rabbits were standing, or moving along at moderate speed, usually after they had been driven from their forms. This enlargement of the white area is always on the side turned toward the chance intruder, and accordingly alternates from side to side as the animal slowly zigzags away. In the bright sunlight the snowy white side flashes bril-liantly, attracting attention from afar, and affording a fine example of directive coloration. In the case of *L. flavigularis* I had the opportunity on several occasions of observing this display within 20 yards, and in that of *L. callotis* at a some-what greater distance. One individual of *flavigularis* hopped slowly from its form, not 10 yards away, as I rode by on horseback, and, standing broadside, shifted the buffy dorsal area over, at the same time slowly drawing the white area up like a curtain until the side toward me was pure white, except a narrow buffy line along the top of the back. The rabbit then hopped slowly along in the direction I was riding, but gradually moved farther away, keeping the white area in the same position until it had traveled 50 or 60 yards, when the color areas slowly resumed their normal positions. I have seen *callotis* zigzag along, changing its course every 10 or 15 yards, and each time it turned it flashed the white on the side toward me. I am inclined to think this flashing of the white is most frequent during the rutting time.

There are undoubtedly more rabbits killed for food in Mexico than any other type of game mammal. Most of these are shot or trapped for home consumption, but in the past, many thousands were sold in the markets. In any of the large cities, and in many smaller villages, it was common to see strings of freshly killed jackrabbits or cottontails for sale on the meat counter. Inadequate refrigeration made it difficult to ship the animals long distances or hold them for extended periods after they were killed. Most of the rabbits were sold locally within a day or so after they were taken. On the streets of Mexico City I talked one morning to a resident of southern Hidalgo who was peddling a string of about a dozen white-sided jackrabbits that had been killed the day before near Pachuca. He had brought them to the city in a truck during the night and was asking six to nine pesos apiece for them, the larger ones bringing the highest price. The animals had been killed with shot-guns by two men hunting together. Market hunting is now illegal, although some of it still goes on.

Most of the rabbits killed in Mexico, however, have always been eaten by the families of the hunters rather than offered for sale on the market. It is impossible to estimate the number of animals so utilized each year, but it must be in the millions.

In addition to being hunted for food, both jackrabbits and cottontails are often shot for sport, as described by López and López (1911). Especially near the larger cities of Mexico, where most kinds of game are scarce, hares and rabbits are attracting much of the attention of sportsmen.

On the red side of the ledger, jackrabbits and to a lesser extent cottontails, when they become too abundant, cause a good deal of damage to cultivated crops, orchards, vineyards, and livestock range. The food habits of all the Leporidae are more or less similar in that the animals prefer the tender green parts of growing plants, or, when greens are not available, the bark and twigs of various shrubs and trees. In arid regions, crops are grown through the dry season of the year by irrigation, and jackrabbits in particular will come down from the hills to live exclusively on alfalfa and other green crops when no greens are available elsewhere. When there are many rabbits, the loss to the farmer may be considerable. Under other circumstances the animals turn to the bark of young fruit trees or grapevines, often killing the plants by girdling them. On range lands, irruptive outbreaks of jackrabbits may result in serious depletion of available forage for stock. In all of these situations local control of the rabbit populations may be necessary.

Black-tailed Jackrabbit. *Lepus californicus*

Other names.—Liebre de cola negra; liebre.

Description.—Approximately the same size as the white-sided jackrabbit but brown dorsally, with buffy underparts (no gray or pure white). Back of ear tips and margins of ears black. Tail relatively long, black above, buffy brown below. Measurements: head and body—450 to 500 mm., tail—75 to 95 mm.

Range in Mexico.—Throughout Baja California, northern and western Sonora, and central desert from Chihuahua and northern Tamaulipas south to Hidalgo.

Black-tailed jackrabbits in Mexico are almost entirely desert dwellers. They often are found in abundance on the most desolate stretches of cactus desert or on adjoining mesquite-grasslands that have been so overgrazed that the ground is almost bare. Even a sparse ground cover of grama grass seems to suppress populations of this species on range lands.

Black-tailed jackrabbits are similar to the white-sided species in their general life history, except that they prefer more open cover. However, the black-tailed species is often higher in population density, and it is considered the most noxious of rabbit pests. When abundant it can cause untold damage to crops and range, and in both the United States and Mexico considerable effort is expended annually to reduce the populations.

On open range, cattlemen frequently complain that black-tailed jackrabbits eat much of the forage needed for livestock. The overgrazed condition of the range is blamed in large part on the rabbits. To be sure, an abundance of rabbits can be a plague on range lands, but this very abundance is usually a *result* of overgrazing by stock rather than the primary *cause* of the range depletion. Well-managed grama grass ranges on which a more or less continuous sod is preserved do not support high populations of black-tailed jackrabbits. This was demonstrated in southern Arizona where populations on heavily grazed and on lightly grazed ranges were compared; the highest densities of jackrabbits were found invariably on the overgrazed range (Taylor, Vorhies, and Lister, 1935).

Damage to agricultural crops usually occurs in irrigated valleys adjoined by overgrazed pasture or range. The rabbit population first becomes high on the bare hills, and then the animals invade the cultivated lands to eat the green alfalfa or other highly palatable crops.

Good range management, in other words, is usually the key to control of this species of jackrabbit. Shooting, poisoning, and encouraging natural predators may help to hold down numbers, but sudden large increases in population can be prevented only by environmental control.

Although often a pest, the black-tailed jackrabbit is still a game animal of some consequence. On the central and northern plains many sportsmen hunt this species with enthusiasm, for sport as well as for food. There is a good deal of such hunting near Monterrey, for example.

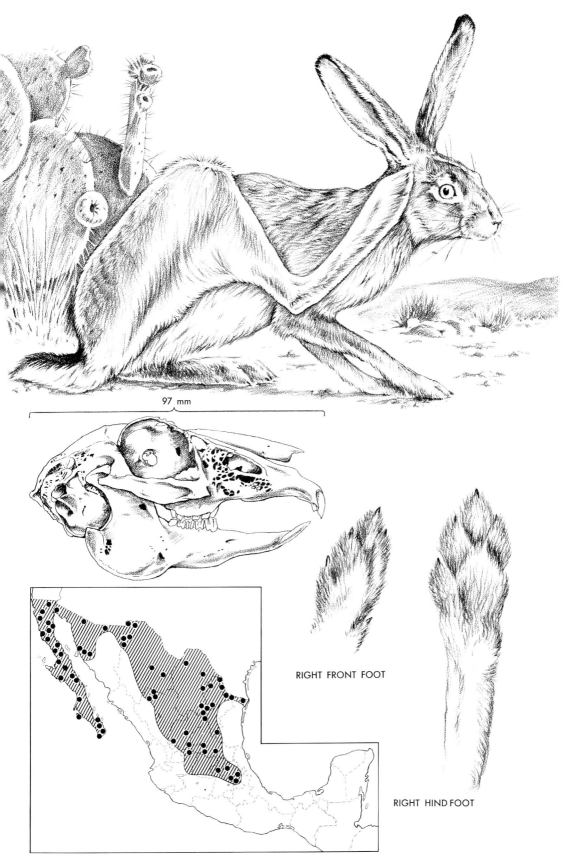

97 mm

RIGHT FRONT FOOT

RIGHT HIND FOOT

Fig. 130. Black-tailed jackrabbit, *Lepus californicus*.

At some seasons of the year the black-tailed jacks are infested with "warbles"—the larvae of a species of parastic fly. The warbles, which are deposited just under the skin, develop into good-sized worms, often in the neck region, but occasionally in other areas of the body. Although worms are not dangerous in any way, their presence tends to discourage hunters from eating the hares.

Cottontail Rabbits. *Sylvilagus floridanus* and Related Species

Other names.—Conejo; conejo de Castilla; conejo castellano; conejo serrano; conejo de monte.

Species included here.—Sylvilagus floridanus, S. audubonii, S. cunicularius, S. bachmani, and S. brasiliensis.

Description.—The five clearly distinct species of cottontails in Mexico vary somewhat in size and slightly in color but all are rather similar in appearance. Only one, *Sylvilagus floridanus*, is illustrated here with a full plate; the rest are shown in relative size and proportion in figure 128. Cottontails are smaller than hares of the genus *Lepus* and have shorter ears and legs. But since the Mexican cottontail (*Sylvilagus cunicularius*) is virtually as large as a small jackrabbit, size cannot always be relied upon as a criterion of identification. All the *Sylvilagus* rabbits have short, fluffy tails, like little powder puffs, usually white, but gray or buff in some species. Hares have longer, pointed tails (see fig. 128).

Eastern cottontail (*Sylvilagus floridanus*): Medium-sized, buffy brown dorsally, white beneath, with a reddish brown patch on back of head; reddish legs ordinarily brighter than in other cottontails. Center of distribution the pine-oak zone in most parts of Mexico, but range extends into the tropics in the southeast.

Audubon cottontail (*Sylvilagus audubonii*): Small; inhabits open, arid lands. Usually pale brownish gray with dull reddish brown on back of head and on legs.

Brush rabbit (*Sylvilagus bachmani*): Small, with a very small tail. Brown, with scarcely any reddish color on head or legs. In Mexico this rabbit lives only in Baja California, where it frequents dense thickets of chaparral or cactus.

Mexican cottontail (*Sylvilagus cunicularius*): Very large; size alone is enough to differentiate *cunicularius* from other members of the genus. Ranges throughout semiarid tropics in central and southern Mexico, extending into the pine-oak zone in some places.

Tropical forest rabbit (*Sylvilagus brasiliensis*): Medium-sized, with short ears and extremely small, buff tail. Dark brown with a good deal of reddish color on legs and head. This species frequents the humid tropical forests of southeastern Mexico.

The brief general descriptions, and the weights and measurements given in table 14, are not enough really to distinguish between the species. Even in a museum where comparative material is available, reference must be made to various characters of the skull to identify a cottontail with certainty. Peculiarities of the skull and skeleton are described by Nelson (1909) but are not repeated here. It is therefore advisable for sure identification to submit a specimen to some properly equipped museum, such as the Instituto de Biología in México, D.F.

Ranges in Mexico.—Shown on maps in figures 131, 132, and 133. One or more species of the genus *Sylvilagus* are found in every part of the Republic.

TABLE 14

MEASUREMENTS AND WEIGHTS OF THE COTTONTAILS

Species	Head and body (mm.)	Tail (mm.)	Hind foot (mm.)	Ear from notch (mm.)	Average weight (gm.)
Eastern cottontail (*Sylvilagus floridanus*)	350–400	40–55	89–104	50–67	900–1,000
Audubon cottontail (*S. audubonii*)	300–330	50–65	75–85	55–65	750–800
Brush rabbit (*S. bachmani*)	280–300	30–40	70–75	55–63	600–700
Mexican cottontail (*S. cunicularius*)	430–445	51–67	95–110	70–75	1,800–2,300
Tropical forest rabbit (*S. brasiliensis*)	360–400	10–20	70–75	45–50	No data

Each of the five species of Mexican cottontails has its own peculiar requirements of habitat. Two are definitely forest species—the eastern cottontail, predominantly of the pine-oak zone, and the tropical forest rabbit of the humid southeast. The Audubon cottontail is strictly a resident of desert and open, arid grassland. The other two are brushland species—the brush rabbit living in the chaparral and cactus thickets of Baja California, the Mexican cottontail in the semiarid thorn forest and tropical deciduous forest. All, however, depend on a certain amount of grass or weed ground cover. Excessive livestock grazing that leaves the ground bare will drive out the cottontails more surely than hunting, predators, or anything else. It may be said, then, that cottontail populations usually are pretty much in inverse proportion to livestock populations. This, it will be recalled is quite the converse of the situation in black-tailed jackrabbits; that species thrives on overgrazed ranges.

Ground cover is needed by cottontails for protection from predators. These smaller and less fleet rabbits also take shelter, at least part of the time, in underground burrows, which they usually acquire by appropriating abandoned homes of skunks, armadillos, or other diggers. They spend much time above ground feeding, however, and in fair weather may live outside entirely, spending their days in surface forms like those of the jackrabbits. But several ground holes are always maintained by each cottontail for escape from enemies and for use in inclement weather.

A cottontail has a "home range" on which all its activities are centered. Studies of marked cottontails indicate that home ranges are surprisingly small —rarely more than a few hundred yards in diameter. The ranges of several rabbits may overlap, but each animal maintains its own personal forms and burrows. When pursued by a dog or a predator, a cottontail will tend to follow a circular course, staying if possible within the bounds of its own home range.

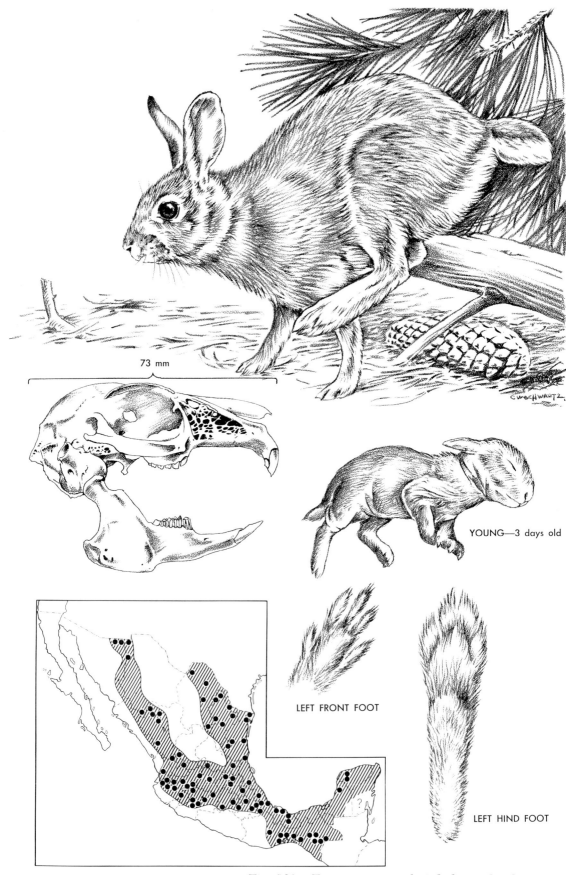

73 mm

YOUNG—3 days old

LEFT FRONT FOOT

LEFT HIND FOOT

Fig. 131. Eastern cottontail, *Sylvilagus floridanus*.

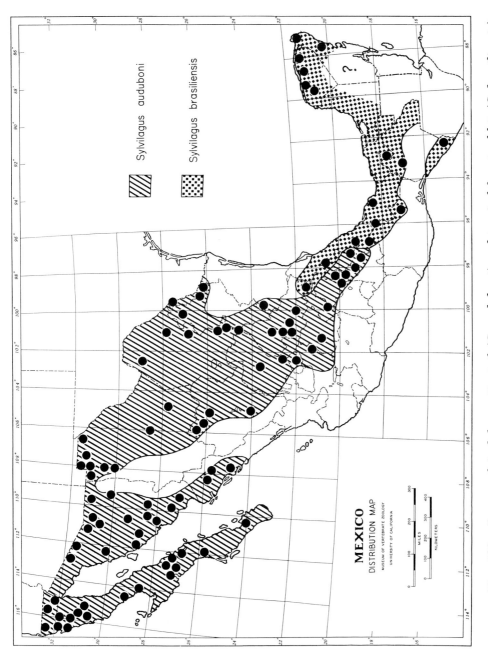

Fig. 132. Ranges of Audubon cottontail (*S. auduboni*) and tropical forest rabbit (*S. brasiliensis*).

Sylvilagus auduboni

Sylvilagus brasiliensis

MEXICO
DISTRIBUTION MAP

MUSEUM OF VERTEBRATE ZOOLOGY
UNIVERSITY OF CALIFORNIA

MILES

KILOMETERS

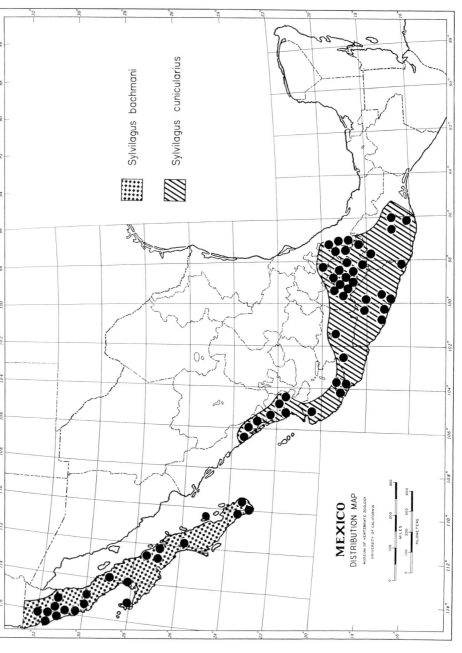

Fig. 133. Ranges of the brush rabbit (*S. bachmani*) and the Mexican cottontail (*S. cunicularius*).

This habit is well known to hunters, who encourage their hounds to trail the rabbit while they wait at the point from which the chase started, knowing that the rabbit will soon circle back. If pursued too closely it will dodge into one of its burrows.

Cottontails are preyed upon by many more predators than are the jackrabbits, because of their smaller size and because they occur in a wider variety of habitats—particularly the tropical forests. Several dozen species of canids, mustelids, cats, owls, hawks, and snakes levy upon their populations. Studies of population turnover of cottontails have shown that a young one has about one chance in twenty of attaining the age of one year. The high death rate is matched by an equally high reproductive rate. Gestation is about a month. Litters are usually 4 to 6 young, and if food conditions are good, a female may have 4 or 5 litters a year.

One of the puzzling phenomena of rabbit populations is the violent fluctuation of numbers that occurs in all species from time to time. In the northern United States the periodic highs and lows in numbers of cottontails come at fairly regular ten-year intervals, and game managers have come to expect these cyclic changes. But in the southern United States and throughout Mexico the fluctuations are usually irregular both as to the time and the place of occurrence. In any given year, the jackrabbits may be high in one area and low a few miles away, while cottontails show an entirely different population pattern. For example, in 1946 I found cottontails scarce near Hipólito, Coahuila, and abundant at San Juan, Durango, whereas the black-tailed jackrabbit population was higher at Hipólito than at San Juan. Both localities are in the central desert about a hundred miles apart, and habitat conditions appeared to me to be very similar. A few years hence, the situations of these local populations may well be reversed.

Gaumer (1917 : 152) makes some interesting statements in regard to the abundance of rabbits over a period of years near Mérida, Yucatán. Although his definition of the species of cottontails does not conform with modern taxonomic nomenclature, he makes it clear that a cottontail which he calls *Lepus yucatanicus* (actually *Sylvilagus floridanus*) was rare in the vicinity of Mérida in 1878, whereas in 1917 the species was an abundant article of commerce, sold in all the markets of Yucatán. In 1945 I hunted for two weeks in central Yucatán without seeing a single cottontail of any type. Gaumer's statement of the abundance of these rabbits in 1917 just before his book was published would suggest a cyclic or irruptive "high," and their scarcity in 1878 and 1945 would correspond to population depressions, or "lows." Whether it has any bearing on the matter or not, it is interesting to note that 1913 to 1915 were high years in the northern ten-year rabbit cycle and 1945 was a low year. Unfortunately, I have no other evidence of fluctuation in the populations of this species elsewhere in its Mexican range.

Environmental conditions, of course, affect rabbit densities. Cottontails usually do best in habitat that is not denuded by livestock. In the highlands of Michoacán, eastern cottontails are numerous on the rough, unwatered and hence ungrazable volcanic cones, and very scarce on the heavily grazed gentler slopes. At Poliutla, Guerrero, we found the Mexican cottontail (*S. cunicularius*) common in the heavy grass and weeds around fenced milpas but absent from overgrazed pasture outside the milpa fences (see fig. 30). The highest populations of Audubon cottontails found during the survey were near Pitahaya, Sonora, and San Juan, Durango, both areas well grown with grama grass and lightly grazed.

Although I shall not attempt to explain exactly the cause-and-effect relationships of these several examples, I can safely say that grazing and other kinds of land use are closely associated with the ups and downs in rabbit numbers. Additional population phenomena, such as those which control the northern rabbits in their regular periodic cycles, may be involved as well.

Jackrabbit and cottontail populations can withstand heavy shooting without appreciable reduction in density. In southwestern Missouri a quarter of a million rabbits a year are put on the market without in any degree lowering the general level of the population below that of surrounding areas. Recent studies in California have shown that predators in one year may remove from a cottontail population many more animals than can be found on the ground at any one time. As mentioned above, under favorable environmental conditions the rate of reproduction is so rapid as to sustain the local populations in spite of very heavy drains on them. In Mexico, therefore, hunting is not to be construed as a cause of rabbit shortages. Rabbit hunting should be widely encouraged so as to make maximum use of this abundant and prolific source of human food.

Volcano Rabbit. *Romerolagus diazi*

Other names.—Zacatuche; teporingo; tepolito; conejo de los volcanes.

Description.—Utterly unlike any other member of the Leporidae in Mexico. Fur uniformly dark brown on back, dark brownish gray below. Ears short (40 to 44 mm.) and rounded, legs and feet short. No visible tail. This rabbit lives in burrows and uses well-defined runways in heavy grass. Measurements: head and body—270 to 315 mm.; tail rudimentary.

Range in Mexico.—Middle slopes of Popocatépetl and Ixtacihuatl, and adjoining ridges bordering the Valley of Mexico on the east and south. This rabbit occurs in open pine forests undergrown with a heavy ground cover of *zacatón* grasses (*Epicampes* and *Festuca*), usually between 9,000 and 10,500 feet elevation, in the boreal zone.

The volcano rabbit has perhaps the most limited range of any mammal in Mexico. It occupies only one habitat type—the pine-*zacatón* association on the rim of the Valley of Mexico. There it lives in burrows in the ground or under rock piles, traversing the dense bunchgrass by way of an intricate

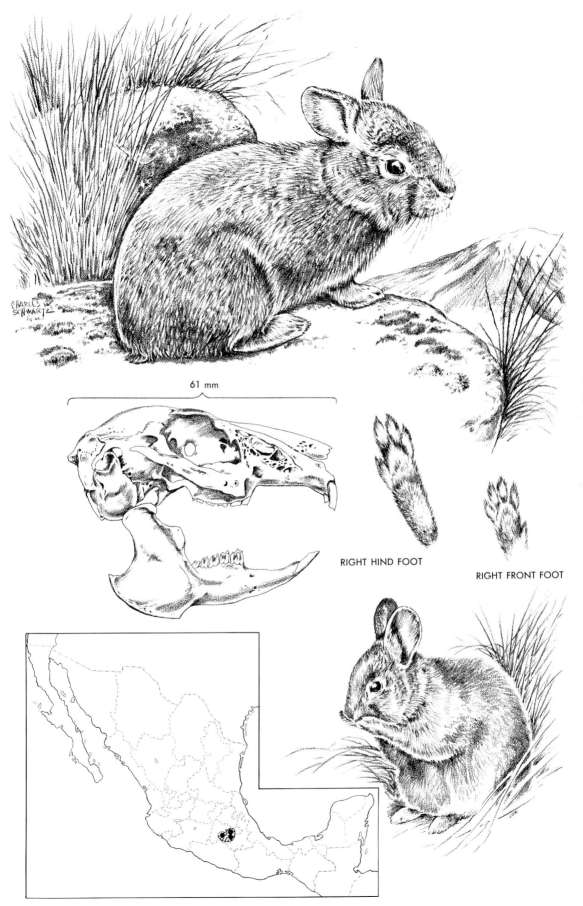

61 mm

RIGHT HIND FOOT

RIGHT FRONT FOOT

Fig. 134. Volcano rabbit, *Romerolagus diazi*.

system of well-kept surface runways. Everyone who has studied the volcano rabbit has commented upon its resemblance to the northern pika, or cony (*Ochotona*), another high mountain Leporid with short ears, no tail, and a propensity to frequent rock piles. The resemblance goes farther in that both the volcano rabbit and the pika have high-pitched, penetrating voices, which they use frequently. No other member of the Leporidae is normally vocal.

Of the food habits of the volcano rabbit little is known. Villa (1953a) states that one favorite forage plant seems to be the aromatic mint *Cunila tritifolium*, which grows in mats in the pine-*zacatón* formation. He has noted the rabbits congregating in stands of this forb, and the strong odor of the plant may sometimes be detected on the animals themselves.

In good weather the volcano rabbit spends much time aboveground, playing, fighting, foraging, or sleeping among the clumps of bunchgrass. It is especially active in the evening and early morning, usually resting quietly in the middle of the day. When surprised it utters its sharp call and scuttles away along a runway to one of its burrows. The nest is underground in a burrow

Fig. 135.   Pine-*zacatón* habitat of the volcano rabbit
on the rim of the Valley of Mexico.

with more than one opening for escape. On June 3, 1949, Villa dug out a nest with young under a pine root and found it made of pine needles, lined with the rabbit's own fur. Young are reared in such a nest until ready to seek homes of their own. The breeding season is in the spring and early summer— March to June or early July. Paulino Rojas collected pregnant females in May and June. Villa suggests that the gestation period is probably a month more or less. Litters average about three young (1 to 4).

Volcano rabbits are hunted a good deal by sportsmen from Mexico City, mostly for target practice, apparently. Neither gunners nor the natives eat them, why I do not know. It has been suggested that the diet of strong mint perhaps spoils the flavor. Villa speaks of coming across a band of city hunters along the Mexico-Cuernavaca highway with twenty-seven volcano rabbits they intended to feed to their dogs. Such wanton destruction of this interesting little animal hardly seems warranted.

Order Rodentia

FAMILY SCIURIDAE

Squirrels

Tree squirrels of the genera *Sciurus* and *Tamiasciurus* are found in all the wooded areas of Mexico except on the tip of Baja California and on some isolated mountain ranges of the northern desert. Mexican tree squirrels are an unusually variable group of animals the taxonomy of which is at present in a very unsatisfactory state. The last major attempt to understand the relationships of the squirrels was made in 1899 by Dr. E. W. Nelson, who arranged these animals in a number of subgenera or species groups. According to his arrangement, all the species belonging to a given subgenus or group have geographically complementary ranges, without overlap. Subsequent study, however, has proved that some of Nelson's "species" may blend or intergrade and thus are really geographic races (subspecies) of a single species; but members of different species groups often occupy the same range without interbreeding and therefore must be specifically distinct. The whole complicated problem is being restudied by Dr. E. T. Hooper of Michigan. Pending his revision I have chosen to treat the squirrels under five main group headings which correspond more or less to Nelson's subgenera. These are:

| | Number of "Species" Known |
Species Group	from Mexico
Gray squirrels	10
Fox squirrels	6
Abert squirrel	1
Deppe squirrel	1
Chickaree	1

Of these five major types of tree squirrels, the last three are easily recognized by such gross morphologic characters as size, color, or presence of ear tufts. But members of the two largest and most widely distributed groups— the gray squirrels and the fox squirrels—are not always distinguishable by external criteria, and it is necessary to refer to a character of the teeth to tell them apart. Most tree squirrels found in Mexico, including the numerous gray squirrels, have a minute, peg-shaped, extra premolar in front of the four regular grinding teeth (1 premolar, 3 molars) in the upper jaw. Fox squirrels (see fig. 137) do not have this tooth (technically Pm 3), and its presence or absence is the only sure way of differentiating members of the gray squirrel and fox squirrel groups. Various species of these two groups are almost identical in size and color, but one can easily be distinguished from the other by a glance at the teeth.

Approximate identification of the tree squirrels can be made from the materials presented below, by reference to (a) geographic locality of capture, (b) presence or absence of the peg-shaped premolars in the upper jaw, and (c) size and color, which are described briefly. For more certain identification, however, the reader is referred to Nelson's treatise of 1899—or, better yet, to a qualified museum.

In addition to the tree squirrels, there occur in Mexico several species of prairie dogs, chipmunks, and ground squirrels, of which the most widely distributed is the rock squirrel, *Citellus variegatus*. This common pest of the milpas is salt-and-pepper gray with a darker saddle. It lives in ground burrows and partakes freely of crops, especially grains. None of the ground-dwelling Sciurids, however, are described here. The accounts which follow concern only the tree squirrels.

Gray Squirrels. *Sciurus aureogaster* and Related Species

Other names.—Ardilla; ardilla arbórea; ardilla arborícola; ardilla volador.

Species included here.—Sciurus aureogaster, S. poliopus, S. nelsoni, S. colliaei, S. sinaloensis, S. truei, S. socialis, S. griseoflavus, S. variegatoides, and S. yucatanensis.

Description.—All species of medium size, with predominantly gray backs. Weights and measurements are compared in table 15. *S. aureogaster* and *socialis* have reddish bellies; *nelsoni* is dark all over, with blackish belly; bellies of other species are usually gray or white. Any medium-sized squirrel taken within the zone designated on the map and having the tiny second premolar tooth in the upper jaw and no ear tufts belongs to the gray squirrel clan.

Range in Mexico.—Coastal plains from Sonora and Tamaulipas south to Chiapas and Quintana Roo, and also the uplands of southern Mexico below Jalisco and Hidalgo. Ranges of the individual species are shown in fig. 136.

TABLE 15

MEASUREMENTS AND WEIGHTS OF THE GRAY SQUIRRELS

Species	Head and body (mm.)	Tail (mm.)	Hind foot (mm.)	Ear from notch (mm.)	Weight (gm.)
S. aureogaster	249–256	249–267	61–69	29–31	411–502
S. poliopus	248–270	249–272	60–70	29–34	475–600
S. nelsoni	255–290	240–263	62–70	28–31	440–590
S. colliaei	250–270	250–275	55–68	28	440–490
S. sinaloensis	269	255	62	. . .	. . .
S. truei	220–247	250–287	61–67	29–33	380–490
S. socialis	250–279	230–270	65–70	30–33	. . .
S. griseoflavus	250–270	256–270	68	. . .	489
S. variegatoides	270	281	66	. . .	. . .
S. yucatanensis	229	222	55	. . .	. . .

Gray squirrels are found principally in tropical forests, ranging from the semiarid thorn forest to wet rain forest. South of latitude 20°, however, gray squirrels invade the temperate uplands much as the tropical Mexican cotton-tail (*Sylvilagus cunicularius*) invades the same area. Three of the ten species live mostly or entirely in temperate forest zones. These are S. *nelsoni* in the mountains surrounding the Valley of Mexico, S. *poliopus* in the pine-oak belt from Jalisco to Oaxaca, and S. *griseoflavus* in the Chiapas highlands. The red-bellied squirrel of Veracruz, S. *aureogaster,* likewise ascends the eastern escarpment to occupy a marginal pine-oak belt in Hidalgo and Querétaro.

The California gray squirrel, *Sciurus griseus,* was reported to occur in the pine-oak belt of northern Baja California by Mearns (1907 : 267), who states that "its range [extends] south at least to the Laguna Mountains of Lower California, 50 miles south of Campo . . ." But no specimens have ever come to light, and it seems probable now that *griseus* does not regularly occur south of the United States border. However, the species was introduced in the vicinity of the Melling Ranch by Mr. C. E. Utt of Tustin, California, who liberated a dozen animals in June, 1945, and some additional individuals later the same year, in pine-oak forest at an elevation of 7,000 feet. The stock presumably was trapped near Tustin. Whether the introduction was successful I do not know.

Nelson, in his treatise on the squirrels, comments repeatedly upon the wide individual variation that occurs in populations of Mexican gray squirrels. Not only are there striking differences in color between adjacent populations of a single species, but even in one locality there may be a great divergence of color patterns. Near Omilteme, Guerrero, our party collected six specimens of *Sciurus poliopus,* and no two of these were identically marked. The exact

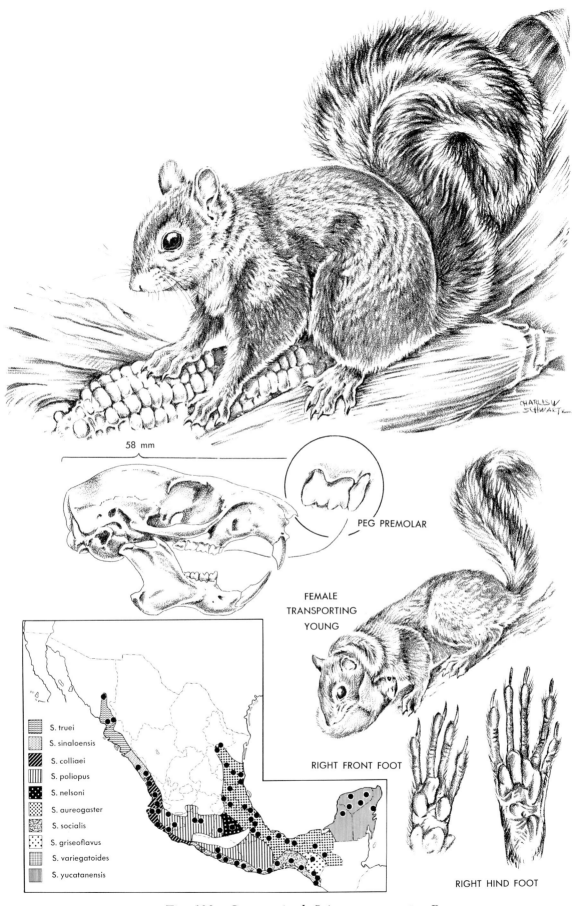

58 mm

PEG PREMOLAR

FEMALE
TRANSPORTING
YOUNG

RIGHT FRONT FOOT

RIGHT HIND FOOT

S. truei
S. sinaloensis
S. colliaei
S. poliopus
S. nelsoni
S. aureogaster
S. socialis
S. griseoflavus
S. variegatoides
S. yucatanensis

Fig. 136. Gray squirrel, *Sciurus aureogaster*. Range map
shows the distribution of this and other species of
gray squirrels in Mexico.

shade of gray on the back and the intensity of the reddish patches on nape and rump varied with each individual. In some areas there is also a large degree of melanism among these animals, jet black individuals being quite common. Such variability makes identification doubly difficult.

In my experience, the gray squirrels usually occur locally in greater abundance than any of the other types of Mexican squirrels. Particularly along the Pacific coastal plain, I have seen dozens of gray squirrels a day in several localities where our camps were in good squirrel woods. Near Santiago, Nayarit, one morning I counted eleven squirrels (*S. colliaei*) in a single tree.

All tree squirrels live in trees, as their name implies, coming down to the ground only to forage for food and water or to travel from one tree to another. The young are reared in arboreal nests. These are usually in cavities in the trees, but some nests, made of leaves and twigs, are in the upper branches. Tree squirrels never live in ground burrows as do the ground squirrels (*Citellus*) or prairie dogs (*Cynomys*). Among the gray squirrels, breeding may occur at any time of year, although it probably is inhibited during drought periods when food is scarce. Litters of 2 to 6 young (4 or 5 usually) are born after a gestation period of about forty-four days. The young develop slowly in the nest and are more than a month old before they open their eyes. They stay with the mother for several months before venturing forth on their own. The long period of care of the young seems to preclude the possibility that one female gives birth to more than one litter a year, although this point is not settled.

Squirrels eat a great variety of plant foods and even some animal foods, such as insects, bird eggs, and small reptiles. In the pine-oak zone, acorns and pine nuts are perhaps the staple foods of squirrels; whereas in the tropics, various fruits—figs, cherimoyas, capulin berries, and similar fleshy foods— are the more dependable source of sustenance. During the dry season when no fruits are available the animals may resort to buds and green parts of plants. Allen and Chapman (1897 : 7) remark of the Yucatán gray squirrel: "These squirrels were common at Chichen-Itza, and were daily seen 'budding' in the small leafless trees."

Elsewhere during periods of food shortage squirrels frequently make altitudinal migrations to better feeding grounds, as noted by Nelson (p. 21):

Many species change their environment by periodical migrations in search of food, moving from one locality to another with the ripening of fruits or seeds upon which they subsist. This is most marked on high mountains where species may have a vertical range of many thousands of feet. Dr. Buller obtained a specimen of *Sciurus poliopus cervicalis* among the pines on the Sierra Nevada de Colima at an altitude of 12,000 feet, but when we visited this mountain at another season, gnawed pine cones were abundant near the summit, but the squirrels had descended to lower levels and were feeding on wild figs and acorns at an altitude of 4000–6000 feet. In eastern Querétaro and northern Hidalgo, *S. aureogaster*, a tropical species which usually ranges below 4000 feet, was found in winter among the oaks and pines above 8000 feet altitude. S. *deppei* likewise at times wanders high above its normal range.

Some economic damage may be attributed to squirrels. They rob corn ears from the milpas and sometimes take nuts and fruits from cultivated trees. Of S. *aureogaster*, Nelson (p. 42) says: "Throughout their range these squirrels do considerable damage to cornfields, and while corn is in the ear it is an easy matter to find them about the edges of fields cleared in the forest. At other times they are dispersed, seeking food wherever wild fruits or nuts may be in season." I observed similar concentrations of gray squirrels (S. *poliopus*) around cornfields in Guerrero and of Deppe squirrels (S. *deppei*) around fields in Campeche. The farmers are aware of crop damage when it occurs, and they try to guard their fields by shooting the squirrels or, as I observed on one occasion, assigning a small boy the task of patrolling the field borders to drive the squirrels out.

There is little sport hunting for squirrels in Mexico. Tree squirrels are hunted mainly as a source of food by the poorer people of rural areas. All types of firearms are used in their capture, as well as some more primitive weapons. In the mountains of Guerrero I hunted one morning with a native who claimed that he killed a few squirrels almost every day with his muzzle-loading twenty-gauge shotgun of ancient vintage (fig. 37). Elsewhere in the same state we saw boys and even adult men hunting birds and small mammals (including squirrels) with slingshots, and the Lacandone Indians of north-eastern Chiapas still shoot their small game with bows and arrows. The .22 rifle, which is a characteristic squirrel gun among farm boys in the United States, is used in some areas, but not many *campesinos* can afford this kind of arm.

In the main, squirrels are hunted for home consumption, and not many are offered for sale in the big commercial markets. As compared with the sale of rabbits, the traffic in squirrels is minor. Even for home use, in the country as a whole there are many more rabbits taken than squirrels. This is due in part to the larger size of rabbits, which makes them more attractive game for hunters, and in part to the limited distribution of squirrels, which of course occupy only the wooded parts of the country. Locally, in some mountain areas where squirrels are numerous and rabbits scarce, the former may be hunted the more heavily. This was true, for example, around Omilteme, Guerrero, when we visited there in October, 1944.

Most of the gray squirrels in Mexico live in tropical forests that have been fairly recently opened up by clearing. The combination of remnants of native forest interspersed with cornfields is actually very favorable habitat for gray squirrels—better, perhaps, than the virgin forest—and may account for the abundance of these animals in some coastal areas. The upland species of gray squirrels (*poliopus, nelsoni,* and *griseoflavus*), however, which live in the central and southern pine-oak lands, have had their homes destroyed by clearing and forest depreciation, and these species are relatively scarce. At one time, when cornfields first began to encroach into the upland timber, these species may have gone through a cycle of abundance. But continued grazing, burning, and overcutting have reduced the cover and food for squirrels until they can live only in certain localities, and even there the populations are small.

Fox Squirrels. *Sciurus niger* and Related Species

Other names.—Ardilla; ardilla arbórea.

Species included here.—*Sciurus niger, S. alleni, S. oculatus, S. nayaritensis, S. apache,* and *S. arizonensis.*

Description.—Fox squirrels all medium-sized to large and without the peg premolar. Some average weights and measurements are compared in table 16. Three of the species (*S. oculatus, apache,* and *nayaritensis*) dark on back, with yellowish or rusty sides and underparts as in the fox squirrel of northern Coahuila and eastern United States (*S. niger*). Other two species more like the gray squirrels in coloration. *S. arizonensis* has a gray back, white belly, and only a faint yellowish wash on ears and back. *S. alleni* is plain gray with a white belly.

Range in Mexico.—Bottom lands of the Río Grande and its principal tributaries in northern Coahuila; northern and central mountains, including the Sierra Madre Occidental, Sierra Madre Oriental, eastern escarpment and southern reaches of the central plateau. The group is not represented south of the Río Balsas valley, and there is a curious gap in the upland range through Michoacán. To my knowledge, no fox squirrels are known from that state.

TABLE 16

MEASUREMENTS AND WEIGHTS OF THE FOX SQUIRRELS

Species	Head and body (mm.)	Tail (mm.)	Hind foot (mm.)	Ear from notch (mm.)	Weight (gm.)
S. niger	247–256	200–238	62–65	30–35	390–545
S. oculatus	268–274	263–269	69–73	...	...
S. alleni	220–254	217–247	60–65	24–30	426–485
S. nayaritensis	294	272	78	...	...
S. apache	240–292	235–286	68–74	27–35	630–800
S. arizonensis	270	247	71	...	...

Most fox squirrels live in temperate mountain forests, principally in the pine-oak zone. *Sciurus alleni* in Nuevo León and Tamaulipas descends onto the edges of the coastal plain; *Sciurus niger* in Coahuila occurs in alluvial bottom lands. But all other species of the group live only in the mountains.

In one locality I observed a good deal of melanism in the local population of *S. alleni.* This was near General Terán, Nuevo León. A note made at the time of my visit indicates that nearly half of all the squirrels seen were black, but no actual counts were made to check this estimate. Elsewhere I saw no black individuals. Nelson (1899) observed no signs of melanism in this species, although he mentions black individuals of *oculatus.* On the basis of my

65 mm

S. arizonensis
S. apache
S. nayaritensis
S. niger
S. alleni
S. oculatus

Fig. 137. Fox squirrel, *Sciurus apache*. Range map shows the distribution of this and other species of fox squirrels in Mexico.

limited experience with this group, and of Nelson's descriptions based on large series of specimens, I believe that on the whole there is less individual variation in color among the fox squirrels than in the gray squirrel group.

Fox squirrels are generally more phlegmatic than their sprightly relatives the gray squirrels; at least this is true of S. *apache* and S. *niger*, the species of fox squirrels that I know best. Although arboreal, they are simply not as agile as the smaller gray squirrels. They negotiate the treetops adequately but without the spectacular leaps and dashes of their nimble cousins.

Like the grays, fox squirrels den in hollow trees or build leaf nests in the treetops. In the United States, fox squirrels breed in early spring and produce 3 to 5 young after a gestation period of forty-five days. Presumably the Mexican relatives have similar breeding habits, although the timing seems to be keyed to the rainy season rather than to the spring. In northwestern Chihuahua we collected two pregnant females of S. *apache* on July 19, one with two embryos of 15 mm. and the other with three of 10 mm. As these young would not have been ready for birth for some weeks, parturition would have occurred in the period of summer rains—a time of plenty in squirreldom. Spring is the period of acute food shortage in the Mexican mountains.

Fox squirrels are similar to the grays in their feeding habits, preferring acorns and other nuts when these are available but otherwise subsisting on fruits, plant seeds of various kinds, some insects and other animal foods, and in times of austerity on buds and greens. When the acorns are falling, the squirrels cache quantities of them in ground holes for later excavation. They relocate the caches by smell. Some caches, however, are forgotten, and often oak trees grow from these acorns.

Fox squirrels are hunted much as the gray squirrels, but since their populations are usually sparse in Mexico they make up only a small part of the total kill. Only in an area of bottom-land timber near General Terán, Nuevo León, did I find a truly dense population of fox squirrels; these were S. *alleni*. Usually it was difficult to obtain even one or two specimens per camp.

Since the fox squirrels live for the most part in pine-oak forest, their habitat has been greatly reduced by the forest cutting that has gone on in central Mexico for several hundred years. Similarly, most of the river-bottom forests of Coahuila have been cleared for agriculture. Even where the stands have not been completely destroyed, their value as a home for squirrels has been impaired by excessive cutting, burning, and overgrazing. The scarcity of fox squirrels in the central uplands is probably in large part a result of forest abuse. In the mountain forests of northern Mexico, however, where the timber has been more recently invaded by man, fox squirrels are still fairly numerous.

Abert Squirrel. *Sciurus aberti*

Other names.—Ardilla; ardilla arbórea.

Description.—Medium large (head and body—260 to 280 mm.; tail—205 to

247 mm.; weight—585 to 750 gm.). Gray dorsally, with white belly. The peg premolar is present. Species most readily identified by the long ears (38 to 44 mm.) and the tufts of hair which grow straight up from the tips of the ears. The tufts are longest in winter, but even in summer when the winter pelage has been shed they are enough in evidence to separate the species from all other Mexican squirrels. The tail is so light a gray that the species is sometimes called "white-tailed squirrel."

Range in Mexico.—Sierra Madre Occidental, from northern Sonora and Chihuahua to southern Durango. This species occurs only in pine-oak forest and islands of boreal forest.

Abert squirrels as a rule occur sparsely in the pine woods, rarely attaining real abundance, even locally. There are relatively few skins in museums, and considering the amount of collecting that has gone on in the Sierra Madre, this in itself is evidence of scarcity. In only two camps in Chihuahua did I find the Abert squirrel in good numbers—near Colonia García in 1948 and at Yaguirachic in 1957. On those occasions I had the chance to learn something of this picturesque animal.

Throughout its total range the Abert squirrel is associated with the yellow pine—a tree that offers both shelter and food to the squirrels. Bulky nests, often two feet in diameter, of cut pine twigs are constructed high in the trees, and there the animals live and raise their young. According to Goldman (1928), Abert squirrels do not use tree holes; but we found them doing so at Yaguirachic, where abundant hollows were available in oaks. In pure pine stands there are not many cavities.

Little is known about the breeding habits of these animals. Near Colonia García a female containing three embryos was taken on May 22. Ten other females collected in Chihuahua during the summer months were not pregnant. At Yaguirachic we saw many half-grown young in late June and early July. It appears that Abert squirrels in northern Mexico breed once in the spring and do not rebreed during the period of summer rains.

Like other squirrels, this species is most active in the early morning and late afternoon. When a good many individuals are about, they often scold and call to each other. The characteristic note is a soft "whicker," very different from the harsh grating scold of most squirrels. The call suggests that of a small owl or the "flicker, flicker . . ." call of the red-shaft. When disturbed, the squirrel may dash up a tree to hide among the branches or in one of its nests, or it may flee through the treetops, leaping from branch to branch. I chased one for a hundred yards before getting within shotgun range.

Of the feeding habits of this animal, Goldman (p. 128) states:

The white-tailed squirrel gnaws the cones of the yellow pine, but as this tree produces few seeds except in good seed years that come at irregular intervals it must depend largely upon other food. It seems doubtful whether any stores are gathered, the cambium of the pine providing a never-failing supply. In feeding, the leaf-bearing branch tip is commonly severed and allowed to drop to

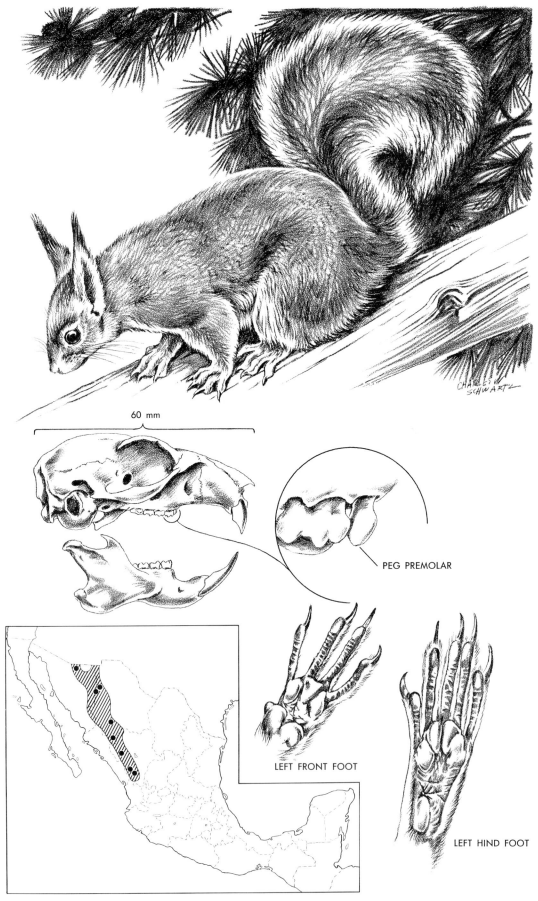

60 mm

PEG PREMOLAR

LEFT FRONT FOOT

LEFT HIND FOOT

Fig. 138. Abert squirrel, *Sciurus aberti*.

the ground. A subterminal section of tender stem 2 to 4 inches in length is cut off, scaled, and when the cambium sought as food has been neatly removed the peeled wood remaining is also dropped. While branches are cut at all seasons of the year, evidence of the specialized feeding habits of these squirrels is most abundant in winter. Tracks in the snow indicate where they have passed between trees standing some distance apart. A preference for certain trees seems to be exhibited, and it is not unusual to find the snow under these thickly strewn with the discarded branch tips and peeled stems. In summer, however, they evidently indulge in a more varied diet. Much time is spent in foraging upon the ground and I have at various times observed them feeding upon mushrooms and other funguses, and they doubtless eat many other things.

In late summer I found Abert squirrels near Colonia García gathering and burying acorns in the manner of other squirrels, from which I inferred that these stores may be used to tide them over the winter. On August 31, 1948, I observed in detail the actions of one of these squirrels. After "whickering" in a pine, the squirrel worked its way from limb to limb down to the ground and then started picking acorns from a clump of low scrub oaks one to two feet high. The animal could reach the acorns by sitting up or standing on its hind legs and pulling down the stems with its front paws. It grasped the acorns in its mouth and pulled them from the cups and then buried them. It would gather from one to three acorns, hop a foot or two away, dig a hole, drop in the nuts, and then cover them, patting the mound down firmly with its front feet and replacing the pine needles over the area. I carefully noted the locations of several of these caches but could not find the spots when I walked over to the vicinity later, so cleverly had the squirrel replaced the ground litter. In the stomachs of several animals that we collected we found remains of the same kind of green acorns. Scattered about the forest were many old stripped pine cones, which indicated that these were important items of diet at other seasons.

So far, the changes in the pine forests of northern Sierra Madre Occidental have not been extensive enough to account for the scarcity of Abert squirrels. I suspect that this species never was really abundant and its present distribution and density is probably the original pattern. It is hunted very little because of the abundance of larger game in its mountain domain.

Deppe Squirrel. *Sciurus deppei*

Other names.—Moto; ardilla; *Sciurus negligens*.

Description.—A small dark squirrel. Measurements: head and body—180 to 205 mm.; tail—150 to 188 mm. Weight—140 to 260 gm. Olive brown dorsally, with white or grayish underparts. Peg premolar present.

Range in Mexico.—Gulf coast and throughout Yucatán Peninsula. The Deppe squirrel is limited almost entirely to rain forests and tropical evergreen forests. Along the eastern escarpment in Oaxaca and on the Chiapas uplands it occurs locally in areas of cloud forest.

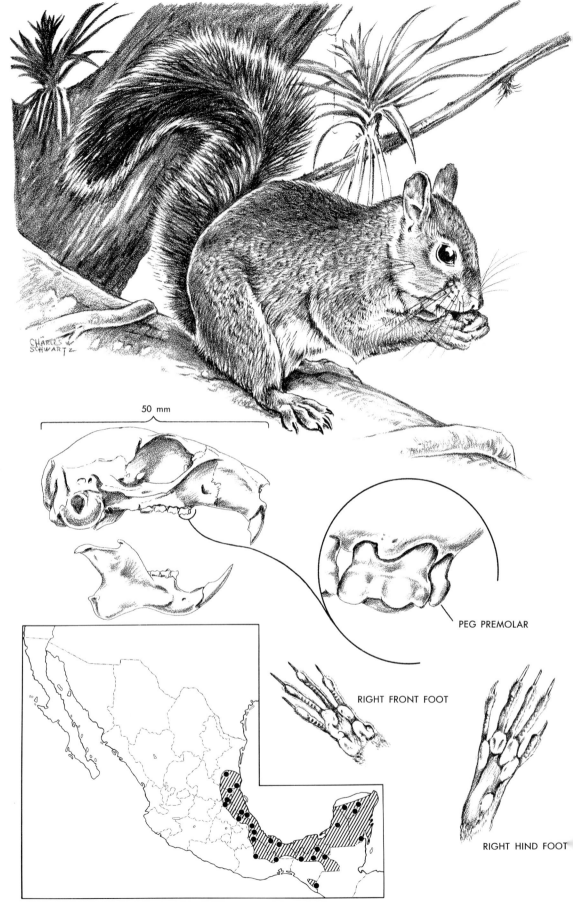

50 mm

PEG PREMOLAR

RIGHT FRONT FOOT

RIGHT HIND FOOT

Fig. 139. Deppe squirrel, *Sciurus deppei*.

The highest population of Deppe squirrels found during the survey was in a semiwilderness near San Juan, Campeche, where new cornfields were being cleared in the virgin rain forest. There, around the edges of the fields, we saw dozens of the active little animals, living handsomely on a diet of ear corn. The combination of milpas and tall, cool forest seemed to produce an exceptional squirrel population.

In areas where the forest is impoverished after being cut over several times —for example, near Chichén Itzá in Yucatán—Deppe squirrels become scarce or disappear even though corn is readily available. Apparently, tall forest is a requisite in the habitat of this animal.

In the Sierra de Chiapas, Villa (1948) found the Deppe squirrel abundant in the cloud forest near Finca Prusia. Among the tall pine trees, heavily grown with lianas and epiphytic plants, it was so hard to see the animals that collecting specimens was difficult. I had a similar experience in the heavy tropical evergreen forest on the flanks of Volcán San Martín Tuxtla in southern Veracruz. The active little scamps would dash to safety in the dense tangles of the tallest trees, there to crouch quietly until the danger had passed.

Little is known about the life history of the Deppe squirrel. It customarily dens in tree cavities, rarely building leaf nests. I have no information whatsoever on its breeding habits. In Yucatán, Gaumer (1917) kept a female in captivity; he claims that she mated with a male gray squirrel (*S. yucatanensis*), giving birth in February to five young, some of which resembled one parent, some the other. He does not comment further upon the fate of the hybrid litter except to indicate that the young matured. It would be of interest to know whether they were fertile.

Besides eating corn, the Deppe squirrels eat the seeds and fruits of many wild plants. Nelson (1899) speaks of them as being abundant in stunted forests of ebony, 15 to 25 feet high, which not only provided shelter but also food for the squirrels. Near Velasco, San Luis Potosí, the ground under the ebony trees was strewn with gnawed seed pods. Alvarez del Toro says that, in Chiapas, *S. deppei* eats the fruits of such trees as the amate, chicle zapote, and the *moju* (*Brosimum*).

Occasionally, great aggregations of Deppe squirrels are found together, swarming through the trees like locusts. Alvarez del Toro reports having seen such mobs in March of two different years in the rain forest of the Selva del Ocote, Chiapas. The causes or purposes of squirrel conventions are not known. In the eastern United States similar gatherings have been noted among the gray squirrels, and in the north among the chickarees. The swarms often migrate great distances. Alvarez del Toro did not know whether the squirrels of the Selva del Ocote were migrating or not.

Deppe squirrels are severely persecuted when they damage corn; but ordinarily they are not hunted much, because of their small size. Hunting, in other words, has little effect on numbers.

Chickaree. *Tamiasciurus douglasii*

Other names.—Ardilla; Douglas squirrel; *Sciurus douglassii.*

Description.—About the size of a house rat. Reddish brown dorsally, white below. Specimens from the Sierra San Pedro Mártir somewhat smaller than California specimens: head and body about 194 mm., tail 111 mm. Second premolar usually present, but small, weakly developed, and in some individuals not visible.

Range in Mexico.—Sierra Laguna and Sierra San Pedro Mártir in northern Baja California. Habitat: Coniferous forests in the high mountains.

The lively little "chickaree," or Douglas squirrel, is well known in the mountains of California. Its occurrence in northwestern Mexico is the extreme southward extension of its range.

In California this species is found mostly in the boreal zones and only sparingly in the yellow pine belt. Similarly, in Baja California the only available records come from localities 7,000 feet or more in elevation in the Sierra San Pedro Mártir and the Sierra Laguna.

Of all the squirrels, the chickaree is perhaps the noisiest and most obstreperous. It livens the woods with its constant chatter, directed at every intruder in its home area or, in the absence of intruders, at neighboring chickarees. Dashing about from limb to limb or hanging on a tree trunk, head down and tail jerking, the little noisemaker warns the world of all dangers, real or supposititious.

Chickarees make their homes in the conifers, coming to the ground only to gather cones that they have cut, or to reach some area not accessible by means of the branches. Nests are usually in tree cavities, often old woodpecker holes. Mating occurs in early spring, and the 3 to 7 young (5 or 6 in a litter ordinarily) are born naked and helpless in the nest. The period of gestation is not known, but it is believed to be between thirty-six and forty days (Cahalane, 1947). The young are tended by the mother until they are nearly half grown, when they scatter to seek homes for themselves. By autumn most chickaree families have broken up and the individual young have adopted the solitary habits of adults.

Chickarees feed on a variety of fruits, nuts, and other comestibles during the warm months, but in winter they depend chiefly on the seeds of conifers which were gathered and stored at the time of ripening. Grinnell and Storer (1924 : 203) describe the chickaree's preparation for winter:

In the late summer and early autumn, when the cones of many of the evergreen trees have attained full or nearly full size but are still green, the chickarees begin their annual harvest. The busy animals gnaw off the cones, and as a person walks through the forest where the squirrels are operating, cones may be seen or heard falling at frequent intervals.

After cutting for a while a squirrel will descend to the ground and proceed to dispose of the cones which it has detached. Such cones as are not wanted for

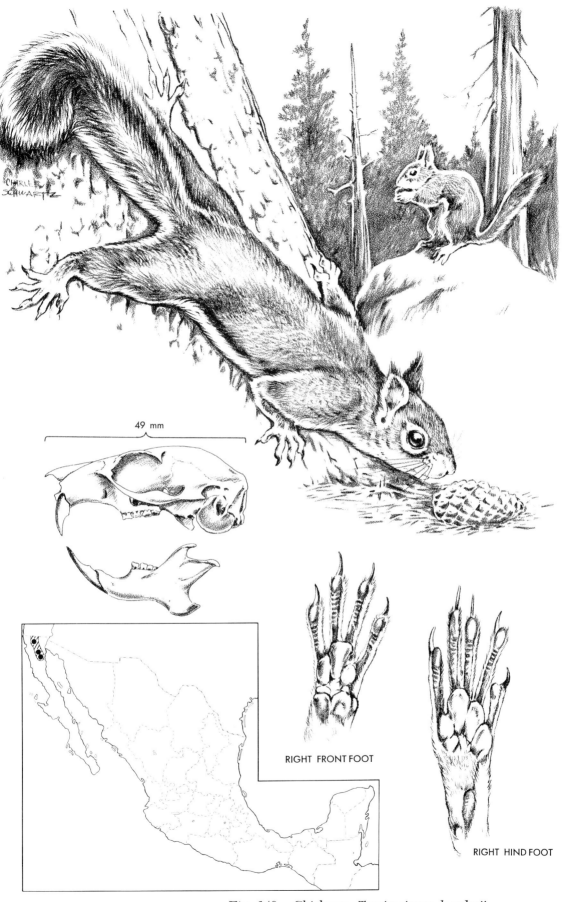

49 mm

RIGHT FRONT FOOT

RIGHT HIND FOOT

Fig. 140.   Chickaree. *Tamiasciurus douglasii.*

immediate use are cached on the ground under the sides of downed tree trunks and in other nooks and crannies in the vicinity of the animal's home.

Practically all the cone-bearing trees within the range of the chickaree are levied upon for food.

Chickaree populations in good habitat ordinarily do not exceed one animal per two to three acres, but occasionally very high densities have been noted. Presumably these large populations are the result of unusually favorable seed crops among the conifers and correspondingly high survival and productivity among the squirrels. At least this has been demonstrated in some of the squirrels of northern Europe that like the chickaree winter on conifer mast. In times of high density, large numbers of chickarees may migrate; but I have no record of such an occurrence in Baja California, which is strictly marginal range for this species. In fact, populations in Baja California are usually reported as relatively low.

Chickarees are too small to have any significance as game animals. But their lively demeanor lends life and color to the mountain forests they inhabit.

FAMILY CASTORIDAE

BEAVERS

Beaver. *Castor canadensis*

Other names.—Castor; nutria; *Castor fiber*.

Description.—The largest North American rodent, adults weighing 13 to 17 kg. (28 to 37 lbs.). Body heavy and squat, with short, powerful legs. Eyes and ears small. Fur a rich brown, somewhat darker on the back than below; underfur thick and woolly. Hind feet completely webbed. Tail horizontally flattened and paddle-shaped, covered with coarse scales. Measurements: head and body—600 to 850 mm.; tail—275 to 325 mm.

Range in Mexico.—Locally along the United States boundary, in the delta of the Colorado River, in streams of northeastern Sonora, along the Río Grande from Juárez, Chihuahua, to its mouth, and in north-flowing rivers of northern Coahuila, Nuevo León, and Tamaulipas.

Beavers are, of course, among the most valuable fur bearers of North America. On the whole, beavers occur in northern latitudes and in the mountains; but along the southern edge of their continental range, in extreme northern Mexico, are local populations adapted to live in warm rivers traversing arid plains. It is only in such situations that beavers occur in Mexico. Why the animals did not occupy the mountain streams of the Sierra Madre Occidental is not known, but shortage of appropriate food doubtless was a factor.

The early trappers in the southwestern United States found beavers abundant even on the extreme southern fringe of their range. James O. Pattie's party in 1827 had excellent success trapping in the lower Colorado River near Yuma. Pattie records taking thirty-six beavers in forty traps in one night.

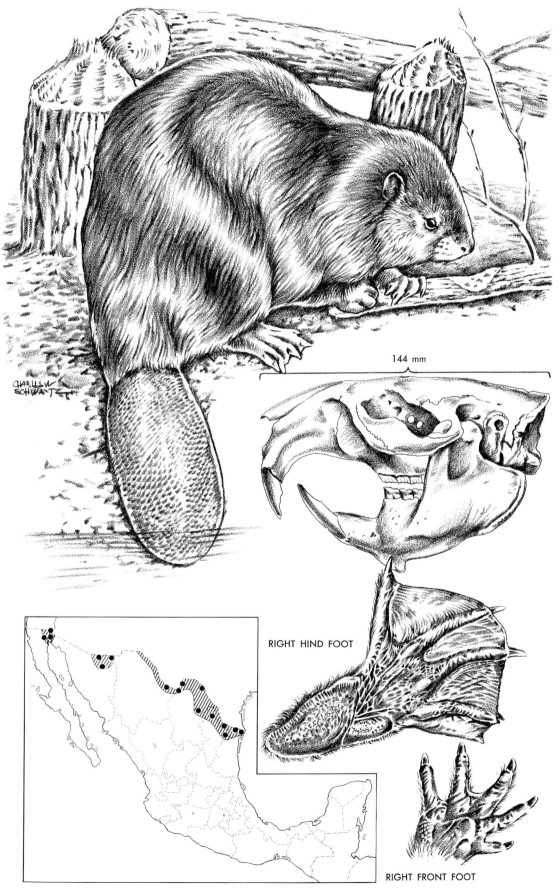

144 mm

RIGHT HIND FOOT

RIGHT FRONT FOOT

Fig. 141.   Beaver, *Castor canadensis.*

"Ever since then," write Grinnell, Dixon, and Linsdale (1937 : 725), "this has been a famous trapping ground. At intervals it has been 'trapped out' and deserted by the trappers. With the lapse of a few years, the beavers have then bred up to a point where they have again become profitable to trap. In 1930 one trapper, Robert P. Bolam, reported taking ninety-seven beaver pelts along the Colorado River, for which he received $1300." Leopold (1953) found many beavers in the Colorado delta in 1922.

Beavers in the lower Río Grande likewise were numerous when trapping first started in the mid-1800's, but they are held down now by intermittent heavy trapping. Bailey (1905) cites evidence of a good deal of trapping along the Río Grande from 1891 to 1902, and states that numbers were decreasing in 1902. Still, in the winter of 1902–1903 Bailey heard of one trapper who caught two hundred beavers in the Río Grande between the Grand Canyon and Del Rio. Others made good catches about that time in the lower river near Matamoros.

Borell and Bryant (1942) report that beavers were still present along the Río Grande "from the mouth of Santa Helena Canyon to the mouth of Boquillas Canyon," in the early 1940's, but do not say how abundant they were. Presumably the animals are scarce there now.

The most up-to date account of beavers in Mexico is a paper published in 1954 by Bernardo Villa R., citing recent records of the animals in the Río San Juan near China, Nuevo León, in the Río Salado of northern Nuevo León, and in the Río Sabinas of eastern Coahuila. Apparently, beavers are thriving in these localities, although Baker (1956) believes that the colonies are being overtrapped.

Beavers live most of their lives in water, or in their dens or houses which have underwater entrances. They come out on dry land only to forage for food. Beavers are agile swimmers, both on the surface and submerged, although on land they are clumsy and slow. No predator can catch or overpower a beaver in deep water, but whenever beavers come ashore they are subject to attack by coyotes or the larger cats, which are glad of the chance to feed upon fat beavers.

Most of the beavers along the Colorado and Río Grande bottom lands live in dens excavated by the animals in the soft alluvial soils of the banks. Tunnels start under water and usually penetrate 5 to 20 feet into the bank, terminating in a home chamber several feet in diameter and above water level. Often the roofs of the dens are covered with great piles of branches and poles to prevent coyotes from digging away the tops. In the north country and in the mountains, the pole "houses" usually are built in the water. Each den normally is occupied by several beavers, which may include a pair of adults or one or more adults and a family of young. Several families do not usually share a single den, however. In California,

14 litters consisted of 1 to 5 young, the average number being about 3 (Grinnell, Dixon and Linsdale, 1937).

In the north, beavers often build dams across small streams, thereby creating deep ponds in which to live. But the beavers of Mexico all live along the banks of large rivers where dams are unnecessary and also would be impossible to build. There may be some tributaries or oxbows that beavers have dammed in Mexico, but I have not heard of any.

The main food of beavers is the bark and tender wood of trees such as willow, cottonwood, ash, or oak. The colony in the Río San Juan was feeding principally on willow (*Salix goodingii*), according to Villa. Food is obtained by felling young trees and dragging them into the water, where feeding can proceed in safety and at leisure. The heavy, chisel-shaped incisors and stout jaws and skull of the beaver are adapted to tree cutting and to chewing up the edible parts after the tree is down. Some herbaceous plants are eaten, and occasionally beavers have been known to cut cornstalks, hauling them to the water to be nibbled at leisure.

Food supply often is the factor which limits the size of beaver populations. A thriving colony frequently "cleans out" all the available food in a given stretch of river bottom and must scatter out to new areas until a new crop of trees grows (a matter of some years) and beavers can once more find enough to eat. Besides the beavers themselves, other factors, such as the clearing of river bottoms for agriculture, floods, and grazing, may tend to deplete food supplies. Exhausted food sources, as well as intermittent trapping, may account for some of the local fluctuations in numbers of beavers.

Since Mexico is on the extreme fringe of the beaver range, *C. canadensis* cannot be designated as a potentially important fur bearer in the country, even though the quality of the fur is excellent. The numbers of beavers in Mexico will always be limited unless the species is introduced into new areas of range. At present the beaver is given complete legal protection in Mexico, although there is still some trapping. The colonies undoubtedly suffer severe losses from intermittent floods that plague the Río Grande and its tributary rivers.

FAMILY CRICETIDAE

Cricetine Rodents

Muskrat. *Ondatra zibethicus*

Other name.—Rata almizclera.

Description.—Size of a half-grown house cat, with weak front legs and short but stout hind legs. Hind feet large, with long toes, partly webbed. Eyes and ears small. Tail vertically flattened (greater in depth than in width), covered with scales and scattered hairs. Fur rich brown, slightly paler below than on the back and sides. Measurements: head and body—240 to 300 mm.; tail—180 to 225 mm. Weight: 550 to 800 gm.

Range in Mexico.—Along the United States border in the delta of the Colorado River, along rivers of northeastern Sonora, and on the Río Grande near the mouth of the Pecos River (Texas) in northern Coahuila. The muskrat was recently introduced in Lake Texcoco, Valley of Mexico.

The muskrat is one of the two native rodents of importance as fur bearers in North America, the other being the beaver. Although muskrats over most of the continent occur in habitats different from those of beavers and eat different foods, the ranges of the two species in Mexico are similar. Only along the Río Grande is the range of the muskrat more limited than that of the beaver.

In their range in northern Mexico, muskrats live ordinarily in holes in the banks of streams or lakes, rather than in houses of vegetation and mud such as they build in the marshes of the United States. Entrance holes normally are under water, the burrow system extending slightly upward and back into the bank for many feet. Some burrows are for feeding or for temporary shelter, and only a few contain nests of leaves or shredded plant stems. A burrow system may shelter as many as a dozen animals.

In Lake Texcoco in the Valley of Mexico, however, muskrats that have been introduced are building their characteristic conical houses in the cat-tail marshes. Villa observed such houses, and muskrat feces as well, in 1953; but no specimens of the animal have been taken. The present extent of this introduced population is not known.

Muskrats are even more strictly aquatic than beavers, since they feed on vegetation which grows in the water and they rarely have occasion to venture out on land. They swim and dive expertly, using the hind feet in alternate strokes for propulsion. During the day they rest in their burrows. Most of their feeding is done at night. Green cattail leaves or other available foods are cut with the sharp incisor teeth and carried in the mouth back to the burrow, where the animal feeds in comfort and shelter. Piles of uneaten leaf fragments often accumulate in burrows that have been used as feeding stations. Muskrats eat the leaves, roots, and stems of a variety of herbaceous plants that occur along the water edge. However, the cattail (*Typha*) supplies the bulk of their diet along the rivers of northern Mexico.

Mating among the muskrats along the lower Colorado takes place at almost any time of year; young have been taken in every calendar month (Grinnell, Dixon, and Linsdale, 1937). Gestation is about thirty days. A litter usually consists of 3 to 9 young, and each female has two or three litters a year if food is abundant. The young are reared in the safety of

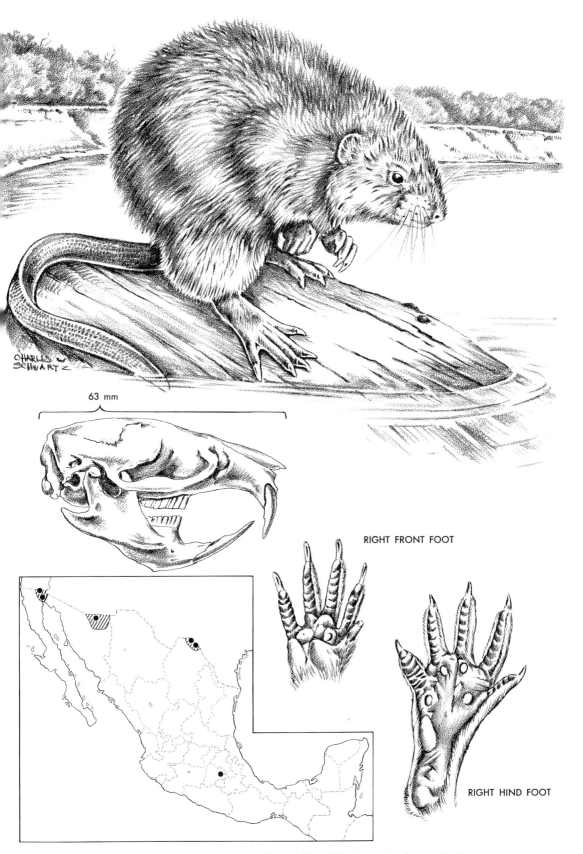

63 mm

RIGHT FRONT FOOT

RIGHT HIND FOOT

Fig. 142. Muskrat, *Ondatra zibethicus*.

underground nests; but often after they are weaned the female drives them from the burrow, and thereafter they must fend for themselves.

Muskrats have many natural enemies, including coyotes, foxes, bobcats, weasels, turtles, snakes, and various birds of prey. The success of these predators in catching muskrats depends upon the number of muskrats in relation to the amount of food and cover for their sustenance. A population well situated in good habitat will suffer few losses to predators, since the animals can feed and live without exposing themselves away from cover. But when a population becomes too large for the available facilities, the muskrats fight among themselves and the weaker ones are either killed outright or are driven from cover and thus become easy prey for predators. Production of a muskrat crop is more contingent upon the presence of suitable food and cover facilities than upon numbers of predators or protection from overtrapping.

Muskrat pelts in the United States bring to the trappers more money than any other type of fur. In Mexico, however, the crop has never been of much importance, because of the limited distribution of muskrats in the country. Under the new law, pelts cannot be sold at all.

The animals cause some damage to dikes and ditch banks by burrowing in them. Grinnell speaks of such difficulties encountered by the irrigation companies along the Colorado River, and Bailey (1905) mentions broken dikes caused by muskrats along the Río Grande. In situations where muskrats are interfering seriously with the function of irrigation systems they must be controlled.

FAMILY ERETHIZONTIDAE

Porcupines

There are two species of North American porcupines—*Erethizon dorsatum*, the common porcupine of the north, and *Coendù mexicanus*, the Mexican porcupine of the tropics. Only the latter is accorded a full account here. The northern species is not ordinarily found in Mexico; but, curiously for so slow-moving an animal, wandering individuals, presumably from Arizona, have been recorded in northern Sonora as far south as Puerto Kino at the mouth of the Río Sonora. Benson (1953) collected one complete specimen and fragments of another in that area. There is no positive evidence, however, that the northern porcupine regularly lives in the mountains of Sonora, although the pine forests there would seem to be favorable habitat.

Marsh (1937) states that he heard reports of porcupines in the Sierra del Carmen of northern Coahuila, and Baker (1956) likewise gathered secondhand reports that the animals had been seen in several mountain ranges of northern Coahuila. Presumably there is a sparse population there, but no specimens have been preserved.

Mexican Porcupine. *Coendu mexicanus*

Other names.—Puerco espín; zorro espín; *Hystrix mexicana; Hystrix prehensilis.*

Description.—Size of a large cat, with long prehensile tail and small legs. Short, stiff spines cover dorsal parts of body. Spines white basally and black at tips like those of northern porcupine but much shorter. Underfur soft, black, and long, almost covering the spines. The eyes small, like shiny brown shoe buttons; ears minute. Measurements: head and body—360 to 515 mm.; tail—435 to 485 mm. Males somewhat larger than females.

Range in Mexico.—Tropical forests south from eastern San Luis Potosí on the Gulf side and from Guerrero (perhaps Michoacán) on the Pacific to Chiapas and east throughout the Yucatán Peninsula. Hunters in the vicinity of Apo, Michoacán, told me that there were porcupines in that area, but specimens have never been collected there.

The Mexican porcupine has been found in widely separated localities of tropical Mexico, but it is rarely seen and specimens are few, as the map will attest. Perhaps this is due to the arboreal and nocturnal habits of the animal. It lives in the tall trees and rarely comes to the ground. Also, it is said to sleep all day and to move about almost entirely at night. This combination would minimize the probability of finding the animal if one were searching for it.

This porcupine, like its northern cousin, is sluggish in movement and generally stupid in demeanor. On the ground its top speed is a slow scuttle, and in the branches of the tall trees it crawls along even more slowly. It forages chiefly in the treetops, feeding on fruits, epiphytic plants, and tender twigs, bark, and cambium. Gaumer (1917) says that it ordinarily holds the food in its front paws when eating, like a squirrel. He also describes how the animal peels the bark from branches of some kinds of trees (not named) to get at the cambium layer beneath.

Again, according to Gaumer, porcupines breed in February, the females giving birth to about four young after a gestation period of sixty to seventy days. The young are born in a nest situated in a tree hole and lined with leaves. The young are said to arrive with their eyes open and with the body clothed in fur and soft, short spines. The spines soon harden.

The spines presumably are a defense against predators, but they do not seem to be very effective. I found the remains of a porcupine near Omilteme, Guerrero, that appeared to have been killed and eaten by a bird of prey. Jaguars and probably other cats kill and eat porcupines without serious injury from the spines. Gaumer thinks that the spines are more of a camouflage than a defense, making the animals difficult for a hawk to see as they sleep during the day among the epiphytic plants of the treetops.

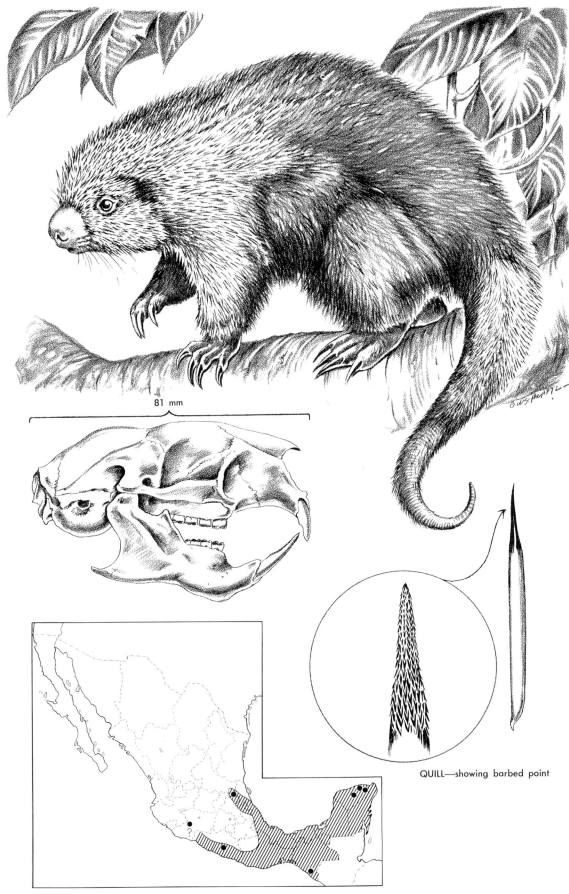

81 mm

QUILL—showing barbed point

Fig. 143. Mexican porcupine, *Coendu mexicanus*.

When attacked, a porcupine raises its tail and rattles it among the erected spines, making a threatening noise. It stamps its rear feet when really annoyed. Sometimes the animal rolls into a bristling ball. But all this pantomime and bluster probably is scant protection from determined enemies.

There is a widespread belief in southern Mexico that the porcupine can throw its quills and hence is dangerous even at a distance. This is decidedly

Fig. 144.   A Mexican porcupine captured in Chiapas.
Photograph by C. W. Schwartz.

not true. The animal can safely be picked up by the unarmed tail if actual contact with the quills is avoided.

The porcupine has a strong odor, detectable even on the trees that it frequents. It also is said to have a very strong and disagreeable taste, although Alvarez del Toro states that some of the Indians of Chiapas eat the flesh. The soft black pelt can be used after all the quills are pulled. On the whole, the animal is little sought by hunters.

FAMILY DASYPROCTIDAE

Pacas and Agoutis

The pacas and the agoutis are large rodents which in flavor and tenderness of flesh are the equal of any game in southern Mexico. They frequent the dense tropical forests where, as a result of constant persecution, they spend the days in underground burrows, coming out to feed mostly at night. The agouti is smaller than the paca and is limited to a smaller range in Mexico.

Paca. *Cuniculus paca*

Other names.—Tepescuintle; tuza real; spotted cavie; *Agouti paca; Coelogenys paca.*

Description.—Size of a raccoon with typical rodent incisors, small ears, very short tail, and short slender legs. Rich brown with whitish spots and stripes on back and sides much like those of a spotted fawn. Underparts and legs dull white. Measurements: head and body—650 to 750 mm.; tail—25 to 35 mm.

Range in Mexico.—Tropical forests from eastern San Luis Potosí southward and eastward through Veracruz, Chiapas, and the Yucatán Peninsula. The pacas, like the agoutis, prefer dense rain forest interspersed with clearings.

The pacas, or cavies, are not common over most of southern Mexico. We hunted for them at night near Xocempich, Yucatán, without seeing a single one, although we found sign and tracks along the edge of a cornfield. At San Juan, Campeche, a paca was observed in a cornfield in late afternoon. Local hunters throughout the peninsula spoke of the *tepescuintle* as an uncommon and much-sought game animal. It seems to be more numerous in parts of its range farther west and north along the Gulf coast. Villa (1948) refers to the paca as being "abundant" near Soconusco, Chiapas, and we found it fairly plentiful in the Sierra de Tuxtla of southern Veracruz. Dalquest (1950) collected five specimens near Xilitla, San Luis Potosí, which suggests that the animals are by no means scarce there.

The home of the paca is the dense, moist undergrowth of the rain forest and tropical evergreen forest. There the animals maintain cleared paths and runways—almost tunnels where the vegetation is thick—which serve

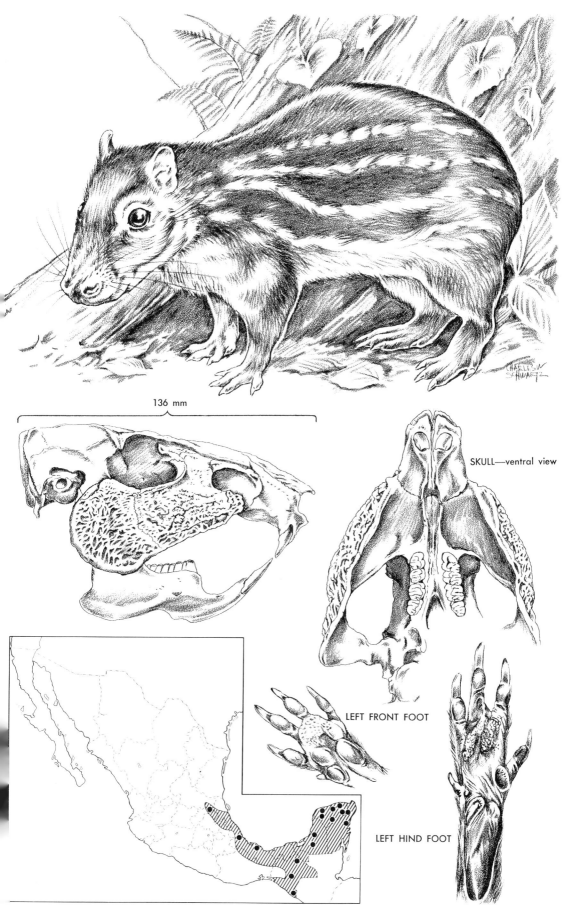

136 mm

SKULL—ventral view

LEFT FRONT FOOT

LEFT HIND FOOT

Fig. 145. Paca. *Cuniculus paca.*

as lanes of escape from their many enemies. During the day they tend to stay in their burrows, which they dig themselves or expropriate from other animals. Most of the burrows are shallow and, unless they lead under too many tree roots, are easily dug out by hunters. An animal will usually have several burrows or will use as alternate shelters hollow logs and stumps or rock piles. In the limestone country of Yucatán, pacas frequent caves or *cenotes* and do not dig burrows. By and large, they tend to stay in these shelters during the day, emerging at night to feed.

Pacas are not social animals. They live singly, each one having its own pathways and hidey-holes. They are shy in temperament and try—with good reason—to avoid man and his dogs. But even in the near vicinity of villages these animals will live in quiet seclusion if there is enough dense ground cover in the moist hollows and draws.

According to Gaumer (1917), pacas breed in the early winter, the females producing litters of two young in the dry season, which in Yucatán is winter and early spring. The period of gestation is not known. The young, which are reared in an underground den, stay with the mother until they are half grown.

Pacas are strict vegetarians, normally preferring various wild fruits and seeds but turning on occasion to such cultivated crops as corn, sugar cane, melons, and squash. They can be somewhat of an agricultural pest where they are abundant, for a paca is large enough to eat a good-sized hole in a milpa. The paca's tendency to frequent cornfields at night is taken advantage of by hunters, who go out with flashlight and shotgun. According to Alvarez del Toro (1952a), another feeding habit of the paca that works to its disadvantage is the tendency to carry food to some secluded dining area. Hunters, after locating such spots—recognized by the hulls and leavings from many previous paca meals—find them favorable places in which to sit and wait for the animal to emerge.

Pacas also are hunted with dogs, which chase the animal from den to den until it is cornered or shot. I attended such a hunt near Tapalapan, Veracruz, in which an animal was trapped in a great hollow log full of ramified cavities, many of them large enough for the smaller dogs in our pack to enter. For a time the log was half full of dogs, their muffled baying indicating that the quarry was somewhere inside. At length the paca burst out of one of the many openings and with a loud grunt scampered off along a runway with astonishing speed. A charge of shot slowed the animal down, and the dogs soon overtook him at his next den. A little work with the machete then finished him off.

In areas where the dense forest has been cleared, as for example in much of Yucatán, pacas are scarce or absent. The shrinkage of the deep, cool forests is probably the major factor leading to scarcity of these animals. But pacas are severely overhunted in much of their range, and this is a contributing factor to their scarcity. The flesh of the paca is so outstandingly delicious that hunters throughout the southeast are forever on its trail. There is some commercial traffic in paca meat, too, especially around Mérida. The hides likewise are valuable and make soft, handsome leather when well tanned.

Agouti. *Dasyprocta punctata* and Related Species

Other names.—Aguti; cuautuza; guaqueque.

Species included here.—*Dasyprocta punctata* and *D. mexicana.*

Description.—Size of a jackrabbit, with small ears and virtually no tail. Legs relatively more slender than a rabbit's. Two color phases—reddish brown (*punctata*) and blackish brown (*mexicana*). Pelage more or less uniform in color on back and sides. (The larger paca has white spots and stripes.) Measurements: head and body—450 to 525 mm.; tail—20 to 35 mm.

Range in Mexico.—Tropical forests from southern Veracruz eastward through most of Chiapas and the Yucatán Peninsula. Rain forest comprises most of the range, but scattered individuals occur in the somewhat drier forests of northern Yucatán and southern Veracruz. Like the pacas, agoutis seem to prefer dense moist forest, interspersed with clearings in which to feed.

The agoutis, like the howler monkeys, jaguarundi cats, jaguars, and various other mammals, have two color phases—reddish brown and black. For none of these mammals has the genetics of color inheritance been worked out, to my knowledge, but for most of them the color phases were first described as characteristics of separate species and later were found to be variant forms of a single species. Populations in any given area tend to be dominated by one or the other color factor. In agoutis, the black animals predominate in southern Veracruz and northern Chiapas, and they are still recognized as *Dasyprocta mexicana,* whereas the agoutis of the whole Yucatán Peninsula and southern Chiapas are mostly reddish and are called *Dasyprocta punctata.* Whether these color phases will prove to be specifically distinct under careful scrutiny is still not known.

Agoutis are similar to pacas in most of their habits. They live in the dense undergrowth of tropical forests, spending much of their time in burrows and other shelters and coming out to feed in the evening and night. Alvarez del Toro (1952*a*) asserts that in undisturbed virgin areas agoutis are largely diurnal and that only where they are regularly persecuted do they become nocturnal like the pacas. Goldman (1913) likewise states that agoutis come out to feed in the morning and evening, and in rainy weather even in the middle of the day; but normally he found them active at night.

The dens of agoutis are excavated burrows, or the animals may utilize hollow logs, stumps, or caves. In Chiapas, Alvarez del Toro found them mostly using log dens with several entrances. Agoutis have systems of trails and pathways similar to those of pacas but narrower. In the virgin

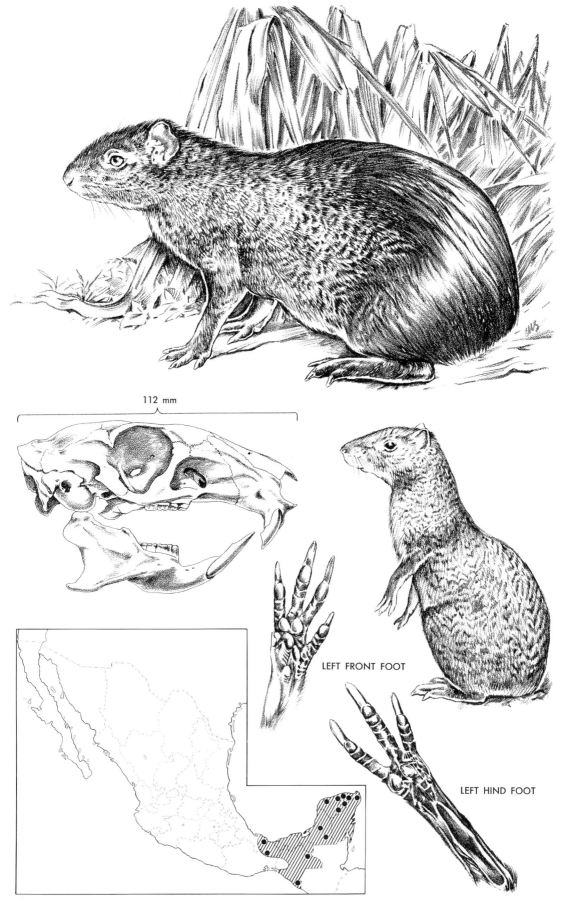

112 mm

LEFT FRONT FOOT

LEFT HIND FOOT

Fig. 146. Agouti. *Dasyprocta punctata*.

rain forest east of El Real, Chiapas, we examined numerous ground burrows of agoutis and occasionally saw one of the animals running like a frightened rabbit for its hole. In Campeche I came across one in a cornfield early one morning, presumably eating the fallen ears. It ran rapidly into the adjoining forest as I approached.

Gaumer (1917) gives the following notes on natural history. Agoutis usually occur singly, rarely in pairs. Females may bear young at any season, but March is the time when most litters are born. An average litter consists of four young. Various plant foods enter the diet of agoutis, including tender leaves and green parts of plants, roots, bark, grains, and fruits. In cane plantations and orchards the animals occasionally cause some damage.

Agoutis are shy and are not easily hunted. Goldman (1913 : 12) states:

They become alarmed at the slightest noise and scamper away, often giving the characteristic squeak or short bark, rapidly repeated several times as they go. The usual method of hunting them is to proceed slowly and cautiously, mainly along trails through the forest, or to wait in the vicinity of their holes until they come out. One day, during the dry season, I heard a rustling noise in the dry leaves, and remaining motionless soon saw an agouti which came rapidly nearer and was shot as it stopped suddenly about 20 yards away. The Indians . . . hunt the agouti for its flesh, and it is one of the favorite game animals of the region.

In Yucatán the accepted manner of hunting agoutis is to slip quietly through cornfields or along forest trails at night, seeking the eye shine with a flashlight. They may also be pursued with dogs or dug from their burrows with machetes.

Although hunted regularly, agoutis often are common or even abundant in good habitat. They withstand hunting better than their relatives the pacas, probably because of their higher reproductive rate. Only clearing of the tropical forest will bring about local extermination. Alvarez del Toro states that the range of the agouti in Chiapas is shrinking steadily as forest clearing advances. Preservation of the tropical forest is the key to conservation of both the agouti and the paca.

Order Carnivora

FAMILY CANIDAE

Coyote, Wolf, Foxes

The order Carnivora, a large and varied group of flesh-eating mammals, is represented in Mexico by five families. Two of these families—Canidae, the dogs, and Ursidae, the bears—include species that are mostly or entirely associated with temperate zones. Only the gray fox ranges widely in the tropics, all the other Mexican canids occurring in the temperate uplands. At the other extreme, the cats of the family Felidae are mostly tropical in their affinities. The remaining two families—the raccoon tribe Procyonidae and the weasel tribe Mustelidae—have about half temperate and half tropical species.

As a group the carnivores are important as fur bearers or as predators on other wildlife or domestic animals. Only a few are commonly thought of as game species.

Coyote. *Canis latrans*

Other name.—Coyote.
Description.—Size of a shepherd dog, with erect, pointed ears, slender muzzle, small eyes set rather close together, and a bushy tail carried ordinarily at a

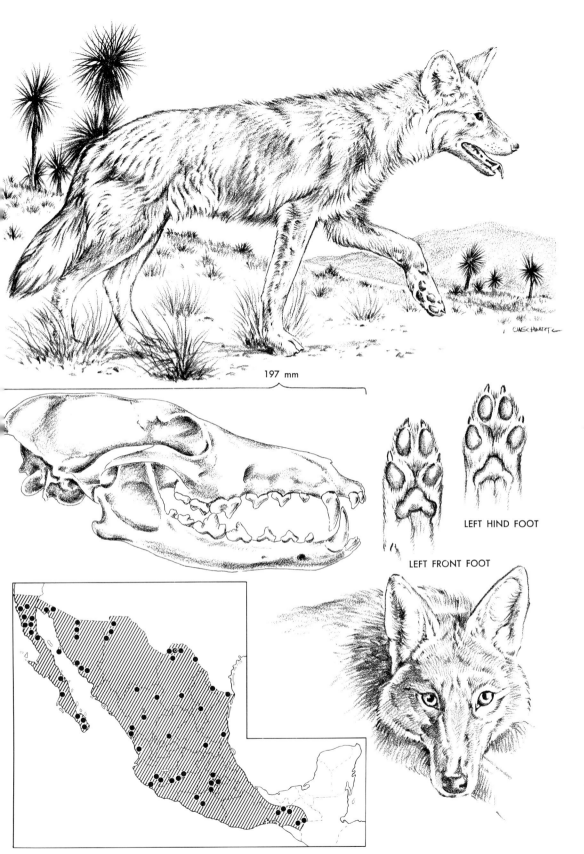

197 mm

LEFT HIND FOOT

LEFT FRONT FOOT

Fig. 147. Coyote. *Canis latrans.*

downward angle (not horizontally like that of a fox). Fur grizzled tan or brown on the back, buffy or whitish underneath. Tail tipped with black. Measurements: head and body—700 to 875 mm.; tail—270 to 375 mm. Weight: 10 to 16 kg. (22 to 35 lbs.).

Range in Mexico.—Throughout the country as far south as the Isthmus of Tehuantepec and the Chiapas highlands. The coyote is ordinarily most numerous in semiarid valleys and plains, scarce in heavily forested areas.

Of all the large carnivores in Mexico, the coyote is the most frequently seen or heard. One cannot drive many miles without catching sight of one of these indolent fellows trotting across the road or sitting, doglike, a safe distance from the highway, watching the passing cars. And in many a camp one hears at night the wild yapping chorus on some nearby hillside serenading the campfire or the moon. Within its normal range the coyote is well known to probably every native and to most casual city travelers.

The coyote is one of the species that has benefited and increased as a result of human settlement. Originally, coyotes probably were only moderately abundant on the plains, deserts, and arid scrublands, and they may not have occurred at all in the pine forests and dense tropical forests. Even today there are no coyotes in the rain forest and cloud forest areas of southern Mexico, and they are rare in the tropical evergreen forest of Veracruz and Oaxaca. Dense vegetation seems to preclude high coyote populations, and it was only after extensive clearing that the species penetrated the coastal plain of Veracruz in small numbers.

In the virgin pine forests of the Sierra Madre Occidental, where wolves are still plentiful, there are few or no coyotes. However, after logging, grazing, and wolf control have been initiated (and they usually come together), coyotes seem to move in. Near Colonia Pacheco in northwestern Chihauhua I have watched this process over the past twenty years. In 1937 the Río Gavilán basin west of Colonia Pacheco was an untouched wilderness with many wolves and no coyotes whatsoever. By 1948, after ten years of development and encroachment by man, wolves had become scarce and a few coyotes had penetrated the area. In 1952 one could drive throughout the basin on logging roads, and much of the country was severely grazed. From our campfire that year we heard much musical yapping by coyotes and not one of the deep, stirring howls of the wolf, although we saw a few wolf tracks.

Similarly, 50 miles southwest of Durango City in the southern Sierra Madre I found wolves in the pine woods in 1945 but no coyotes. Today I am told that ranchers in that area are complaining about coyote depredations on calves. Elsewhere in Mexico, where wolves never inhabitated the pinelands or where they have been eliminated, coyotes generally are common. An exception to this rule is the Sierra del Carmen in Coahuila, where neither wolves nor coyotes are found in the virgin pine forests, but where mountain lions are abundant. Local ranchers suggested to Baker (1956) that lions were suppressing the coyote population there. Whatever the real explanation may be, settlement seemingly has made Mexico a better place for coyotes.

The coyote benefited by the Conquest in still other ways. The introduction of domestic livestock has provided a source of food far exceeding that supplied by the native big game. Livestock carrion, and to a lesser extent live sheep, calves, and colts, have become standard items of diet in the coyote's fare. On top of this, heavy grazing of the prairies and ranges has brought an enormous increase in the populations of ground squirrels, prairie dogs, and black-tailed jackrabbits, all of which are "bread and butter" for the coyote. In short, despite the warfare waged by man—the shooting, trapping, and poisoning that goes on constantly—coyotes probably have increased severalfold in the past two or three hundred years. This is a good example of the importance of environment and food in determining the population of a wild species, irrespective of the amount of hunting and direct kill by man.

Ordinarily coyotes live singly or in pairs, each animal having a home range or hunting area which may overlap that of other coyotes. Family groups often run together until the young are nearly full grown, but adult coyotes do not usually form organized packs as wolves do. Loose aggregations of five or ten animals often gather at a carcass to feed, and several adults may even hunt together temporarily, but there is little evidence of the close ties of an organized pack.

In the western United States and northern Mexico, mating occurs in late winter, and the young are born early in spring. In southern Mexico, where the rains come in summer rather than in winter, breeding may be timed otherwise, although Alvarez del Toro (1952a) finds that in Chiapas the young arrive also in spring (March to July). Most coyote dens are in underground burrows, dug by the mated pair before the young arrive. Often, old ground squirrel burrows or abandoned badger diggings are enlarged to form the den. Occasionally, hollow logs or cavities in the rocks are selected. Most ground burrows are eight or ten feet long with a terminal den about three feet in diameter.

The period of gestation is about nine weeks (63 to 65 days). Litters range from 3 to 9, averaging 6 young (Grinnell, Dixon, and Linsdale, 1937). The mother coyote assumes the principal responsibility for rearing the young, but the male parent often brings food to the family, and he helps train the half-grown pups in hunting. After the young are well grown the family ties disintegrate, and by the subsequent breeding season the young are running independently on their own adopted home ranges.

Because of the relation of coyotes to domestic livestock and to game populations, a great deal of study has been devoted to the food habits of the species in the western United States. Two of the best papers are by Sperry (1941) and Ferrel *et al.* (1953), both of which reports are based on examination of the contents of hundreds of coyote stomachs. The materials presented in these studies indicate that (1) small mammals such as gophers, mice, ground squirrels, rabbits, and (2) carrion, constitute the bulk of the diet of coyotes. Coyotes also eat fruits, grains, and other plant foods—even greens—at times. To be sure, coyotes on occasion kill sheep, goats, calves, colts, pigs, and deer; but these economically important animals are not the main food as is commonly supposed by stockmen and hunters in the United States.

Coyotes are popularly believed to prey heavily on deer, and indeed they do kill a good many, especially fawns. Yet healthy deer in ordinary circumstances seem more or less immune. Of observed coyote-deer encounters, there are nearly as many cases of deer chasing coyotes as the reverse. An irate doe has little difficulty driving a coyote from her fawn, and she may even kill it with a blow of the front feet. In deep snow, however, or when deer are weakened by starvation, the tables are turned in favor of the coyote. But considering Mexican deer ranges as a whole, coyotes have little or no effect on deer numbers.

Coyotes feeding on carrion are often blamed for the death of the animal. A cowpuncher who comes upon a coyote eating a calf usually assumes that the coyote did the killing, which may or may not have been the case. Near Uruapan, Michoacán, I drove a coyote from the fresh carcass of a large horse which obviously must have died from some cause unconnected with the coyote. Had the body been that of a deer or calf I too might have suspected the coyote's guilt. In short, the coyotes' liking for carrion frequently earns them undeserved blame for more damage than they actually cause.

Of coyote depredations on livestock I heard surprisingly few complaints in central and southern Mexico, although I raised the question frequently. Coyotes are not generally abundant in the south, and sheep and goats are customarily herded by at least a boy and a dog and rarely are left unguarded in fenced pastures as is the custom in parts of the United States. When herds are so guarded, they are virtually immune from attack by coyotes.

In the range country of northern Mexico, however, where coyotes are abundant and where stock is permitted to roam unguarded, coyote damage is often significant. In 1903, J. A. Allen wrote of coyotes in northwestern Durango:

In the valley of the Rio Sestin, says Mr. [J. H.] Batty in his notes, "the coyotes greatly annoy the ranchmen in the winter months. They are very bold, often entering corrals in the daytime, killing calves, sheep, and goats. I have known them to take small pigs from the steps of the squatters' huts." He also refers to a night attack on his camp by a pack of about twenty coyotes, who dragged away five deer skins from within twenty feet of where he was lying. (Allen, 1903 : 611.)

This statement of the voracity of Durangan coyotes exceeds any accounts I personally heard in northern Mexico, but several ranchers mentioned losses of range stock which they attributed to coyotes.

The killing of coyotes to protect livestock probably started in Mexico when the Spaniards first brought their flocks and herds into the country, and it is still going on. Allen (1881 : 183) quotes a statement of Edward Palmer's on the coyote population of northeastern Mexico (Coahuila?): "Generally dispersed but not common, having been to a large extent destroyed by poisoning and shooting." Palmer collected coyote specimens in Coahuila and San Luis Potosí in 1879 and 1880.

Rancheros of the northern plains still carry a .30-30 on the saddle so that they can greet each coyote with a fusillade of lead. Moreover, in 1950 various governmental organizations began systematic efforts to keep down the coyote populations in parts of northern Mexico. Poison stations have been set out under a coöperative program between the Subsecretaría de Ganadería (a branch of the Mexican Secretariat of Agriculture and Livestock), the Oficina Sanitaria Panamericana (a branch of the World Health Organization interested in rabies control), and the United States Fish and Wildlife Service. In 1954 the highly toxic poison known as 1080 (sodium fluoroacetate) came into use by these groups, principally in Chihuahua and Durango but, I understand, in other parts of northern Mexico as well. Poisoning of coyotes with 1080 as practiced by the Fish and Wildlife Service in the western United States can be highly effective as a control measure. Substantial kills are reported from the Mexican poison stations.

Perhaps this type of control, although directed primarily to livestock protection, will facilitate antelope restoration on the mesquite-grasslands; but it will not likely be of any particular benefit to other game populations, since coyotes on the whole are predators of rodents, not of game. Furthermore, many other animals will be killed inadvertently by the poison. There is a growing sentiment in the western United States against the use of poisons in predator control. It will be well if this practice is avoided in Mexico, or at least is rigidly regulated.

Wolf. *Canis lupus*

Other names.—Lobo; *Canis nubilus*.

Description.—Size of a large police dog, with broad heavy muzzle, wide-set eyes, and small, erect ears. (Even a small wolf is noticeably larger than a coyote and of heavier frame and build.) Forefeet large, leaving tracks 7 to 10 cm. across. Body grizzled brown or gray, not very different from that of the coyote. Shoulders and back darker than underparts. Measurements: head and body—1,000 to 1,200 mm.; tail—390 to 410 mm. Weight: 30 to 45 km.

Range in Mexico.—Formerly throughout the temperate uplands, from Sonora and Tamaulipas south to Michoacán and Puebla. Wolves now exterminated in

246 mm

FORMER RANGE
•
PRESENT RANGE
▲

LEFT FRONT FOOT

LEFT HIND FOOT

Fig. 148. Wolf. *Canis lupus.*

central uplands and along eastern escarpment. The two remaining extensive blocks of occupied range are (1) the Sierra Madre Occidental, and (2) the arid mountains of western Coahuila and eastern Chihuahua. Additionally, Dalquest (1953) reports a population of wolves in western San Luis Potosí.

There can be no doubt that the wolf in its original abundance was the most formidable and destructive of livestock predators in Mexico. The other large carnivores, such as the mountain lion, jaguar, and grizzly bear, kill some stock, but animal for animal their depredations are minor compared with those of wolves. We can assume, therefore, that from the earliest days of Spanish settlement when domestic cattle, sheep, goats, burros, and horses were brought to this country, the wolves turned at least some of their attention from native game to the more vulnerable domestic herds and flocks, to the considerable detriment of the latter. Undoubtedly, also, the Spaniards took advantage of every opportunity and used every possible means to destroy the wolves. But in spite of persecution, wolves persisted throughout nearly all of their original range until fifty to seventy-five years ago, when technological improvements in firearms, traps, and poisons finally gave a conclusive advantage to the settlers. Now the range of the wolf is shrinking rapidly.

In the vicinity of Lake Pátzcuaro, Michoacán, the wolf was listed in the "Relación de Xiquilpan," written in 1579 (Barlow, 1944), and it was still present in 1884 according to León (1887). But in 1945 I could find no resident of the area who specifically remembered a wolf. Several old men knew vaguely that there had been wolves in past times. Similarly, at Los Reyes in western Michoacán a local hunter stated that he did not know the wolf but he had heard his father speak of it. Lumholtz (1902, vol. 2 : 362) says that the wolf was exterminated in this area (Tancítaro) about 1870.

On the northern slope of Nevado de Toluca, Estado de México, E. W. Nelson found an elaborate pit trap for wolves which had been in use until about 1880. The following description of the trap is taken from Young and Goldman (1944 : 288).

This trap was made by digging a ringshaped trench about 20 feet deep, from 7 to 8 feet across the top, and tapering to a V at the bottom. The diameter of the circular trench across the outer walls was approximately 25 feet and the round, island-like center was 8 or 9 feet across. Both walls of the trench were carefully built from bottom to top with fairly smoothly-faced rock. To operate this trap, a young goat was staked on top of the round island in the middle, and poles loosely covered with branches and other vegetation were so laid across the trench that when a wolf tried to make his way to the bait, he would slip through and become helplessly wedged at the bottom of the pit. Such traps proved very effective in an area of heavy wolf infestation. Nelson was informed that the pits had not been used for more than 10 years previous to the time of his visit to this area in 1893.

Hans Gadow (1908) in his travels through central Mexico found wolves on the east slope of Mount Orizaba, Veracruz, about the beginning of this century.

In each of the accounts cited above, the wolf is carefully distinguished from the coyote, and I am satisfied that the records are valid. It is since the adoption of the breech-loading rifle and parallel improvements in other killing methods that wolves have disappeared in the southern reaches of the Mexican plateau.

In the sparsely settled uplands of northern Mexico, however, wolves still occupy large blocks of range. In some of the wilder parts of the Sierra Madre Occidental I found evidence of fairly large residual wolf populations in the recent past. Ten miles west of Colonia Pacheco, Chihuahua, we saw many tracks in 1937 and found remains of several deer at least some of which were wolf kills. However, this population is shrinking now. One hundred miles north of there, along the United States line, wolves regularly swing up from the Sierra Madre to raid the cattle herds in the Animas Valley and on other ranches near Cloverdale, New Mexico. The wolves in adjoining parts of northeastern Sonora are fewer, but a rancher near Casita complained to us in 1946 of losing some cattle to wolves. West and south of Durango City in the southern reaches of the Sierra I saw wolf tracks several times and heard of at least one cattle rancher who was seeking help in trapping wolves. As grazing and settlement continue to pinch down the wilderness areas of the Sierra Madre, however, the number of wolves and the range that they occupy will continue to shrink.

Reports of the abundance of wolves in Coahuila and eastern Chihuahua are conflicting. Marsh (1937) gives a lurid account of the ravages of "abundant" wolves on livestock in the region of the Sierra del Carmen, whereas Taylor et al. (1945) and Baker (1956) refer to the animal as uncommon in that area. In 1953 I spent a month in the Carmens and found no wolves at all. Eduardo López, a lifelong resident there, told me that a single wolf had come into the region in the late 1920's and preyed on cattle until about 1938, when it disappeared. Sr. López asserted, however, that there still are a few wolves to the south, and to the west in the Sierra Blanca along the Coahuila-Chihuahua border. Dalquest (1953) reports a thriving population south of there, in San Luis Potosí. It would seem, however, that although wolves may have been generally distributed in northern and central Mexico at one time, they were never abundant (Young and Goldman, 1944). The animals are scarce and scattered there now.

In winter, wolves are prone to hunt together in organized packs which are capable of inflicting big losses on livestock herds in one night. Originally, the wolf packs of the prairies attacked and pulled down bison—a task too great for a single wolf to attempt. This pattern of group attack on a large prey animal works admirably on cattle, and there is no steer on the range strong enough or fleet enough to escape a band of wolves when he has been "cut out" or isolated from the main herd. As a rule, a wolf pack will make a new kill each night rather than return to an old carcass; this protects the animals, at least in part, from the traps and poison set out by ranchers. Young and Goldman (1944) cite many instances in which cattle-killing packs have operated successfully for long periods in the face of all-out warfare of stockmen and government trappers. But even the wariest individuals can be taken eventually by a clever and persistent trapper.

Not all wolves are stock killers. Cattle killing is a habit acquired by particular bands or individual wolves, and cattle losses often can be stopped by eliminating the individual killers without having to exterminate all the wolves in an area. Fascinating stories have been told of some of the more infamous wolves that have raided the cattle ranges of the West. Lobo, the "King of the Currumpaw Valley," New Mexico, whose biography is recorded by Ernest Thompson Seton, was one such animal.

The normal diet of the Mexican wolf consists mainly of deer but includes such other native mammals as peccaries, antelope, bighorn sheep, rabbits, and many of the rodents. At times wolves eat some plant foods, such as manzanita berries and other fruits, but this tendency is less marked than in the coyotes. In the Río Gavilán basin of northwestern Chihuahua we found many deer carcasses representing wolf kills, and one adult male wolf that we collected contained in its stomach a whole fawn—head, hoofs, and all—eaten in great chunks. Curiously, there was one extra ear, which had come from an adult deer, presumably the mother of the fawn. In her efforts to defend her young the doe must have leaped in too close. The bobbed-off ear was a record of her valor.

As the breeding season approaches, the packs break up into pairs, which seek their own dens for rearing their litters of young. Mating occurs in late winter, and the young are born after a sixty- to sixty-three-day gestation period, usually in March (Young and Goldman, p. 96). Litters range from 5 to 14 pups, averaging about 7. Until the whelps are a third grown they are kept in a den by the parents and come out only to feed and to romp in the sun for short periods. Most dens are in ground burrows; but wolves, like coyotes, sometimes use caves in the rocks, or hollow logs or stumps as den sites. The male is solicitous of the family and works as hard as the female to bring food for the growing young.

The den is abandoned when the young are about three months old, and thereafter the family hunts together, the parents teaching the young to do their own hunting. As winter approaches, family groups become the nuclei of winter packs, which outsiders or nonbreeding individuals may be permitted to join. Young wolves do not breed as yearlings; they become fully adult at the age of two years. While the adults are busy raising a new batch of pups, the yearlings forage a good deal on their own, often without much success. A young wolf that we took in July, 1948, along the Río Gavilán contained in its stomach only shreds of desiccated deer hide, stripped from the carcass of some long-dead animal. The period of emancipation from parental care is probably a difficult one.

Fig. 149.   An adult male wolf collected along the Río Gavilán in northern Chihuahua, in 1948.

The foregoing paragraphs have shown that wolves do extensive damage to domestic livestock. But what of their predation on game? At least some wolves live mostly on deer and smaller game such as rabbits and rodents. The wolves occupying the wilderness of the northern Sierra Madre Occidental must have lived entirely on game (mostly deer), since up to a few years ago there were virtually no cattle or other stock in the mountains. Yet deer were abundant. Under completely natural conditions, wolves and mountain lions seem to harvest merely the surplus or annual crop of deer, keeping the breeding herd at a reasonable level. In this sense, the population of the predator (wolf) is determined by the abundance and availability of the prey (deer), rather than vice versa. The deer in turn exist in numbers conforming to the carrying capacity of the range, as determined by supplies of food, cover, and water. Such a natural balance is advantageous to both the deer and the wolves in the long run, and it is erroneous to suppose that we must destroy the large predators in order to protect the game populations in wilderness areas.

On cattle range, it is usually necessary to kill wolves to prevent serious depredations on the vulnerable domestic animals. It may be necessary also to take some measures to restore vanishing game species, such as the antelope; for a few wolves along with coyotes seem to be preying on the remaining antelope in northern Chihuahua. But on the whole, keeping down the wolf population is not an important aspect of game management in Mexico.

As mentioned in the preceding chapter, there appears to be some degree of social intolerance between wolves and coyotes. To be sure, there are many areas where the two occur together on the same range, but I suspect that there are not as many coyotes on wolf range as in similar areas where the wolves have been exterminated. Retaining a few wolves, then, may be one way to hold down excessive coyote populations.

Whatever the economic importance of the wolf may be in Mexico, it is one of the most interesting of the native mammals, and definite provision should be made to prevent its complete extermination. Setting aside a great national park or wilderness preserve in the northern Sierra Madre Occidental would be one of the best ways of maintaining at least a fragment of the shrinking population. The Mexican lobo is as much a part of the lore of the country as the feathered serpent, and we would be poorspirited indeed if we could not find at least one place in Mexico where the wolf may persist, safe from the incessant warfare of the cattlemen.

Kit Fox. *Vulpes macrotis*

Other name.—Zorra norteña.
Description.—Very small, with enormous pointed ears and cylindrical bushy

tail. Pale gray on back, with buffy underparts; tip of tail black. Measurements: head and body—440 to 500 mm.; tail—280 to 325 mm. Weight: 2 to 2.5 kg.

Range in Mexico.—Deserts of Baja California, western Sonora, and central desert from Chihuahua and Coahuila south probably to San Luis Potosí. I have found only seven definite locality records of the kit fox in Mexico, but it is probable that a sparse population occurs (or formerly occurred) throughout the desert regions, and the range is so designated in fig. 150.

The beautiful kit fox is an evasive and virtually unknown member of the desert fauna. Apparently it is nowhere abundant but rather occurs in moderate numbers on the desert plains far removed from human habitation, where it feeds on kangaroo rats and other native rodents. Kit foxes are nocturnal, spending the daylight hours in cool underground burrows, which usually are 8 to 10 feet long and reach a level several feet below the surface of the desert. The entrance to a kit fox burrow is round, with a tunnel 8 to 10 inches in diameter. Coyote burrows are much larger, and badger holes are eliptical in cross section—wider than they are deep. A mound of loose dirt is piled in front of the burrow of the kit fox, and ordinarily in or near it are many scattered remains of rodents. The kit fox apparently carries home its prey to eat it near the safety of the burrow rather than where it was caught.

The kit fox is reputed to be one of the fastest of mammals, at least on short runs. Cahalane (1947 : 235) describes the escape habits as follows:

This burst of speed does not last long. The little kit fox either pops down a burrow, to hide out from trouble, or begins to dodge. This in itself is an efficient defense against a pursuing eagle, dog, or coyote. The fleeing "swift" zigzags sharply, with great speed, and so suddenly that the human eye cannot see just how it is done. One instant the fox may be racing north. The next moment it is traveling west or east at undiminished speed. Meanwhile the baffled pursuer is slowing down, and violently trying to turn. All the time the kit fox runs low, hugging the ground, with its tail straight to the rear. The chances are that the kit fox will be able to find an old badger hole or similar shelter before tiring out.

When hunting, the kit fox glides over the desert in a fast trot until it scents or sees a rabbit, a kangaroo rat, or other prey, whereupon it hugs the ground and stalks and pounces much like a cat. A good part of its food probably is derived from insects, snakes, lizards, and fruits, but small mammals are the mainstay of the diet.

From 2 to 7 young (average number 4 or 5) are born in the underground den in late winter, usually in February. They are reared by both parents, as in other species of wild canids, and become independent late in summer.

Despite their agility in escaping natural enemies, kit foxes seem to be incapable of adapting their habits so as to avoid the guns, traps, and poisons of men. Benson (1938 : 17) states:

They are so unsuspicious that they are easily trapped and even more easily poisoned. Consequently, wherever trappers are active, and especially wherever

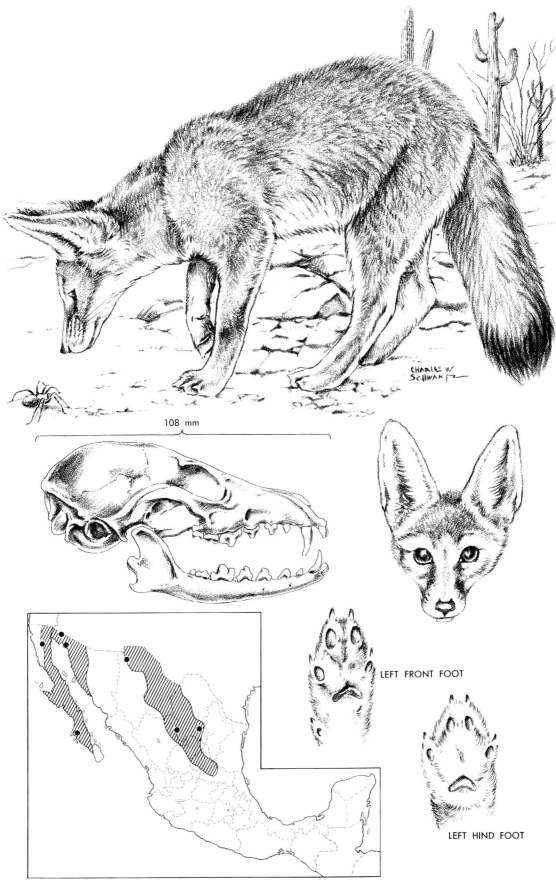

108 mm

LEFT FRONT FOOT

LEFT HIND FOOT

Fig. 150. Kit fox, *Vulpes macrotis*.

control campaigns involving the use of poison have been carried out against predatory animals on areas inhabited by kit foxes, the foxes have been greatly reduced in number or entirely eliminated.

This susceptibility to trapping and poisoning has been one of the chief causes of the present scarcity of kit foxes in the western United States and doubtless also in northern Mexico. It is tragic indeed that as a consequence of our efforts to control coyotes and other predators of possible economic importance the beautiful and wholly beneficial little kit fox has in some places been reduced to the verge of extinction. This well illustrates the dangers of indiscriminate and unselective predator control by the use of poison.

Gray Fox. *Urocyon cinereoargenteus*

Other names.—Zorra; zorra gris; gato de monte (southern Mexico).

Description.—Medium-sized, decidedly larger than the kit fox, much smaller than the coyote. Tail long and fairly slender (not like the heavy cylindrical bush of the kit fox), carried straight out in back in typical fox fashion. Ears large and pointed. Back grizzled and blackish; throat and belly white; along each side a band of rusty brown separates these contrasting colors. Tail blackish dorsally, with coal-black tip. Feet small and round, leaving tracks much like those of a house cat and very little larger. Measurements: Head and body—500 to 600 mm.; tail—300 to 400 mm. Weight: 3 to 4 kg.

Range in Mexico.—Throughout the Republic, in varying density according to vegetation type. Highest populations of this fox occur in semiarid brushlands, both temperate and tropical. I have no records of occurrence in the central desert, but the species lives in brushy watercourses in the deserts of Sonora and Baja California and probably exists in small numbers along the draws and ravines of the central desert. Records are lacking from the virgin rain forest; if gray foxes occur in this type of habitat it must be around savannas and clearings.

The gray fox is the most numerous and widely distributed carnivore in Mexico. Its abundance in the highly settled southern and central uplands is a tribute to the sagacity and adaptability of the species. Gray foxes seem to thrive as well on the outskirts of big cities as in the remote, unpopulated ranges, so long as the food supply is good and the vegetation is sufficiently scrubby and dense. Whereas kit foxes prefer the open desert, the gray foxes are always associated with brush. Forested regions which have been partly cleared and have reverted to second growth may become better habitat for gray foxes than they were originally. The numbers of gray foxes and the total range in Mexico undoubtedly have increased as a result of man's activities.

The highest local population I found in Mexico was on the Hacienda de Acuña in the Sierra de Tamaulipas. There a combination of dense, brushy draws and oak openings made ideal habitat for gray foxes; scarcely a day passed without our seeing one or more foxes hunting along the edges of the draws or crossing under the oaks from one ravine to another. A family of

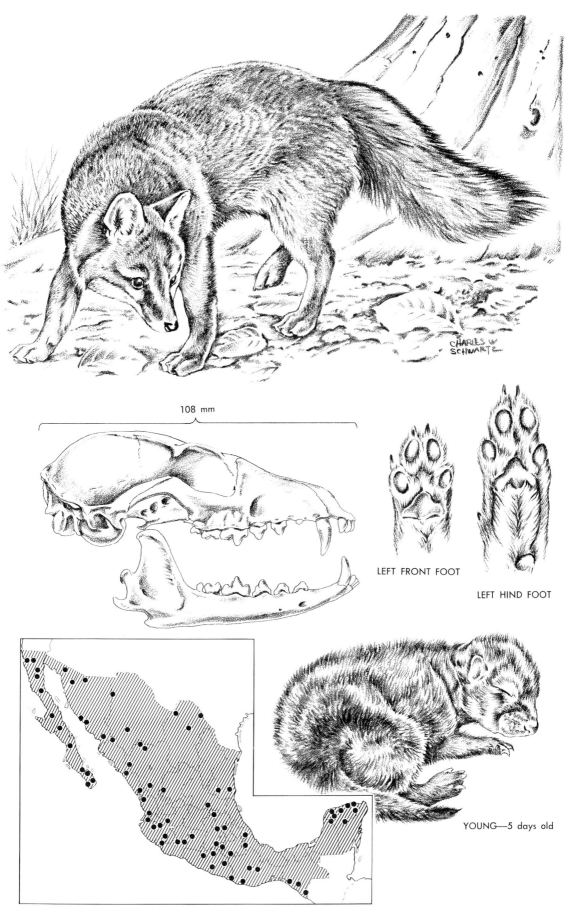

108 mm

LEFT FRONT FOOT

LEFT HIND FOOT

YOUNG—5 days old

Fig. 151.   Gray fox, *Urocyon cinereoargenteus*.

four well-grown young and their parents lived in a brushy rockslide within view of our camp, and we often watched the young playing like puppies in the early morning sun. When not persecuted, gray foxes are surprisingly gentle and confiding, showing no fear of man even in broad daylight. The parents of the family mentioned above more than once jumped on big boulders to watch us pass within thirty yards of them. We carried guns and could easily have killed them; but as we did not, they became even more fearless as our stay in this camp continued. One day, half a mile from camp I met face to face on a trail an adult gray fox, possibly one of the camp pair. We saw each other simultaneously at a range of about twenty yards. The fox crouched, then raised its head slowly above the low scrub to study me with obvious curiosity. When I resumed walking directly toward the animal, it glided swiftly into the brush beside the trail, to reappear thirty yards to the side, from which vantage point it watched me go by without in any way attempting to conceal its position. After I had passed it trotted back to the trail and resumed its original course.

In a camp near Poliutla, Guerrero, we were writing notes one night by the light of an oil lantern when there commenced near by a crunching noise of an animal eating bones. A flashlight beam revealed two gray foxes within thirty feet of us cleaning up camp scraps that had been thrown into the brush. They were unconcerned by our close proximity, our conversation, the campfire, or the flashlight and continued to exploit the rich find of edibles with scarcely a glance in our direction. We did not interfere with their foraging, which continued for almost half an hour.

The above examples illustrate the fearlessness of gray foxes that have not been pursued or shot at. In contrast, when the animals are regularly hunted or chased with dogs they become as wary and secretive as the proverbial foxes of nursery tales. They may be locally abundant but are rarely seen except along the highways at night or when surprised in their daytime beds.

The gray fox is the only member of the dog family that is really adept at climbing trees. To escape a pack of hounds a gray fox often will scramble up a tree and hide in the upper branches. It will even climb up vertical trunks with no branches closer to the ground than ten or twelve feet. More than once a fox has been observed sunning itself comfortably in the fork of a limb. According to Goldman (1938) the gray foxes of the tropics have sharper and more recurved claws than those of the temperate uplands and are even more aboreal.

Gray foxes forage mostly at night, although, as related above, under some circumstances they go abroad in the early morning and late afternoon. Small mammals, from mouse to jackrabbit size, make up the bulk of the diet. But these foxes are more omnivorous than most canids: fruits, berries, insects, reptiles, amphibians, birds, and their eggs are important parts of their diet at certain times of year. Gray foxes are also active scavengers, eating garbage and carrion freely.

The young are born and reared in ground dens or in cavities in rocks, logs, or stumps. Mating takes place in late winter, and the young arrive in March or April after a sixty-three-day gestation period. In southern Mexico the breeding season is much the same as in the north, according to Alvarez del Toro (1952a); that is, pups may be expected in Chiapas in April and May. Litters range from 2 to 5, averaging about 4 young. Their development and training follows the normal course for wild canids, and the families separate in late summer or early autumn. The 4 three-quarter grown young seen in southern Tamaulipas early in August, 1945, would have been ready to abandon parental care by September or October. During the fall and winter, gray foxes are more or less solitary in their habits. They do not form packs but hunt alone and thus are limited to the small game that a single animal can catch and kill.

Under some circumstances gray foxes may become pests by preying upon poultry. Chickens, domestic ducks, or turkeys that are allowed to wander into the brush are subject to heavy predation when foxes are abundant.

Gray foxes also prey freely upon quail, cottontails, and other species of small game, but ordinarily this predation does not reduce the game populations below the carrying capacity of the habitat. Quail, for example, in territories well supplied with cover, food, and water will not suffer many losses to gray foxes or to other predators. But a quail covey forced to occupy a poor habitat (because the good locations are already filled by other quail) will be subject to loss from predation. Although under such circumstances gray foxes have killed a good many quail, it is not to be construed that the foxes are an important factor in limiting the quail population. Control of foxes is not a remedy for scarcities of small game as is often supposed by hunters.

On the whole, the role of the gray fox is a neutral one, the occasional damages to poultry and game being offset by the benefits of rodent control and the value of the fur (which is slight in the warm Mexican climate). Regardless of our attitude toward this species, the gray fox has demonstrated its ability to cope with modern changes in land use and with persecution by hunters, which is not true of the guileless kit fox of the desert.

FAMILY URSIDAE

BEARS

Black Bear. *Ursus americanus*

Other names.—Oso; oso negro; *Euarctos americanus.*
Description.—Small to medium-sized. Fur may be black, blackish brown, or

cinnamon brown. These color phases represent natural variants within the species *americanus;* a "cinnamon bear" may come from the same litter as a "black bear." Bears of this species are generally smaller than grizzly bears and have appreciably shorter front claws (fig. 152). Measurements: head and body—1.2 to 1.8 m.; tail —about 100 mm. Weight: 50 to 150 kg. A three-year-old male that we trapped in Coahuila weighed 56 kg. (125 lbs.). Older males are much larger. Females usually are 20 per cent smaller than males.

Range in Mexico.—Pine-oak forests of the Sierra Madre Occidental as far south as southern Zacatecas; desert mountain ranges of northeastern Sonora, Chihuahua, Coahuila, and northern Nuevo León; forests and brushlands of the Sierra Madre Oriental in southern Nuevo León and Tamaulipas. The range outlined above and shown in fig. 152 is that now occupied by black bears. I have found no evidence of black bears ever having occupied the southern uplands, although it is possible that the species once ranged much farther south than at present. Ranges in some places have shrunk as a result of extermination by hunting and of habitat changes, but on the whole the black bear has been surprisingly persistant over much of its range in northern Mexico.

It is a matter of some astonishment that the black bears of Mexico have maintained themselves so well in the face of ceaseless hunting and persecution. Nominally, bears may be taken in Mexico only between October 1 and January 15, but actually there is no enforcement of the closed season, and hunting goes on throughout the year. From conversations with numerous cowboys, loggers, and backwoods farmers I gathered that a man would be considered foolish who passed up the opportunity to kill a bear, whatever the season. The meat is highly edible, the fat is useful for cooking and for dressing leather, and the pelt has considerable commercial value—so why let a bear get away? The bear's survival over so wide a range is due, then, to the animal's own wariness and cunning in keeping out of rifleshot.

To be sure, populations are sparse in most parts of the range. Marsh (1937) reports that black bears are common in the mountains of northern Coahuila despite hunting by American and Mexican sportsmen and by local cowboys. Before 1932 the average number of bears killed each year on the Jardín Ranch in the northern Sierra del Carmen was two or three. After that date the owner of the ranch forbade hunting parties to enter his property, and in the ensuing five years only three bears were killed—all by residents who had stock on the range. Marsh intimates that the bears increased as a result of this voluntary protection. We visited the Carmens in a very dry year, 1953, and found relatively little bear sign, but we were told there had been many bears a few years previously and that they would come back—from where no one seemed to know. I personally suspect that the bear population of the Carmens is in serious decline.

Baker (1956) mentions several other localities in Coahuila where bears are still common, including the Sierra de la Madera, Sierra del Pino, and Sierra de San Marcos. But he is far less optimistic than Marsh was twenty years ago about the future of the black bear in this region. He states (p. 298):

The bear population is being slowly reduced because the animal is shot at every opportunity. Ranch riders are often equipped with rifles for this purpose. On June 21, 1938, two bears, a female and her cub, were killed in a mountain cañon near La Babia by a rider and left where they fell. We retrieved the specimens being able to save only the skeletons. It was reported to me by Señor Juan José Zapata of the Hacienda Rincón in 1953, that bear are entirely gone in the Sierra de los Hecheros and that the last one had been killed three years before. These mountains contain abundant montane chaparral, attractive to black bear, but intensive hunting seems to have eliminated the population. The mountains in the vicinity of Saltillo have few bear present because of the great number of hunters operating in the area.

Fairly good bear populations still occur in the Sierra Madre Occidental. I have seen much sign west of Colonia Pacheco, Chihuahua, and 50 kilometers south of Durango City, Durango, and I understand that all parts of the intervening mountain chain are still inhabited by bears. In the Sierra del Nido northwest of Chihuahua City black bears seem likewise to be still common, along with grizzlies, and I am told that they are numerous in the Mesquital Indian Reservation of southern Durango and in the mountains west of the Río Bolaños along the Jalisco-Nayarit line.

Bears are scarce now in northern Sonora, along most of the foothills of the Sierra Madre Occidental (on both east and west), and in the Sierra Madre Oriental of Nuevo León. Near Cerro de Potosí, one of the higher mountains in the latter range, we were told by local residents that there were very few bears; in 1946 Chester Lamb saw the skin of a bear killed the previous year in this vicinity.

Adult black bears are solitary in habit except during the short mating season in early summer, when pairs run together for a few weeks. After that, the pairs separate. The bears then partake heartily of the fall harvest of nuts and berries, storing up fat for the period of winter dormancy. In the higher mountains of Mexico bears are dormant for several months—at least through December, January, and February. At an elevation of 6,500 feet in the pine forests west of Colonia Pacheco, Chihuahua, we found no fresh bear sign from mid-December to mid-January, 1937. Our guide, the late Clarence Lunt, stated that the animals had retired to their winter beds early in December. Also, in the mountains south of Durango City in early March, 1946, all the droppings and sign appeared to be several months old and there was no indication that any of the bears had yet become active, although it was time for them to reappear.

It is said that at lower elevations the period of dormancy is shorter and some individuals may remain active all winter and not retire at all. The idea is proposed by Grinnell et al. (1937 : 116) that bears den up in winter to escape the period of acute food shortage as well as to avoid cold weather. At elevations below 5,000 feet in northern Mexico a bear probably could find plenty to eat through the winter months, at least in good years.

A dormant bear is not truly hibernating, since its body temperature remains normal and the rate of metabolism is not materially reduced. The animal is simply in a deep sleep, drawing its sustenance from the thick layer of fat that was built up during the autumn months of plenty. These winter sleeps take place in caves or sheltered dens, usually on warm south slopes. The arrival of spring and warm sunshine arouses the sleeping bears, which emerge thin and hungry to resume their normal habits.

It is in the winter dens that the females have their young. A young female bear first becomes pregnant at the age of three years, and usually her first litter is a single cub. Subsequent litters consist of 2, 3, or rarely 4 cubs, 2 being the normal number. The period of gestation is about seven months or a little longer, and the young are born in or about January. At birth the cubs are very small (some 250 gm.), naked, toothless, and generally helpless. They find their way to the nipples, however, and develop rapidly while the mother contentedly sleeps on. When it is time for the family to emerge in spring the young are well furred and are able to follow the mother and to climb trees when so ordered by their parent. They weigh about two kilograms at this stage of life.

Throughout the summer the female bear rears her young and protects them from possible enemies, of which male bears are perhaps the most dangerous. The mother of a new litter does not breed again that year but avoids the males and tends her family on through the fall. She may den for the winter with the well-grown young of the previous season. By the second summer the cubs are able to care for themselves and the female breeds again. From this schedule it may be seen that the breeding potential of the black bear is very low. A female six years old may have borne a single cub in her third year and twins in her fifth year—an average of one young for every two years of her life. With such a slow reproductive rate, a population of bears cannot withstand a heavy harvest, and overshooting may lead quickly to local extinction of the animals.

Although black bears ordinarily are very shy of human beings, avoiding encounters with them whenever possible, a female with cubs, in her zeal to protect her young, may be quite dangerous. It is well not to bother such a family or to get between the mother and her young. A wounded or cornered adult also will fight effectively and aggressively to defend itself from a man or a pack of dogs. Under most other circumstances black bears are harmless and little to be feared.

Black bears will eat a great variety of plant and animal foods, but the usual diet consists for the most part of fruits, nuts, and insects. Dozens of bear droppings that I have examined in the mountains of northern Mexico contained mostly the remains of manzanita berries or acorns. These are undoubtedly the most important autumn foods. Almost all types of fruits and berries are eaten through the summer months, including wild cherries, madrone

273 mm

RIGHT FRONT FOOT

RIGHT HIND FOOT

Fig. 152. Black bear, *Ursus americanus.*

berries, gooseberries, mahonia, and cultivated fruits. Occasionally bears damage corn by eating the ripening ears. Lumholtz (1902 : 226) reported such damage in the Chihuahua highlands. Splintered stumps and logs which have been broken up by bears searching for ants are commonly observed on bear ranges. Having stirred up an ant nest, a bear will allow the angry insects to swarm on its paws and then will lick them off scores at a time. Other foods are grasshoppers, crickets, and especially bees and their honey whenever these are available.

A black bear is not averse to eating meat, but it is not particularly adept at obtaining it. In foraging under rocks and logs, a bear sometimes uncovers rodents and flattens them with a swat of the paw; rarely, one will stumble upon a fawn or a calf too young to run away and will kill it. Grown deer or livestock are not usually taken, however, unless they have died from some other cause and are available to the bear as carrion. Sometimes a super-annuated and almost toothless old black bear will learn to kill livestock, but such renegades are rare.

On the whole, the habits of black bears are in no way deleterious to the interests of human beings, and it is never justifiable to exterminate these animals on the pretext of protecting livestock, game, or human life. It may be necessary to kill an occasional dangerous or destructive individual, but not a whole population.

Bear hunting with hounds is a rigorous and exciting sport. A good many American and Mexican sportsmen come to northern Mexico each autumn to hunt bears, and unquestionably the black bear is one of the more important of the Mexican big game mammals. Professional guides take many parties out each year, and as long as the supply of bears is maintained, this business, which pays thousands of pesos annually to local residents, will continue and probably expand. The black bear not only should be protected as a part of the native fauna, but it can well be put under careful management for its monetary value in the important tourist trade. Conservation of the forests and local regulation of the kill are essential for the preservation of the black bear. Because of the slow reproductive rate, probably no more than a fourth or a fifth of a bear population should be killed each year.

Grizzly Bear. *Ursus horribilis*

Other names.—Oso plateado; oso gris; oso grande; *Ursus nelsoni; U. kennerleyi; U. magister; U. horriaeus.*

Description.—Very large, with massive head, small ears, and high forehead, which gives the face a concave or "dished" profile. Adults have a distinct shoulder hump which black bears lack. Claws of forefeet long (up to 80 mm.), only slightly curved, and light-colored. (Black bears have short, black claws, "hooked" to permit tree climbing.) Fur brown but may vary from pale golden to dark umber. The skin of an old male killed in the Sierra del Nido, Chihuahua, in 1955 is dark umber in general color, with areas of tan on the face and backs

335 mm

RIGHT HIND FOOT

RIGHT FRONT FOOT

FORMER RANGE

PRESENT RANGE

Fig. 153.   Grizzly bear, *Ursus horribilis*.

of the legs; scattered white hairs on the back give a grizzled appearance. A yearling bear from the same area (pelt examined at Rancho Providencia) is rather uniformly chocolate brown.

Size of grizzly bears varies greatly; no body measurements of Mexican specimens are available. All descriptions of Mexican grizzlies state that they are "small" relative to northern grizzlies. Measurements: head and body—1.5 to 2.0 m. Weight: 140 to 320 kg.

Range in Mexico.—Originally northern Baja California, northeastern Sonora, most of Chihuahua and Coahuila, and northern Durango. Currently grizzlies are known only from the Cerro Campana (50 mi. north of Chihuahua City) and the adjoining Santa Clara and Nido ranges extending to the northwest of that point. However, in the rough cumbres of those contiguous ranges the species is still present in fairly large numbers.

Of all the mammals native to Mexico there is not one to take the measure of the grizzly bear. In size, in power, and in self-reliant independence the grizzly has no match. He fears no beast. Mountain lions, wolves, and black bears withdraw discreetly, even from their own kills, when the grizzly comes to feed. The strongest range bull cannot match his strength. Yet for all his majesty, the grizzly has been virtually exterminated by man and his dogs, traps, poisons, and .30-30 rifles. That so noble a species, the very symbol of wildness and rugged freedom, should be trampled to extinction under the heel of "progress" is a sad commentary on our civilization.

The earliest certain account of the grizzly in Mexico is that of James O. Pattie, an American trapper who visited northwestern Mexico in the 1820's. He knew the grizzly from New Mexico and Arizona and reported its presence near Santa Catarina Mission in the Sierra Juárez, Baja California (Pattie, 1905 : 221). An earlier reference to grizzlies in extreme southern California (and possibly northern Baja California) is that of José Longinos Martínez, who traveled through the region in 1792. Somewhere near San Diego he wrote (Simpson, 1938 : 35): "The animals which attack man are the bears and vipers, the bear especially killing many gentiles [Indians]. Within a short time I have seen two dead gentiles, victims of this ferocious animal." Whether the bear referred to was north or south of the present international boundary it was undoubtedly the grizzly, and one can detect an attitude of awe and respect toward the great beast. How long the grizzly persisted in Baja California is not known, but it has been extinct there for at least several decades.

In the northern Sierra Madre, many grizzly bears were encountered by the members of the United States and Mexican Boundary Survey party that located the present international boundary in 1855. The following quotation is taken from the field notes of Dr. C. B. Kennerly, one of the naturalists of the survey party (Baird, 1859 : 28). Although Dr. Kennerly distinguished between the small grizzly of northern Mexico, which he called the "brown bear," and the large grizzly of California, both are in reality grizzly bears.

These animals [small grizzlies or "brown bears"] were observed by us in greater or lesser numbers in the San Luis mountains, the Sierra Madre, and at Los Nogales; being particularly numerous at the first and last named localities. We are assured by the Mexicans of Sonora, who also distinguished this animal from the grizzly, that it was feared by themselves, as well as by the Indians, more than the latter, on account of its ferocity. This, however, admits of a considerable degree of doubt; for, notwithstanding some very good proofs of its boldness within our own knowledge, we also observed almost unexampled evidence of its cowardice. While, on one occasion, a very old male rushed unexpectedly from the bushes and made a fierce and unprovoked attack upon a gentleman of the Boundary Commission, who, probably, only saved his life by a fortunate escape into a neighboring tree, we observed, on a subsequent occasion, in the same vicinity, a female entirely forsake her cubs by a rapid retreat, and without being wounded; and this, too, notwithstanding the cries of the little ones while we pursued and captured them; she only looked around once, at a distance of half a mile, raising herself on her hind feet in a menacing manner, then again fled rapidly over the hills and disappeared. In the same region, a very large female grizzly defended her young with great desperation, and only fled after the cubs were entirely beyond the reach of the hunters, when she made her escape, covered with wounds. . . .

Near the highest crest of the Sierra Madre, called "San Luis mountains," I had an opportunity to witness a rare butchery, by which, in less than one hour, a whole family of grizzlies was killed, without one offering the slightest resistance. It was about noon on the 11th of October, 1855, when our long trains, coming from Guadaloupe Pass, in the Sierra Madre, towards the San Luis springs, met on the plains these unexpected mountaineers. When surprised, they were lying on the ground not far from each other digging roots. The position in which they performed this work naturally caused long narrow strips of grass lands to be turned up and searched as if it had been done by a bad plough. I could not learn what kind of roots they had been looking for. After taking off the thick skin of these root-diggers, we found them all in a very poor condition, and this may account for the want of that resistance which they failed to offer. The ungrizzly-like behavior of these poor brutes induced the majority of our party to doubt their being grizzlies at all. They evidently had descended from the surrounding mountains, where they have their stronghold in the rough trachytic recesses of this part of the Sierra Madre, the highest crest of which is densely crowned by a dark growth of pines. There their fruit stores had probably given out in the late season, and they were obliged to resort to roots to satisfy their hunger.

Dr. Kennerly preserved one specimen of grizzly, taken at Los Nogales, northeastern Sonora, in June, 1855.

In 1892, Dr. E. A. Mearns visited the San Luis Mountains with the (second) International Boundary Survey. Apparently grizzlies were still abundant, for he states (Mearns, 1907 : 12): "The presence at the time of numerous Sonoran grizzly bears and of the 'Kid' and his band of renegade Apache Indians added danger to this and subsequent trips into this still wild region." In 1948, Floyd Johnson of Colonia Pacheco told me that he had seen very large bear tracks in the San Luis Mountains a few years before, and it is barely possible that some of the animals persist there even today. Black bears are still common in that range.

In 1894, W. W. Price, collecting mammals for the American Museum along the Arizona-Sonora border, found grizzlies already scarce. He records only one "silver tip" as having been killed in the region in several years—in Guadalupe Cañon in extreme northeastern Sonora along the Arizona border (Allen, 1895 : 255). The skin was in the possession of Mr. J. H. Slaughter, owner of San Bernardino Ranch.

In 1899, Dr. E. W. Nelson collected in the vicinity of Casas Grandes and Colonia García, Chihuahua, and brought back several specimens of grizzlies which were named by Merriam "*Ursus nelsoni.*" I cannot ascertain from the writings of either Nelson or Merriam whether the big bears were common or scarce at that time. However, in 1937 I visited the same area and found that the grizzly was by then locally extinct, the last individuals having been killed in 1928 and 1932 along the Chihuahua-Sonora boundary west of Pacheco.

Thus in a period of less than half a century the grizzly bear was reduced from abundance to extinction along the United States border and in the northern Sierra Madre.

Farther south and east in Chihuahua, grizzlies have held out somewhat longer. Imaz Baume (1938 : 548) published a photograph of a bear, said to be a young grizzly, killed by Crisóforo B. Peralta at Los Metates, Chihuahua, in October, 1935. This place is near the Cerro de la Yedra, as nearly as I can locate it, which would be close to wild country where grizzlies may still occur.

A recent account of grizzlies in Chihuahua was given to me orally by Mr. Ernest E. Lee of Tucson, Arizona, who with his several brothers has hunted all the species of large carnivores in Mexico. In the 1930's the Lee brothers started going to the northern Sierra del Nido in central Chihuahua after mountain lions and bears. On their first trips they encountered grizzlies frequently, and with their hounds they tracked down and killed one or more each visit. But on each succeeding trip they found fewer grizzlies, until finally they could find no more. The last grizzly killed by the Lees in the Sierra del Nido was taken in 1941. In 1945 the brothers followed the track of a single animal but failed to overtake it.

However, there is abundant evidence that grizzlies still exist in the Sierra del Nido. In September, 1955, Mr. Dan Webster saw a live yearling grizzly in the possession of Alejandro López Escalera, a taxidermist in Chihuahua City. The animal had been captured as a cub in the Sierra del Nido in 1954. Sr. López had photographs of other grizzlies killed there in recent years.

In 1957 I examined the skin of a magnificent male grizzly killed by Sr. Isaías T. García in Cañon de Madera on the east slope of the Sierra del Nido, on October 24, 1955. The bear measured 1.98 meters from nose to tail and was estimated to weigh 320 kilograms (see fig. 154). Subsequently, on

October 4, 1957, Sr. García killed a female grizzly in the same general area; this animal is shown in figure 155. The hide of a yearling grizzly, shot in the same area in 1955, was shown to us by Sr. Filomeno Barrios, owner of Rancho Providencia. The skull of a young adult was obtained on the adjoining Rancho del Nido; this animal was killed in 1954 or 1955.

With a field party from the Museum of Vertebrate Zoölogy I camped in the Sierra del Nido for ten days in June, 1957. Along the cumbre we found the fresh tracks of 10 bears, some of which certainly were grizzlies, judging by the size of tracks and the long foreclaws. Our guide, Camarillo, twenty-eight years of age, stated that he had seen 13 grizzlies in his lifetime—6 in the Sierra del Nido, 4 in the Santa Claras, and 3 on Cerro Campana. He had not seen that many black bears, and he considered the grizzly more abundant. However, he and other local residents asserted that the number of bears of both species had been shrinking in recent years. The few remaining grizzlies are endangered by overhunting, and unless some rapid and decisive

Fig. 154.   Large male grizzly bear killed by Sr. Isaías T. García on the east slope of the Sierra del Nido, Chihuahua, on October 24, 1955.

action is taken by the government to protect these majestic animals, there will soon be no more.

The preferred habitat of the grizzly bear seems to have been the brush-covered foothills rather than the high, forested mountains. All the places mentioned above which were frequented by grizzlies lie in the scrub-oak belt or along the lower (xeric) fringe of the pine forest. Perhaps this predilection for the lower country hastened the disappearance of the species, since the foothills were developed for livestock production long before the mountains were invaded by stock raisers. Even today, parts of the Sierra Madre pine forests are practically virgin, but there are no grizzlies there and probably never were many. The principal foods of the big bears are nuts and fruits of various shrubs and small trees that do not occur in a heavy pine forest.

Kennerly commented on the diet of the grizzly (Baird, 1859 : 29): "The food of these animals, in this country [northern Chihuahua], consists of acorns, walnuts, piñones (the fruit of *Pinus edulis*), manzanillas, the fruit of an ericaceous shrub, and such animals as they are able to capture." As noted above, Kennerly also found grizzlies digging for roots on the plains. Else-

Fig. 155.   Female grizzly bear killed by Sr. Isaías T. García near the Sierra del Nido, Chihuahua, October 4, 1957.

where in the Southwest, grizzlies have been found to eat carrion, insects, honey, almost all kinds of fruits and berries, ground squirrels and other rodents (which the bears dig out of the burrows), and occasionally livestock and such big game as they happen to catch. In short, the grizzly, like the small black bear, is omnivorous.

The social habits, too, of the grizzly are similar to those of other bears. Adults usually are solitary except during the mating season or when females are accompanied by dependent young. It is believed that young grizzlies do not mate until they are four or five years old, and thereafter the female gives birth to young only every second or third year. A litter consists usually of one or two cubs, rarely of triplets. With so low a breeding potential it is self-evident that a grizzly population cannot withstand a heavy annual kill.

Grizzlies retire in winter in the manner of black bears, and the females have their young in January or February during the winter sleep. Newborn cubs are about the size of little black bears and they develop even more slowly. The mother cares for the young through two full seasons before they are able to make their own living. Full growth is not attained until the age of eight or ten years. Thereafter, under natural conditions, the life expectancy of a grizzly is long. In zoölogical parks some individuals have lived to be thirty years old, and the larger carnivores ordinarily live longer in the wild than they do in captivity.

Grizzly bears usually attend to their own business and expect others to do likewise. When aroused, however, they do not hesitate to attack a man. A wounded grizzly or a mother defending her cubs is perhaps the most dangerous wild animal in North America. Yet, in Yellowstone National Park and elsewhere where grizzlies are still numerous, people live in the immediate vicinity of these great bears and seldom are attacked by them. There is no justification for believing that it is necessary to kill all grizzlies in order to protect human lives.

Occasionally an individual bear becomes a stock killer or turns crotchety and attacks people without provocation. Such an individual, usually a superannuated adult, must be destroyed. Incidentally, a grizzly in killing stock does not deal a crushing blow with the paw as has been commonly supposed but grasps the animal in an embrace with the powerful forearms and kills by biting the neck or back of the skull. An adult grizzly can thus dispose of a full-grown bull or cow; but the grizzlies' usual livestock kills are calves, yearling cattle, sheep, or pigs. The livestock loss from the few grizzlies that have persisted in Mexico in the last twenty years, however, is negligible.

The grizzly bear is so nearly extinct in Mexico that it should be given immediate legal protection. A field survey should be made at once to find out how many grizzlies still survive in that country, and to ascertain what measures can be taken to protect the remaining animals. It is not impossible that the creation of a national preserve or park might still save the species in

Mexico, just as Yellowstone Park did in the United States. Tentative plans for such a park are discussed elsewhere in this volume.

FAMILY PROCYONIDAE

Raccoons and Their Relatives

Ring-tailed Cats. *Bassariscus astutus* and Related Species

Other names.—Cacomixtle; mico de noche; babisuri; sal coyote; mico rayado; rintél; pintorabo.

Species included here.—*Bassariscus astutus* and *B. sumichrasti* (sometimes called *Jentinkia sumichrasti*).

Description.—Size of a half-grown house cat, with rather slender body, short legs, and very long, bushy tail. Face pointed, ears long, eyes large. General color yellowish brown, the hairs along the back tipped with black. Underparts whitish. Eyes narrowly ringed with black; lips, cheeks, and superocular spots whitish. Tail conspicuously ringed with seven white and seven black bands; the black rings incomplete on ventral side. (Differences between *astutus* and *sumichrasti* shown in table 17.) Measurements: head and body—340 to 425 mm.; tail—350 to 500 mm. Weight: 670 to 1,400 gm. Within these ranges, *astutus* tends to be small, *sumichrasti* large.

Range in Mexico.—Of *B. astutus:* all of northern and central Mexico from deserts of Baja California and arid shrublands of Tamaulipas south to semiarid tropics of Oaxaca and probably Chiapas (fig. 156). Of *B. sumichrasti:* a complementary range in wet tropics of southeastern Mexico (fig. 157). Northernmost record at Mirador, central Veracruz, but species probably follows the tropical evergreen forest north to San Luis Potosí. Ranges of the two species overlap along eastern escarpment and on Isthmus of Tehuantepec.

The two species of ring-tailed cats are similar in behavior and in appearance, except that *sumichrasti* is somewhat larger. They occupy very different habitats, however, and they are not known to interbreed. Numerous slight morphological differences (table 17), pointed out by Nelson and Goldman

TABLE 17

Morphologic Differences Between the Two Species of Ring-tailed Cats

(After Nelson and Goldman, 1932. Additional differences in cranial details are omitted here.)

Bassariscus (*Jentinkia*) *sumichrasti*	*Bassariscus astutus*
Muzzle and feet distinctly blackish; tail with light rings becoming indistinct toward end.	Muzzle and feet grayish; tail with light rings distinct throughout its length.
Pelage finer, softer, and more lax.	Pelage coarser and stiffer.
Ears more broadly and evenly rounded.	Ears more narrowly rounded.
Second, third, fourth, and fifth digits of fore and hind limbs naked on lower surface behind digital pads, which are narrower, more elongated.	Second, third, fourth, and fifth digits of fore and hind limbs densely hairy on lower surface behind and around digital pads, which are broader, more rounded.
Claws longer, more strongly curved, more compressed, nonretractile [perhaps an adaptation to tree living].	Claws shorter, straighter, less compressed, retractile.

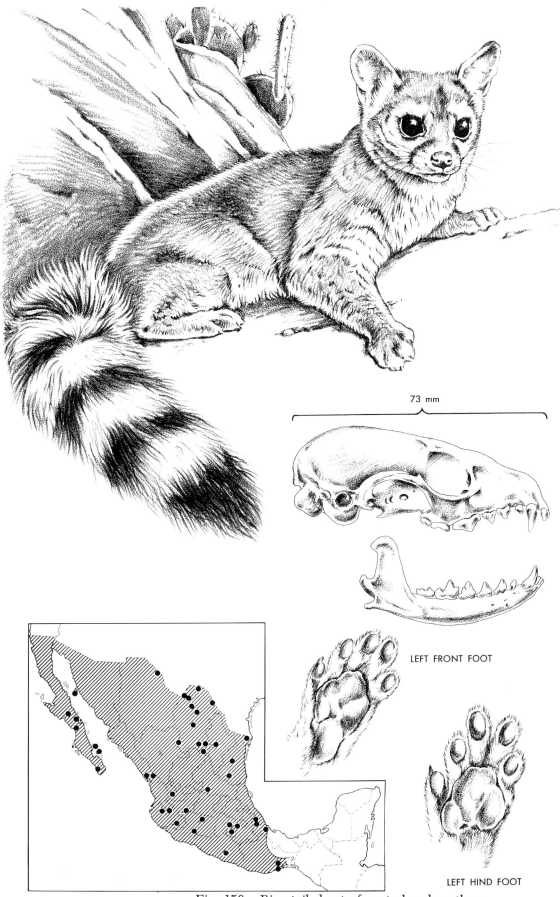

73 mm

LEFT FRONT FOOT

LEFT HIND FOOT

Fig. 156.   Ring-tailed cat of central and northern
Mexico, *Bassariscus astutus*.

(1932), led these authors to classify the two species in distinct genera, a view supported by Miller and Kellogg (1955). But I shall follow the traditional classification under the single genus *Bassariscus*.

Ringtails are strictly prowlers of the night. They sleep by day, usually in caves, rock crevices, or hollow trees, and forage after dark. The northern ringtail (*astutus*) occurs in highly diverse environments, from arid desert and dry tropics up to the pine-oak belt. In many places there are no available trees and the animals den in rocks, cliffs, or even buildings. According to Cahalane (1947 : 166), they prefer "broken ledges well supplied with caves and large crevices and a supply of drinking water." The tropical species (*sumichrasti*) inhabits areas heavily forested but often lacking cliffs or outcroppings. It dens almost exclusively in trees and, in fact, rarely comes to the ground (Gaumer, 1917).

Adult ringtails normally are solitary in habit. During the breeding season, however, some males and females seem to be stable pairs, and the males have sometimes been known to assist the females in rearing young. The young are born in the nests or dens and remain there until approximately two months old, when they begin to accompany the adults on hunting parties. The gestation period is not known. Richardson (1942) kept three pairs in captivity in southern Arizona, 2 females of which gave birth to litters of 4 and 1 young on June 3 and 12, respectively. Davis (1944b) captured 4 lactating females in central Mexico in late July and the first week of August; from this he postulates that the young were born in June or July. Of *sumichrasti* in Yucatán, Gaumer states that March is the time of parturition, and he lists 2 young as the usual number. Female ringtails have 4 nipples, from which it might be assumed that 4 is the maximum size of a normal litter.

The young start taking meat when about three weeks old. From then on to adulthood they eat increasing amounts of meat. Adults are mainly carnivorous, although, like raccoons, they will eat many plant foods on occasion. Lists of foods presented by four authors follow.

Bassariscus astutus

1. In Arizona: "Native foods: Prickly pear fruit, saguaro fruit, rats and mice, birds, lizards, grasshoppers, round-tailed squirrels. However, a rock squirrel, *Citellus variegatus grammurus*, which was in the adults' cage for several weeks, was not killed by them.

"Non-native foods: Meat scraps of all kinds (both cooked and uncooked), dog food (canned), fish, apples, peaches, pears, tomatoes, carrots, string beans, peas, corn, cauliflower, celery, lettuce, spinach, swiss chard, romaine, oatmeal (uncooked), milk." (Richardson, 1942 : 17.)

2. In Arizona: Staple food—woodrats. "Insects and their larvae, and centipedes are also eaten. Sleeping birds may be killed or their nests robbed of young . . . fruits, including figs, the fruit of many low-growing cacti, madrone, yew, cascara,

87 mm

RIGHT FRONT
FOOT

RIGHT HIND FOOT

Fig. 157. Ring-tailed cat of southeastern Mexico,
Bassariscus sumichrasti.

manzanita, and blackberry. My captive animals were fond of oranges." (Cahalane, 1947 : 168.)

3. In Jalisco: "Nocturnal in habits, hunting cat-like for rodents and large insects. Fruit furnishes its main food in the wet season, especially wild figs and the coporno balls." (Batty, quoted in Allen, 1906 : 254.)

Bassariscus sumichrasti

1. In Yucatan: Staple food—tree squirrels. Also birds, their eggs and young, rats and mice, domestic poultry. (Gaumer, 1917.)

Collectively these accounts suggest that ringtails eat almost anything but that small mammals are the staple items of diet. Northern ringtails sometimes take up residence in cabins and barns, where they effectively suppress populations of rats and mice.

There are no available figures on population densities of ring-tailed cats, but these animals seem to be especially abundant in northern Coahuila. Marsh (1937) speaks of ringtails as "common" in the Carmen Mountains, and Borell and Bryant (1942) designate *astutus* as the most abundant fur bearer in the Big Bend region. In most parts of Mexico the populations of ringtails seem to be of moderate density.

In Mexico, ring-tailed cats have a bad reputation as robbers of the chicken house. Being good climbers, they can enter all but the tightest buildings and can catch chickens on their roost even high above the ground.

Aside from their predation on poultry, the only economic importance of the ring-tailed cats is in the fur market; their pelts are of low quality and little monetary value. Cahalane (1947 : 168) states:

Only in "boom times" on the fur market, is the ringtail trapped intentionally on a large scale. Frequently, its curiosity gets it into traps set for more valuable furbearers. . . . The fur, which on the living animal is fluffy and beautiful, mats down and loses its "life" and color and is used as trimming only on the cheapest cloth coats.

If captured young, ringtails are easily tamed, and they make attractive pets. Gaumer speaks of using captured ringtails (*sumichrasti*) in hunting rabbits, but he does not specify just how this is done.

Raccoon. *Procyon lotor*

Other names.—Mapache; osito lavador; tejón (Chihuahua); culú (Yucatán).
Species included here—Procyon lotor, P. insularis, P. pygmaeus.
Description.—Size of a small cocker spaniel, with stocky body and short legs. Tail short relative to body length, banded alternately with black and grayish-white rings (usually 6 or 7 black rings). Face masked with black, pale gray around the muzzle and above the eyes. Body grizzled, grading to black in the middle of the back. Toes long and slender. Measurements: head and body—450 to 600 mm.; tail—250 to 320 mm. Weight: 3 to 4 kg.; some very large males weigh up to 7 kg.

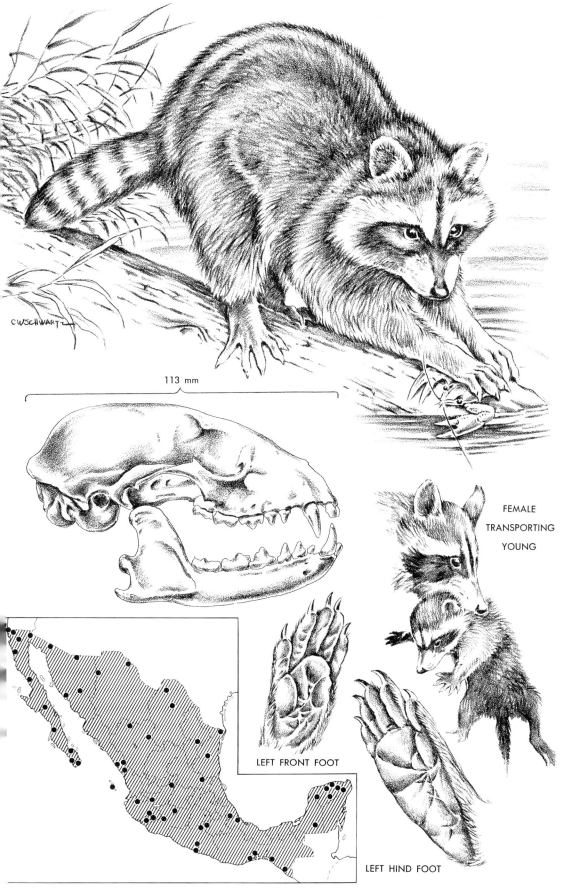

113 mm

FEMALE
TRANSPORTING
YOUNG

LEFT FRONT FOOT

LEFT HIND FOOT

Fig. 158. Raccoon, *Procyon lotor*.

Range in Mexico.—Throughout the country in well-watered places. The raccoon is rare or locally absent in the high mountains. On the northern desert areas it is confined to stream bottoms and the vicinity of water impoundments.

Almost anywhere in Mexico along the bank of a stream or on the margin of a lagoon one may find the tracks of a raccoon. This adaptable little fur bearer is one of the few mammals that occur in virtually all parts of the country, from the cottonwood groves of desert streams to the alligator bogs in the deep rain forest. The only indispensable element in raccoon habitat is year-round water. A large part of a coon's diet is obtained in and around the water. Crayfish and frogs, for example, are two favorite items on the bill of fare, and these of course are found only in wet places. At some periods of the year when an abundance of fruit and berries may be had easily, individual coons will wander far from water; but during the dry season they make their way back to the wet places, where food is always available. The highest populations of raccoons occur in Mexico along the coastal plains, where streams and lagoons are most numerous. Alvarez del Toro (1952*a*), for example, speaks of the "exaggerated abundance" of raccoons along the shores of the Mar Muerto in western Chiapas. Conversely, the lowest densities are in the great desert areas and in timbered mountains where water is scarce.

Ordinarily, adult raccoons are solitary in habit. A mother may keep her litter of young with her through the first winter, or until they are virtually full grown, but it is not usual for two adults of the same sex to run together for long. Two females with their families have been known to share a den where dens were scarce, but this is exceptional. Old males are unsociable and solitary, except during the breeding season, when they seek the company of females.

Mating takes place in December in the southern United States, but farther south it may be much later, to conform with the period of summer rains. In southern Nuevo León, on July 23, 1945, I saw a mother coon with a litter of five young which I estimated to be a little more than two months old. Calculating back, they would have been born sometime in May, and mating must have occurred in March.

Male coons are polygamous and may serve several females in a season. Each female, however, after service by an acceptable male, will not associate further with any other male coon but goes about her own affairs—preparing a den for the expected family, for one thing. The young arrive about nine weeks after copulation. Dens usually are in hollow trees, but if none are available a family may den in a rock ledge, or even in an abandoned skunk or badger burrow. Litters consist of 3 to 6 young, 4 or 5 being the usual number.

When the young are about a month old they begin to accompany their mother on nightly foraging parties. By the time they are two months old they are catching some of their own food and learning the tricks of hunting. A mother coon is a strict disciplinarian and does not hesitate to deal out severe spankings when the young get too independent. In this regard a coon mother is much like her larger cousins, the bears. The family of five young and their mother, mentioned above, was observed traveling single file along the shore of a lagoon early one morning, when a frog leaped from the shore into a tangle of cattails in the adjoining shallow water. The mother kept on her course, uttering a low churring noise, and the three young immediately in back of her followed close behind. But the two in the rear of the procession plunged into the cattails and started groping for the frog. They followed the quarry eight or ten feet into the thicket without making a capture. Then, discovering that they had lost their mother, both set up a loud whimpering. The mother coon had moved twenty yards or so down the shore, and as nearly as I could tell she did not miss the tail-enders of the procession until they called. She turned back with the expression common to all tired mothers and walked resolutely into the cattail patch, from which there immediately emerged the mixed sounds of slaps, squeals, and splashes. The two young came into view scrambling for the shore, with the old female slapping their rears at every step. On the bank the procession re-formed, and this time all five young followed dutifully in line until I lost sight of the group a hundred yards down the shore.

Coons, like the bears, are omnivorous. Besides crayfish and frogs, already mentioned, foods found in or around water are snails, mussels, water insects, and occasionally a fish. Coons will eat almost any fleshy fruit—grapes, cherries, apples, cherimoyas, mangos, and the berries of manzanita and dogwood are the main ones taken. Acorns and other nuts are eaten in quantity when these are available. In addition, coons freely steal eggs from the nests of both wild birds and domestic fowls, and they eat such birds and small mammals as they can catch. The latitude of diet accounts in part for the raccoon's ability to live almost anywhere in Mexico.

Occasionally coons cause considerable damage to orchards and crops. Cultivated orchards and vineyards are subject to the nightly raids of coons when the fruits are ripe. In Sonora, W. W. Price reported in 1895: "At Cooley's they [raccoons] were destructive to growing corn, pulling down the stalks, and eating the soft ears. The Apache Indians are in many places compelled to guard their fields during the corn season on account of the ravages of this pest." (Allen, 1895 : 250.) At Colonia Pacheco, Chihuahua, in August, 1948, Floyd Johnson complained to us that his corn was being damaged by the coons that lived along Piedra Verde Creek. He was setting traps in the hope of catching the culprits. Bernardo Villa tells me that damage to corn is often severe in Guerrero and Oaxaca, and Alvarez del Toro (1952a) mentions the same problem in Chiapas. Gaumer (1917 : 213) speaks of coon damage to gardens in Yucatán and to such commercial crops as peanuts, sweet potatoes, and sugar cane. The coons eat the sweet, tender shoots of the cane and thereby inhibit growth of the plants.

Coons have a reputation for cleanliness in their eating habits, since they customarily wash their food before eating it. Of course they do this only when water is readily available. So marked is this habit that the coon is known locally in Mexico as *osito lavador* (little bear washer) and its Latin name, *lotor,* likewise means "the washer."

In the United States coon hunting is an important sport and the fur of the animal is of considerable commercial value. In Mexico coons are hunted only for meat, and even this is done on a small scale. López and López (1911 : 292) express the opinion that coon hunting is not popular as a sport in Mexico because there are very few good hounds in the country. The whole point of coon hunting is to test the trailing ability of the hounds. The actual shooting of a treed coon with the aid of a jack light is more or less anti-climactic to the chase. Without the hounds, the sport is pointless. It is unfortunate, in a sense, that the running of good hounds never has been developed in Mexico, for the high population of coons along the coastal plains would make exciting hunting. The opportunities for fine sport in this region are being neglected.

Coons are relatively easy to trap, but they are clever in eluding pursuing dogs. They double back on their tracks, swim or wade in water, walk logs or brush fences, and adopt other stratagems that slow down the dogs and confuse the trail.

The poor quality of the fur of Mexican coons accounts for the low commercial value of the pelts. The hair is sparse and the underfur thin, as in many Mexican fur bearers. Hides are used locally, but even when their sale was legal, relatively few ever reached the commercial market.

The only place in Mexico where I found evidence of much coon hunting was near El Rincón, Guerrero. Local hunters there apparently hunt *mapaches* a good deal with flashlights and shotguns. They are interested principally in the meat—only secondarily in the sport. Two young men claimed to have killed eleven coons and coatis along the river in one night. In most rural communities coons are taken for food only casually, and although a good many doubtless are shot and eaten, the hunting is incidental to the pursuit of other game. It is widely recognized, however, that coons are very good eating. The difficulties incident to night hunting and the lack of such equipment as flashlights probably preclude more widespread pursuit of this species.

Since coons are little hunted in Mexico, the only factors limiting their abundance are environmental. Where forests have been destroyed and water sources have dried up there doubtless has been a decrease in raccoons.

Coati. *Nasua narica*

Other names.—Tejón; pisote; choluga; "solitario" (old males); coatimundi.
Description.—Rather long, slender; about the size of a small cocker spaniel. Tail and snout long and tapered. Ears short and rounded. Front claws 20 mm.

or more in length, slightly curved. Rear claws shorter and sharply hooked. General body color grizzled brown or tan, varying greatly in tone. Coatis of southern Mexico usually dark, those of the northeast and northwest golden tan. A dusky mask extends across the face. Tail often ringed with dusky bands; on many individuals these scarcely visible. Measurements: head and body—430 to 630 mm.; tail—420 to 635 mm. Weight: 3 to 5 kg., old males being considerably heavier than females.

Range in Mexico.—Coastal plains and adjoining forested uplands as far north as the United States border in Sonora and Tamaulipas. Coatis are most numerous in tropical forests, along the coasts and lower foothills. In lesser numbers they follow the river channels high into the pine-clad mountains.

Every animal has some "badge" by which it is most easily recognized in the field. The coati's badge is its tail. Frequently the ramrod-straight tail will be seen extending vertically above the grass like a periscope when the animal's body is not visible. Or a group of coatis may be discovered in the trees by the movement of their tails above the horizontal limbs. A coati cannot hang by its tail—the appendage is merely a tall balance staff; it is as long as the head and body together and is carried in a jaunty, upright position. At closer range the long snout is another diagnostic character.

Coatis occur principally in the tropics. The Mexican species and its near relatives range throughout the lowlands of Central and South America. In Mexico the highest population densities are on the coastal plains where the tropical forests are interspersed with grassy clearings. We found the animals especially abundant along the lower Santiago River in Nayarit and on the Río Salto in eastern San Luis Potosí. Widely separated as these places are, they are very similar in vegetation—tall, dense stands of fig trees and other timber along streams and in cool ravines, with palmetto-studded grasslands and brush patches on exposed sites. Mixed vegetation of this kind seems to be ideal coati habitat.

The animals are by no means confined to the tropics, however. Even well up in the pine forests and in mesquite-grasslands and oak scrub along the fringes of the desert there are sparse populations. We came across occasional individuals or family groups at 6,500 feet elevation in the pinelands west of Chilpancingo, Guerrero, and in the pine-oak forests of northwestern Chihuahua. Bernardo Villa saw specimens in the vicinity of Piedra Volada, at 9,600 feet, in Sierra del Norte, Chihuahua, in January, 1955. Marsh (1937) designates the species as "fairly common" in the more humid canyons of the mountains in northern Coahuila. Burt (1938) states that the coati probably occurs throughout most of Sonora except the northwest desert area, and he cites specimens from San Javier and Ures, on the desert border. And the coati is known as a resident of the mesquite bottom lands of southern Arizona.

Female coatis and their young are highly sociable. It is not uncommon to find groups of 15 or 20, and aggregations of as many as 200 are mentioned in

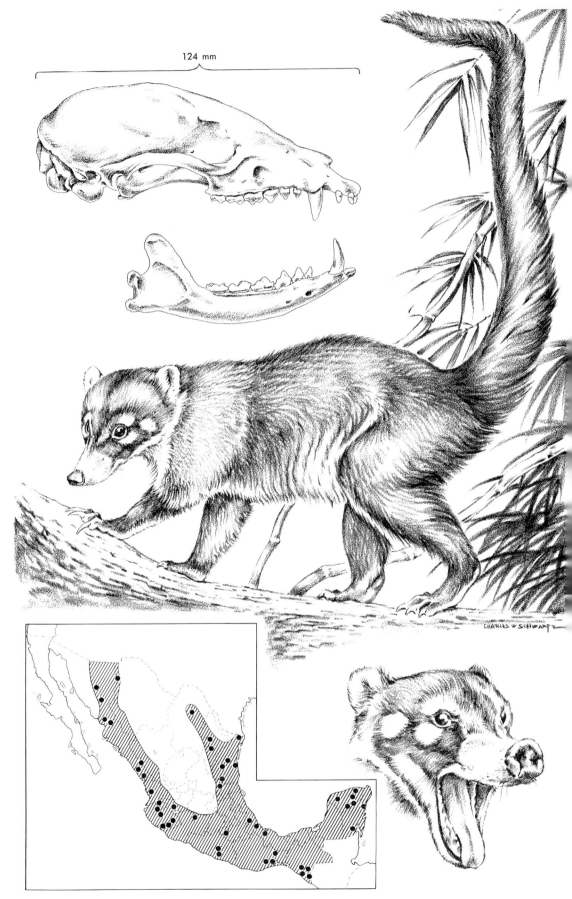

124 mm

Fig. 159. Coati, *Nasua narica*.

the literature. Some old males, on the other hand, are solitary in habit. This differential behavior is well known to the rural people of Mexico; in many localities the lone males are designated as *solitarios* and the mixed bands of young males, females, and young are called simply *tejones* or *cholugas*. There is even confusion over whether these animals are all of the same species.

When frightened, coatis seem to try to escape on the ground rather than take shelter in the trees. I have never seen a fleeing coati go up a tree, although when hard pressed one might do so. In Nayarit I once saw a group of a dozen females and half-grown young in a giant fig tree; when startled they rained to the ground and dashed away through the brush rather than seek refuge in the limbs where they were.

Coatis are most active early in the morning and in the evening. Although they feed and move about some at night, they are less nocturnal than are their relatives the raccoons. Gaumer (1917) states that they are strictly diurnal. Foraging bands are frequently come upon well into the middle of the morning. During the heat of the day, however, coatis rest in the treetops or on the ground beneath sheltering vegetation. It is said that females customarily rear their young in hollow trees or on rocky ledges, and perhaps they also rest in these retreats.

Presumably breeding among wild coatis is promiscuous, as it is among raccoons. Gestation is said to be approximately eleven weeks. An average litter consists of 4 or 5 young. I was told of a litter of 7, but my informant may not have obtained an accurate count. The time of breeding varies in different parts of Mexico, as it does for so many other species. My evidence on this matter is summarized in table 18.

TABLE 18

BREEDING RECORDS OF THE COATI IN MEXICO

Date	Place	Observation	Approximate time of birth
July 31, 1948	Río Gavilán, NW Chihuahua	Lactating female collected	June or July
Aug. 2, 1948	Río Gavilán, NW Chihuahua	Two young captured; estimated 2 mos. old	June
July 24, 1904	Escuinapa, Sinaloa	Newborn young taken from den by J. H. Batty (Allen, 1906)	July
Oct. 21, 1944	Amojileca, Guerrero	Female and two young collected, the young bet. 2 and 3 mos. old	July or August
Dec. 14, 1944	El Rincón, Guerrero	One young captured alive, estimated 3 to 4 mos. old	August or September
	Chiapas	Alvarez del Toro (1952a)	May (March to June)

Coatis, like many of their near relatives, are omnivorous. Various observers have found them eating fruits, berries, nuts, tender green vegetation, insects, snails, lizards, small mammals, and carrion. Gaumer speaks of their digging in the ground for worms and insect pupae. The stomachs of three individuals collected in Guerrero in October, 1944, contained some unidentified fibrous bulbs or roots and crushed pine seeds. Two specimens taken in northwestern Chihuahua in late summer, 1948, contained acorns exclusively. In eastern San Luis Potosí I watched coatis foraging through the dead leaves of palmetto trees, and it seemed at the time that they might be catching lizards, mice, or perhaps bats. In Nayarit we frequently saw coatis in fig trees laden with ripe fruit, which they undoubtedly were eating.

As a game mammal or fur bearer the coati is of relatively little importance in Mexico. López and López (1911) speak of its pursuit with dogs, but in my experience this is an uncommon practice. Such coatis as are taken—and they are very few—are bagged incidentally to the pursuit of other game.

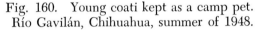

Fig. 160.   Young coati kept as a camp pet.
Río Gavilán, Chihuahua, summer of 1948.

The flesh of young coatis is tender and flavorsome, but adults tend to be tough and of strong flavor. The fur is coarse and of no commercial value.

The capture of coatis to serve as pets, however, is of some consequence. When reared in captivity a coati will become entirely tame and a very entertaining addition to a household. Hundreds and perhaps thousands of young are captured each year and are either sold in the larger cities or taken into the homes of their captors. In a camp on the Río Gavilán, Chihuahua, we kept two young animals for almost two months, at first in a makeshift cage and later on leashes. They were wild and distrustful when first taken, but after a month of confinement they could be handled without undue danger to one's fingers, and they "churred" with pleasure when food was brought. Both lived and grew on a diet of milk and raw meat; but the diet was in some way inadequate, for one of the two developed rickets. They were particularly fond of sugar, syrup, and candy, and we found that they would eat almost anything that had been sweetened sufficiently. When sleeping in broad daylight these two would curl up on the ground and cover their eyes with their two front paws. They were usually active by day, particularly in the morning and evening, and quiet most of the night; this presumably indicates the normal activity pattern in the wild. The one that matured became surly as an adult and had to be disposed of.

Although coatis ordinarily are entertaining and harmless members of the Mexican fauna, they sometimes make themselves unpopular by raiding the cornfields in the manner of raccoons. A large band can cause a good deal of damage to the ripening ears in even one night.

Kinkajou. *Potos flavus*

Other names.—Martucha; marta; martes; kinkaju; tancho; oso mielero; mico de noche; micoleón; godoy.

Description.—Monkey-like, with long, prehensile tail (tail longer than head and body) and a somewhat flattened puglike face. Eyes large. Ears very small, rounded, and thinly furred. Body stocky, with short legs. General color pale grayish brown, slightly darker brown along back and on top of head. Underparts buff. Measurements: head and body—425 to 515 mm.; tail—460 to 535 mm. No weights available.

Range in Mexico.—Principally rain forest and tropical evergreen forest throughout southeastern Mexico, up the Gulf coast as far as extreme southern Tamaulipas and up the Pacific coast to Guerrero. In Oaxaca and Guerrero kinkajous live in pockets of lush tropical forest which are localized in unusually wet sites. This tongue of range may extend northwest to Michoacán or even farther, but records are lacking.

The kinkajou is almost entirely nocturnal, and for this reason it is not at all well known in the wild. My only meeting with the species occurred near Acuña, Tamaulipas, August 12, 1945, when we happened to find a kinkajou abroad in full morning sunlight. It was standing in a wagon track watching

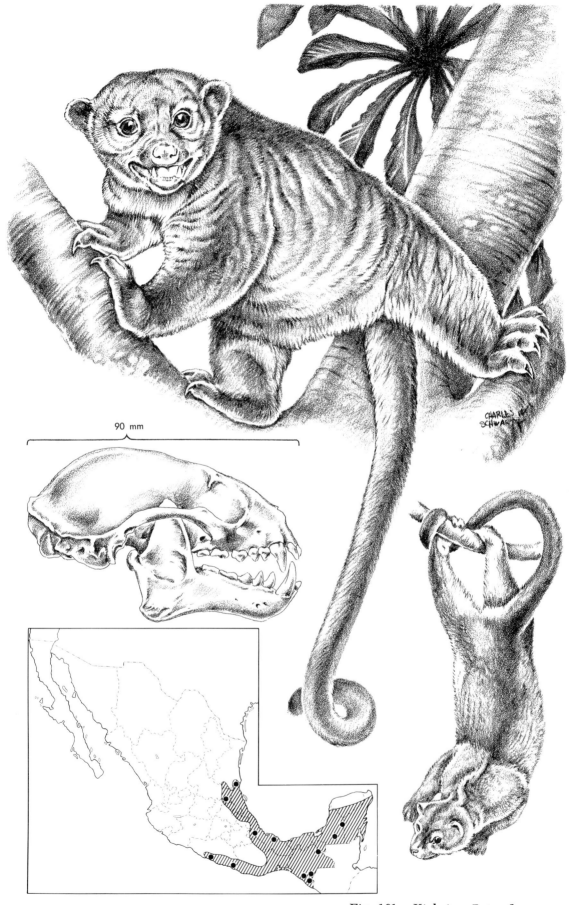

90 mm

Fig. 161. Kinkajou, *Potos flavus.*

the approach of our car, and at 50 yards it leaped into the thorn forest and scampered down a hill toward a deep ravine where the tropical forest was somewhat taller. The animal had wandered out of its normal habitat of tall, cool jungle; this may account for its diurnal activity. The posture and running gait were not unlike those of a monkey, with obvious differences in heaviness of body and shortness of limbs. The tail was curled back like that of a monkey. This, incidentally, is the northernmost record of occurrence of the kinkajou; unfortunately the specimen was not obtained.

A few observations on life history and habit are offered by Gaumer (1917). He states that kinkajous prefer virgin tropical forests near sources of water. They spend the daylight hours sleeping in hollow trees and come out at night to feed. In the trees they are active and lively, swinging gracefully from limb to limb with the tail and four feet "as if they had wings." They commonly run in bands, which maintain a noisy chatter as they forage through the forest.

Gaumer lists the food of kinkajous as small mammals, birds, eggs, insects, grubs, honey, and fruits, particularly bananas and figs. Honey apparently is a preferred food, for the animal is known in some localities as "honey bear" (oso mielero). The kinkajou inserts its long tongue into a hive to break up the comb and lick out the honey.

Alvarez del Toro (1952a), however, states that kinkajous are almost exclusively vegetarian and that they are not fond of meat. He emphasizes fruit as the principal food but comments on the sharp and strong teeth of this fruit-eating mammal.

Female kinkajous bear and rear their young in tree holes. Single births seem to be the rule, although the females have two teats. Villa (1948) collected two pregnant females in December, 1944, near Finca Prusia, Chiapas; each bore a single embryo. The young are much sought as pets, and there is a brisk trade in tame kinkajous despite legal protection. The young are very attractive and are easily tamed. However, Gaumer states that captive individuals usually sleep all day and are active only at night, just as they would be in the wild. They will accept food when aroused from the daytime nap but return immediately after eating to resume their slumber. It would seem that an animal so strictly nocturnal would be less desirable as a pet than a coati, which will come out and play during the day.

Kinkajous are rarely hunted except in the search for live young. They have no importance as game animals nor as fur bearers.

Presumably the shrinkage of the virgin tropical forests is effecting a decrease in the range and abundance of kinkajous, but there is no available evidence on this matter.

FAMILY MUSTELIDAE

The Weasel Tribe

Members of the Mustelidae share one unique character from which the name of the family is derived. All have a pair of musk glands at the base of the tail on each side of the anus. In the skunks these glands are highly developed weapons of defense, the acrid liquid being fired as a fine spray in the face of an attacker. The liquid is choking in the lungs and causes great discomfort in the eyes, although no permanent damage results. With this defense skunks command the respect of larger predators. The musk of other members of the group, such as weasels, otters, and badgers, likewise is emitted in times of excitement or fear, but with no more serious consequence than an unpleasant odor.

Mustelids known to occur in Mexico are one species of weasel, two otters, the tayra, grison, badger, and three types of skunks each represented by several species. The mink (*Mustela vison*) is known from Texas and conceivably may enter northeastern Mexico. Marsh (1937) reports a secondhand description of an animal killed along the Sabinas River in Coahuila which might have been a mink. The sea otter (*Enhydra lutris*) once frequented the shore of northern Baja California, but it has not been known there for several decades (Nelson, 1921). Hunters locally exterminated the species many years ago. In recent years, however, sea otters have reappeared along the California coast, and they seem to be increasing. Perhaps in the future they may reënter the waters of Baja California.

Some of the finest furs are produced by members of the family. Most mustelids prey on small mammals, including injurious rodents. None of them does any appreciable damage, so far as man is concerned.

Weasel. *Mustela frenata*

Other names.—Comadreja; sabín; oncita.

Description.—A slender, lithe animal, smaller than a gray squirrel, with short legs and a moderately short tail. Head flattened, eyes small, ears short and rounded. Color generally rich brown dorsally, creamy white below. Tail tip black. Head black, with a white band across the face above the eyes (in Baja California the head would be mostly brown as in the weasels of southern California, with black only on the muzzle). Easily differentiated from the jaguarundi, mink, or otter by the smaller size. Males normally half again as large as females. Measurements: head and body—250 to 300 mm.; tail—140 to 205 mm. Weight of one male from Chiapas: 365 gm.

Range in Mexico.—Throughout the country except in the most arid regions. The weasel occurs in San Diego County, California, and its range probably extends into northern Baja California, although specimens are lacking. Occurrence in the Sierra Madre Occidental likewise is presumed without any supporting specimens. The species is known from southern Arizona and New Mexico and was reported near El Paso, Texas, by Bailey (1905). If present in north-central Mexico, weasels must be very scarce. It appears that the highest populations are in the uplands of southeastern Mexico.

The vivacious weasel is not often seen, even in localities where it is known to be abundant. It frequents rock piles, impenetrable tangles of ground vege- tation, old buildings, and other secure shelters, and only rarely is one seen in the open. A weasel may forage both by day and by night, and in seeking its prey (mostly small mammals) it wriggles through the smallest cracks and passages. It can follow a gopher through its underground tunnels or a wood- pecker into its tree hole. The alert and agile little predator can also run down a rabbit in open chase if the ground vegetation is dense.

Weasel dens usually are underground or in the farthest recesses of rock or log shelters. Gaumer (1917) states that breeding takes place in March and April in Yucatán, the young being born five weeks later, in May or June. However, recent studies of the breeding biology of weasels indicate that there may be a long period of delay between fertilization of the ova and their implantation in the uterus. Wright (1948 : 338) outlines the breeding habits of the weasel:

a single litter of young is born in the spring, usually in April. The young de- velop rapidly and at 3 months of age the females are full grown. The young males remain in a sexually immature condition during the first summer, but the young females as well as the parous females come into heat in mid-summer and are bred by the adult males. After a long period of quiescence lasting for several months, the embryos resulting from these matings become active in early spring and develop to term in less than 27 days after they become im- planted.

The actual period between mating and birth averaged 279 days in Wright's experimental animals.

Weasel litters may be as small as 3 or as large as 8, about 6 being the usual number of young. Soon after the young open their eyes, meat is brought to them by the parents, or at least by the mother—it is uncertain what part the male plays in bringing up a weasel family. Nests have been unearthed that contain numerous small rodents and birds—the larder for the growing young, apparently. At the age of six or eight weeks the young begin to forage with the mother.

Although rats and mice probably constitute the bulk of the weasel diet, the voracious and bloodthirsty animals will prey upon nearly any vertebrate they can master, even those that are many times their own weight. Weasels capture and kill large rats, domestic chickens, rabbits, squirrels, and even sizable snakes, dispatching their victims by biting them in the neck or on the back of the skull. They also kill some small birds. I saw a weasel cross a road near Mexico City with a finch or sparrow in its mouth. Although weasels eat

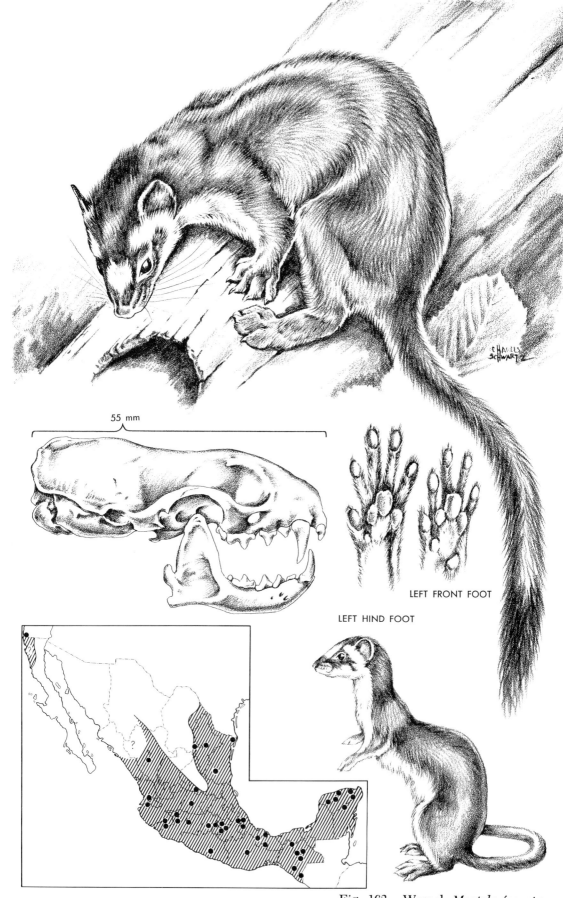

55 mm

LEFT FRONT FOOT

LEFT HIND FOOT

Fig. 162. Weasel, *Mustela frenata*.

small prey animals entire, they only suck the blood of a large animal such as a rabbit or chicken and leave the body as waste. This well-known habit has given the weasel a bad name as a wanton killer.

Although weasels are believed to hunt chiefly by scent, they respond readily to the sound or sight of possible prey. In the Chiapas uplands I once was attempting to call the scattered members of a covey of ocellated quail when I observed at some distance a weasel hurrying directly toward me. It bounded along logs and through the dense oak brush, apparently attracted by the quail whistle. I shot the animal at twenty yards as it paused on a log, peering intently in my direction as though seeking the location of the calling quail.

Weasels on the whole are beneficial predators since they eat mostly rodents. Damage to small game populations is negligible. Occasionally an individual animal will cause havoc in a chicken roost, but such instances are not usual. The rats killed by weasels are capable of far more destruction to poultry than are the weasels themselves.

In northern North America weasels turn white in winter, and the fur (known as ermine) is of considerable value. Mexican weasels are not known to assume a white pelage, and the pelts are of little commercial importance.

Tayra. *Tayra barbara*

Other names.—Tayra; cabeza de viejo; cabeza blanca; viejo de monte; *Galera barbara*.

Description.—Size of an otter, with long body, fairly short legs, long tail, flattened musteline head, and small rounded ears. General coloration black; white head and neck grading to gray and then to black on shoulders; white spot on breast. Extent of white on head and shoulders reportedly varies widely. Light-colored "hood" sometimes yellowish rather than white. Underparts, feet, legs, tail, and posterior half of back always black or blackish brown. Measurements: head and body—560 to 625 mm.; tail—375 to 450 mm. No weights available.

Range in Mexico.—Wet tropical forests of southeastern Mexico, up the Gulf coast to eastern San Luis Potosí and locally along the Pacific coast as far north as southern Sinaloa.

The northernmost record of the tayra on the west coast is supplied by Allen (1906), who reported two specimens from Escuinapa, Sinaloa. On the eastern coastal plain I observed a group of four tayras foraging along the bank of the Río Salto, which is probably the northernmost recorded occurrence on the Gulf coast (Rancho Maitínez, 30 km. east of Ciudad Maíz, San Luis Potosí, Feb. 18, 1946). Dalquest (1953) cites another record from the same general area. The species is widely distributed, although nowhere abundant, in the tropical forests of southern Mexico.

The tayra is a large mustelid, minklike in form. The grayish-white head and shoulders on a jet-black body have given rise to the local names *cabeza de viejo* and *cabeza blanca*. Gaumer (1917) lists the principal foods as rats, mice, squirrels, rabbits, agoutis, and birds. The tayra feeds also on larger animals up at least to the size of brocket deer. Villa (1948) observed in Chiapas a dramatic pursuit of a brocket by a tayra. The little deer took refuge in a pond and was swimming valiantly for the other shore with the tayra in close pursuit. The chase proceeded into the forest, and Villa did not see the outcome. José Tárano of El Real, Chiapas, also told me that tayras prey on brockets. Villa took another tayra near the site of the deer chase; its stomach contained only some ripe coffee berries—an odd food for this flesh-eating animal. But tayras often are accused of eating sugar cane, so perhaps plant foods enter the diet more than is generally believed.

The four animals that I watched on the Río Salto were foraging on the ground and through the trees. They were spread out 10 to 30 yards apart and they moved so rapidly that it was impossible for the eye to follow all four at once. The leader leaped from the riverbank to a leaning tree trunk and in a few seconds appeared in the topmost branches, 30 feet above the river. A flash of black, and it was in the adjoining tree, thence straight down the trunk to the ground and on down the riverbank, where it disappeared round a bend. The other three followed in like manner, springing with incredible agility up through vines and lower branches of trees, over or under logs and tangled brush, and thence swiftly along the ground. They covered a hundred yards in much less than a minute and disappeared; but downstream I could hear the rustling and see branches and leaves shake for another minute or so before the animals were gone. After the tayras passed, an abnormal silence was noticeable along the river; it was fully five minutes before the birds began to stir again.

Communal hunting by groups of tayras has been remarked by several authors. According to Leyland, troops of 15 to 20 have been seen hunting together on the pine ridges of Belize, British Honduras (Alston, 1879–1882). Often, however, tayras are encountered singly. On one of our field trips, David L. Spencer came upon a single tayra in a trail near Xocempich, Yucatán; and Efraín Hernandez mentioned seeing one cross a railroad track in western Tabasco.

Little is known of the life history of this interesting animal. Gaumer (1917) says that females construct nests in tree forks, lining them carefully with soft bark and leaves. He further states that two young are born, in February, that they open their eyes two weeks after birth, and that by the time they are two months old the young are accompanying the mother on foraging trips. At the time the group of four was observed in San Luis Potosí, I suspected that it might be a family of three grown young with their mother; there was no real evidence of relationships in the group, however.

Alvarez del Toro (1952a) states that female tayras have their young in hollow logs in spring or summer, and that they vigorously defend the den from intruders.

Allen (1906) described two young tayras captured by J. H. Batty near

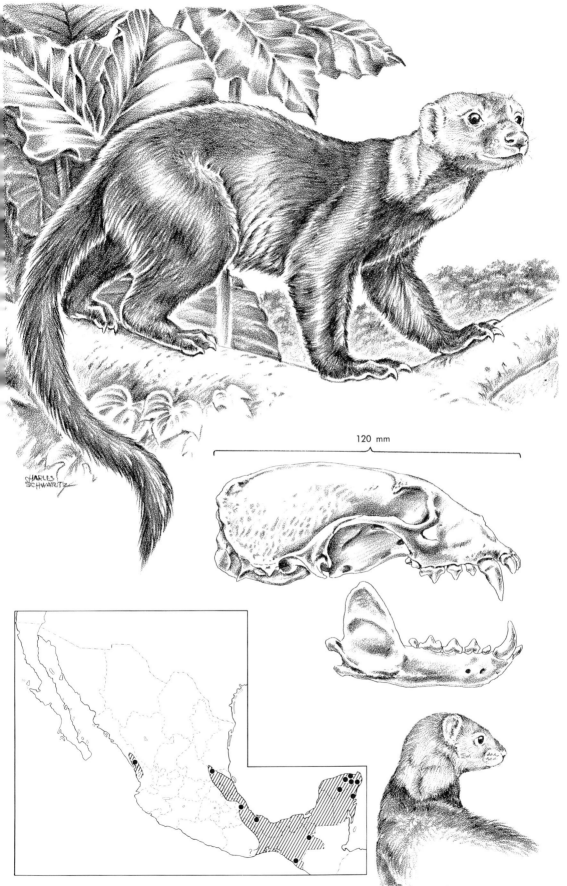

Fig. 163. Tayra, *Tayra barbara*.

Escuinapa, Sinaloa, on November 10, 1904. They were thought to be only three or four days old, which would imply a breeding season different from that given by either Gaumer or Alvarez del Toro. The color pattern of juveniles is given by Allen (p. 235) as follows: "From the shoulders posteriorly the pelage is wholly deep black; at the shoulders it is mixed with rufous, passing into nearly uniform rusty brown on the head and neck. There is a small blackish spot at the posterior base of the ear, and an indistinct blackish lateral face stripe."

Although Gaumer indicates that tayras are principally nocturnal, he goes on to say that in cloudy weather they may be out through the morning. Most of the observations cited above were made in broad daylight. Apparently tayras, like weasels and otters, are active either by day or by night.

The tayra is an exceedingly interesting predator, but it is of no particular economic importance, either in its destruction of game or as a fur bearer. Although it is accused of raiding poultry flocks, Gaumer could not cite a single proved case of such damage. Like the weasel, it probably eats more rodents than game or poultry.

Grison. *Grison canaster*

Other names.—Grisón; rey de las ardillas; *Galictes canaster.*

Description.—Size of a house cat, with very short legs, a short tail, and a long sinuous neck. Upper parts of body and the bushy tail salt-and-pepper gray. Lower parts including legs jet black. A white line half an inch wide extends above the eyes, passes through the short ears, and fades out along the sides of the neck; it separates the dorsal gray from the black of the face and lower parts. Toes partly webbed. Measurements: head and body—400 to 470 mm.; tail—200 to 230 mm. Weights: young male almost full grown, 3,305 gm.; young female, 1,830 gm. Females are nearly as long as males but are more slender.

Range in Mexico.—Wet tropical forests from northern Veracruz and eastern San Luis Potosí south along the Gulf coast to the Isthmus of Tehuantepec and eastward through Chiapas and the Yucatán Peninsula. The animal is nowhere abundant. It has never been recorded on the west coast above the isthmus.

The grison was unknown north of Guiana and northern Brazil until Nelson (1901) saw a live specimen captured by the natives near Tunkas, Yucatán. Subsequently Gaumer (1917) listed the species from several localities in Yucatán and from southeastern Chiapas. Recently taken specimens extend the known range far up the Gulf coast, almost to the border of Tamaulipas. Dalquest (1951) kept two pet grisons which had been taken near Potrero in northern Veracruz; his published account of these animals includes much valuable material on behavior.

Wherever it occurs in Mexico the grison seems to favor humid tropical forests, although it has been found in cane fields and other open situations. The presence of webs on the feet suggests that the animal may be semi-aquatic, and Dalquest attests that it is a deft swimmer. Alvarez del Toro

89 mm

Fig. 164.   Grison, *Grison canaster*.

(1952a) says that grisons are usually found near rivers and in wet lowlands where much swimming would be necessary.

Not much is known of the normal habits and behavior of wild grisons. They hunt singly or in pairs and supposedly do not form packs like the larger tayras. Presumably they den in burrows or hollow logs and rear their young there. Gaumer states that litters of about two young are born in March; but the pets obtained by Dalquest were captured at a very early age (one with its eyes still closed) from separate litters on August 14 and September 16, respectively. Details of the dens or the size of the two litters were not obtained. As adults these animals were principally diurnal, sleeping most of the night. They rolled and played together a great deal, according to Dalquest, and their occasional fights—mostly over food—were accompanied by shrill squeals. As is true of all mustelids, grisons have paired anal glands containing strong-smelling musk. Until it was three months old, Dalquest's captive female when frightened or excited would spray this disagreeable liquid, much in the manner of a skunk. However, the habit ceased. The young male never was known to discharge musk. Adult grisons do not emit any strong odor, a fact attested by both Dalquest and Alvarez del Toro.

Grisons in the wild are said to feed principally on small mammals, birds and their eggs, and large insects. Various authors say that they eat a good deal of fruit also, and they are known to do so in captivity. Dalquest's captives took bananas readily. They killed live mice, rats, and birds up to the size of domestic pigeons and ate them, feathers, fur, bones, and all. Curiously, no bones, not even teeth, could be found in the droppings. These animals also drank large amounts of water, 350 to 750 milliliters daily.

Grisons have no importance as game or predators, but they are among the rarest and perhaps the most interesting of the Mexican carnivores. The young seemingly are easy to tame, and they make lively and entertaining pets.

Badger. *Taxidea taxus*

Other names.—Tlalcoyote; tejón.

Description.—Size of a cocker spaniel, with squat, powerful body, flattened head, short but stout legs, and stubby tail. Ears short and rounded. Feet large and strong, equipped with massive claws for digging (claws of forefeet more than 25 mm. long). General coloration grizzled, the long fur projecting laterally from the sides of the body making the animal appear even wider than it really is. Head predominantly blackish, with dorsal white stripe from nose over head to shoulders, and white stripes from chin upward past eye and from throat to ear. Underparts whitish tan except feet and legs, which are blackish. Measurements: head and body—500 to 550 mm.; tail—100 to 150 mm. Weights: 3,500 to 5,000 gm.

Range in Mexico.—Throughout northern Mexico, south on the central plateau to the Valley of Mexico (Ajusco Mountains). The badger is found principally in mesquite-grassland and desert zones, but may penetrate the pine and oak forests up to high elevations.

112 mm

RIGHT FRONT FOOT

RIGHT HIND FOOT

Fig. 165. Badger, *Taxidea taxus*.

The badger is best known for its ability as a digger. There is probably no animal of comparable size that can move as much dirt in so short a time as a badger. One that was overtaken in open country dug itself into hard ground and was out of sight with the hole plugged behind it in less than a minute and a half. Badgers live in underground burrows and they feed principally on ground-dwelling rodents, which they systematically excavate in foraging operations. The squat body and powerful digging legs adapt the animal well to a fossorial existence.

Badgers usually prefer open plains where small rodents are abundant and the soil is loose and easily excavated. The highest populations in Mexico probably are in the temperate mesquite-grasslands or in alluvial valleys in the pine-oak zone, though the animals are found sparingly on the most arid deserts and even in heavy timber. They never live on excessively rocky ground.

Foraging is done mostly at night, the badgers spending most of the day-light hours in underground retreats. Because of their nocturnal habits and generally shy and unobtrusive manner, badgers are rarely seen, even in country where they are relatively abundant. Their diggings and sign, how-ever, are readily observed. A feeding badger will leave a prairie pitted with excavations, and horsemen sometimes complain of the danger to horses legs caused by the holes.

Young badgers are born in ground dens, usually 2 to 6 feet beneath the surface. The entering tunnel may be as long as 30 feet. In central California the young are born in February or March, but the time of breeding in Mexico is not known. Litters usually consist of 2 to 5 young. The young are cared for by the female until they are perhaps two-thirds grown; after that they adopt the solitary habits of adults.

As already mentioned, the main foods of badgers are burrowing rodents such as ground squirrels, prairie dogs, gophers, rats, and mice. Occasionally they will take a cottontail trapped in a ground hole or even a jackrabbit surprised in its surface form. Other casual items of diet are small birds and their eggs, carrion, insects, snakes, and lizards. On the whole, the badger is a valuable animal in range country because of its depredations on rodents which compete with livestock for forage. On irrigated lands badgers may cause some damage to dikes and ditch banks by digging after ground squirrels and thereby weakening the earth structures. Such troubles are uncommon.

Ordinarily badger fur is of little commercial value, but at times the demand on the fur market has pushed the price up to a point where commercial trapping was worth while. Badger fur makes serviceable trimming for cloth coats. It is too shaggy to be made into whole coats.

Perhaps the greatest danger to the badger population of the United States and northern Mexico is the increasing use of poison for destroying range rodents. Badgers are incautious in picking up carrion or baits of any kind, and they easily can be eliminated by the wholesale use of poison.

Striped Skunks. *Mephitis macroura* and Related Species

Other names.—Zorillo listado; mofeta rayada; zorillo.

Species included here.—*Mephitis macroura*, often called the "hooded skunk," and *M. mephitis*, specifically called the "striped skunk."

Description.—Size of a house cat, with chunky body, relatively small head, short legs, and a long bushy tail. General color black, with continuous white bands on each side of body or along middorsal line. The white patterns vary greatly in both the hooded skunk (*Mephitis macroura*) and the striped skunk (*Mephitis mephitis*). (See fig. 167.) Hooded skunks have relatively longer tails than striped skunks, whence the name *macroura*.

	Head and Body	Length of Tail	Percentage of Total Length Represented by Tail (Average)
M. macroura	300–340 mm.	350–420 mm.	52
M. mephitis	350–380	250–320	44

Additional differences in the skulls of these two species are described by Howell (1901 : 39).

Striped skunks can be differentiated from spotted skunks by their larger size and by the continuity of lateral white bands—spotted skunks have irregular, broken white bands over most of the body—and from most hog-nosed skunks by the black hairs in the middorsal region of the back and in the tail. In northern and central Mexico, hog-nosed skunks are pure white dorsally and have a white tail. Only the hog-nosed skunk of the southeastern tropics might resemble *Mephitis* (see description of *Conepatus*).

Range in Mexico.—Of *M. macroura*: throughout the Republic except in northwestern deserts and very dense rain forest (fig. 166). Of *M. mephitis*: only temperate northern localities (mostly wooded uplands), such as northern Baja California, the Sierra Madre Occidental from Sonora and Chihuahua south at least to Durango, the Sierra del Carmen in northern Coahuila, and the lower reaches of the Río Grande in Tamaulipas (fig. 167). In 1957 we took a specimen of *M. mephitis* by a wooded stream near the city of Chihuahua. To what extent the species may live in oases in the northern desert is not known.

Armed with a particularly efficient weapon of defense, the striped skunk wanders at will over its range without apparent fear of man or beast. The paired scent glands of the mustelids (to which the family name Mustelidae refers) are best developed in the skunks. These glands, on each side of the anus, consist of receptacles enclosed by strong muscles and connected with erectile jets from which the acrid musk can be ejected in a powerful spray. When danger threatens, the skunk assumes a U-shape, with head and anus both directed toward the intruder. The tail is held vertically, with the long hairs extended to form a broad plume—a clear warning, "Look out"! The vents of the two glands protrude from the partly everted anus. Often the warning is accented by a growl or a hiss, or by patting the front feet on the

66 mm

PORTRAIT—showing "hood"

Fig. 166. Hooded skunk, *Mephitis macroura*.

ground. If an attack is pressed in the face of these portents, the skunk opens fire by contracting the muscles which surround the glands. The spray of blinding, choking liquid will hit its mark from a distance of ten feet or even more, and usually sends the attacker into precipitous retreat.

The possession of so formidable a means of defense seems to instill in the skunk a confidence and self-assurance that is rare in wild animals. A skunk goes about its business in a methodical, plodding way, paying little attention to anything but its own affairs. It is not in any sense alert or wary. A passing dog or speeding automobile arouses little interest unless it appears to the skunk as a challenge or a danger. Then the skunk resorts to its scent weapon for protection. This confidence in anal artillery as a defense against motor vehicles is ill founded, as is evident from the many highway kills along roads where skunks happen to be abundant. And a good many predators, including the coyote, bobcat, great horned owl, and certain hawks, will often capture and eat skunks in spite of the scent. Thus the defense is not invulnerable.

A skunk normally is solitary. It spends the warm daylight hours in an underground burrow, a hollow tree, an old building, a cave in the rocks, or a similar shelter and comes out to forage at night. The striped skunks are more likely to be seen abroad in daylight (especially at dawn or dusk) than either the spotted or the hog-nosed skunk. In fog or warm, soft rain the striped skunk may even be about in midday. Adults usually forage alone and den alone, but favorable dens sometimes harbor several individuals at one time. In cold climates skunks may sleep in dens for many weeks, but in most parts of Mexico the weather is not severe enough to induce retirement for so long a period.

Mating takes place in late winter, and the young are born approximately eight weeks afterward. Litters consist of 3 to 8 young, averaging about 5. Females of the species *mephitis* have 6 pairs of nipples, whereas those of *macroura* have 5; it is not known whether there is a corresponding difference in litter size. After four or five weeks in the nest, the young start to follow their mother on her nightly foraging trips. In the lights of a car it is not uncommon to see a female leading an obedient file of several youngsters, each with its own tail plume held just like mother's. By late summer the young attain their independence and wander off to forage for themselves. Young skunks are easily tamed and make attractive pets if the scent glands are removed.

Although most members of the family Musteldae are predominantly carnivorous, skunks are omnivorous. However, insects and other invertebrates are the staple diet, and the normal method of foraging is adapted to the capture of such prey. At daylight one morning I watched a striped skunk busily searching for breakfast in an open grove of oaks It hurried from one rock to another, turning over the small ones and walking completely around larger ones, its nose close to the ground to detect a possible cricket or beetle;

occasionally it would dig a small hole with the front feet, seeking a grub or a pupa, which it located doubtless by scent. The animal never looked beyond the immediate foreground nor paid any attention to its general course, which was an apparently aimless wandering. It caught a grasshopper within twenty feet of me without detecting my presence. I did not see this particular animal capture any small mammals, but studies of skunk scats and stomachs indicate that mice and rats contribute materially to the striped skunk's diet. Other vertebrates preyed upon by skunks are birds (and their eggs), lizards,

Fig. 167.   Variation in the color patterns of *Mephitis macroura* (four specimens on left) and *Mephitis mephitis* (four specimens on right).

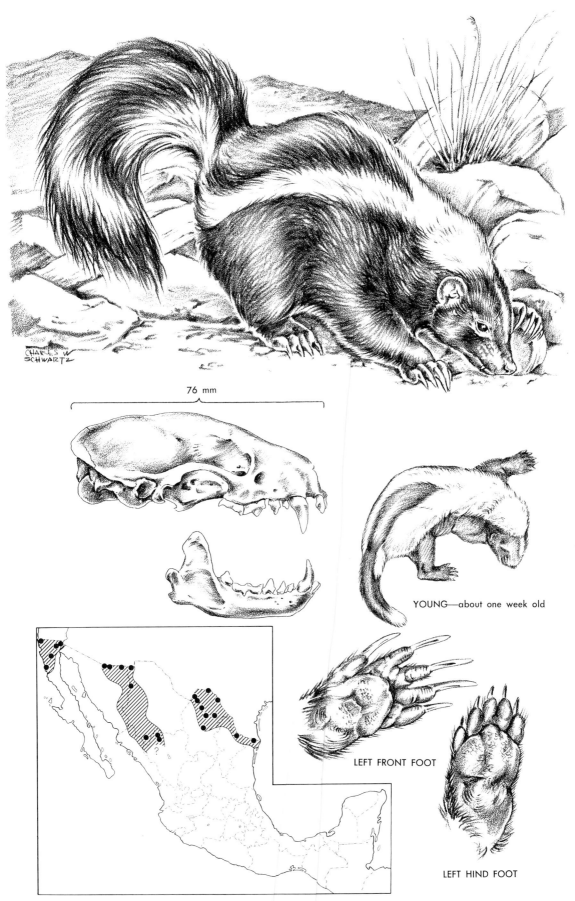

76 mm

YOUNG—about one week old

LEFT FRONT FOOT

LEFT HIND FOOT

Fig. 168.   Striped skunk, *Mephitis mephitis.*

snakes, frogs, salamanders, and even small fishes. And skunks readily eat carrion of all kinds.

Of plant foods the striped skunk is known to eat a wide variety of fruits and berries, including cherries, apples, strawberries, manzanita berries, and a host of others. In southern Mexico, M. macroura doubtless eats such tropical fruits as annonas, cherimoyas, mangos, and bananas, but I have no specific data about this. Gaumer (1917) lists "roots" as a prominent food of the striped skunk in Yucatán; he does not specify what kinds.

Skunks are known to eat birds' eggs readily, and occasionally they even capture an incubating bird. Often they catch crippled game birds left in the field by hunters, or eat the bodies of birds that have been shot and lost. There are no grounds for belief, however, that skunks are adept at searching out bird nests or at capturing many healthy wild birds, though they do cause real damage in poultry yards. In the wild, skunk predation usually has little effect on bird populations. The benefits derived from skunk predation on mammalian pests such as mice, and upon insects, far exceed the damages to poultry and wild birds.

Striped skunks occupy a variety of habitats, as may be inferrred from their wide distribution in Mexico. However, the highest population densities are in farming areas where cultivated fields are interspersed with brushy draws, dense fence rows, small wood lots, orchards, rock fences, or deserted buildings. In such situations the skunk finds adequate cover and a maximum food supply. The skunk, like the coyote and jackrabbit, is a species that probably has increased with agricultural development. Only when land use becomes too intense, resulting in destruction of the cover and loss of soil fertility, is the skunk population adversely affected by farming.

In the United States, skunks collectively (that is, striped and spotted skunks) are among the most important of the fur-bearing mammals. The pelts are not individually of great value, but the number taken annually is in the millions. High-quality skunk pelts, from northern regions or high altitudes, are used for fur coats or for trimming cloth coats. Mexican skunks have sparse underfur and are of less commercial value, although in the past a good many were marketed despite the low price. The blackest pelts have the highest value.

Spotted Skunks. *Spilogale gracilis* and Related Species

Other names.—Zorillo manchado; zorillo pinto; zorillo rayado; zorillo.

Species included here.—Spilogale gracilis, S. indianola, S. pygmaea, and S. augustifrons.

Description.—Size of a half-grown house cat (much smaller than striped or hog-nosed skunks), with short legs and slender body. Body longitudinally streaked with alternate black and white bands 1 to 2 cm. wide; bands not continuous but broken, particularly on rump, giving a spotted or blotched pattern. Underparts mostly black. Bushy, relatively short tail mostly black with a white tip. Measurements: head and body—230 to 330 mm.; tail—130 to 200 mm. Weight—425 to 950 gm. Spotted skunks of northern Mexico appreciably larger than those in the south.

Range in Mexico.—Spotted skunks apparently occur throughout Mexico except in extreme desert or in pine-forested mountains. At present several species are recognized; their approximate distribution is shown in fig. 169. It is probable that careful taxonomic study will reveal these geographic populations to be intergrading races of a single species rather than distinct species. Distributional records compiled here are admittedly incomplete.

The spotted skunk is somewhat less numerous in most parts of Mexico than its larger relatives, the striped and hog-nosed skunks. It seems to prefer semi-arid brushlands in northern Mexico and the United States, but it occurs also in wet tropical forests where the other skunks do not. Gaumer (1917 : 223) states that the spotted skunk is found throughout Yucatán, in the forests as well as in brushlands, farmlands, and even in villages. He specifically states that *Mephitis* and *Conepatus* live around clearings and not in the forest.

In general habits the spotted skunk is not unlike the striped skunk. It is, on the whole, solitary, spending the days in a den or burrow and coming out to feed at night. I have the impression that it is more strictly nocturnal than the striped skunk; at least, I rarely have seen one abroad in daylight. The spotted skunk is somewhat more alert, agile, and aggressive than the larger skunks. When threatened, it often actively attacks the intruder, and this habit has given rise to a widespread belief that all spotted skunks are rabid. In allusion to this belief the animal is commonly called *hidrofobico* in northern Mexico, although it is no more subject to rabies than any other carnivore. In Yucatán I was told that the smallest species of skunk (presumably *Spilogale*) would attack without provocation. It is said that some of the rash attacks are made by males during the mating season. The scent of the spotted skunk is fully as powerful as that of larger skunks.

Spotted skunks are much better climbers than their larger and less nimble cousins. Rather than defend themselves against a dog, they sometimes scramble into the limbs of a nearby tree. Chicken yards are not safe from raids, because these skunks can scale almost any sort of wall or fence.

Little is known of the breeding habits of spotted skunks. Litters apparently consist of about four young, born in the spring. The period of gestation is not known. The young, like those of the striped skunk, leave the nest about a month after birth and follow their mother until almost grown, whereupon they adopt the solitary habits of adults.

The diet of the spotted skunk is as varied as that of *Mephitis*. Insects and other invertebrates, small mammals, birds and their eggs, reptiles, amphibians, and many types of fruits and berries are included in the fare, insects being the most important item. Gaumer (1917) correctly states that the benefits of this skunk's predation upon mice, rats, and insects far outweigh the occasional damages to poultry.

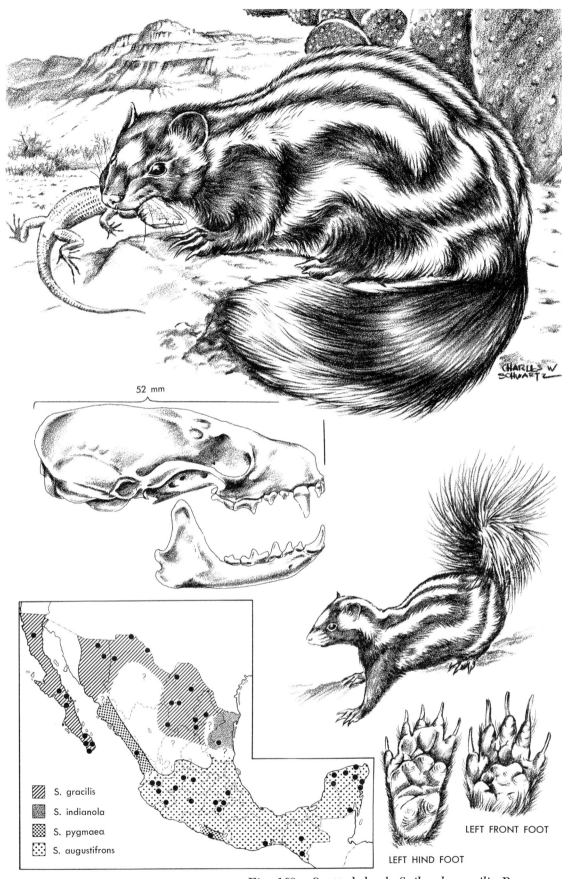

52 mm

S. gracilis
S. indianola
S. pygmaea
S. augustifrons

LEFT HIND FOOT

LEFT FRONT FOOT

Fig. 169. Spotted skunk, *Spilogale gracilis*. Range
map shows the distribution of this and other
species of spotted skunks in Mexico.

Although the fur of spotted skunks is fine and soft, it is worth less than that of striped skunks on the commercial market. The spotted skunks are trapped for profit in Mexico.

Hog-nosed Skunks. *Conepatus mesoleucus* and Related Species

Other names.—Zorillo espalda blanca; zorro coleto; zorillo.

Species included here.—*Conepatus mesoleucus, C. leuconotus,* and *C. semistriatus.*

Description.—Size of a house cat, with stout body, small head, short bushy tail. Long snout bare dorsally. Forelegs strong-muscled and armed with stout digging claws 15 to 20 mm. long. *C. mesoleucus* and *C. leuconotus* are pure white dorsally, including tail, with black sides and underparts. The distinct *semistriatus* has two broad white stripes down the back from nape to hips, separated by a median stripe of black as in *Mephitis.* Very short tail mostly white except basal portion, which is black. All species of *Conepatus* have a black face, lacking the median, white nose stripe of *Mephitis.* Measurements of *mesoleucus* and *leuconotus:* head and body—360 to 460 mm.; tail—240 to 365 mm. The species *semistriatus* has a shorter tail (129 mm. in type specimen).

Range in Mexico.—Throughout Mexico except in Baja California and in the northern deserts. These skunks are abundant in some parts of the pine-oak forest, but are decidedly uncommon in unbroken tropical forests. In fact, they seem to be rare throughout southeastern Mexico. Gaumer (1917) states that in thirty-three years of mammal study in Yucatán he saw hog-nosed skunks only three times.

Although hog-nosed skunks are not often seen in Mexico, and specimens are scarce in most collections, they actually may be more common than is generally supposed. Once I became familiar with their distinctive diggings and long-clawed tracks, I noted their presence in many localities from which no specimens were obtained. They are more nocturnal than *Mephitis*—only once have I seen one abroad in daylight. Furthermore, they are more strictly insectivorous in their feeding habits than other skunks and are correspondingly more difficult to trap. Bailey (1905 : 203) describes his failure in western Texas to attract hog-nosed skunks to his traps with any kind of bait he had to offer, even though the animals were abundant; they fed exclusively upon beetles dug from the ground and were not interested in other foods. In the pine-oak forests near Colonia Pacheco, Chihuahua, we had a similar experience. For some weeks in the summer of 1948, fresh diggings were evident around our camp each morning, but all trapping efforts were unsuccessful. We finally collected several specimens with shotgun and flashlight, which is the only method by which a hog-nose has been taken on any collecting trip in which I have participated. Hog-nosed skunks can, however, be taken in trail sets. The difficulty of capture does not necessarily imply that the animals are scarce.

Outside of being more specialized in diet, hog-nosed skunks are generally similar to striped skunks in temperament and behavior. They are solitary in

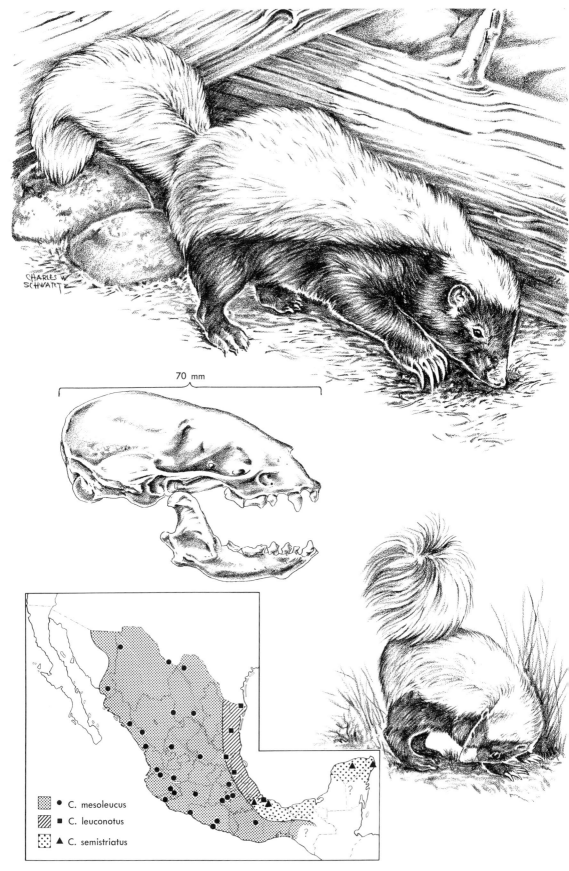

70 mm

C. mesoleucus •

C. leuconotus ■

C. semistriatus ▲

Fig. 170. Hog-nosed skunk, *Conepatus mesoleucus.*
Range map shows the distribution of this and other
species of hog-nosed skunks in Mexico.

habit, den in the ground or in appropriate surface shelters, such as rock piles or hollow logs, and depend principally upon their scent for protection. When accosted they hoist a warning tail plume like others of their kind, and they possess a fully functional scent mechanism. The one hog-nosed skunk that I met abroad in daylight backed under a manzanita bush and threatened me with low growls and a vigorous patting of the ground with both front feet. The implications of its warnings were clear enough, and I left it in full possession of the ground.

Little is known of the breeding habits. Litters are said to consist of 1 to 4 young (Cahalane, 1947). The female has only 3 pairs of nipples, as compared with 4 to 6 pairs in other skunks. Young are presumed to be born in early spring. Bailey (1905) mentions taking in western Texas a female containing a single embryo on March 24; the embryo was nearly ready for birth. He further records two females nursing young in April; one of these had her litter of 2 young in a hollow stump. On August 19, 1949, in the mountains of northwestern Chihuahua we collected a half-grown skunk which apparently had left its mother and was foraging alone.

On April 24, 1953, Ward C. Russell found a female hog-nosed skunk with a litter of 3 young, eyes still closed, under a flat rock in the Sierra del Carmen, Coahuila. He was attracted to the spot by the faint cries of the young. On opening the den, he saw the female tending the young, but she did not discharge her scent. He took the young ones to camp, and one of them subsequently grew to maturity in captivity.

As indicated above, ground insects, including beetles, grasshoppers and various grubs and worms, seem to be the staple foods of hog-nosed skunks. Bailey (1905 : 203, 205) mentions finding such insect foods in a number of stomachs, but two specimens contained also ripe fruits of the cactus *Opuntia engelmanni*. Various authors, including Gaumer (1917) and Cahalane (1947), speak of hog-nosed skunks eating small mammals, birds, and carrion, but I doubt that the animals partake of such foods in any quantity. At least they are much more prone to stay strictly on an insect diet than the other skunks, which have more catholic tastes.

In the warm lowlands of Mexico, hog-nosed skunks produce a sparse pelage and the pelts are of little commercial value. It is said that the fur is finer and denser in the high mountains, but the preponderance of white on the back keeps the value below that of the blacker striped skunk.

River Otters. *Lutra canadensis* and Related Species

Other names.—Nutria; perro de agua.
Species included here.—*Lutra canadensis* and *L. annectens.*
Description.—Long-bodied, aquatic mammals with short legs and webbed feet. Tail long and tapered, very heavy at the base. Body a good deal longer than that of a large house cat but not much larger in circumference. Head broad

and flat. Ears very small and rounded. Pelage short and dense, of fine texture. General color rich brown, paler on throat and underparts. Measurements: head and body—650 to 750 mm.; tail—350 to 500 mm. Weight: 5 to 9 kg.

Range in Mexico.—Of northern river otter (*canadensis*): the lower Colorado River between Baja California and Sonora. Of Central American river otter (*annectens*): the mountain rivers of Sonora and Chihuahua and streams along the coastal plains from northern Sinaloa to Chiapas on the Pacific side. This species reported also near Tapalapan, Veracruz, and near Mérida, Yucatán, on the Gulf of Mexico side. Knowledge of distribution of neither species is complete.

The northern river otter (*canadensis*) is well known over most of the United States. However, the only published record of its occurrence in Mexico is the description of a specimen taken by Mearns near where the international boundary intersects the Colorado River.

Otters from other parts of Mexico are considered to belong to the Central American species, *annectens*. Not enough specimens are available to determine whether these two populations are specifically distinct, but they appear very similar to me. I suspect that eventually all Mexican otters will be considered of one species.

Most Mexican otters are found in rivers along the coastal plains; but there seem to be a good many of the animals in larger rivers of the Sierra Madre Occidental. In 1937 I saw an otter on the Río Gavilán about 7 miles west of Pacheco, Chihuahua. It glided down the river past me, shot a rapid, and disappeared round a bend. The pelage was rich, glossy brown. Upon returning to Pacheco in 1948 I inquired about the occurrence of otters in the rivers of this region. Floyd Johnson displayed the pelt of an otter purchased from a local hunter along the Río Gavilán near the Sonora border. He stated that his father, Harl Johnson, had seen a good many such pelts taken in this area in past years. I purchased the skin of a fine big male otter taken on the Río Tutuaca in west-central Chihuahua in October, 1956. Lumholtz (1902) mentions otters a little south of there, in the Barranca de San Carlos (p. 393) and 17 miles northwest of Guadalupe y Calvo (p. 436).

Very little is known of the Central American river otter of the tropical coasts. The species was described in 1897 from a skull taken in the Río de Tepic, Nayarit (Major, 1897). A skin was purchased from a hunter by J. H. Batty near Escuinapa, Sinaloa (Allen, 1906). A mounted specimen without label is in the collection of the Estación Limnológica de Pátzcuaro, Michoacán. W. W. Brown obtained a skin in 1937 from a hunter near Omilteme, Guerrero. Additional scattered records are indicated on the map.

Otters are to a large degree aquatic. They den along the banks of streams and feed upon fish, crayfish, and other aquatic animals. In disposition and habit the otter is utterly unlike its nervous relatives, the weasels and minks. It is slower in action, more docile in temperament, and much less ferocious.

The young are born usually in underground nests, or more rarely in surface nests built in tangles of water-border vegetation. The gestation period

132 mm

LEFT FRONT FOOT

L. canadensis

L. annectens

LEFT HIND FOOT

Fig. 171.   River otter, *Lutra canadensis*. Range map
shows the distribution of *L. canadensis* and of the
much more widespread *L. annectens* in Mexico.

of English otters is often given as sixty-one days; but Liers (1951) states that his captive otters give birth anywhere from nine and a half to twelve and a half months after mating, which suggests delayed implantation as in the weasel. Litters of northern otters consist of 1 to 4 young, 3 being the usual number. The young develop slowly and remain with the mother until they are nearly full grown.

Nowhere in Mexico are otters abundant enough to be of importance, either as fur bearers or as predators of fish. Olegario Sonora of Tierra Colorada and also hunters of Dos Caminos, both localities on a branch of the Río Papagayo, Guerrero, spoke to me of taking *nutria* for the commercial fur market. I doubt that they caught many. Individual pelts are quite valuable, however, and it is not unusual for an otter population to be overtrapped—the more so since the species has a low breeding potential.

FAMILY FELIDAE

Cats

Of the seven species of cats found in North America, all but the Canada lynx occur in Mexico. Four of the six Mexican cats are tropical in distribution, and the mountain lion occurs both in tropical and in temperate zones. Only the bobcat is essentially restricted to the temperate zone.

In tropical forests the large cats are the only predators capable of controlling populations of hoofed game such as deer, peccaries, and tapir. In other words, in the tropics, cats take over completely the ecological function performed in part by the wolf and coyote in temperate zones.

Jaguar. *Felis onca*

Other names.—Tigre; tigre real; leopardo; *Felis hernandesii; Panthera onca.*
Description.—The largest American cat. Body stout, with heavy chest and strong-muscled forelegs. Tail relatively short and tapering. Ears small and rounded. Hair short and rather bristly. Ground color golden tan above, paling to white below. Whole body heavily spotted with black "rosettes," or irregular-shaped blotches. Measurements of males: head and body—1,100 to 1,600 mm.; tail—525 to 640 mm. Weight: 64 to 114 kg. (140 to 250 lbs.). Measurements of females: head and body—1,000 to 1,300 mm.; tail—400 to 550 mm. Weight: 45 to 82 kg. (100 to 180 lbs.).
Range in Mexico.—Tropical forests of southeastern Mexico, up the coastal plains to the mouth of the Río Grande on the Gulf side and the Sonoran foothills of the Sierra Madre Occidental on the Pacific side. Occasional wandering individuals are found far from this normal area of occupancy; a few such extralimital records are indicated on the range map.

Around the camp fires of Mexico there is no animal more talked about, more romanticized and glamorized, than *el tigre*. The chesty roar of a jaguar

Ocelot with Turkey

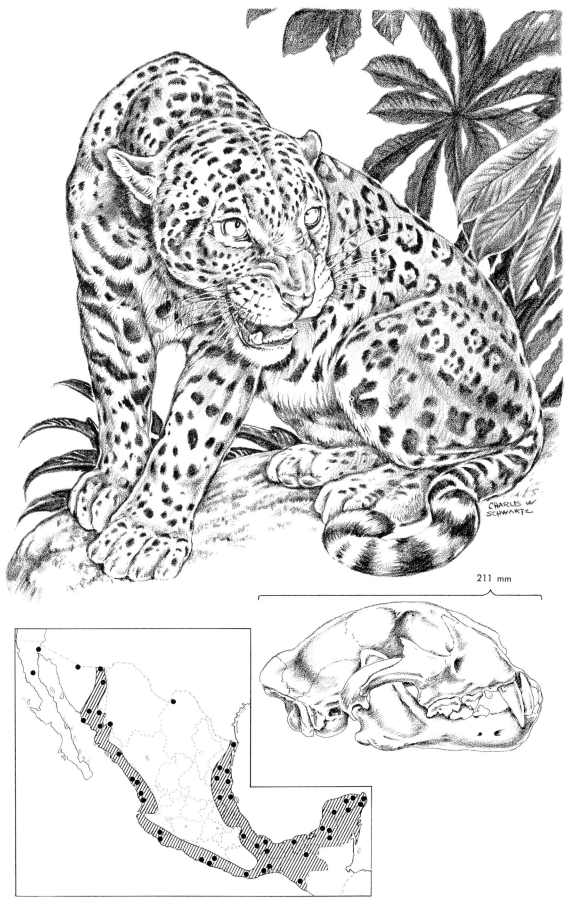

Fig. 172. Jaguar, *Felis onca*.

in the night causes men to edge toward the blaze and draw serapes tighter. It silences the yapping dogs and starts the tethered horses milling. In announcing its mere presence in the blackness of night, the jaguar puts the animate world on edge. For this very reason it is the most interesting and exciting of all the wild animals of Mexico.

The realm of the jaguar is the dense tropical *monte*. The big cat is most at home in the tall, shady forests along streams and watercourses that traverse the coastal lowlands. The highest densities of jaguars noted in the course of this survey were along the heavily forested flatlands and foothills of southern Sinaloa, the swamps of coastal Nayarit, the remaining uncut forests along the Gulf coast as far east as central Campeche, and the great rain forests of northern Chiapas. But some individuals follow the tropical gorges far up into the pine-clad mountains, and on occasion they wander great distances from their normal habitat. Jaguars have been recorded in various parts of the Mexican uplands and even well into the southwestern United States, as far west as California. They are particularly prone to follow the big rivers on their northern peregrinations—the Brazos, Pecos, Río Grande, Gila, and Colorado. I recently examined the tanned hide of a jaguar killed in September, 1955, near the southern tip of the San Pedro Mártir range, Baja California. This animal, an old male, must have wandered across the whole Sonoran desert, crossed the Colorado River, and traveled south for 100 miles—a trip of at least 500 miles from regularly occupied jaguar range. Most vagrant jaguars are males, presumably driven from home in territorial disputes with other males. Once on the road, such vagrants seem to adopt travel as a way of life, like itinerant Englishmen.

But for all the evidence of long travel by a few jaguars, the animals in their preferred habitat are normally highly sedentary—far more so than mountain lions. Hunters who pursue jaguars with hounds are impressed with the great distance a jaguar can run before coming to bay, and from this type of observation has come the general belief that all jaguars must range many miles every night. But J. F. Ferreira of San Ignacio, Sinaloa, a guide and hunter who has killed approximately 60 of the beasts, told me emphatically that undisturbed animals have very small home ranges, no more than 2 to 5 km. in extent, within which they can normally be found. Furthermore, Sr. Ferreira was of the belief that male jaguars guarded these home territories from encroachment by other males, although the ranges of females may overlap those of males. One method of hunting jaguars in Sinaloa is to take a station in the known territory of a male and after dark simulate the roar of another male. At any time of year (not solely during the mating period) the local "owner" may come posthaste to the call, presumably to drive out the intruder. The old saying that each hill has its own tiger may hold true for the actual arrangement of a jaguar population.

Jaguars are almost exclusively nocturnal, only rarely coming out during daylight hours. Ordinarily, during the day they rest in some secluded hide-away in the rocks or thick brush. At nightfall they emerge to find a meal. Like other cats, jaguars stalk their prey or wait in ambush by a game trail or water hole. Hunting is done mostly on the ground, but various authors report that jaguars occasionally go into the trees to hunt monkeys. Jaguars have an almost catholic taste in prey. The mountain lion prefers deer, and the bobcat feeds chiefly on rabbits and small rodents, but the jaguar apparently has no special preference. Where peccaries are numerous, *el tigre* may live mainly on them. But the diet can include deer, monkeys, tapirs, rabbits and other small mammals, birds, fish, dogs, or even turtles and their eggs. Sr. Ferreira, who has opened the stomachs of many jaguars killed in Sinaloa, tells me that the contents of no two are the same. He has often found mice, small birds, lizards, and snakes, along with the remains of the larger, grazing animals. In places along the sea coast, jaguars seem to search for the turtles that come in at night to lay their eggs, and they frequently dig up and eat the eggs themselves. Jaguars have been observed lying quietly on the shore of a lagoon or on a projecting log waiting for fish. In Brazil there is a widespread belief that the jaguar taps its tail on the water to attract fish, hooking them out onto the bank with its claws when they come to investigate the disturbance. This story is carefully documented by Gudger (1946), who accepts it as probably true.

Jaguars may prey heavily on livestock. Being fond of wild peccaries, they are especially prone to attack domestic swine. At El Real, Chiapas, we were told that herds of swine often are driven to market in Tabasco over dim trails through the great virgin rain forest. The greatest hazard in this operation is that a jaguar will attack the herd at night, scattering the animals far and wide through the forest. Any type of stock, including horses, cattle, burros, goats, or sheep, may be subject to predation by jaguars, and sometimes losses are severe. It is a question whether all jaguars on occasion attack stock, or whether certain individuals become habitual stock killers and the damage is blamed on jaguars collectively. Quoting again my friend Sr. Ferreira, the evidence as he sees it suggests that only certain animals form the habit of killing stock, and when these individuals are killed, losses cease even though there are other jaguars in the vicinity.

Fabulous tales are told of the ability of jaguars to carry their victims away from dangerous clearings to safe retreats where they can eat in peace. López and López (1911), for example, cite reports of jaguars carrying animals of 200 kg. and more long distances (20 or 30 km.). In the first place, it seems unlikely that a jaguar would have any reason to carry food so far; secondly, it is doubtful that this would be possible. However, all cats are astonishingly strong, and a jaguar could certainly move a horse or a cow some little distance if it wanted to.

Female jaguars rear their litters in caves or other shelters, bringing food

Fig. 173.   Portrait of a jaguar, by C. W. Schwartz.

to them during the period of growing up, and later leading them in the hunt for at least a year, and probably more, until the young can hunt satisfactorily by themselves. The gestation period is one hundred days. Litters usually consist of 2 kittens, occasionally 3, and sometimes (though rarely) even 4. Breeding in Yucatán is said by Gaumer (1917) to occur in August and September, during which time the jaguars do much roaring and caterwauling. The young would arrive, then, in midwinter. In Sinaloa, according to J. H. Batty (Allen, 1906), the young are born in July or August. After the honeymoon, the male jaguar leaves his mate, and she rears the young alone. The female zealously guards her brood and is likely to attack with vigor and determination if the young are threatened.

From time to time, it is rumored that a jaguar has become a man-eater, but nowhere in Mexico have I been able to authenticate any such report. Men undoubtedly have been killed by cornered or wounded jaguars, but unprovoked attacks are rare. In this respect the jaguar differs from its relatives in the Old World. Lions, tigers, and leopards may all become confirmed man-eaters under certain conditions; the American cats fortunately do not.

Fig. 174.   Jaguar captured in the mangrove swamps of coastal Nayarit. Photograph by E. E. Lee.

Jaguars are hunted in various ways. Probably more kills are made hunting with dogs than in any other manner. Packs of trailing dogs are put on the fresh track of a jaguar and are followed by the hunters afoot or on horseback until the animal is brought to bay. The hunters then make the kill at close range with a rifle or shotgun. The chase may take many hours and often goes through thickets of thorny brush and up and down rocky precipices and other difficult places. Along the coast of Nayarit the Lee brothers of Tucson, Arizona, hunt jaguars and ocelots in the extensive mangrove swamps, following the hounds by boat. Both of these spotted cats are very much at home in water, and they lead the dogs on extensive semiaquatic runs. When a jaguar comes to bay it sometimes trees but more frequently faces the dogs on the ground, with its back protected by a tree, rock, or other defense. There it fights the snapping pack and often kills or maims several dogs before the hunters arrive to dispatch it.

Another method of jaguar hunting is to wait at night in a tree perch above a bait or the remains of an animal killed previously by the jaguar itself. When the cat comes to feed, hunters shoot it with the aid of a flashlight. López and López (1911) describe elaborately the preparations that should be made for this type of still hunting.

The procedure of calling male jaguars within their home territories by simulating the roar of a trespassing male already has been mentioned. Some jaguars are trapped near kills or along trails, and some, of course, are come upon by pure accident and are shot before they can escape.

As a result of constant persecution, jaguars have become scarce or even been exterminated in the more highly developed sections of tropical lowland; but in wilder regions they seem to be holding their own very well indeed. Sr. Ferreira has seen no diminution of numbers in Sinaloa during his lifetime. The Lee brothers find about as many animals in Nayarit as formerly. According to livestock ranchers in Campeche, Tabasco, and northern Chiapas there are still too many jaguars in the rain forest for livestock to be permitted free range. The lordly *tigre* will probably persist in the Mexican lowlands in much better numbers than the big carnivores of the temperate uplands.

Ocelot. *Felis pardalis*

Other names.—Ocelote; tigrillo; xacxicin; *Leopardus pardalis.*

Description.—A medium-sized spotted cat, with body about as large as that of a cocker spaniel, small head, and relatively short tail. Base color of body, legs, and tail buffy gray but heavily marked with rich brown spots, each surrounded with a black border. Spots on shoulders and neck elongate, those to the rear more nearly round. Head brown with black streaks and vermiculations. Underparts whitish with dusky spots. Tail heavily marked with black, tip mostly black. Feet and lower legs gray, finely spotted with black. Measurements: head and body—550 to 780 mm.; tail—300 to 435 mm. Weight of a young male from

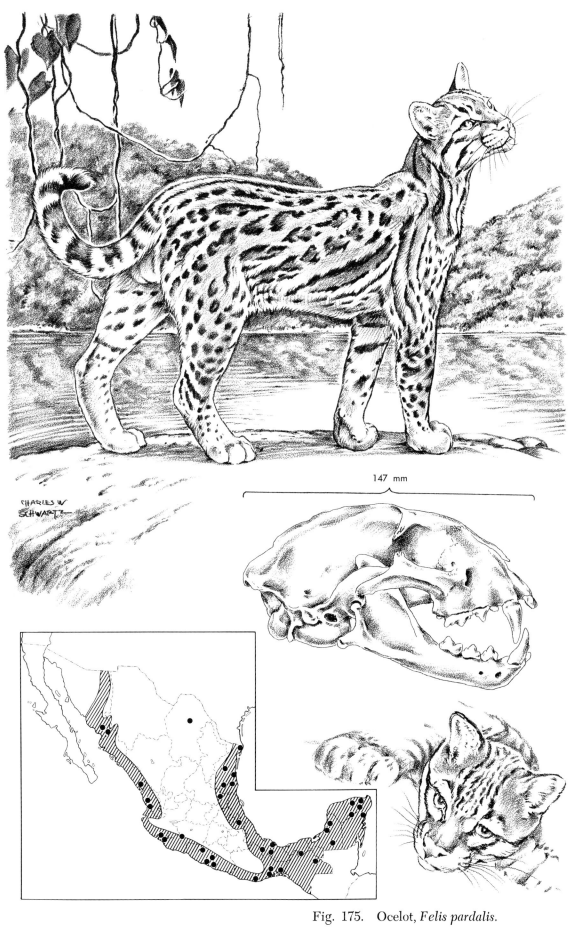

147 mm

CHARLES W SCHWARTZ

Fig. 175. Ocelot, *Felis pardalis.*

eastern San Luis Potosí: 4.5 kg. (10 lbs.); some individuals are said to weigh up to 11 kg. (25 lbs.). Females are only slightly smaller than males.

Range in Mexico.—Tropical coastal plains and foothills on both sides of Mexico from Sonora and Tamaulipas south to Isthmus of Tehuantepec, thence eastward through Chiapas and the Yucatán Peninsula. Wandering individuals have been recorded in Coahuila and in various parts of the southern United States.

There are two medium-sized spotted cats in Mexico—the ocelot and the margay. Both range throughout the Mexican tropics, and most Mexican hunters do not differentiate between the two, calling both *tigrillos*. But a *tigrillo* nearly always turns out to be an ocelot, for it is the more common species. The margay is very rare indeed.

The ocelot is one of the handsomest of all cats. Its richly marked pelt has always been a valuable item of commerce and still is, despite the prohibition on the sale of wildlife products. Ocelots are widely distributed in tropical zones, from the heavy rain forest to the sparse tropical deciduous forest. They do not occur regularly in arid tropical country. Areas known to be well populated with ocelots are southern Sinaloa, coastal Nayarit, eastern San Luis Potosí and adjoining parts of Tamaulipas and Veracruz, the Isthmus of Tehuantepec, and Gulf coast of Tabasco and Campeche. In these areas especially, jaguar hunters run down with their hounds many ocelots while hunting the bigger cats. In the lowlands of Nayarit the Lee brothers, it is said, kill about as many ocelots as jaguars, although they attempt to direct their hounds to the jaguars.

Ocelots are nocturnal for the most part, spending their days lying quietly in the branches of large trees and coming out to hunt after dark. Though normally solitary, ocelots frequently are found in pairs—a male and a female together. They hunt both on the ground and in the trees, and their diet includes a wide variety of small and medium-sized mammals and birds. J. H. Batty states that the ocelot "feeds on rabbits and other small mammals, birds, iguanas, frogs, fish, crabs, and small turtles" (Allen, 1906 : 219). Alvarez del Toro says that it preys on mammals up to the size of brocket deer, an opinion expressed also by Epileme Tagoma of Tapalapan, Veracruz. Gaumer (1917) adds pacas, agoutis, and especially monkeys to the bill of fare. He also tells of observing an ocelot catch an ocellated turkey on its roost and fall with it from the limb to the ground. It is often noted that ocelots frequent riverbanks and the shores of other bodies of water, where presumably they do a good deal of fishing. Ocelots occasionally kill domestic animals, an indulgence that earns them the enmity of farmers. Young pigs, kids, and lambs are favorite prey, as are chickens and turkeys. But on the whole, the economic damage done by these beautiful cats is a very minor problem in tropical ranching.

Ocelots breed in the fall and the kittens are born in early winter. Bailey (1905) tells of several newborn litters found in November in southern

Texas. Gaumer says that mating takes place in October in Yucatán and the young arrive in January. The gestation period is not known. Litters of 2 are normal, according to most accounts, although Batty states that there may be 3 or 4 young. The nursery is usually a cave or a hollow tree. It is said that kittens captured young and raised in captivity make very tractable and responsive pets. In this respect ocelots differ markedly from other North American cats, which on the whole are morose and unresponsive in captivity.

The hunting of ocelots is done mostly with dogs. The animals are rather easily taken, for they tree readily after a short run. Some ocelots are shot at night with the aid of a spotlight, and some are encountered accidentally in the daytime. Individuals that have adopted the habit of raiding a chicken roost or corral are most readily captured with steel traps, for they are not particularly wary of such devices.

In addition to utilizing the pelts, many Mexican hunters eat the flesh of ocelots, asserting not only that it is very good meat but also that it imparts strength and good health to the person who eats it. Bernardo Villa told me of participating in a hunt near Coyutla, Veracruz. While butchering an ocelot for eating, the men drank the warm blood accumulated in the thorax. To some extent this belief in the medicinal and even supernatural properties of the meat and blood of cats is found throughout Mexico.

Margay. *Felis wiedii*

Other names.—Tigrillo; tiger cat; chulul; pichigueta; *Margay glaucula; Felis glaucula; Felis tigrina.*

Description.—Size of a large house cat, with stocky body and relatively long tail. Smaller than an ocelot. Base color tawny gray, heavily marked with black or dark-brown spots and streaks. Along the middorsal line the dark markings tend to be linear, becoming irregularly round on the sides and flanks. These spots are all *dark.* (The ocelot has brown spots bordered in black.) Measurements: head and body—450 to 560 mm.; tail—330 to 385 mm. No weights available.

Range in Mexico.—Probably along both coasts from southern Sinaloa on the west and eastern San Luis Potosí on the Gulf southward to the Isthmus of Tehuantepec and thence throughout Chiapas and the Yucatán Peninsula. The margay is known from only a few specimens. A single specimen was taken at Eagle Pass, Texas, sometime before 1852, which quite apparently was a stray, far out of its normal range in the wet tropics.

The margay is another beautiful spotted cat, not easily distinguished from the ocelot. Yet, Mayans of Yucatán call it *chulul* in contradistinction to the ocelot, *xacxicin,* and in Chiapas it is called *pichigueta,* the ocelot having various other names. Thus native peoples do differentiate between the two in some places. But, as mentioned previously, both the ocelot and the margay are widely called *tigrillos* in most of Mexico. I am following Alvarez del Toro (1952*a*) in restricting the name *tigrillo* to the margay.

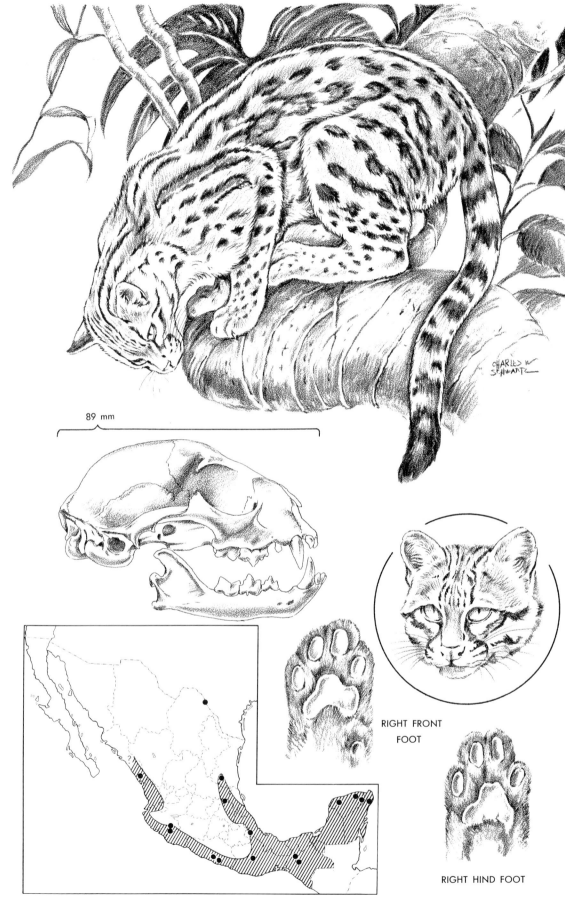

89 mm

RIGHT FRONT
FOOT

RIGHT HIND FOOT

Fig. 176. Margay, *Felis wiedii.*

The margay is an exceedingly rare animal, judging from the paucity of specimens that have been preserved. Goldman (1943) remarks that during the twelve years that he and E. W. Nelson collected 15,000 mammals in every part of Mexico only 2 specimens of the margay were taken. In the past twenty-five years I have record of only 2 additional specimens—an adult female taken near Xilitla, San Luis Potosí, described by Dalquest (1950), and a skull picked up in the forest near San Fernando, Chiapas, by Robert Selander. Any specimen suspected of being a margay should be submitted to a qualified museum for checking.

As one might expect, little is known of the natural history of the margay. Alvarez del Toro (p. 215) states that it resembles the ocelot in being arboreal, frequenting the tree tops in the great tropical forests by day and coming out to hunt at night. He gives its food as "rats, rabbits, birds . . . and an occasional chicken." Nothing has been recorded about the breeding biology of the species.

Gaumer (1917) says that the margay makes an intelligent and affectionate pet if taken young enough. It "wages incessant war against the mice and rats that infest the house."

Fig. 177.   A margay held captive at the Desert
Museum, Tucson, Arizona. Photograph
by Prentice Bloedel.

Puma. *Felis concolor*

Other names.—León; mountain lion; cougar.

Description.—A large cat of slender build, with long legs and tail. General color tawny or sandy to rather rich reddish brown; whitish beneath; dark ears and tail tip; no spots nor stripes. Measurements of males: head and body—1,100 to 1,400 mm.; tail—680 to 960 mm. Weight: 45 to 73 kg. (100 to 160 lbs.). Measurements of females: head and body—1,000 to 1,250 mm.; tail—650 to 730 mm. Weight: 27 to 50 kg. (60 to 110 lbs.).

Range in Mexico.—Throughout the Republic, although the puma is now scarce or exterminated locally in settled areas.

The puma, or mountain lion, is one of the few mammals that range literally throughout Mexico. Equally at home in the mountain pines, on the parched desert ranges, or in the steaming jungle, this remarkably adaptable animal has one essential requirement, and that is a good supply of deer. Although the puma does take other prey, the deer is its bread and butter. I know of no place in North America where pumas thrive in the absence of deer. Since all parts of Mexico have one or another species of deer, this basic necessity of the puma is widely available, except where the deer themselves have been exterminated. Nevertheless, it is still remarkable that so large and specialized a carnivore is able to live in such a variety of habitats as occur in Mexico.

However, puma populations vary greatly in density. The highest populations seemingly occur in the pine-oak zone of northern Mexico. Two localities where I have found pumas especially abundant are the Río Gavilán basin in northwestern Chihuahua and the Sierra del Carmen in northern Coahuila. To the south, pumas are progressively fewer, perhaps because there are fewer deer, and in the tropics because there are other large cats as competitors.

The puma is a much more mobile animal than the jaguar. In hunting, males especially seem to follow long circuits that require a week or even two weeks to complete. Females unhampered by family cares likewise hunt over extensive areas. These individual "beats" are not defended from other pumas in a territorial sense, for they often overlap. Young and Goldman (1946) cite abundant evidence of the wide range of individual pumas.

However, females with young—even well-grown yearlings that hunt with the mother—have much smaller home ranges, judging from my experience. In camps along the Río Gavilán and in the Sierra del Carmen we found signs of family groups hunting day after day in the same canyon or series of adjoining canyons. There was no evidence that these lions were making a circuit. Only occasionally did we find larger tracks, which we assumed to be those of males. The males appeared to be covering more country than the females.

203 mm

RIGHT FRONT
FOOT

Fig. 178. Puma, *Felis concolor*.

Female pumas first breed when two or perhaps three years old, and thereafter they produce a litter every second or third year. Dens for the young are chosen in isolated rocky places, usually in natural caves. The litters, ordinarily of 2 to 4 kittens, are cared for and reared entirely by the mother, who has no single mate, for during heat she may have mated with several males. Gestation is about ninety-six days. The newly arrived kittens weigh from 230 to 450 gm. and are heavily spotted, with rings on the tail. These marks are lost as the animals mature. The young stay with the mother for at least a year and sometimes perhaps longer. One foggy morning I observed a family group coming "home" from a night's foray in the Chihuahua pinelands. The mother stalked majestically ahead, and the two young, which looked to be essentially as large as the mother, followed forty yards behind. When she stopped to survey the ground ahead, they stopped also. When she started off again, they followed at the same distance as before.

Much has been written about the voice of the puma. There are those who have lived in puma country all their lives without hearing a puma make a sound. However, many outdoorsmen have heard the roar, or "scream," which apparently is given only rarely. On August 2, 1948, not only did Robert A. McCabe and I hear the call, but he saw the animal give it (McCabe, 1949). It sounded much like the roar of an African lion but was of higher pitch and shorter duration. The animal was large and presumably was a male.

Although pumas are rarely heard and are not often seen, they leave much sign to betray their presence. Besides tracks and kill remains, pumas are prone to scratch up a pile of leaves or pine needles to cover feces or urine; these characteristic mounds made along trails or in low gaps in a ridge last for some time and are easily recognized. I once found a rubbing post identified as that of a puma by the hair stuck in the pine bark. A trap set near this post caught a puma the second night.

The puma hunts at night and locates its prey by sight, smell, or hearing, then stalks it in the typical manner of a cat, closing in finally with a swift rush to pounce upon the chosen victim before it can gain headway in flight. Characteristically, the kill is made by a deep bite in the neck or back of the head. I have examined the remains of many deer killed by pumas and have found that almost invariably the base of the skull had been punctured by the long canine teeth, or the neck vertebrae just below the skull had been crushed. The claws are used only to hang on to the prey while the fatal bite is delivered. After the kill, a puma often moves its prey to a sheltered spot before feeding, and the ability of the cat to transport animals many times its own weight up hills and over rough terrain has amazed numerous observers. I once found where a puma had carried a white-tailed doe across a sandy road without leaving a drag mark of any kind. Beyond the road the deer had caught on a snag and had fallen to the ground, but the lioness had

Fig. 179.   Photographic portrait of a puma in repose,
by C. W. Schwartz.

picked it up again and carried it to a deep and brushy canyon and thence up the rocky bottom to a cozy nook under a leaning rock, where two well-grown young joined her in the feast. The three animals ate all the deer in one sitting, leaving only fragments of the skull and the heads of the leg bones.

Before feeding, pumas eviscerate their kills, piling the entrails neatly to the side and often burying them with leaves and sticks; and they sometimes cover with limbs and debris the remains of an unfinished carcass, presumably to save it for another meal. In 1938 in Chihuahua I found a freshly killed horse only partly eaten and carefully covered up. For two mornings thereafter I visited the carcass, noting that the lion had returned each night for another meal and each time had left the remains covered over again.

Quantitative studies of the stomach contents of pumas indicate that their diet usually consists of 50 to 90 per cent deer; the rest is made up of livestock, smaller mammals, birds, and carrion. On the east face of the Sierra San Pedro Mártir in Baja California, pumas reputedly kill a good many bighorns. As foods regularly eaten in the tropics, Gaumer (1917) lists also peccaries, agoutis, pacas, coatis, and occasionally monkeys. Small quantities of grass may be eaten at times. On many cattle ranges, pumas live happily on deer and kill cows only occasionally. When deer are scarce, depredations on stock are of course much more severe than when deer are abundant. Sheep, goats, and pigs are preferred by pumas, and horses and burros are particularly subject to predation.

In general, pumas are not in the least dangerous to human life. A wounded or cornered animal will fight valiantly and may maim or kill a person. But this seldom happens. For all North America there are only a few records which show that a puma has eaten a human victim. Despite their size and power, pumas are fearful and respectful of man and flee his approach whenever they can.

Mountain lions in Mexico are killed at every opportunity, but the effort to find and kill them is always intensified when livestock are being taken. Clavigero relates in his history of Baja California that the native Indians were afraid, for superstitious reasons, to kill the lions which raised havoc with the livestock introduced at the Jesuit missions. Finally, in 1701, Padre Ugarte, who took over the mission at Loreto, killed a puma with rocks and induced the natives to start killing off these animals. In northern Sonora the United States border survey party of 1849–1853 found the Mexican ranchers using strychnine, which they applied to fresh kills, poisoning the lions that came back for a second meal. A good many wolves also were dispatched in this way (Baird, 1859). In more recent times I have found that Mexican ranchers trap pumas or hunt them with dogs and rifles. Poison, I think, is used very little.

Hunting lions for sport is done almost entirely with trained hounds, the hunters following the pack on horseback. This is a rugged and exciting sport, for the lion may go many miles over exceedingly rough terrain before the chase ends. When overtaken, a lion usually takes refuge in a tree, where it is easily shot. Unlike jaguars, pumas do not often bay on the ground and fight the dogs. For this reason, any damage to the dogs in a lion hunt is usually minor.

The puma has proved its ability to persist in rough country, despite persistent persecution, so long as deer are present. A program of deer restoration and management in Mexico would almost guarantee a continuing supply of mountain lions.

In western Mexico, from southern Sonora to Nayarit, there is a persistent rumor of another big cat which is neither the puma, nor the jaguar, nor the jaguarundi. It is called the *onza* (ounce), and it is said to be about the size and build of a puma but to have faint stripes over the shoulders. Other characteristics of the *onza* are an elongate track (rather than the typical round track of other cats) and a tendency to refuse to come to bay, even when hard-pressed by dogs. Such an animal has never come to the

Fig. 180.   Puma captured in the Sierra Madre of Sonora. Photograph by E. E. Lee.

attention of taxonomic zoölogists, and until specimens are obtained and determined to be distinct from known species, the *onza* must remain in the status of a myth—admittedly, a very intriguing one.

Jaguarundi. *Felis yagouaroundi*

Other names.—Leoncillo; onza; *Felis cacomitli; Felis eyra.*

Description.—A long, slender cat, as big around as a house cat but much longer. Shaped like an otter, with long neck, rather small legs, small head, and long tail. Occurs in two color phases—reddish brown and dusky black. Both are paler ventrally, and both have a speckled, salt-and-pepper appearance, without any spots or streaks. Measurements: head and body—630 to 750 mm.; tail—300 to 460 mm. No weights available.

Range in Mexico.—The jaguarundi is most frequently recorded from the Tamaulipas plains and from northern Yucatán. Scattered records along the Pacific coast suggest that it might be found throughout tropical Mexico, and the range is so indicated on the map. Jaguarundis have been recorded in southern Arizona, hence they might occur in the Sonoran foothills west of the Sierra Madre.

Curiously, little is known of the jaguarundi. It frequents very dense ground thickets and is naturally secretive. Still for an animal said to be quite common in places, it is very poorly represented in collections, and few observations on its natural history have come to print. I saw a jaguarundi only once during the Mexican survey. This was along the Río Salto in eastern San Luis Potosí. A long reddish form darted across a narrow trail ahead of me and into a thicket of palmettos. It was not seen again.

Of this animal in the Río Grande delta region, F. B. Armstrong wrote (Bailey, 1905 : 168):

. . . Yaguarundi cats inhabit the densest thickets where the timber (mesquite) is not very high but the underbrush—catsclaw and granjeno—is very thick and impenetrable for any large-sized animal. Their food is mice, rats, birds, and rabbits. Their slender bodies and agile movements enable them to capture their prey in the thickest of places. They climb trees, as I have shot them out of trees at night by "shining their eyes" while deer hunting. I capture them by burying traps at intervals along the trails that run through these thick places. I don't think they have any regular time for breeding, as I have seen young in both summer and winter, born probably in August and March. They move around a good deal in daytime, as I have often seen them come down to a pond to drink at midday . . .

Gaumer (1917) kept a pet jaguarundi in the patio of his home in Mérida and seems from his writing to have been quite familiar with the species in the wild as well. He concurs with Armstrong that it feeds on various small mammals and birds, but he thinks gallinaceous birds are its specialty. Quails, chachalacas, guans, and wild turkeys are named as favorite prey species. The jaguarundi is said to extend this preference to include domestic

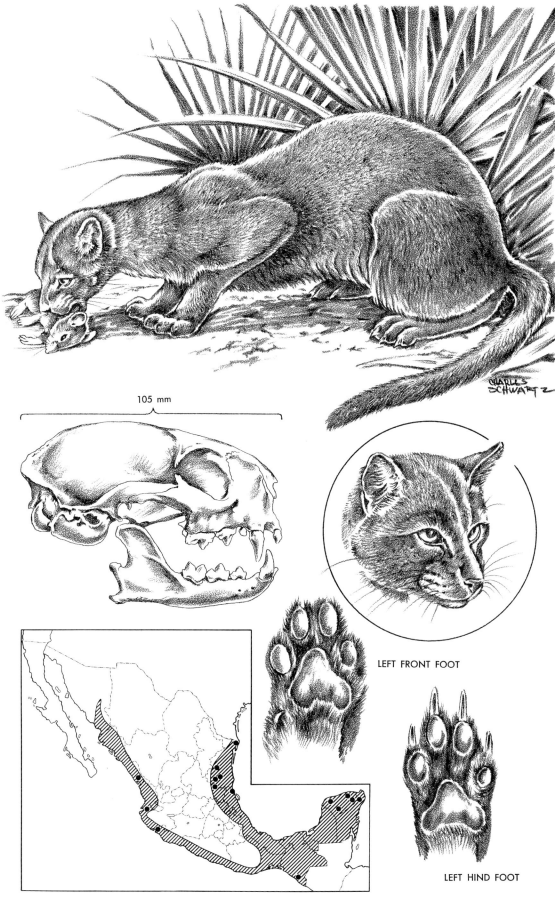

105 mm

LEFT FRONT FOOT

LEFT HIND FOOT

Fig. 181. Jaguarundi, *Felis yagouaroundi*.

chickens and is considered quite a pest of the poultry yard in both Yucatán and Chiapas (Alvarez del Toro, 1952a).

In Yucatán, Gaumer states, breeding occurs among the jaguarundis in November and December, accompanied by much noisy caterwauling and fighting. The young are born in a hollow tree or other shelter nine or ten weeks later, a normal litter consisting of 2 (Bailey mentions one litter of 4). The kittens are unspotted, thus differing from all other wild cats. There may be both red and dusky individuals in the same litter, according to Cahalane (1947).

Jaguarundis are little hunted in Mexico, although some undoubtedly are killed in hunts for other game. They tree readily before dogs, and in Yucatán they are said to escape by hiding in the bromeliads on the higher branches. The pelts are of poor quality and scant value.

Bobcat. *Lynx rufus*

Other names.—Gato montes; gato del monte; lince.

Description.—Size of a small dog, but with long legs and a very short tail (whence the name "bobcat"). Mottled brown mixed with gray and black on the upper parts, becoming white beneath with black spots. Face surrounded by a ruff; ears and tip of tail usually tufted with black. Measurements: head and body—580 to 700 mm.; tail—130 to 170 mm. Weight: 5 to 12 kg.

Range in Mexico.—Species most abundant in northern Mexico, but range extends southward in the temperate uplands at least to Michoacán and the Valley of Mexico, where the animal is generally uncommon. Bobcats do not ordinarily range in the tropical lowlands, nor are they known from the temperate highlands of the southern states.

The bobcat, like the coyote, is a native predator that has adjusted very well to conditions of land settlement. Rodents and rabbits are the bobcat's principal prey, and these sources of food are usually available even on heavily used lands. Bobcats prefer dense brushy cover, especially in conjunction with rocky canyon walls. Areas combining brush, rocks, and abundant rodents are common in northern Mexico, and there the bobcat maintains itself in large numbers.

It is not clear—to me, at least—why there are fewer bobcats in central Mexico and none at all in the south. Many areas in the central and southern uplands superficially appear to be excellent habitat for this animal. We know only that it does not thrive there now, nor is there any evidence that it did so in the past. Among the *relaciones* of south-central Mexico, written by priests in the period from 1538 on, are some excellent accounts of natural history, none of which mention the bobcat as a common animal. Other predators, including the wolf, coyote, and various other cats, are described in detail. It is easier to understand the absence of the bobcat in the tropics, where its place is taken by the ocelot and other medium-sized carnivores.

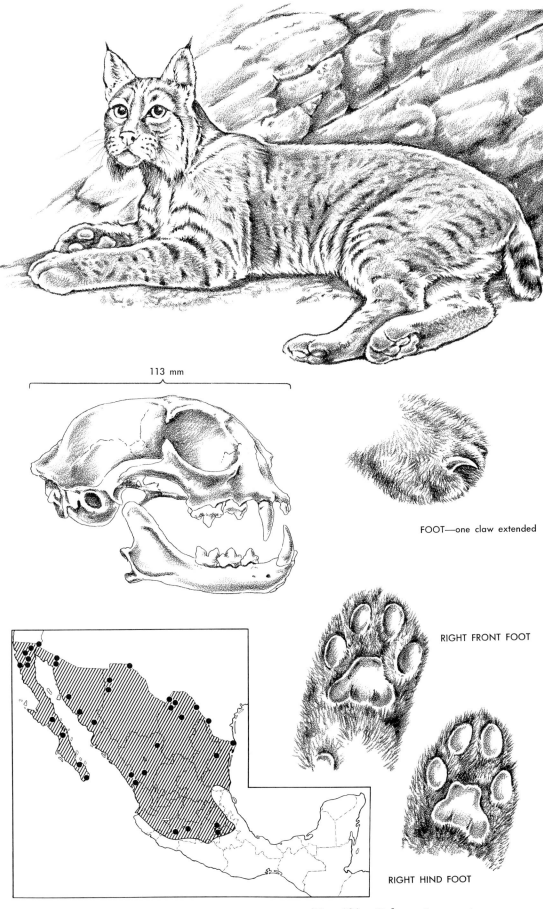

113 mm

FOOT—one claw extended

RIGHT FRONT FOOT

RIGHT HIND FOOT

Fig. 182. Bobcat, *Lynx rufus*.

Bobcats are mainly nocturnal, but they venture forth in daylight more than most other wild cats. Especially on crisp, cool days I have seen bobcats stalking rabbits or mousing in the meadows in bright sunlight. Bobcats generally hunt alone. It is not often that they are seen in groups or even in pairs. After a mother cat teaches her kittens to hunt, she leaves them and resumes her independent life. Males are solitary at all times except when seeking the females during the brief mating period.

Each bobcat has a more or less fixed hunting area, or "beat," several miles in diameter, within which it has a number of daytime resting places or retreats. These may be in rocky caves or hollow trees, but many are simply bedding areas in dense brush or grass without shelter from the weather. Females utilize one or another of their better dens for rearing of the young. When pursued, especially by dogs, bobcats may take refuge in caves or they may simply climb a tree. In very dense brush they sometimes refuse to come to bay but run in circles in the manner of rabbits, keeping well ahead of their pursuers.

Although the bobcat is ordinarily a shy and retiring animal, it is a fighting demon when cornered or captured. Seldom can a single dog overcome one. In a steel trap a bobcat usually will crouch and hide until the trapper approaches closely, whereupon the animal springs out, snarling, spitting, and clawing. It does not become cowed as a coyote or fox usually does. Young bobcats make cute but generally intractable pets. When mature they rarely remain gentle, but more often become sullen and resentful.

The precise breeding season of the bobcat in Mexico is not known, but apparently mating occurs most commonly in the early summer, the 1 to 5 young (averaging 3) being born after a gestation period of about fifty days. Near Escuinapa, Sinaloa, J. H. Batty captured young bobcats estimated to be a month old on August 16 and September 5, 1904; another group of 3, assumed to be a week old, was removed from a nest on October 7 (Allen, 1906). Bernardo Villa (1953a) took 2 very young kittens from a rocky den near Mexico City on June 25, 1949. At Ramos, Chihuahua, Alden H. Miller killed an adult female bobcat weighing 19½ pounds, with milk in her four nipples, on September 4, 1948. The summer breeding period is considerably later than that known in California, where most of the young arrive in April (Grinnell et al., 1937).

As already mentioned, bobcats subsist principally on rodents and rabbits. A recent study in California, based on an analysis of the stomach contents of 219 bobcats taken in semiarid country much like northern Mexico, showed that approximately 60 per cent of the food consisted of mice, rats, ground squirrels, and other rodents, and 30 per cent of rabbits and hares. Contrary to popular belief, bobcats capture very few birds, and of these only a small part are game birds. Seasonally, bobcats may eat a few quail and occasionally they take a fawn. But the bobcat cannot be considered an important predator of game animals, except, of course, rabbits. Nor is it dangerous to domestic livestock, although it has been known to kill a lamb now and then and, very rarely, even a calf. Free-ranging poultry may suffer from depredations of bobcats. But considered all in all, the bobcat in its feeding habits is much more beneficial than harmful to man's interests, a fact that has long been recognized by many ranchers. Bailey (1905 : 169) reported that along the lower Río Grande "most of the ranchmen will not allow the wildcats to be killed for fear their ranches will be overrun with wood rats, mice, and rabbits"—an overestimate, perhaps, of the control value of predators but a recognition nevertheless that the animals are not harmful.

Bobcats have few enemies besides man and his dogs, but two that may be troublesome or even dangerous at times are the mountain lion and the deer. As a rule, bobcats are scarce where mountain lions are numerous, and it seems probable that the larger cat actually preys upon the smaller; not infrequently bobcat remains have been found in mountain lion stomachs. There are many sight records of deer pursuing bobcats and chasing them into trees—especially does during the fawning season. I myself once observed such a chase. How frequently the deer overtake the cats and harm or kill them is not known, but the presence of irritable does must discourage bobcats from venturing far from trees or rocks.

In Mexico, bobcats are generally killed on sight, although the fur is of little value. The flesh is eaten quite commonly, as is that of other cats. I tried it once and cannot endorse it with any real enthusiasm.

Order Perissodactyla

FAMILY TAPIRIDAE

TAPIRS

The tapir is the only North American representative of the order Perisso-dactyla, the odd-toed ungulates. The horse and burro are familiar relatives that have been introduced from the Old World.

Tapir. *Tapirella bairdii*

Other names.—Tapír; danta; anteburro; tzimin; *Tapirella dowii.*

Description.—A large, heavy-bodied ungulate the size of a pony but chunkier and with much shorter legs. Nose elongate, bending downward over the mouth like a short trunk, or proboscis. Ears short, rounded, and white-tipped. Tail stubby. Four toes on front feet, three on rear. Dusky brown, much paler on face, throat, and breast. I have no measurements or weights taken in the flesh, but Gaumer (1917) states that tapirs are about 2 m. long and 1 m. high at the shoulder. A skin in the Museum of Vertebrate Zoölogy is 1.7 m. long, lacking the tip of the nose and the tail. Small (1956) estimates the weight of an adult at 600 lbs. (270 kg.).

Range in Mexico.—Wet tropical forests of southeastern Mexico, west to south-ern Veracruz and eastern Oaxaca. The tapir has been exterminated in much of this range and now lives in only the wildest and least disturbed forests.

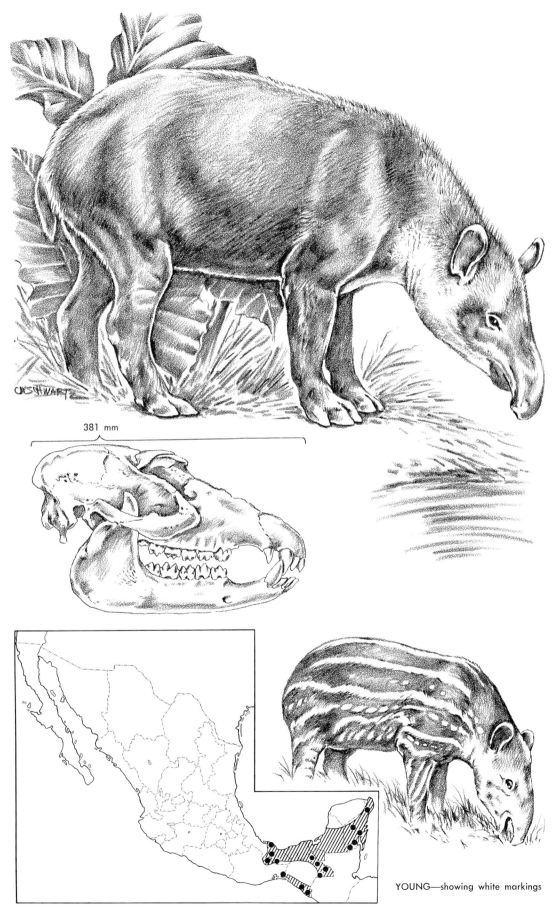

381 mm

YOUNG—showing white markings

Fig. 183.   Tapir, *Tapirella bairdii*.

The tapir is a rather primitive member of the order of mammals to which the horse and its relatives belong. Unlike the horse, the tapir has not lost all of its lateral toes, although the weight is applied principally on the middle toe (no. 3) of each foot as in the horse. Only the thumb (no. 1) has disappeared from the front feet, and the two outer digits (nos. 1 and 5) are gone from the rear. The stubby proboscis is a development peculiar to the tapir. It is too short to serve as an effective grasping organ, like the elephant's trunk, yet it is supple enough to be an aid in feeding and in smelling.

Even at the time of the Conquest the tapirs were gone from Yucatán, presumably as a result of Mayan settlement and clearing of the forest. The first bishop of Valladolid, Diego de Landa, wrote in his *Relación de las Cosas de Yucatán* of 1566:

There are tapirs in only one corner [of the bishopric of Yucatán] which lies back of the mountains of Campeche and there are many of them. . . . They go more in that piece of land than in all the rest, since it is an animal very fond of water and in that region there are many lagoons in those woods and mountains. . . . The Indians consider it an act of great bravery to kill them and the skin or parts of it lasted as a memorial down to the great grandsons as I have seen myself. They call it *tzimin* and from these they have given their name to horses. (Tozzer, 1941 : 203).

I am not sure what area Landa was referring to, since there are no "mountains" in Campeche, but presumably he meant the Tabasco lowlands.

The best remaining tapir habitat in Mexico is the marshy lowland forest which has been little altered by settlement. Originally tapirs occurred in much of the upland rain forest as well, and there still are a few in the more remote tracts. But most of the uplands are now too heavily settled to afford a home for this shy and retiring animal. Even in the lowlands the encroachment of settlers who persistently pursue the tapir has reduced populations to a dangerously low level. Until a few years ago, it was believed that there were substantial numbers of tapirs in the wilder parts of Quintana Roo and Belize, where Gaumer and others spoke of finding herds of the animals not very many years ago. But in 1947, D. B. Legters, a missionary who has tramped all over Quintana Roo, wrote me: "Tapirs are just about done for in this [territory]. The only place I know where a few abound is south of Dzula where there is a network of lakes and very few inhabitants. They are not hunted because there are so few but they are shot on sight. . . . If no effort is made to save the animals there will be none left."

I know nothing of the present status of tapirs in Campeche or Tabasco, but I heard no word of the animals in my brief travels there. A few remain on the Gulf side of the Sierra de Tuxtla in southern Veracruz, and Small (1956) saw several animals and found abundant sign along the Río Chalchijatapa in the headwaters of the Río Coatzacoalcos, near the Oaxaca-Veracruz border. There is also a scattered handful along the Pacific slope of the Sierra de

Chiapas. Villa (1948) reported the presence of tapirs near Paval. Ingles (1956) found numerous tracks near Bonampak on the northern edge of the Chiapas highlands. Frans Blom (personal letter) reports tapirs persisting in a dozen scattered localities in eastern Chiapas.

C. L. Sibley came upon a tapir on the highway 10 miles east of Tapana-tepec, Oaxaca, on April 9, 1948. His notes recount the incident:

In the arid tropical scrub country we came suddenly upon a tapir in the middle of the road (at midnight). The animal made no attempt to flee but moved back and forth in the light of the automobile headlights and walked ahead of us for about ¼ mile. Often it came back toward the car and actually came along-side almost close enough to touch from the window. We could see that it was a male, and also could see minute markings such as white-tipped ears, a white spot at the base of the ear, the 3 hind toes, short tail, brownish iris, and the movements of the proboscis as the animal tried to catch a scent of the source of light. After following the tapir slowly along the road for more than 10 minutes I got out of the car and as the tapir trotted ahead I ran up behind him and slapped him sharply on the rump! Off he went down the road and over the bank into the brush. We could hear him crashing through the brush up a hill for several minutes.

The occurrence of this animal in arid scrub would appear to be abnormal. From whence he may have strayed is not known.

Considering southeastern Mexico collectively, current reports of tapirs are all of the nature of these accounts—one seen here, a few known to persist there. There remains no secure and assured population anywhere. The tapir, in other words, must be added to the list of important species that are dangerously reduced in number and very much in need of active protection.

As stated above, tapirs dwell in the densest forest, retiring to the thickets or swamps by day and coming out to feed at night. They are shy animals, highly intolerant of disturbance by man or his dogs. In their jungle fastnesses tapirs maintain networks of trails which they use in moving from resting to feeding grounds and in fleeing from enemies. Alvarez del Toro (1952a) points out that tapir trails often pass under low limbs or trunks, and that when attacked by a jaguar (the only important natural enemy) a tapir tries to charge under these obstructions, knocking the cat off its back and on occa-sion even killing it. Tapirs are excellent swimmers. They often plunge into the water to escape from man and his dogs, and they do a good deal of swim-ming and mud bathing for pleasure and to avoid mosquitoes and other troublesome insects. Tapirs, in fact, are almost amphibious. Rivers, lakes, or swamps seem to be an essential part of tapir habitat, along with dense forest.

The tapir has an acute sense of hearing and smell but is deficient in eye-sight. It is said that a hunter walking upwind on a quiet forest trail can ap-proach within a few yards of a tapir. The jaguar undoubtably can do this even more successfully. Ordinarily, the tapir makes no vocal sound, although when alarmed or excited it emits a sharp squeal like that of a horse. Though not usually aggressive, a tapir can put up a good fight when cornered, using its feet and especially its teeth to attack dogs or other tormentors. In southern Mexico it is widely believed that tapirs tear the hide off dogs with the proboscis, but this is a physical impossibility. Rather, the animal may grasp a dog in its mouth and injure it severely by biting and tearing. Potentially, a tapir could inflict similar wounds on a person, but this rarely happens. Gaumer reports that in Yucatán eight men killed a cornered tapir with machetes without its attempting any defense whatsoever, so great was its terror. But a mother tapir may valiantly defend her young, even from man. She is then a dangerous adversary.

According to Gaumer, tapirs breed in March, and the period of gestation is about four months. At what age they start to breed is not known, but evidently it is not before they are two years old. A litter consists of a single young one, which is streaked and spotted with white, like a fawn. The growing animal stays with its mother until it is a year old. By that time it has lost its spots and is more than half adult size. Young tapirs are subject to predation by several of the smaller cats and by the tayra, in addition to the prime enemy, the jaguar.

Tapirs are exclusively herbivorous, browsing on the leaves and twigs of various trees and shrubs, particularly palms and palmettos. They eat many kinds of tropical fruits and occasionally damage agricultural crops such as corn, sugar cane, and melons. However, losses of this sort are negligible because few tapirs live in cultivated areas.

The tapir is associated with and completely dependent upon undisturbed climax rain forest for its existence. It adjusts poorly or not at all to settlement and seemingly can be retained only in virgin areas; it is hoped that some of these will be set aside as national parks or wilderness preserves. One such area that might well be designated as a permanent rain forest reserve for tapirs and other elements of the wet tropical fauna and flora is the northeastern slope of Volcán San Martín in the Tuxtla range of southern Veracruz. There may still be other suitable sites in southern Campeche, Quintana Roo, or Chiapas. The creation of one or more rain forest preserves and the extension of effective legal protection to tapirs everywhere in southern Mexico are steps that should be taken quickly to save this unique member of the Mexican fauna from ultimate extinction.

Order Artiodactyla

Most of the ungulates native to Mexico are of this order of two-toed or cloven-hoofed mammals. Four families comprise the Artiodactyla of Mexico: the peccaries, the deer, the pronghorn antelope, and the bighorn sheep. These animals walk on their third and fourth toes, the other toes having been lost or much reduced in the course of evolution. Imported relatives are the cow, sheep, goat, and pig.

FAMILY TAYASSUIDAE

Peccaries

Collared Peccary. *Pecari tajacu*

Other names. Jabalí; pecari de collar; javelina; *Pecari angulatus; Dicotyles torquatus; Tayassu angulatus.*

Description.—A small wild pig with stocky body, large head, and short spindly legs. Body mostly grizzled, paler ventrally and on sides of head, darker along middorsal line. In most specimens, but not all, a light-colored band extends diagonally across both shoulders from back to breast (hence the name *collared* peccary). Measurements: head and body—800 to 970 mm. Tail vestigial, although encased within the stub is an extension of caudal vertebrae 25 to 35 mm. in length. Live weight 14 to 25 kg. (30 to 55 lbs.). Females approximately as large as males, or even larger, according to Allen (1906). One large sow collected in Chihuahua during this survey weighed 52 lbs. Near Tucson, Ariz., Bobby J. Neal found the average weight of 23 live-trapped adult females to be 45 pounds; that of 13 males was 43 pounds. The animals are smaller in Texas (and presumably in eastern Mexico). Jennings and Harris (1953) found the average weight of 52 adult peccaries of both sexes to be 36.5 pounds.

Range in Mexico.—Throughout the Republic except in Baja California. The javelina is rare on the deserts of the central plateau.

The collared peccary, or javelina, is another of the highly adaptable mammals found in many vegetational types of both the tropics and the temperate uplands of Mexico. It occurs in highest density, however, in the tropical thickets along both coasts, especially on the Pacific side from Sinaloa to Oaxaca. The javelina is present in undisturbed rain forest but does not attain maximum abundance there. Cutover rain forest or naturally thick and stunted growth, as typified by thorn forest, the mesquite thickets of northeastern Mexico, or the richer parts of the tropical deciduous forest, are more nearly optimal habitat for this animal. In the pine-oak uplands, peccaries may occur in good numbers where there is enough thick growth, such as manzanita or scrub oak. I know of no situation where javelinas thrive in the absence of dense, scrubby ground cover. The Sonoran desert is perhaps the most barren javelina range; but even there, S. B. Benson found them principally in thickets of mesquite and ironwood.

The javelina is a gregarious animal and tends to live in bands or herds. The denser the population, the larger the bands. A sparse population is usually broken up into little groups of two or three or half a dozen animals, whereas in areas of plenty the bands number ten to twenty and sometimes, though rarely, more. Collared peccaries do not form the great droves characteristic of white-lipped peccaries. Some individual males, presumably old animals, avoid the bands and live alone. Such a recluse is often referred to as a *jabalí solitario* in contradistinction to the majority, which like each others' company. In certain areas, especially on the flat coastal plains, javelina bands range widely over the country, but they seem to have definite home ranges and are by no means vagrant in their wanderings. In the pinelands of Chihuahua I found bands living in very circumscribed areas, feeding at night in certain manzanita patches and retiring each day to some nearby rocky canyon. We occasionally met the animals abroad in early morning or in the evening.

Often a foraging band of peccaries can be heard grunting contentedly and rooting through the leaves long before they are seen. When surprised, one or more members of the band emit a loud grunt of warning and all take off with astonishing speed and agility. A javelina dodging through a thicket is a difficult target. Occasionally the strong musky odor of the animals can be detected at some distance. A javelina has a large, puffy gland on the mid-line of the back 8 inches forward of the tail. From this gland is emitted a strong-smelling musk, especially when the animal is frightened or annoyed. Other

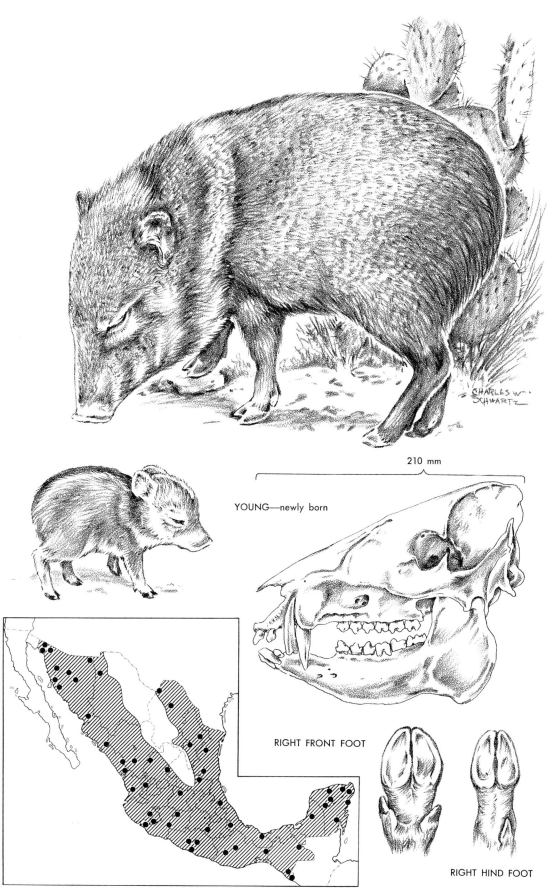

210 mm

YOUNG—newly born

RIGHT FRONT FOOT

RIGHT HIND FOOT

Fig. 184. Collared peccary, *Pecari tajacu*.

characteristic signs that reveal the presence of javelinas are the droppings, shaped like those of a pig, the rooted up ground, and the small blunt tracks, much more rounded than those of deer.

Javelinas may bear their litters of 1 to 3 young (usually 2) at any time of year. In the Gavilán basin west of Pacheco, Chihuahua, I collected a family group—an old sow, 2 yearlings, and 2 tiny piglets—on August 19, 1948, and in the same area I came across a sow with one equally small piglet on February 5, 1952. McCullough (1955) likewise states that there is no set breeding time in Arizona. However, Neal found that of 44 birth records gathered in the Tucson area, 34 occurred in July or August, the rest being scattered through the year. There is a tendency then, toward a primary breeding season, births occurring mostly in the summer rainy season. The gestation period has been variously reported as 96, 112, and 116 days. The age at which females first breed is not known, but judging from the size and scant sexual development of the yearlings, I suspect it must be at least two years. Young javelinas are reddish brown with a black streak down the back. The two piglets mentioned above were about 400 mm. long and weighed approximately 1,800 gm. Javelinas are precocial at birth and follow their mother from the first day or two until they are at least a year old. When very small they develop the spirit and fight of adults. One of the piglets captured in Chihuahua slashed at our hands with its little needle teeth and showed no fear whatsoever. This particular animal was released later near the point of its capture and went squealing off through the oaks in the general direction in which its mother had disappeared. It is said that young javelinas can be easily tamed and that they make excellent pets.

Collared peccaries, like domestic hogs, are omnivorous, but most of their diet in the wild is derived from plants and plant products. A wide variety of fruits, roots, bulbs, and greens contribute to the normal fare. Acorns, pine nuts, and manzanita berries are favorite foods in the pine-oak uplands. Cactus fruits and the beans of mesquite, catclaw, and juniper are other common items of diet in the uplands. In Texas, Jennings and Harris (1953) found the fleshy stems of prickly pear (*Opuntia*) to constitute the bulk of the diet. Gaumer (1917) mentions the fruits of various tropical trees as staples, particularly those of palms, figs, and the zapote. Javelinas may turn to cultivated crops on occasion and cause great damage in the milpas. They will eat the eggs of birds and turtles when these are available, and even some carrion. In the stomachs of peccaries killed in Chihuahua I found green grass a dominant item. Javelinas drink a good deal of water, too; the shortage of drinking water may account for their absence from many otherwise suitable desert ranges. Fleshy cactus, when available, may supply the need for water.

In severe winter weather, peccaries may perish either from inability to find food or from the cold itself, their coarse bristly fur being no protection at all. Floyd Johnson of Pacheco, Chihuahua, tells of finding dead and dying javelinas during the hard winter of 1945–46, when deep snow covered the mountains for weeks and temperatures reached 20° below zero.

In Mexico, peccaries are hunted mostly with dogs, which run down the animals and force them to turn in defense. The hunter then overtakes the pack and kills the quarry with a gun, if he has one, otherwise with a machete, spear, or club. Javelinas at bay are formidable opponents, as can be seen from the following passage, written by J. H. Batty in Sinaloa:

Many dogs are killed by Peccaries, being torn open or gashed by their long, sharp-edged canine teeth. When about to attack, the Peccary lowers its head, champs its teeth, and advances sideways with its mouth open and under jaw turned to one side, ready for an upward lunge to rip up its enemy. When a band is attacked by many dogs, the Peccaries immediately close up in a bunch, forming a ring with heads outward, which position they stubbornly maintain, fighting until the dogs leave them, the dogs knowing that they cannot break the circle without being killed or badly cut by the Peccaries' tusks. (Allen, 1906 : 199.)

Even jaguars that feed regularly on peccaries have been known to be severely wounded by their spunky prey. Occasionally a man is attacked by javelinas, but the popular notion that these animals go about chasing people into trees is a gross exaggeration. They are timid and are quick to flee when anyone approaches.

Javelinas are hunted everywhere in Mexico both for food and for the hides, which make up into fine leather. The meat of females and of the young is excellent, although great care must be taken not to smear the musk onto the flesh. It is customary to remove the dorsal musk gland and then wash hands and knife before proceeding with the skinning. Old males are poor eating, being tough and strong no matter how the musk is cared for.

At one time there was substantial trade in peccary hides, the leather being used chiefly in the manufacture of gloves. Villa (1951) reports that in 1949 there were exported to the United States 18,000 javelina hides for glove manufacture. Commercial hide hunting led to serious shortage of javelinas in some places. I am especially aware of the problem as it existed in Sonora. Today open sale of hides is prohibited and there is much less commerce in them, although it has by no means ceased.

Javelinas are still overhunted in much of Mexico, but like the white-tailed deer, they have shown a remarkable capacity to persist, at least in low numbers, on suitable ranges. With even a minimum of protection the javelina can be expected to hold its own indefinitely.

White-lipped Peccary. *Tayassu pecari*

Other names.—Senso; marina; *Dicotyles labiatus*.

Description.—A large wild pig with massive head, short legs, and a stub of a tail. Body pelage grayish black. Bristles of mane very long (up to 150 mm.). Nose, lips, and cheeks clear white. Dorsal gland like that of the javelina. Measurements: head and body—1,100 to 1,200 mm.; tail—50 mm. No weights available. Females and males about the same size.

Range in Mexico.—Dense tropical forests from southern Veracruz eastward through the Yucatán Peninsula.

The white-lipped peccary is an animal of the virgin forest and does not frequent cutover or scrub forest as does the javelina. It is much more gregarious than the javelina, running in great droves of hundreds of individuals. Such an aggregation of animals seen in the half-light of the rain forest is an imposing spectacle. According to Alvarez del Toro (1952a) there is a certain amount of organization in such a drove, the younger animals (which are reddish) coming first, subadults next, and the large adults following, with the very young at the heels of their mothers. There is a vocal noise like the distant beat of drums, and the rustling of the many feet through the leaves sounds like wind in the trees. The strong, acrid odor of the herd hangs in the air long after the animals have passed.

Large groups of white-lipped peccaries require a tremendous amount of food; hence the bands roam widely in search of new supplies of fallen fruit. The passage of a herd leaves a broad band of disturbed and uprooted ground cover; hunters often locate the animals by following in the wake of their passage. But the peccaries travel far and often pass through an area without being overtaken by the local hunters. Just how far a given band will cruise is unknown. It is safe to presume, however, that white-lipped peccaries have home ranges of some sort and do not wander completely at will.

Like those of the javelina, the bands of *sensos* are proportionate in size to the density of the over-all population. The fewer animals there are in a given region, the smaller the herds. Alvarez del Toro states that in the fringe areas of virgin forest in Chiapas the surviving groups of white-lipped peccaries are small and scattered, whereas in the great selva of the northeast the aggregations are still large.

Little is known of the breeding habits of white-lipped peccaries. Newborn young have been seen by several observers at all seasons of the year; hence there does not seem to be a fixed time of breeding. The age of breeding and period of gestation are not recorded. O. P. Pearson offers the following observations on numbers of young. On March 25, 1938, in eastern Panama, he examined 4 newly killed females, 3 of which were pregnant and contained 2 embryos each. On February 13, 1941, at Maldonado, Madre de Díos, Peru, he autopsied 2 females, one of which had 2 embryos, the other 3. A single young pig, "still probably suckling, came back to the carcasses while we were skinning." This would suggest that females may breed again soon after giving birth. In any event, the normal litter seems to consist of two young, with three occasionally.

The young apparently are able to follow their mothers soon after birth, since the females do not drop out of the wandering herds at the time of

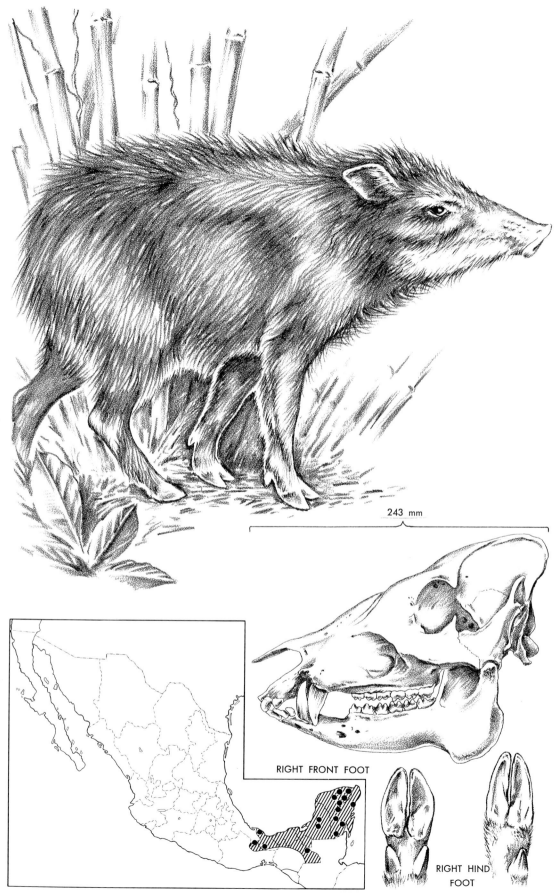

243 mm

RIGHT FRONT FOOT

RIGHT HIND FOOT

Fig. 185. White-lipped peccary, *Tayassu pecari*.

parturition. The young are reddish brown, and, as noted by Pearson, "definitely paler in color than adults, not noticeably spotted or marked." They turn slowly to the grizzled black of adulthood.

White-lipped peccaries eat a wide variety of foods, principally fruits, greens, and roots of plants. Probably all of the mast-bearing trees of the rain forest contribute to their fare. Additionally, Alvarez del Toro states that *sensos* eat a good many insects and other invertebrates uncovered in their rooting.

In southern Mexico, as throughout Central America, the white-lipped peccary is hunted assiduously for its highly edible meat and durable hide. Dalquest (1949) indicates that in southern Veracruz hunters sometimes travel far in pursuit of this animal, known locally as *marina*. Hunting the white-lipped peccary not only is exciting but may be dangerous. Many dogs have been killed by the slashing, razor-sharp tusks of a *senso*, and men are often driven to the shelter of the trees by a charging band. When a hunter overtakes a herd and shoots one or more of the animals, the rest flee or charge, according to the mood of the moment. If a large contingent charges simultaneously, there is no option but to start climbing. Even the large cats, such as the jaguar and puma, that prey regularly on white-lipped peccaries are careful to select a victim apart from a large herd and not place themselves in the middle of an angry band.

The white-lipped peccary is disappearing from Mexico as settlement is extending into the wet tropics. Overhunting is the most immediate cause of the decrease, but even if hunting were brought under rigid control the loss of suitable habitat eventually would eliminate the species. Hence a program of conservation for the white-lipped peccary must include permanent preservation of suitable blocks of climax rain forest along with protection from hunters. Fortunately, the *senso* persists in several areas still occupied by tapirs, howler monkeys, and other endangered species, and a properly administered set of wilderness reserves would serve to protect all these rare and interesting animals. The northeastern slope of Volcán San Martín Tuxtla in southern Veracruz is one such site, and there are others in the remaining wild lands to the east.

As stated in the Introduction, the objectives of wildlife conservation are many. Supplying hunters with game to shoot is one that has much popular appeal. But on an even higher moral and ethical plane is the endeavor to preserve in perpetuity samples of the native biota that cannot withstand exploitation and use. The preservation of parts of the rain forest with its complement of such sensitive species as the white-lipped peccary should be accepted as a national responsibility.

FAMILY CERVIDAE

DEER

The deer family was represented originally in Mexico by four species—three deer that will be considered in detail here, and the wapiti or elk that occurred along the extreme northern border but was exterminated at an early date. The elk of New Mexico, Arizona, and northern Mexico was given the name *Cervus merriami*. A good general account of this animal may be found in the report of Mearns (1907), who accompanied the International Boundary Survey of 1892–1894. Most of the scant knowledge of this animal was obtained in New Mexico and Arizona before it disappeared in the early 1900's, but Mearns

Fig. 186.   Elk from the Wichita Wildlife Refuge in Oklahoma being released in the Sierra del Carmen, Coahuila, in March, 1941. Photograph by Dallas *Morning News*.

cites one record of two bulls seen on San José Mountain in northeastern Sonora. There is no evidence to suggest that the native elk ever penetrated far into the Sierra Madre.

Interest in the elk in Mexico has been renewed by two recent efforts to introduce the northern form, *Cervus canadensis,* into Coahuila.

In March, 1941, 18 elk were transported by truck from the Wichita National Wildlife Refuge near Cache, Oklahoma, to headquarters of the Carmen Mountain Hunting Club 5 miles west of Piedra Blanca in northern Coahuila. There they were liberated. The project was undertaken by the club in an effort to introduce elk hunting on their property of 114,000 acres. In 1947, Ted Dealey of Dallas, a member of the club, wrote me to the effect that, although the elk had scattered about in the region, "a good percentage of them were alive as late as 1943." Some cows were said to have dropped calves. However, in 1953 when I visited the area all the elk had disappeared. Eduardo López, caretaker of the Carmen Mountain Hunting Club, stated that most of the animals had died within a few months after liberation, although a few old bulls lived for a year or more. One of these stayed on Centinela Peak for nearly a year but then drifted north toward the Río Grande, where he probably was killed. Another bull traveled about 70 miles east across the dry plains before disappearing; presumably he too was shot.

In 1956 I learned from Rollin Baker of Michigan State University that two shipments of elk had been sent from Yellowstone National Park to a Sr. Jaime T. García of Monterrey for liberation in Nuevo León and eastern Coahuila. The numbers sent were as follows: On January 31, 1952—5 bulls, 15 cows, and 10 calves. These animals were liberated in February on "Rancho Santa Hermosa, approximately 50 kilometers west of Ciudad Muzquiz [Coahuila], and on the west side of Sierra Hermosa de Santa Rosa. Nineteen animals, including 8 calves born at the rancho, remained in March, 1956." (Baker, 1956 : 318.) On January 25, 1955, Sr. García imported a second shipment of Yellowstone elk, including 2 bulls, 14 cows, and 14 calves. I do not know what became of this shipment, but I believe the animals were liberated in western Nuevo León.

Whether elk ever will become acclimated in Mexico is doubtful. As things stand now, the species must be considered a potential rather than an actual member of the game fauna of Mexico.

Mule Deer. *Odocoileus hemionus*

Other names.—Bura; venado mula; venado cola negra.

Description.—Large, with very long ears and small narrow tail. Body color gray or brown (changes seasonally), white beneath, males with a dark (sometimes black) crown. Tail white below and on sides and black-tufted at tip. Antlers of adult males dichotomously forked. Metatarsal gland on outer surface of each hind leg just below hock 40 mm. long or more. Large preorbital gland

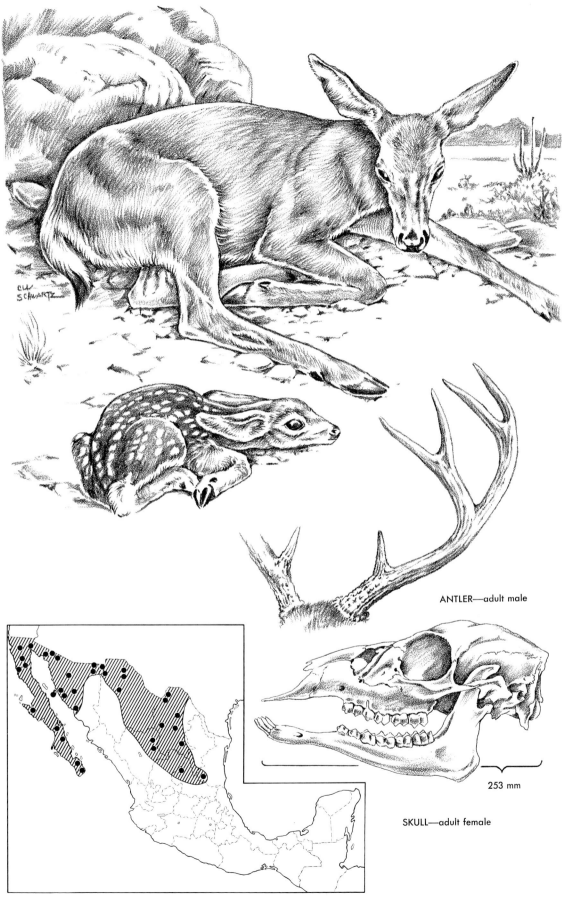

ANTLER—adult male

SKULL—adult female

253 mm

Fig. 187.   Mule deer, *Odocoileus hemionus*.

in pit in lacrimal bone at inner "corner" of eye; this pit distinguishes skull of mule deer from that of whitetail. Average measurements: head and body—1,300 to 1,600 mm.; tail—115 to 190 mm. Live weights: males—64 to 114 kg. (140 to 250 lbs.); females—45 to 70 kg. (100 to 150 lbs.). Removal of paunch and intestines reduces weights by about 20 per cent.

Range in Mexico.—Throughout Baja California and desert ranges of Sonora and central uplands as far south as northern San Luis Potosí and southwestern Tamaulipas (Cerro del Tigre).

There are two principal types of mule deer in Mexico. The animals of Baja California are similar to the deer of the southern Coast Ranges of California in size, in appearance, and in their preference for a habitat well vegetated with chaparral, oak, or pine. The somewhat larger and paler desert mule deer, or "burro deer," of Sonora and interior Mexico is much more of a barren-ground animal, living comfortably on the most desolate desert ranges with scant vegetation. This deer does not penetrate the pine-oak zone of the higher mountains, even where it has ample opportunity to do so. Hence, in the discussion that follows, the two segments of the mule deer population will have to be treated separately from time to time.

The mule deer of Mexico are appreciably larger than white-tailed deer and have much larger antlers. Females, of course, are antlerless, but adult males normally have a heavy, widely spread rack of ten points, eight of which are bifurcations of the two main branches into which each antler divides, the other two being brow tines that emerge near the bases of the respective antlers (see fig. 187). Occasionally the brow tines are missing. The antlers of younger animals have fewer points, and those of exceptional bucks may have many more than ten. The largest burro deer have antlers that compare favorably in size with those of mule deer from anywhere in North America. The records of the Boone and Crocket Club list a specimen from Chihuahua that measures 26½ inches round the outside curve of one antler (Gray, 1932), which puts it in the championship class. The mule deer of Baja California are smaller and have much lighter antlers. The smallest of all are found on Cedros Island.

Deer antlers are shed and grown anew each year. While growing, the antler is covered with a highly vascularized tissue known as "velvet," the blood vessels of which transport the calcium and other materials of which the antler is made. After growth is completed, the velvet dies and is sloughed off, leaving the finished bony antler, which is itself a dead structure firmly cemented to the live pedicel on the skull. After the breeding season, the attachment between the antler base and the pedicel is dissolved away (decalcified) as a secondary result of the sharp decrease in the male hormone testosterone, and the antler drops off. A scab of live tissue quickly forms over the exposed pedicel, and within a few weeks another antler begins to form under new velvet. In Baja California the antlers fall in February or March. Since burro deer breed later, the antler drop probably does not occur until late March or April.

The size of antlers grown by an individual buck varies with the age and with the vigor or condition of the animal. Buck fawns have only tiny nubs of antlers. Yearling mule deer have either slender spikes or forked antlers, depending on the size, health, and quality of diet of the individual. Two-year-olds may have two to four points on each side. Ordinarily, the full rack of ten points is achieved in the third or fourth year. Thereafter the antlers of an adult buck tend to increase each year in massiveness, and sometimes in number of points, until the animal passes its prime (five to eight years), whereupon they begin to decrease in size and numbers of points. Very old bucks often have big forks, or even spikes. In a year of exceptionally good food, as for example a wet year in the range of the desert deer, the antlers of all the bucks will be larger than normal. A poor (dry) year conversely will result in small antlers.

Mule deer live most of the year in small groups, the females with their fawns and yearlings tending to form stable social units of two to six animals, and the males running together in little bands of like size. Segregation is never complete, however; for some bucks, especially younger ones, associate regularly with does, and some deer of either sex live entirely alone. Each deer or band of deer has a specific home range within which it lives. The size of these home ranges varies according to the nature of the cover and food and the availability of water; but they are surprisingly small—usually less than half a mile in diameter in good cover and probably much larger on the desert. The deer may shift their home ranges seasonally. Burro deer live in the washes and river bottoms during the dry season but move to the uplands in time of rain. In the San Pedro Mártir and similar mountains the deer summer near the crest and drop down to lower elevations when the snows come. But at no time do deer wander aimlessly. They always have a "home" area. Adult males travel widely during the breeding season but return faithfully to their respective ranges when the excitement is over.

Breeding takes place in late autumn in most parts of Mexico, probably in November or December in Baja California, and in January in desert areas. Virtually all the adult does and some yearlings come into heat more or less at the same time. The better the food, the more yearling does will breed. Concurrently the bucks attain breeding condition as a result of an upsurge of sex hormones that cause a noticeable swelling of the neck. They become bold and aggressive and fight some among themselves. Mating is promiscuous, on a first-come first-served basis, but the adult males cover most of the does. Two-year-old bucks and even yearlings are physiologically capable of breeding but are driven away from the does by the older males.

The fawns are dropped in the summer, gestation requiring about seven months (205 to 212 days). In Baja California this would bring the period of fawning in late June or July. The desert deer fawn in late July or August after the summer rains have started. In any given area most fawns drop within a short period, but there are always a few that come along a month or even two months later. These are from does that were not bred in the main rut but that came into heat again in a subsequent cycle of ovulation. Yearling does, when they breed, normally produce a single fawn. Adult does may have one fawn or twins. The proportion of twins produced in a herd is a direct result of the quality of diet available to the individual doe. The better the forage, the more likely a does is to ovulate two eggs and produce two young. On very poor ranges, some does do not produce even a single fawn.

For a time after birth the fawns are hidden by their mothers in dense cover, but within a few weeks they follow the does at heel, staying with them through the whole first year. As yearlings the males tend to wander away to find a home range in some different area, but yearling does often stay on in their mother's home ground, adopting it as their own.

Mule deer eat a wide variety of plants, and often the diet changes season-ally in a particular area. Green grass and various weeds are the main foods in the rainy season; but in winter or in times of drought, mule deer eat mostly browse—the twigs and buds of shrubs and trees. Oaks, wild lilacs (*Ceano-thus*), chamise (*Adenostoma*), and redberry (*Rhamnus*) are good browse plants in northern Baja California. On the desert some of the better browse foods are ironwood (*Olneya*), dysodia, atriplex, and palo verde. The fruits and even the fleshy leaves of many cacti are eaten, and these help supply the water needs of desert deer. Bailey (1905) states that mule deer in the dry breaks along the Río Grande eat the green stalks of agaves and paw open the cabbage-like heads of the sotol (*Dasylirion*), obtaining both food and water from them. He believes that in this manner the deer can live for long periods without drinking. Beans of mesquite and catclaw are excellent food when available, as are juniper berries, acorns, and various other kinds of fruits and seeds. A mule deer has to eat from three to four pounds of food daily to main-tain its health, and on the desert this much good food is not easily gathered. Lack of proper food during critical seasons is the principal factor limiting deer populations almost everywhere. The food shortage is often aggravated by the overgrazing caused by domestic livestock. Especially around water holes in arid regions, cattle and burros will consume all the edible forage used formerly by deer. This leads to extermination of the deer even more rapidly than overhunting.

The principal predator of the mule deer in Mexico is the puma. In only a few places are wolves still present on the plains and deserts in numbers suffi-cient to take many deer. Coyotes doubtless kill a few fawns, but their effect on deer populations is usually negligible. In northern Baja California it has been reported that in the vicinity of the Melling Ranch pumas increase periodically and the deer go down in number, presumably as a result of predation. After a few years the pumas thin out and the mule deer again increase. This fluctuat-ing balance between predator and prey has not actually been proved but is reported verbally by the Melling family. Similarly, I learned from José García of Buena Vista (near Cabo San Lucas) that pumas were so abundant in the mountains near the tip of the peninsula that the governor of Baja California Sur (about 1950) offered a bounty for puma scalps in order to lessen the danger to livestock. Sr. García and his sons also thought that the pumas were keeping the mule deer scarce. Some 36 lion skins were turned in for bounty (which, by the way, was never paid), mostly from the cape area, and it is believed locally that deer are increasing as a result of the reduction in pumas.

Despite protective laws, the mule deer in Mexico is hunted the year round, and this never-ending persecution has contributed materially to its scarcity. The burro deer of the desert actually has been exterminated over large areas by the combination of hunting and overgrazing of the ranges. Overshooting was begun at an early date. López and López (1911 : 227) recount the exploits of one Don Donaciano Montero, who killed deer professionally while in the employ of the railroad being built through north-central Mexico. In 1884 and 1885 in the Bolsón de Mapimi of northeastern Durango, Montero killed 400 burro deer, including both bucks and does. Bailey (1905) speaks of excessive hunting along the Río Grande, and Hornaday (1909) while on an extended trip through northwestern Sonora did not see even one live mule deer. Presumably hunting was a factor in reducing the deer population, even at that time. More recently, hunting has increased rather than decreased in intensity as a result of the growing population in northern Mexico.

Management of the mule deer must include, first, enforcement of the protective laws, and second, some degree of protection of ranges from unlimited grazing by livestock. In the Big Bend region of Texas, mule deer are responding very well to this twofold plan of conservation. Borell and Bryant (1942) designate the mule deer as "fairly common" and call it the most important game animal of the district. Even though the deer are heavily hunted in season and their ranges support many livestock, the animals are holding their own, as they definitely are not on the other side of the Río Grande in Mexico. Neither hunting nor grazing need be eliminated but only regulated to insure a sustained mule deer population.

White-tailed Deer. *Odocoileus virginianus*

Other names.—Venado; venado saltón; venado cola blanca.

Description.—Small, with a large tail which is raised vertically like a white flag when the animal runs. Body color grayish brown in winter, reddish brown in summer, white ventrally. Antlers of males consist of a main beam bending forward, with individual unforked tines extending vertically. (In northern Coahuila some white-tailed bucks have dichotomously forked antlers like those of mule deer. See Leopold, 1953.) Full racks usually have 10 or more points, but in some areas 8 or even 6 points are normal for adults. Metatarsal gland on outer surface of each hind leg below middle of tarsal bone is 25 mm. long or less. Preorbital gland at inner corner of eye small; corresponding pit in skull shallow.

Measurements: head and body—1,000 to 1,300 mm.; tail—180 to 270 mm. Live weight: males—36 to 57 kg. (80 to 125 lbs.); females—27 to 45 kg. (60 to 100 lbs.). Removal of paunch and intestines reduces weights by about 20 per cent.

Range in Mexico.—Throughout the Republic except in Baja California. In the more heavily developed regions this deer is much less abundant than formerly.

As I have stated earlier in this book, the white-tailed deer is probably the most important game species in Mexico. Widely distributed throughout the country in both temperate and tropical zones, and amazingly persistent in the face of overhunting and severe habitat disturbance, the whitetail goes on supplying sport and food for Mexican hunters after other big game species are mostly or entirely killed off. There are many places where this deer has been crowded almost to local extinction, though surprisingly few where the last animal has been killed. Because of its adaptability and persistence, the whitetail is a good subject for management.

The highest populations of white-tailed deer in Mexico are to be found in pine-oak woodlands, mostly in the Sierra Madre Occidental. In the Gavilán basin west of Pacheco, Chihuahua, I estimated a density of perhaps 30 to 40 whitetails per square mile in 1938 before the area was invaded by loggers. Populations of like density were found in the virgin mountains of southern Durango in 1946, on the protected pine-oak mesas of the Sierra de Tamaulipas in 1945, and in isolated sections of the Sierra del Carmen of Coahuila in 1953. I am told that whitetails are still moderately plentiful in eastern San Luis Potosí where cactus desert and oak woodland meet, and in the mesquite thickets of southern Sonora and northern Tamaulipas. Nowhere in the tropics, not even in remote and unchanged areas, are whitetails equally abundant. But they certainly are present, especially in the thorn forest and tropical deciduous forest of the more arid zones. The virgin rain forest and the unbroken desert are perhaps the two vegetational types least conducive to occupation by whitetails. But second-growth rain forest is acceptable habitat, and the species actually has spread into parts of southeastern Mexico after partial clearing of the land.

Dense brushland of almost any kind is the favorite haunt of white-tailed deer. It is the thickets of scrub oak, manzanita, mesquite, acacia, and the second-growth *monte* of the tropics that form the deer's castle—not the forest proper. Perhaps this predilection for thick cover is one of the factors that protect whitetails from extermination. In contrast, desert mule deer, antelope, and bighorn are lovers of the open spaces and withstand heavy hunting very poorly.

The scrubby thickets also supply much of the whitetail's food. Although these deer eat green grass and forbs seasonally, they are primarily browsing animals, depending upon the twig tips of various shrubs and trees for sustenance during nongrowing periods (winter or the dry season). In Chihuahua I found mountain mahogany (*Cercocarpus*) and a spiny bush called "Johnny-

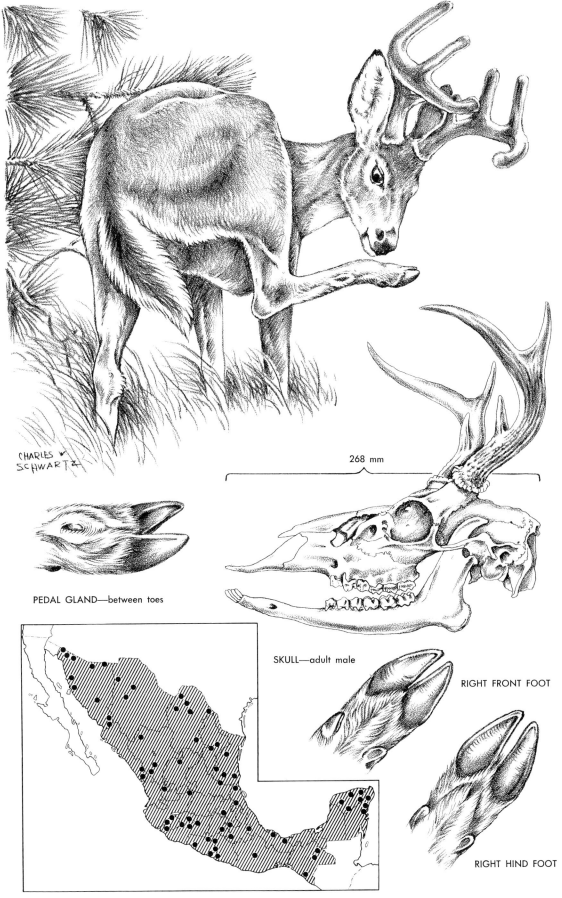

PEDAL GLAND—between toes

268 mm

SKULL—adult male

RIGHT FRONT FOOT

RIGHT HIND FOOT

Fig. 188. White-tailed deer, *Odocoileis virginianus*.

jump-up" (*Ceanothus huichagorare*) to be the mainstays of winter diet. Taylor *et al.* (1945) rank the species of deer browse in northern Coahuila in the following order of importance: Madrone, oak, *Eysenhardtia*, wild rose, snowberry (*Symphoricarpos*), and mountain mahogany. In the dry tropics various leguminous shrubs and the morning-glory tree (*Ipomoea*) are among the favorites. In Morelos I found hunters waiting at night in morning-glory trees for the deer to come. Carrillo Rodriguez (1955) lists dogwood (*Cornus*) and capulincillo (*Monnina*) among the select foods of the deer confined in the large pen at the San Cayetano game farm; other favorites were various forbs. The list of good browse species from all the regions of Mexico would be very large indeed if the data were available to compile it. Most of these preferred plants are secondary invaders of burned or cutover forest lands; it is thus understandable why whitetails thrive even in the face of encroachment and development of the wilderness by man. The deer also eat many kinds of fruit when they are available—acorns, figs, cherimoyas, wild cherries, mangoes, oranges, and the berries of manzanita, juniper, capulin, and a host of others. Adaptability of diet is another attribute of the whitetail.

At times whitetails raid the fields of outlying farms, causing substantial crop damage. Corn, beans, chile, squash, and melons are very much enjoyed by the deer. Grapevines and orchards are subject to damaging browsing. In Mexico this problem is taken care of by the *campesino* whose crops are being damaged. He usually finds some way to kill or snare the deer.

In their day-to-day lives whitetails are much like mule deer. They live in small groups, the adult males tending to segregate from the does and young during all but the breeding season. Home ranges are small and rigidly circumscribed, although there may be seasonal movements in time of snow or drought. J. H. Batty found the deer of southern Sinaloa high on the slopes in the wet season and down in the lowlands during drought (Allen, 1906). Similar shifting about has been noted by Gaumer (1917) and many others. The home range of each deer or group of deer contains thickets for shelter and appropriate feeding areas that are visited at night when the animals come out to forage. Water, too, is important. When any of these necessities become unavailable, as for example during drought, the deer have to move to a new range. There they settle down again in a small area. Like mule deer, they do not wander about aimlessly.

Mating among whitetails is promiscuous. The bucks spar and quarrel over the does, and the largest and strongest do most of the breeding. The time of the rut varies greatly from place to place in Mexico. In the north it usually comes in midwinter (January), the young being born during the favorable period of summer rains, in August. At least this is true in Chihuahua and northern Coahuila. But Batty reports fawning in June and July in Sinaloa, Gaumer places it in spring (April to June) in Yucatán, and Villa (1953*b*) reports that a fawn was dropped as late as September 7 on the game farm at

Fig. 189.　Mountain mahogany (*Cercocarpus*)
heavily browsed by white-tailed deer.
Photograph taken on slope above
the Río Gavilán, Chihuahua,
in July, 1948.

San Cayetano by a doe imported from Guerrero. The period of gestation of this doe, according to Villa, was 245 days, although northern whitetails, like mule deer, have approximately a seven-month gestation. Whether there actually is this difference or there was some error in determining the actual period of pregnancy in the doe at San Cayetano is not known, but I suspect the latter. It seems unlikely that Mexican whitetails would digress far from the established gestation period for the species of 205 to 212 days. The fawns are spotted like other young deer. One that we captured in Chihuahua, estimated to be one week old, weighed 3,150 grams. Floyd Johnson of Pacheco states that in the Gavilán area about one-third of the does have twins, the rest produce single fawns. Our observations seem to bear this out. The proportion of twins, however, is not a constant but may vary with the nature of the range and the quality of diet available to the individual doe.

The time of the antler cycle in the bucks varies locally, like the breeding cycle. Antlers drop in April or May in Chihuahua, slightly later than that in Coahuila, and in March in Yucatán (Gaumer). Villa (1954b) records the antler fall of deer brought to the San Cayetano game farm from widely separated parts of Mexico; the amazing time spread—from February 19 to May 26—shows that the sexual cycles are differently timed locally, even when the deer are placed together in the same environment. The first bucks to lose their antlers seemed to be those from the south—Oaxaca and Guerrero—where the breeding season is earlier.

White-tailed deer are preyed upon by pumas, jaguars, and wolves, and the young may be taken by bears, coyotes, and many of the smaller carnivores. In some areas predation losses are substantial. In the Sierra del Carmen of Coahuila we found numerous lion-killed deer and in northern Chihuahua a good many remains, some left by pumas, others by wolves. I shot one wolf that contained a whole fawn in its stomach, eaten in great chunks. However, in both of these areas deer were abundant. Apparently it is unsound to assume that an abundance of predators killing deer will lead to deer scarcity. The converse seems to be the situation: the abundance of predators is due to the large numbers of deer, because the predators are thus assured of an ample food supply. The density of deer is dependent upon the quality of the range. A healthy herd well supplied with year-round forage cannot easily be suppressed by predators.

Parasites of various kinds may be more significant than predators in depleting the vigor of a deer population. Particularly in the tropics, bloodsucking ticks gather on deer in great numbers and sap the strength of all members of a herd. In addition, whitetails are plagued by nose bots, mosquitoes, deer flies, and various internal pests.

White-tailed deer are hunted in Mexico by every conceivable device. Perhaps the most popular and effective method is driving the deer out of cover with dogs. But even when not hunting, every man who owns a gun carries it in the woods and shoots deer when he sees them, regardless of their sex or age or the season of the year. Spotlighting at night is widely practiced, either from an automobile or afoot with a hand light. At our camp near Omilteme, Guerrero, a carload of deer hunters passed several nights, sweeping the hills with a spotlight, looking for the telltale eye shine. In a burst of gunfire they killed a horse (I was later blamed for its death), but we did not see them kill a deer. Hunters often wait patiently for deer at water holes, customary feeding grounds, or salt licks, sometimes sitting all night uncomfortably perched in a tree. Ingles (1956) states that Mayan hunters near Chochola, Yucatán, use a wooden whistle to lure the deer during the rutting season, and Lumholtz (1902 : 282) describes how the Tarahumara Indians of southwestern Chihuahua run deer down afoot or take them in snares or traps (p. 248). In southern Mexico, when the natives discover a newborn fawn it is standard practice for them to use it as a decoy in order to bring the mother within shooting distance. The hunter simply waits near the fawn or else imitates the plaintive bleat of a fawn in distress in order to hurry the arrival of the doe. Both Gaumer and Alvarez del Toro mention and deplore this practice. Various devices are used for snaring and trapping deer. In Sinaloa a farmer that had been bothered by deer jumping his garden fence placed sharp-pointed stakes at the point where the deer landed inside the garden. Several deer speared themselves in a period of two weeks. These methods of deer killing and others of similar character are socially and ethically accepted in Mexico. As yet there is no public feeling of responsibility for conserving deer or limiting the kill.

The result of this endless persecution of deer is acute shortage in most of Mexico. The situation is aggravated by overgrazing of many of the deer ranges by domestic livestock. But even taking the ranges as they are, Mexico could enjoy a vast increase in deer if hunting were regulated. The present plan to restock depleted areas with deer raised on the game farm at San Cayetano will succeed only if some way is found to interest the local people in protecting the animals. The white-tailed deer is one of the most persistent and prolific of game mammals. It adjusts well to settlement and thrives on cutover or burned forest lands, of which Mexico has plenty. It can withstand an annual harvest of 30 to 40 per cent of the population. But even the whitetail cannot hold up under the unlimited hunting now practiced. With even a modicum of effective protection the white-tailed deer could become an exceedingly important resource of rural Mexico, yielding for the local people meat, hides, recreation for themselves, and income from urban sportsmen that would come to share the hunting.

Brocket Deer. *Mazama americana* and Related Species

Other names.—Temazate; temazame; corzo; venadito rojo.
Species included here.—*Mazama americana,* the "red brocket" of Tamaulipas, Veracruz, Tabasco, and Chiapas; *Mazama gouazoubira,* the "brown brocket" of the Yucatán Peninsula.

Description.—Smallest North American deer. Males have unbranched spike antlers rarely more than 120 mm. long. Body reddish brown, much redder in mainland brockets; rather dull brown in those on Yucatán Peninsula. Neck grayish, underparts white. Tail brown dorsally, white below. Metatarsal gland absent. Measurements: head and body—910 to 980 mm.; tail—110 to 130 mm. Weight of a yearling male from Tapalapan, Veracruz: 17 km. (whole weight). Females virtually as large as males.

Range in Mexico.—Wet tropical forests of the Gulf coast, from near Gómez Farías, Tamaulipas, south to Chiapas and the Yucatán Peninsula.

Brockets are dwellers of the tropical forests. Throughout the total range of these deer, from southern Mexico to central South America, are found two distinct colors—red and brown. The evidence suggests that the two types are genetically distinct and not merely color phases such as occur in the squirrels, jaguarundis, bears, and some other mammals. In any event, until this situation is better understood the Mexican brockets are classed as two species, as above. Except for their color, red and brown brockets are very similar. They are of about the same size, and as far as we know are much the same in behavior and habitat requirements.

In Mexico, brockets are most abundant in the wet forests of the southeast. Their occurrence as far north as Tamaulipas was discovered only recently when a field party from the American Museum took a specimen at Alta Cima, near Gómez Farías (Goodwin, 1954). No verified record of the brocket in western Mexico has come to light, although Beebe (1905 : 328) saw a dried scalp with antlers in the possession of a native of Colima who said that he killed the animal in northwestern Michoacán. This could have been brought in from elsewhere, or it could mean that there is a local population in the west that has not yet been formally recorded. It must be remembered that spider monkeys were first found in western Mexico as recently as 1955!

Because of their predilection for impenetrable thickets, brocket deer are not easily studied; in fact, they are not easy even to see. Near El Real, Chiapas, where we camped for ten days in the great mahogany forest, a brocket lived in a patch of *monte* 75 yards from our tent and was seen only once. We tried repeatedly to collect the animal; but it always dodged out by some new route, and no ambush that we could contrive was successful.

Although brockets frequent dense cover during the day, they venture freely into open areas when they forage at night. Little is known of their food preferences. Alvarez del Toro (1952a) states that they feed on "sprouts and fruits," and both he and Gaumer (1917) assert that brockets may damage such cultivated crops as chile, beans, melons, and corn. Within the virgin rain forest, however, such a choice would not be available; the animals probably live mostly on fallen fruits that typically are available at almost any season of the year. Near Tapalapan, Veracruz, Epimenio Tegoma pointed out to me several fruits that were favorites of the brocket

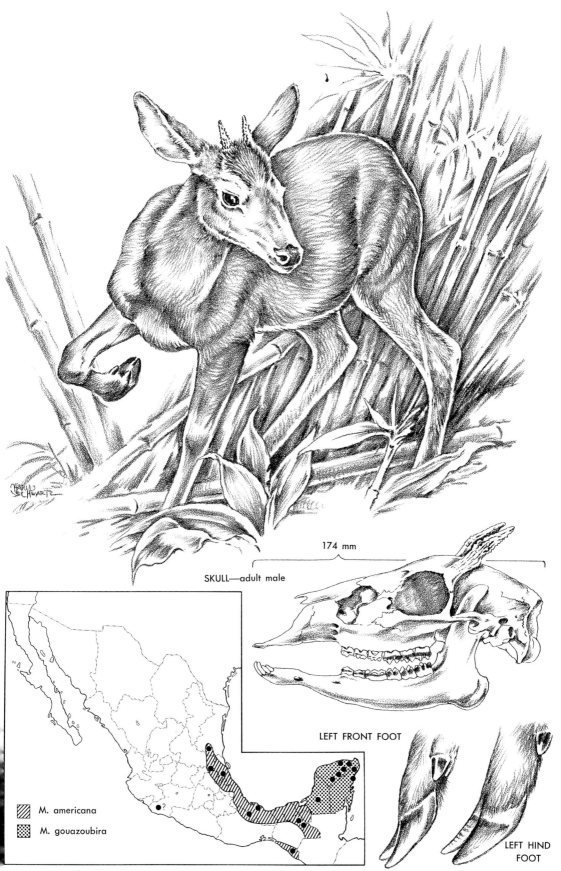

174 mm

SKULL—adult male

LEFT FRONT FOOT

LEFT HIND
FOOT

M. americana

M. gouazoubira

Fig. 190. Brocket deer, *Mazama americana*.

and the paca. Unfortunately, I failed to collect specimens of these for identification.

A controversial facet of brocket natural history is the matter of antler growth and replacement. Alvarez del Toro (1952a : 196) voices the opinion, often expressed in earlier literature, that the sharp little spikes "are not shed annually as in other deer, but grow continuously as in the goats" (my translation). This view is denied emphatically by Cabrera and Yepes (1940 : 277), who point out that the antler drop is highly irregular in timing and that an individual buck may retain its antlers for periods much longer than one year. That brockets do lose their antlers and grow new ones was attested as early as 1802 by Azara, who tells of taking a male *gouazoubira* with velvet spikes on February 24 in Paraguay (Hunter, 1838 : 146). Frans Blom of San Cristóbal las Casas, Chiapas, wrote me on May 24, 1956, that he also has collected brockets in velvet. Examination of brocket skulls suggests no way in which the antlers could grow except by dropping off and regrowing as in other deer.

According to Gaumer, brockets live in pairs. Each buck attends its single mate and helps her raise the fawns. Occasionally, several pairs and their young will band together into loose groups. In my own scant contact with brockets I saw no evidence of fixed pairs, nor even of any tendency to form bands. The brockets we saw during our hunts were alone or were does with fawns. The social arrangement in a brocket population must therefore be put down as not known.

In Yucatán, the fawns, single or twins—"never more than two" Gaumer states—arrive in June. They are spotted like other young deer and stay with their mothers through the first year.

Brockets are small enough to have many natural enemies. The jaguar, puma, and ocelot prey regularly upon them, and probably the larger birds of prey, such as the crested eagles, do also. Tayras have been observed in pursuit of brockets, as stated in the tayra account. Near settlements the cur dog is perhaps the brocket's worst enemy.

The flesh of the brocket is tender and delicious; consequently these deer are hunted intensively. Yet so adept are they at dodging through the *monte* that relatively few are killed. Around Tapalapan, Veracruz, for example, local hunters have completely exterminated the white-tailed deer; yet the brocket thrives literally among the houses of the village. In Panama, Goldman (1920) likewise observed that even the best-organized drives with dogs yielded few brockets in comparison to whitetails. Dogs are virtually a necessity in hunting this elusive animal. One specimen that we obtained led a pack on a merry chase for several hours in a very small area before it had the misfortune to slip off a cliff and drown in the torrent below. We recovered the body the next morning from an eddy in the river.

Although the brocket is adaptable and elusive, it disappears when the

Fig. 191.   Author preparing a male brocket deer as a
scientific specimen, Tapalapan, Veracruz.
Photograph by C. W. Schwartz.

tropical forest is impoverished by too much cutting or burning. Near Xocempich and Chichén Itzá, Yucatán, brockets are scarce in the scrubby growth that remains after centuries of Mayan rotational clearing. They are most abundant around small clearings in the rain forest.

FAMILY ANTILOCAPRIDAE

PRONGHORN ANTELOPE

This family, consisting of a single species, is endemic to the New World. The pronghorn occurred originally throughout the plains and deserts of North America, but today it is limited to the western United States, south-western Canada, and a few places in northern Mexico.

Pronghorn Antelope. *Antilocapra americana*

Other names.—Berrendo; antílope.

Description.—Size of a Mexican white-tailed deer, with small ears that point slightly inward at tip, very large eyes, and short tail. Dorsal color tan to cin-namon; sides, rump, and underparts white, with two white stripes across throat and a white zone on each side of face from lips to base of ear. Both sexes have horns: those of female small (ear length), those of male up to 275 mm. long. Horns have a single prong, facing forward, except when sheaths are shed, when for a period they have none. Measurements: head and body—1,100 to 1,350 mm.; tail—90 to 125 mm. Live weights: males—39 to 60 kg. (85 to 132 lbs.); females—34 to 45 kg. (75 to 100 lbs.). Removal of abdominal contents reduces weights by about 20 per cent.

Range in Mexico.—Formerly throughout northern deserts and grasslands, as far south as western Hidalgo and northern Estado de México. Now only scattered localities within the "occupied range" designated on the map.

On the plains of northern Mexico the antelope originally occurred in abundance. In 1540 a great hunt was held in honor of the first Spanish Viceroy, Antonio de Mendoza, in an area of western Hidalgo and northern Estado de México that represents the most southerly extension of the mesquite-grassland. The Indians killed 600 deer and antelope. Torque-mada's account of the incident, written much later, in 1723, states that the "verrendos . . . not only ran but flew." Fray Juan Agustín Morfi saw antelope near Durango City in 1777 and reported that "they abound in the provinces." The adventuresome Englishman George F. Ruxton (1849) refers repeatedly to the many antelope between Durango and Chihuahua City; and Lumholtz (1902 : 83) found the animals still abundant near Casas Grandes, Chihuahua, in 1891. However, during the late 1800's, after the Apaches and Comanches had been cleared from the north and normal settlement had resumed, the antelope were rapidly depleted, and by the end of the century they had become scarce. In 1907, Mearns wrote: "The

287 mm

SKULL OF ADULT MALE—Left horn with sheath in place. Right horn with sheath removed to show bony core.

• FORMER RANGE

▲ PRESENT RANGE

Fig. 192.   Pronghorn antelope, *Antilocapra americana*.

prong horn antelope is already a rare animal in the region of the South-west, where it ranged in thousands twenty-five years ago." Concern over the disappearance of the species led to a general survey of the status of antelope in North America, results of which were published in 1925 by Nelson. The Mexican population at that time was estimated at 2,395 animals, distributed as follows: Coahuila, 600; Chihuahua, 700; Sonora, 595; and Baja California, 500. As part of the widespread interest in the antelope, a special closed season was declared in Mexico in 1922 by President Obregón, and legal hunting has never been reopened. For a few years, starting in 1923, a special warden (Ben H. Tinker of Arizona) was em-ployed to protect the antelope and bighorn sheep along the Sonora-Arizona border. This worthy but short-lived project was sponsored jointly by the Mexican government and the Permanent Wild Life Protection Fund. Yet the antelope continued to decline, both in numbers and in range occupied.

The scattered areas that still support some antelope are shown on the map in figure 192. Much of the information on which the map is based was obtained by Guillermo Arai Espinosa, who in 1950 conducted a biological reconnaissance of north-central Mexico for the Bureau of Forestry and Game (Villa, 1951). His findings, together with those of Rollin Baker and Bernardo Villa, and mine, give a fair picture of the situation on the Central Plateau, which, in brief, is not very optimistic. The antelope population is still shrinking, in some places with alarming rapidity. For example, Dalquest (1953) reports the species virtually extinct in San Luis Potosí. No estimate of current numbers is available, but the population in the Central Plateau certainly is much lower than it was even ten years ago.

Less is known of the immediate status of the antelope in Sonora and Baja California. S. B. Benson found scattered bands in northwestern Sonora and northeastern Baja California (near San Felipe) on various trips between 1936 and 1948. Raymond Gilmore visited the salt camp on Black Warrior Lagoon in July, 1956, and was told that bands of as many as thirty were often seen on the Vizcaíno plain east of the lagoon and that hunters still pursued these animals. Halloran (1954a) estimates that there are no more than fifty antelope along the Sonora-Arizona border west of Sonoita. The pronghorn, in other words, is a disappearing species very much in need of special attention. A survey of the current status of the antelope in Mexico is now being conducted by Bernardo Villa. His findings should elaborate the incomplete data offered here.

The antelope has been much studied in the southwestern United States and we now know a good deal of its biology. One of the best local investi-gations was conducted in western Texas, just across the Río Grande from Mexico, by Buechner (1950). I have drawn on his work and that of others in compiling the present account of the life history of the animal.

Pronghorns are social in habit, living in bands that range from a few individuals to a hundred or more. As is true of so many other animals, the denser the population the larger the bands. Males do not segregate but join the bands of females and young. When attacked or frightened, an antelope band takes to its heels and flees. If pursued, the animals will travel long distances, at speeds of 35 to 40 miles an hour. In short bursts, individual antelope have been clocked in excess of 60 miles an hour. However, undisturbed antelope are not in the habit of dashing about the country; instead, they live quietly and move about very little from day to day. Buechner reports that the antelope of west Texas rarely use an area larger than a square mile in a given day. But the bands drift slowly about the countryside seeking better food, so that a yearly range for a band may be as much as 10 miles in diameter. On the northern plains, antelope originally made long seasonal migrations, but such migrations are not evident in the southern populations. Sheep-proof fences seriously inhibit antelope movement, for the animals rarely jump. They have been known to starve to death in overgrazed sheep pastures when good forage was available just across a low web fence. But they slip under an ordinary barbed-wire fence with ease, even while traveling at great speed.

Breeding occurs in early autumn, from late August through September. Bucks may chase the does and even mount them at any time of year, but effective breeding is limited to a short period. By the end of August the more vigorous bucks have gathered the does into harems of two to a dozen. Most of the young are driven out of the breeding harems and form temporary bands of their own. Young bucks harass the harems and must constantly be chased away by the master of the herd. The fawns are born in the spring, after a gestation of seven and a half months. Twins are normal, although single fawns and even triplets may occur. In several studies the average fawn crop has been found to approximate 1.75 per doe. For two weeks or more the fawns remain hidden, moving about only when the doe comes to feed them. Being grayish brown, they are surprisingly hard to see when flattened out in the shade of a desert shrub. By the time they are a month old they are following the mother.

It is during the period of early life that antelope are most susceptible to predation. Coyotes sometimes learn to search out hidden fawns, and losses may be severe. In a few of the southwestern states (Arizona, New Mexico) coyote predation on fawns has been found to limit the increase in sparse populations of antelope, and coyote control has been helpful in restoring the herds. Golden eagles catch a few fawns, although serious losses to eagles have never been proved. Wolves and pumas catch fawns and adults as well. Predation on adults may be especially severe in times of deep snow, which in Mexico are rare.

After the mating season, the antelope of both sexes shed their horn sheaths. The horn of an antelope is made up of a living, bony core and a sheath of plastic-like material, actually derived from a fusion or amalgamation of hairs. The sheaths loosen and fall off annually, and are replaced by new sheaths that form over the bony core. Bucks shed immediately after the rut—in late October in Texas, late September in Sonora (Hornaday, 1909 : 234)—and the does a month later. The new horns grow rapidly, and within two months are approaching final size. Prongs grow out after the main horn sheath is well developed. Because of the horn cycle, antelope hunting is usually done early in the fall when the heads make attractive trophies.

Antelope feed mostly on weeds and forbs throughout the year; grass and browse are of lesser importance. In Texas, Buechner identified 228 species

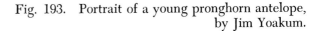

Fig. 193.   Portrait of a young pronghorn antelope, by Jim Yoakum.

of plants eaten by antelope, the most important being such forbs as bitter-weed (*Actinia*), cutleaf daisy (*Aplopappus*), several species of dahlia and of wild buckwheat, gaura, deervetch (*Lotus*), paper flower (*Psilostrophe*), coneflower (*Ratibida*), and woolly senecio. Grama grasses and some shrubs, such as hackberry, walnut, juniper, and javelina bush, are seasonally important. Because antelope eat mostly weeds, and cattle and horses eat mostly grass, there is relatively little food competition between antelope and these domestic animals on good ranges. The diet of sheep and goats, however, is much the same as that of antelope, and range competition is often severe. Thus antelope on the Central Plateau can be expected to get along well on moderately grazed cattle ranges, but they may lack forage on sheep ranges. In the extremely dry situations that occur in Sonora and Baja California, any grazing by domestic livestock, even cattle, probably curtails the food supply for antelope, since there is so little forage of any kind. Lumholtz (1912 : 152) even reports antelope and cattle competing for the leaves of the terrible cholla (*Opuntia mamillata*) in northwestern Sonora. Severely overgrazed ranges anywhere are not favorable antelope habitat.

Although the carrying capacity for antelope of the northern plains and deserts has obviously been lowered by grazing, overgrazing is not the main factor in reducing the species to its present precarious state, but rather overhunting. The antelope lives in open country. It is not particularly adept at keeping away from people, and hunting without regulation or control can easily exceed the productivity of the herds. Most of the shooting of antelope is done by local residents—the vaqueros and *campesinos* that live on the antelope range. But visiting sportsmen, both Mexicans and Americans, add to the toll despite the nominal closed season. Much of this "sport" hunting is done from jeeps and automobiles, and a little of it even from airplanes. The evidence before us clearly suggests that until adequate law enforcement is achieved the antelope will continue to decline toward extinction. Locally, protection for antelope can perhaps be strengthened by establishing special refuges. But refuges will not solve the problem for the whole large area; first there must be created a general public sentiment for saving the animals. It is only thanks to the voluntary interest of scattered individual ranchers that any antelope are left today. This desire of a few landowners to see some antelope retained on the range should be cultivated and given maximum support by the federal government. A few active wardens, working sympathetically with the ranchers to protect and foster the remnant herds, could reverse the steadily declining tide and bring about a sharp increase in numbers of this interesting creature of the plains. Once restored, the antelope again could yield a substantial annual harvest as they are doing in the western United States.

FAMILY BOVIDAE

SHEEP, CATTLE, BISON, AND RELATED ANIMALS

The original Mexican fauna included two members of the family Bovidae—the bighorn discussed below, and the bison, or *cíbola* (*Bison bison*). Records of the bison in Mexico are few; apparently the species did not follow the grasslands very deeply into Mexican territory. Bailey (1905) cites occurrences of bison along the Texas-Mexico border, and Allen (1881 : 184) gives evidence that the animal penetrated at least to central Coahuila. He quotes Dr. Edward Palmer: "According to the testimony of old people, the Bison was very abundant about Monclova and Parras when the first settlers reached these points, probably half a century after the conquest. For some years they killed large numbers for food, but soon they ceased to appear." Brand (1937) cites several records of occurrence in Chihuahua (as far south as Casas Grandes) and one account from Sonora. Baker (1956) adds other data on the species in Coahuila. But the bison disappeared early, and there is no available "niche" left for it today.

Bighorn Sheep. *Ovis canadensis*

Other names.—Borrego; cimarrón; carnero salvaje; *Ovis mexicanus; Ovis nelsoni.*

Description.—Size of a mule deer but with short legs, very small ears, massive curled horns on the males, and slender curved spikes on females. Body color smoky brown, with whitish underparts, muzzle, ear linings, and rump. Tail small—shows as dark line or dot on conspicuous white rump. Measurements: head and body—1,200 to 1,450 mm.; tail—70 to 130 mm. Males somewhat larger than females. Hornaday (1909) gives the whole weight of an old ram killed in the Pinecate Mountains of Sonora as 192½ lbs. (87 kg.) and estimates that another unweighed ram was 40 lbs. heavier. No weights of ewes in Mexico available; they probably weigh 60 to 75 kg. (130 to 165 lbs.).

Range in Mexico.—Formerly most desert ranges of northern Mexico from Baja California to Coahuila. Now only scattered remnants of bighorn remain, as shown on the map, the only substantial populations being in Baja California.

The bighorn of Mexico is exclusively an animal of the desert ranges. It frequents the most arid and forbidding cinder cones, rock upthrusts, and rims of the northern deserts and never has occurred in the well-vegetated and seemingly more hospitable mountains. But in its rocky home the stately bighorn is a noble sight. John M. Phillips, hunting in the Pinecates of Sonora with Hornaday (1909 : 197), wrote this description of four sheep seen during an afternoon thunderstorm:

That magnificent ram, standing like a statue on the pedestal of red bronze lava, washed by the falling rain and lit up by the setting sun; on one side a head with

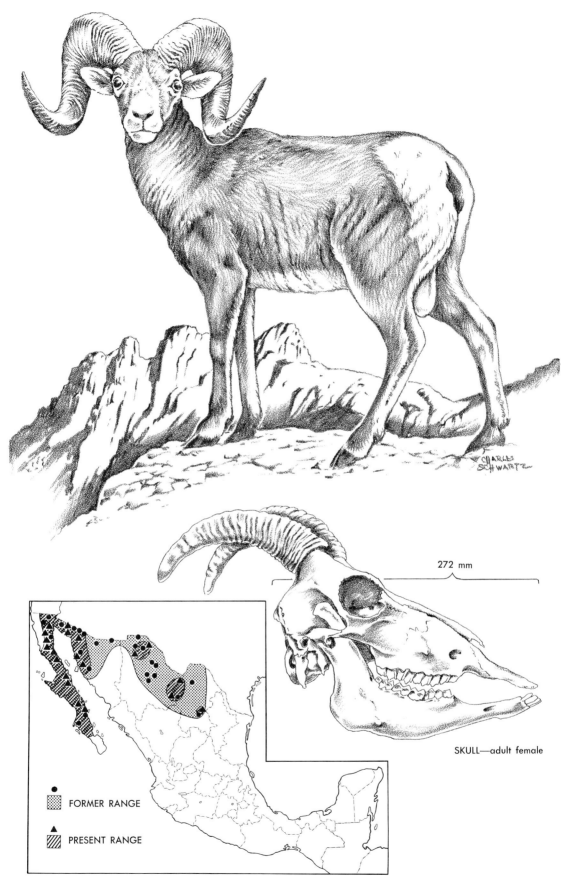

272 mm

SKULL—adult female

● FORMER RANGE

▲ PRESENT RANGE

Fig. 194.   Bighorn sheep. *Ovis canadensis.*

horns quite as massive as those of the central figure, on the other the heads of two younger rams, and the whole group overarched by a gorgeous rainbow!

Such a picture is etched deep in a sportsman's memory.

Although bighorns at one time were present in all or most of the desert mountains in the zone designated on the map, they were never as numerous as their neighbors the antelope and mule deer, for the reason that the actual spots of suitable habitat are small and localized. Within their restricted niche they seemingly occurred in good numbers. But bighorns are not overly wary, and since they, like the other desert ungulates, have to visit the water holes, they are highly vulnerable to hunting. Little by little, continued persecution has brought this species perilously close to extinction. Unlike the antelope, the bighorn is in greatest danger in the central region and has held out best in Baja California and northwestern Sonora. Rollin Baker, who has just completed an exhaustive survey of the mammals of Coahuila, found only three or four little remnants of sheep in that state. He knows of several areas in which the bighorns have been exterminated in the past decade or two. More or less the same situation seems to exist in Chihuahua, although my information there is less reliable. A few scattered animals are all that remain, and the trend is still downward. In the more isolated outcroppings of the Sonoran desert there are somewhat more survivors, estimated by Halloran (1954b) to number between 500 and 3,000. In Baja California the bighorn is likewise holding its own. An informant who was hunting bighorns (illegally) near the south tip of the San Pedro Mártir in September, 1955, saw 27 sheep in eight days, which suggests a reasonably good surviving population at that spot. The whole east face of this rugged mountain mass is said to be populated with sheep. From a low-flying airplane I saw well-marked sheep trails near a water hole in the mountains east of Scammon Lagoon (in central Baja California), and still farther south in the Sierra de la Giganta, I am told, sheep hunting is still carried on successfully. Somehow the sheep of Baja California persist despite the hunting.

Bighorns live in small bands, the ewes and lambs tending to group separately from the rams. Although these animals are ordinarily sedentary in their movements, a band may take off in search of new range during critical periods, as in an extended drought, and they have been seen crossing desert flats between mountain ranges. This is not the usual pattern, however. Bighorns are loath to leave the mountains, since they are poor runners on flat terrain. Only in the rocks can they easily outmaneuver predators, including man.

During the mating season the rams seek out the bands of ewes and stage vigorous combat for breeding privileges. They charge each other and collide head-on with great impetus, but the massive horns seem to cushion the contestants against serious injury. Only the older rams and ewes breed, yearlings and perhaps even some two-year-olds remaining aloof to the proceedings. After the breeding time, the rams drift off to their own society again. The lambs—usually one, rarely twins—are born after a gestation period of about 180 days. In the Nevada desert, lambs drop in April and May (Allen, 1939), but I do not know when lambing occurs in Mexico. I suspect that the time of lambing in Baja California, where rains fall in winter, is different from that on the central plateau, where the rainy season is summer. If there is a difference, it would apply of course to the time of rut as well as to lambing. The lambs are pale-colored, with a dark dorsal stripe, and only gradually assume the brown pelage of adults.

Predation on lambs occurs commonly. Coyotes, wolves, mountain lions, bobcats, and golden eagles are known to take bighorn lambs. Sometimes local control may be needed to bring about a desirable increase in a remnant herd. Among thriving populations the matter is less likely to be critical. Adult bighorns are usually immune to predation except when forced to leave their rocky strongholds in search of water or food. However, in 1955 considerable predation of mountain lions upon adult bighorns was reported to me from the southern end of the San Pedro Mártir, where several fresh kills and many older ones were found. Lions were abnormally abundant, judging by the amount of sign observed.

The diet of the desert bighorn is rather strictly limited by what is available. During the period of plant growth following rain there is no problem, the sheep thriving on a variety of weeds and grasses. They are very fond of the fruits of cacti and yucca when these are in season. But in time of drought the choice is meager indeed. Hornaday (1909 : 339) found the following plants in the stomach of a ram killed in the Pinecates of Sonora: "Galleta grass, palo verde (*Parkinsonia torreyana*), dry flower stalks of white brittle-bush (*Encelia farinosa*), 'torote prieto,' *Terebinthus microphylla*, and *Sphaeralcea*." He states that these are probably staple foods in that region. In the same area, in February, 1894, Mearns (1907 : 244) observed that the sheep were feeding "largely upon a *Cylindropuntia* cactus in valleys at the base of [Gila] Mountain." Desert bighorns move along rapidly as they feed, nipping a bite here and there without stopping. Allen (1939) estimates the rate of movement of a feeding band as 2 to 2½ miles an hour.

Because the chosen home of the bighorn is so rough, it is not easily overrun with livestock that may compete with the sheep for food. Nevertheless, critical areas *near water* very frequently are overgrazed by cattle or burros to the serious detriment of the bighorns. In the deserts of the southwestern United States it has often proved necessary to control livestock use of primary bighorn ranges, and the same is probably true in the arid mountains of northern Mexico.

The critical plight of the bighorn, like that of the antelope, is more the result of overhunting than it is of range difficulties. Although hunting is nominally prohibited, it goes on constantly. As early as 1894, Mearns reported a scarcity of bighorns in northwestern Sonora as a result of excessive hunting by the Papago Indians, and both Hornaday and Lumholtz (1912 : 240) reported a similar situation a few years later. Hornaday further noted the rapid disappearance of sheep in Chihuahua and Baja California, citing examples (pp. 341–345) of good populations reduced to scarcity or even exterminated by native hunters and professional meat hunters. Visiting sportsmen, anxious to add a bighorn head to their trophies, compound the problem, and there are professional guides in Baja California to supply the wants of this group, the law notwithstanding. Effective protection from hunting is the most pressing need of the sheep, especially on the Central Plateau where the population is so low. A field survey is now being conducted by Bernardo Villa to ascertain the status of the surviving remnants and to determine where special protection could most advantageously be supplied. A long-term program of restoration can be developed, using the protected herds as sources of breeding stock for reëstablishing the animals where they have been completely killed out.

A desert peak without bighorns is a dreary place that attracts few men. With a ram crowning its crest, it is a palace to be visited by the royalty of the sporting world. If ever a species deserved the protection of government and sportsmen, it is this statuesque master of the arid crags.

Appendixes

Mexican Game Law

Order Appearing in the Diario Oficial, México, D.F., January 5, 1952
[Translated by Milton J. Lindner and Rae Kaplan]
Law signed December 3, 1951, by President

EXECUTIVE BRANCH
MINISTRY OF AGRICULTURE AND LIVESTOCK
FEDERAL GAME LAW

[At the margin is a seal with the national emblem and the words:] United Mexican States.—Presidency of the Republic.

I, Miguel Alemán, Constitutional President of the United Mexican States make known to the inhabitants thereof:

That the Hon. Congress of the Union has seen fit to transmit to me the following

DECREE

The Congress of the United Mexican States decrees:

FEDERAL GAME LAW

CHAPTER I

Object of the Law

ARTICLE 1. The purpose of this law is to direct and guarantee the conservation, restoration, and development of the wildlife which lives freely in Mexican territory, regulating its exploitation.

ARTICLE 2. Wildlife consists of the animals which live freely and not under human domination. Also considered as wild, for purposes of this law, are those domestic animals which, upon being abandoned, turn wild and consequently are susceptible to capture and appropriation by means authorized in this law and its regulation.

ARTICLE 3. All species of wild animals which live freely in Mexican territory are property of the nation, and the Ministry of Agriculture and Livestock is charged with authorizing the hunting of them and the appropriation of their products.

CHAPTER II

Protection of Wildlife

ARTICLE 4. The following are declared to be of public benefit:

a) The conservation, restoration, and propagation of all the wild animals useful to man, which temporarily or permanently inhabit Mexican territory.

b) The control of wild animals, whether they be useful or harmful to man or to other animal species.

c) The importation, movement, and feeding of wild animals.

d) The conservation and propagation of the resources that serve as food and shelter for wildlife.

ARTICLE 5. The protection of birds and other wild migratory animals shall be undertaken in accordance with the precepts of this law, its regulation, and the international treaties now in force and those which may be effected in the future.

ARTICLE 6. The Ministry of Agriculture and Livestock shall be in charge of the inspection and supervision of all hunting activities in accordance with provisions of this law, its regulation, and any other orders emanating from it.

ARTICLE 7. The federal, local, and municipal authorities, the hunting clubs, and all inhabitants of the Republic should coöperate with the Ministry [of Agriculture and Livestock] in order to achieve the goals indicated in this law.

ARTICLE 8. The Ministry of Agriculture and Livestock shall impart specialized training and diffuse by all available means the necessary knowledge in order to assure the conservation and development of the national wildlife.

CHAPTER III

National Reserve Zones, Refuges for Animals, and Zones Closed for Propagation

ARTICLE 9. The Executive Branch of the Union, after suitable study, shall establish national reserve zones and determine temporary or indefinite closed seasons to secure the repopulation, propagation, acclimatization, or refuge of wild animals and, principally, of species in danger of extinction.

CHAPTER IV

Acclimatization and Propagation

ARTICLE 10. When the Ministry of Agriculture and Livestock considers beneficial the importation of foreign wild animals for their acclimatization, it shall issue the corresponding permit and the importation shall be free of duty.

ARTICLE 11. The capture of wild animals for propagation purposes obligates the permit holder to present to the Ministry of Agriculture and Livestock the live, healthy specimens designated in the regulation and in accordance with specifications contained in the permit.

ARTICLE 12. The holders of permits are also obligated to deliver to the Ministry of Agriculture and Livestock the sick specimens which they may occasionally capture, so that investigation may be made of the causes of the sickness and that epidemics may be controlled and combated efficiently.

CHAPTER V

Hunting Zones

ARTICLE 13. The hunting clubs or associations registered with the Ministry [of Agriculture and Livestock] shall be able to request of the Executive of the Union the declaration of "Cotos de Caza" (hunting zones).

By "coto" is understood a limited area designated for sports hunting.

ARTICLE 14. A prior requisite for the declaration of a hunting zone by the Executive shall be that the Ministry of Agriculture, at the expense of the interested parties, undertake a study showing that the establishment of the "coto" is justified and setting forth the conditions under which it shall function. In this study shall be determined the species and the number of animals that each hunter shall have a right to hunt during the season.

CHAPTER VI

Hunting Rights

ARTICLE 15. There shall be no limitations imposed on hunting other than these established in this law, its regulation, and orders which the Ministry of Agriculture and Livestock may proclaim.

ARTICLE 16. Hunting for commercial purposes is prohibited.

Sport hunting shall be authorized in open seasons and shall be subject to the provisions of this law and its regulation, as well as to the Table of Open Seasons issued by the Ministry of Agriculture and Livestock.

ARTICLE 17. In exceptional cases and subject to approval of the President of the Republic, authorization may be granted for the capture of a specified number of a species which is not considered destructive or harmful, when such authorization is requested for scientific or cultural investigation or for repopulation purposes and the request comes from an official, scientific, or educational organization, either Mexican or foreign.

CHAPTER VII

Permits

ARTICLE 18. Hunting permits shall be issued upon request and payment of the fees fixed in the tariff, to the members of the registered hunting association or clubs recognized by the Ministry of Agriculture and Livestock, subject to permission of the proper authority for the carrying and use of firearms.

ARTICLE 19. Hunting permits are personal and nontransferable and bearers of the permits are obliged to show them to civil or military authorities whenever requested.

ARTICLE 20. Tanners and taxidermists engaged in the preparation of wild animal skins must demand of their clients the proper permits and maintain a control book in the manner designated in the regulation [of this law].

CHAPTER VIII

Hunting Arms and Means of Capture

ARTICLE 21. The Ministry of Agriculture and Livestock is charged with determining the types and calibers of the arms, as well as the means of hunting, which may be employed.

ARTICLE 22. Taking animals by means of poison is prohibited, and decoys can be used only in exceptional cases determined in the regulation.

ARTICLE 23. It is strictly prohibited to hunt aquatic and shore birds by means of "armadas" or knots.

Shotguns (*cañones*) which can be utilized in "armadas" and all types of arms not specified in the regulation are declared prohibited arms.

CHAPTER IX

Transportation of Wild Animals and Their Products

ARTICLE 24. The transportation of wild animals or their products and remains must be covered by the proper permit, without prejudice to the fulfillment of the customary legal regulations of the animal health service.

ARTICLE 25. Transportation companies are obliged to demand of senders the permit covering their shipment.

CHAPTER X

General Provisions

ARTICLE 26. The exportation of game items, living or dead, as well as their products and derivatives, whatever they may be, is prohibited.

Exceptions to this ruling are the game items or products taken by foreign nonresidents, within the number authorized in the permit.

ARTICLE 27. A permanent closed season is decreed within the territory of the national parks and reserves, experimentation fields, and hatcheries.

ARTICLE 28. The hatcheries, experimentation fields, reserves, and national parks shall be considered propagation centers of new species and shall be utilized by the authorities to promote the breeding of all types of nonpredatory animals.

CHAPTER XI

Crimes and Offenses in the Matter of Hunting

ARTICLE 29. The Courts of the Federation shall be informed of crimes relative to hunting.

ARTICLE 30. Hunting crimes are:

I. Engaging in hunting of species that are permanently protected.

II. The use of prohibited arms for hunting.

III. Hunting females and the young of mammals not considered harmful, when it is possible to distinguish clearly the sex of the animals.

IV. The taking or destruction of nests and eggs of wild birds; and

V. Hunting by the use of "armadas" or by other unauthorized methods.

ARTICLE 31. Those persons responsible for the crimes specified in the foregoing chapter shall be penalized by a maximum of three years of prison or a fine of $100.00 to $10,000.00, and in both cases they shall be denied hunting permits for a period of five years. Penalties shall be doubled for second offenders.

ARTICLE 32. Hunting items and arms or equipment employed when committing crimes or offenses shall be collected by the administrative authority and only returned after permission has been obtained from the proper authority and after payment of the corresponding fine, if the offense is slight. In other cases and in the instance of crimes, the Ministry of Agriculture shall declare the arms confiscated by the nation and shall proceed with their auction in accordance with the manner and terms established in the regulation.

ARTICLE 33. The following are offenses with regard to hunting:

I. Engaging in hunting without the proper permit;

II. The taking of wild animals without a permit;

III. Traveling in the wilderness with hunting arms, traps, or other hunting equipment without the respective license;

IV. The capture of predatory animals with unauthorized traps;

V. Engaging in hunting of species during temporary closed seasons;

VI. Engaging in hunting with the help of artificial light, poisons, or decoys;

VII. The sale, commerce in or advertising of meats, products, or remains of wild animals;

VIII. The killing or capture of more animals than those authorized in the permit;

IX. Transportation of game animals or products derived from them, without the proper documentation, or of a larger number than that authorized;

X. Changing the names of game products in order to evade inspection; and

XI. Violation of any of the other provisions of this law or [interfering with] its regulation.

ARTICLE 34. Offenses shall be penalized with a fine of $100.00 to $10,000.00 and with the confiscation of the products and equipment involved, without prejudice to the penalties with respect to arms which may be applicable according to the provisions of Article 32 of this law.

ARTICLE 35. When live animals are seized, they shall be liberated, preferably at the site of their capture.

The products or remains, when susceptible to decomposition, shall be donated to charitable institutions, and those which can be used industrially shall be auctioned by the proper Federal Treasury Office.

ARTICLE 36. The forwarders, consignees, and carriers of game products shall also be considered responsible for offenses committed and for paying penalties imposed upon the hunters or those who have taken the animals.

ARTICLE 37. Offenses shall be judged and imposed by the Forestry and Game Agents in each federal district and shall be revised by the Ministry of Agriculture and Livestock, for purposes of increasing, verifying, or decreasing the amount of the fines and to assure a better application of this law and of its regulation.

With respect to crimes, the Agents or the Ministry shall consign the party involved to the Federal Attorney General in charge of the district concerned.

ARTICLE 38. Persons condemned or declared guilty of the same crime or offense within a lapse of five years are second offenders.

ARTICLE 39. When offenders abandon seized equipment and game the Ministry of Agriculture shall proceed with auctioning these after thirty days have passed since their seizure.

The proceeds of the auctions undertaken by the Ministry of Agriculture shall be turned over to the Ministry of the Treasury, within a period of not more than five days from the date of the auction.

ARTICLE 40. Fines shall be collected by the Federal Treasury Offices, subject to the respective laws.

TRANSITORIES

1. The Game Law of August 28, 1940, and any other order conflicting with this law are hereby revoked.

2. This law shall commence to be effective as of the date of its publication in the *Diario Oficial* of the Federation.

3. Permits now in effect shall continue to be valid until their expiration date; but their application shall be subject to provisions of this law.

4. The Table of Open Seasons for Hunting or Capture shall continue in force and shall be modified by the Ministry of Agriculture and Livestock whenever it is deemed advisable.

In compliance with the provisions of paragraph 1 of Article 89 of the Political Constitution of the United Mexican States, and for its publication and observance, I promulgate this law in the residence of the Federal Executive Power in the City of México, Federal District, on this third day of the month of December in the year one thousand nine hundred and fifty-one.—Miguel Alemán [signature]. The Minister of Agriculture and Livestock, Nazario S. Ortiz Garza [signature]. The Minister of the Treasury and Public Credit, Ramón Beteta [signature]. The Minister of Economy, Antonio Martínez Báez [signature]. The Undersecretary of Government, in Charge of the Office, Ernesto P. Uruchurtu [signature]. The Minister of National Defense, Gilberto R. Limón [signature].

APPENDIX B

Hunting Regulations

Order Appearing in the *Diario Oficial*, México, D.F., September 4, 1954
[Translated by Bernardo Villa R. and L. Farfán B.]

EXECUTIVE BRANCH
MINISTRY OF AGRICULTURE AND LIVESTOCK

Order Which Establishes the Periods During Which Wildlife Species
May Be Captured

[At the margin is a seal with the words:] Federal Executive Branch.—United Mexican States.—México.—Ministry of Agriculture and Livestock.—Directorate General of Forestry and Game. Note number 207.3.]

ORDER TO THE DIRECTORATE GENERAL OF FORESTRY AND GAME

WHEREAS, FIRST: It is essential to protect the species which comprise the wildlife of the country.

WHEREAS, SECOND: Some of our game species are already in danger of extinction, as a consequence of excessive hunting and of the progressive modification of their habitat.

WHEREAS, THIRD: It is necessary to conform to the stipulations of the international treaties effected for the protection of migratory species.

WHEREAS, FOURTH: In accordance with investigations undertaken by the personnel of the Directorate General of Forestry and Game, the conclusion has been reached that it is expedient to modify the regulations which have been governing game activities in the country; based on Articles 9 and 17 of the Game Law of December 3, 1951, I have therefore deemed it advisable to issue the following:

ORDER

ARTICLE 1. As of date of publication of this order in the *Diario Oficial* of the Federation, the open seasons for the hunting or capture of wildlife species mentioned shall be subject to the following table:

BIRDS

SPECIES	OPEN SEASON
Family ANATIDAE Ducks, geese, and swans (patos, gansos, y cisnes) In the entire Republic	November 16 to March 15 inclusive Limit, 15 per day or in possession
Family GRUIDAE Cranes (grullas)	November 1 to January 30 inclusive Limit, 5 per day or in possession
Family RALLIDAE Rails and coots (gallinas de agua, gallaretas)	November 15 to February 15 Limit, 15 per day or in possession
Families CHARADRIIDAE and PHALAROPODIDAE Plovers and phalaropes (chichicuilotes)	August 15 to September 30 inclusive Limit, 25 per day or in possession
Family SCOLOPACIDAE Snipe (agachona) and others of the family except upland plover (ganga)	October 15 to February 15 inclusive Limit, 10 per day or in possession
Family RECURVIROSTRIDAE Avocet (avoceta), stilt (zancuda), and others of the family	November 15 to February 15 inclusive Limit, 15 per day or in possession
Family COLUMBIDAE White-winged dove, mourning dove, Inca dove (paloma de alas blancas, paloma morada, tórtola, huilota)	
In Baja California, Sonora, Sinaloa, Chihuahua, Nuevo León, and Tamaulipas	September 1 to December 31 inclusive Limit, 20 per day or in possession
In the rest of the Republic	November 16 to March 15 inclusive Limit, 15 per day or in possession

SPECIES	OPEN SEASON
Family CRACIDAE	
Chachalacas (chachalacas), curassows (hoco ó faisán), guan (cojolite), and others of the family	October 1 to March 15 inclusive Limit, 5 per day or in possession For the entire season
Family PHASIANIDAE	
Ring-necked pheasant (faisán chino de collar)	
In Mexicali Valley, Baja California	November 1 to 30 inclusive Limit, 2 males per day or in possession
In the rest of the Republic	Prohibited
Mountain quail (codorniz de montaña) and other species of the family, except ring-necked pheasant (faisán de collar) and Montezuma quail	December 1 to February 28 inclusive Limit, 15 per day or in possession
Montezuma quail (codorniz de Montezuma)	
In the Valley of Mexico and high parts of the State of Mexico	January 1 to March 1 inclusive
Family MELEAGRIDIDAE	
Wild turkey (guajalote silvestre)	November 1 to February 1 inclusive Limit, 2 per day or in possession
Family TINAMIDAE	
Tinamous (perdices)	December 1 to March 31 inclusive Limit, 15 per day or in possession
Family PSITTACIDAE	
Parrots, parakeets (loros y pericos)	No season or limit

MAMMALS

Family DESMODONTIDAE	
Bats of the suborder Microchiroptera (murciélagos, chinacos, ratones viejos) except vampire bats (vampiros)	Prohibited
Vampire bats (vampiros)	No season or limit
Family CEBIDAE	
Howler and spider monkeys (mono aullador and mono araña)	November 1 to February 28 inclusive Limit, 2 males per day or in possession

SPECIES	OPEN SEASON
Family DASYPODIDAE	
Armadillo (armadillo)	August 1 to September 30 inclusive Limit, 2 per day or in possession
Family MYRMECOPHAGIDAE	
Anteater or honey bear (oso hormiguero, brazo fuerte, tamandúa, oso mielero)	December 1 to 31 inclusive Limit, 2 per season
Family LEPORIDAE	
Hares (liebres), rabbits (conejos), volcano rabbit (zacatuche ó teporingo)	
In the Valley of Mexico and States of Morelos and Puebla	Prohibited
Hares and rabbits (liebres y conejos)	
In the Valley of Mexico	Prohibited
Hares (liebres)	
In the State of Aguascalientes, municipalities of Cosio, Tepezalá, Rincón de Romos, Asientos, and Aguascalientes	No season or limit
In the State of Durango, municipalities of Ocampo, San Bernardo, Hidalgo, Mapimí, Tlahualillo de Zaragoza, El Oro, Nadé, San Pedro del Gallo, Gómez Palacio, San Luis del Cordero, Dodeo, Nazas, Lerdo, Canatlán, San Juan del Río, Peñón Blanco, Pánuco de Colorado, Guadalupe Victoria, Guencamé, Santa Clara, San Bartolo, San Juan de Guadalupe, Durango, Nombre de Dios, Poanas, Súchil, Coneto de Comonfort	No season or limit
In the State of San Luis Potosí, municipality of Santo Domingo	No season or limit
In the State of Zacatecas, municipalities of Río Grande, Sombrerete, Sain Alto, Villa de Cos, Fresnillo, Calera, Pánuco, Morelos, Veta Grande, Zacatecas, Guadalupe, San	No season or limit

SPECIES	OPEN SEASON
Pedro, Piedra Gorda, Ojo Caliente, and Luis Moya	
Hares and rabbits (liebres y conejos)	
In the rest of the Republic	November 1 to February 28 inclusive Limit, 5 per day or in possession
Family SCIURIDAE Tree and ground squirrels (ardillas arbóres y terrícolas)	
In the Valley of Mexico	Prohibited
In the rest of the Republic	No season or limit
Family DASPYROCTIDAE Agouti (agutí), paca (cuautuza or tuza real)	October 1 to January 30 inclusive Limit, 2 per day or in possession
Family CANIDAE Coyotes (coyotes), wolves (lobos), foxes (zorras)	No season or limit
Family URSIDAE Bears (osos)	October 1 to January 15 inclusive Limit, 2 adults per season
Family PROCYONIDAE Ring-tailed cat (cacomixtle), raccoon (mapache), coati (tejón, genus *Nasua*), kinkajou (marta ó mico de noche)	October 16 to February 28 inclusive Limit, 5 per day or in possession
Family MUSTELIDAE Weasel (comadreja), tayra (cabeza de viejo), skunks (zorrillos), and other species of the family except the badger (tejón ó tlalcoyote, genus *Taxidea*) and otters (perros de agua, genus *Nutria:* i.e., *Lutra*)	October 1 to January 30 inclusive Limit, 5 per day or in possession
Family FELIDAE Jaguar (tigre), wildcats (tigrillo, jaguarondi, gato de monte), ocelot (ocelote), and other members of the family	No season or limit
Family TAYASSUIDAE Peccaries (jabalíes)	
In Sonora, Chihuahua, Nuevo León, and Tamaulipas	October 1 to January 31 inclusive Limit, 5 per day or in possession

SPECIES	OPEN SEASON
Peccaries (*Continued*)	
In the State of Morelos	Prohibited
In the rest of the Republic	November 1 to February 15 inclusive Limit, 5 per day or in possession
Family CERVIDAE	
White-tailed deer (venado cola blanca)	
In the cold zones of Veracruz, Oaxaca, Chiapas, Guerrero, and Michoacán and in the rest of the Republic	October 16 to December 31 inclusive Limit, 2 adult males per season
In the states of Colima, Tabasco, Campeche, Yucatán, and Quintana Roo and the warm zones of the States of Veracruz, Chiapas, Oaxaca, Guerrero, and Michoacán	September 1 to October 15 inclusive Limit, 2 adult males per season
In the Valley of Mexico and states of Querétaro, México, Morelos, Tlaxcala, and Puebla	Prohibited
Mule or black-tailed deer (venado bura or cola prieta)	December 1 to 31 inclusive Limit, 1 adult male per season
Brocket or red deer (temazate ó venado colorado)	October 15 to December 30 inclusive Limit, 2 adult males per season

REPTILES

Iguana (iguana or garrobo)	November 1 to April 30 Limit, 10 per day or in possession
Other reptiles	According to the judgment of this ministry

ANIMALS THE HUNTING OF WHICH IS PERMANENTLY PROHIBITED

MIGRATORY BIRDS

Family CUCULIDAE: Cuckoos, ani, and roadrunners (platero, culillo, vaquero, garrapatero, correcamino, paisano)

Family CAPRIMULGIDAE: Nighthawks and whippoorwills (cuerpo ruín, abubilla, tapacamino)

Family APODIDAE: Swifts (avión listado, aguador, media luna, vencejo, tajadera, granizo tajadera)

Family TROCHILIDAE: Hummingbirds (chupamirto, chupamirto ermitano, chupamirto de guías blancas, chupamirto canelito, chupamirto real azul, chupamirto de corbata blanca, colibrí, chupamirto verde de cola de pescado, chupamirto cola de tijera, matraquita, chupamirto de pecho verde azulado, chupamirto esmeralda, chupaflor)

Family PICIDAE: Woodpecker and flickers (carpintero, carpintero de alas rojas, carpintero de alas amarillas, carpintero de orejas amarillas, carpintero de cabeza amarilla, carpintero verde, carpintero café, carpintero negro, carpintero tigre, carpintero del palmar, carpintero amarillo or saucero, carpintero de pino, pico de marfil, pito real)

Family TYRANNIDAE: Flycatchers (papamoscas, papamoscas de río, mosquero de llano, papamoscas boyero, colmenero, mosquero, abejero, avispero, rey de los papamoscas, tijereta, como chile, justo juez, cardenalito, papamosca de cuello blanco, corre gavilán, triste, portugués, mosquero de monte, papamosca gris, papamosquita, mosquero de barba blanca)

Family ALAUDIDAE: Larks (alondra, calandria monjita llanera, casilda, terito)

Family HIRUNDINIDAE: Swallows (golondrinas, avión negro, vencejo, golondrina de ciénega, golondrina albina, avión verde)

Family PARIDAE: Titmice (mascarita or baloncito, chivito, sastre, paro de matorral, paro de México de cabeza amarilla)

Family CERTHIIDAE: Nuthatches and creepers (carpinterito, saltadorcito, ocoterito, carpintero ocotero)

Family TROGLODYTIDAE: Wrens (reyezuelo, saltapared zanjero, saltapared de canal, saltapared chiquito, saltapared chico de monte, carpinterito, matraca, sonaja, saltapared de los cactos, saltapared aranero, saltón)

Family TURDIDAE: Thrushes, robins, and bluebirds (tordos, primavera, mirulín, primavera de color ocre, primavera del sur, primavera de monte, chivillo, primavera café, primavera real, capulinero, jilguero, clarín, mirlo, zorzal, ruiseñor, azul de tempestad)

Family MIMIDAE: Mocking birds and thrashers (cerción, malviz, cuitlacoche, cuitlacoche de pecho obscuro, cuitlacoche alacranero, mulato, zenzontle, chico, mirlo, ruiseñor, clarín cenizo)

Family SYLVIIDAE: Gnatcatchers and kinglets (cucurrucas, papamoscas aplomadito, pispirria, pitiflor)

Family MOTACILLIDAE: Wagtails and pipits (alondra de la majada, alondra obscura de la majada)

Family BOMBYCILLIDAE: Waxwings (burrito, chinito, tontito, torito)

Family PTILOGONATIDAE: Phainopeplas (muscicapa, chivo negro, negro copetón, copetón negro, capulinero, jarifa, jaltomatero)

Family LANIIDAE: Shrikes (cabezón, pájaro gato, pega reborda, verdugo, zenzontle arriero)

Family VIREONIDAE: Vireos (oropéndola, vireos, vireo, mosquero de ceja amarilla, mosquerito, papamosquita de cabeza aplomada, gusanero, cafetero)

Family PARULIDAE: (COMPSOTHLYPIDAE): Warblers (mezclilla, verdín rayado del sauce, verdín gusanero, verdincito, semillero, aceiturero, calandrita, canarito, verdín de toca amarilla, verdín de corona, verderón, aguador de copete, calandria huertera, arriero, cordelín, guajolotito amarillo, duraznero)

Family ICTERIDAE: Meadowlarks, orioles, and blackbirds (alondra, triguero, tordo de pecho amarillo, capitán, tordo de charreteras, tordo capitán, coronel, canero, comendador, calandria, calandria tunera, calandria negra de quiote, calandria zapotera, calandria de cabeza negra, urraca, zanate)

Family THRAUPIDAE: Tanagers (cerquero, hormiguero, caminero, ahuacatero real, misto, cardenal avispero, cuadrillero, naranjero, higuerillo)

Family FRINGILLIDAE: Grosbeaks, finches, sparrows, and buntings (cardenal, chivito, triguerillo, gorriones, prusianito, cuadrillero, dominico, marinerito, arrocerito, chouis, cerquero, canero, zorzalito, triguero, zacaterito, ojos de lumbre, pepitero, azulejo, mascarita)

NONMIGRATORY BIRDS

Family CATHARTIDAE: Vultures (buitres americanos, aura, zopilote)

Family ACCIPITRIDAE: Hawks and eagles (milanos, águilas y halcones, gavilán ratonero, águila real)

Family PANDIONIDAE: Ospreys (águilas marinas, halietos, osifragas, quebrantahuesos)

Family TYTONIDAE: Barn owls (lechuza, lechuza orejona)

Family STRIGIDAE: Other owls (lechuzas y buhos)

Family PELECANIDAE: Pelicans (alcatraz, chondón, pelícano blanco, pelícano café, flamenco or flamingo, zopelicaneco)

Family SULIDAE: Boobies (pájaro bobo, tonto, zonzo)

Family PHALACROCORACIDAE: Cormorants (cuervo de agua, cormorán, pato sargento, puerca)

Family ARDEIDAE: Herons (garza blanca chica, garza blanca grande, garza morena)

Family CICONIIDAE: Storks, wood ibises, and ibises (ciguenas e ibises arbóreos, garza rosa, espátula)

Family LARIDAE: Gulls and terns (gaviota, golondrina de mar)

Family RAMPHASTIDAE: Toucans (tucán de pecho rojo, tucán verde, pico de canoa)

Family REGULIDAE: Kinglets (reyezuelo)

Family PSITTACIDAE: Red and green macaws (guacamaya roja, guacamaya verde)

Family TROGONIDAE: Quetzal (quetzal—*Pharomachrus mocino*)

MAMMALS

Family CASTORIDAE: Beavers (castor)

Family MUSTELIDAE: Badgers (tlalcoyote—*Taxidea taxus*), perro de agua (otter, nutrias)

Family TAPIRIDAE: Tapirs (anteburro or danta)

Family ANTILOCAPRIDAE: Antelope (berrendo)

Family BOVIDAE: Wild sheep (borrego silvestre)

Family CERVIDAE: Cedros Island deer (venado de la isla de Cedros)

ARTICLE 2. The hunting of wild animals in national parks, hunting reserves, and refuges is strictly prohibited.

ARTICLE 3. In accordance with the Presidential Decree of October 17, 1950, published in the *Diario Oficial* of the Federation on October 24 of the same year, hunting is totally prohibited in the State of Coahuila.

ARTICLE 4. As a means of protecting the national fauna and in accordance with Article 16 of the Federal Game Law, hunting is permitted only for sport; professional hunting and commerce with wild animals, their products, or their remains are prohibited.

ARTICLE 5. Violations of this order shall be penalized in accordance with provisions of the Federal Game Law in effect.

ARTICLE 6. The order of September 4, 1951, regulating hunting seasons is hereby revoked.

For publication and compliance.
México, D.F., September 3, 1954

The Minister of Agriculture and Livestock
GILBERTO FLORES MUÑOZ [signature]

Bibliography

Bibliography

(Listed here are only the publications cited in the text. These represent approximately one-third of the publications utilized in compiling this book.)

Allen, J. A.
1881. List of mammals collected by Dr. Edward Palmer in north-eastern Mexico, with field-notes by the collector. Bull. Mus. Comp. Zoöl., 8 : 183–189.

1895. On a collection of mammals from Arizona and Mexico, made by Mr. W. W. Price, with field notes by the collector. Bull. Amer. Mus. Nat. Hist., 7 : 193–258.

1903. List of mammals collected by Mr. J. H. Batty in New Mexico and Durango, with descriptions of new species and subspecies. Bull. Amer. Mus. Nat. Hist., 19 : 587–612.

1906. Mammals from the states of Sinaloa and Jalisco, Mexico, collected by J. H. Batty during 1904 and 1905. Bull. Amer. Mus. Nat. Hist., 22 : 191–262.

Allen, J. A., and F. M. Chapman
1897. On mammals from Yucatán, with descriptions of new species. Bull. Amer. Mus. Nat. Hist., 9 : 1–12.

Allen, J. C.
1939. Ecology and management of Nelson's bighorn on the Nevada mountain ranges. Trans. N. Amer. Wildlife Conf., 4 : 253–256.

Alston, E. R.
1879–1882. Biologia Centrali-Americana. Mammalia. Taylor & Francis, London. 220 pp.

Alvarez del Toro, M.
1952a. Los animales silvestres de Chiapas. Ediciones del Gobierno del Estado, Tuxtla Gutiérrez, Chiapas. 247 pp.

1952b. New records of birds from Chiapas, Mexico. Condor, 54 : 112–114.

American Ornithologists' Union
1957. Check-list of North American birds. 5th ed. Amer. Ornith. Union, Lord Baltimore Press, Baltimore. 691 pp.

Arellano, M., and P. Rojas M.
1956. Aves acuaticas migratorias en México. Inst. Mex. Recursos Naturales Renovables, México, D.F., 270 pp.

Arnold, L. W.
1943. The western white-winged dove in

Arnold, L. W. (*Continued*)
    Arizona. Arizona Game and Fish Comm., Phoenix. 103 pp.

Azara, Don F.
    1838. *See* Hunter, W. P.

Bailey, V.
    1905. Biological survey of Texas. N. Amer. Fauna, No. 25. 222 pp.

Baird, S. F.
    1859. United States and Mexican Boundary Survey: Part II—Zoölogy of the Boundary. Mammals, pp. 1–62; Birds, pp. 1–32. Dept. of the Interior, Washington, D.C.

Baker, R. H.
    1956. Mammals of Coahuila, Mexico. Univ. Kansas Publ., Mus. Nat. Hist., 9 : 125–335.

Barlow, R. H. (ed.)
    1944. Relación de Xiquilpan y su partido, 1579. Sobretiro de Tlalocán, 1 : 278–306.

Beard, J. S.
    1944. Climax vegetation in tropical America. Ecology, 25 : 127–158.

Beebe, C. W.
    1905. Two bird lovers in Mexico. Houghton Mifflin Co., Boston and New York. 407 pp.
    1925. The variegated tinamou, *Crypturus variegatus variegatus* (Gmelin). Zoölogica, 6 : 195–227.

Beltrán, E.
    1946. Los recursos naturales de México y su conservación. México, D.F., Sec. Educación Publica, La Biblioteca Enciclopédica Popular, 106. 96 pp.

Bennett, L. J.
    1938. The blue-winged teal: Its ecology and management. Collegiate Press, Ames, Iowa. 144 pp.

Benson, S. B.
    1938. Notes on kit foxes (*Vulpes macrotis*) from Mexico. Proc. Biol. Soc. Wash., 51 : 17–24.
    1953. A record of the porcupine (*Erethizon dorsatum*) from Sonora, Mexico. Jour. Mamm., 34 : 511–512.

Bent, A. C.
    1932. Life histories of North American gallinaceous birds. Bull. U. S. Nat. Mus., 162. 490 pp.

Blake, E. R.
    1953. Birds of Mexico. Univ. Chicago Press. 644 pp.

Blake, E. R., and H. C. Hanson
    1942. Notes on a collection of birds from Michoacán, Mexico. Field Mus. Nat. Hist., Zoöl. Ser., 22 : 513–551.

Booth, E. S.
    1953. American golden-eye in Sonora, Mexico. Condor, 55 : 160.

Borell, A. E., and M. D. Bryant
    1942. Mammals of the Big Bend area of Texas. Univ. Calif. Publ. Zoöl., 48 : 1–62.

Brand, D. D.
    1937. The natural landscape of northwestern Chihuahua. Univ. New Mexico Bull., No. 316. 74 pp.

Brodkorb, P.
    1943. Birds from the Gulf lowlands of southern Mexico. Univ. Mich. Mus. Zoöl., Misc. Publ., No. 55. 88 pp.

Buechner, H. K.
    1950. Life history, ecology, and range use of the pronghorn antelope in Trans-Pecos Texas. Amer. Midl. Nat., 43 : 257–354.

Burt, W. H.
    1938. Faunal relationships and geographic distribution of mammals in Sonora, Mexico. Univ. Mich. Mus. Zoöl., Misc. Publ., No. 39. 77 pp.

Cabrera, A., and J. Yepes
    1940. Historia natural ediar: mamiferos sud-americanos. Cia. Argentina de Editores, Buenos Aires. 370 pp.

Cahalane, V. H.
    1947. Mammals of North America. The Macmillan Co., New York. 682 pp.

Carpenter, C. R.
    1934. A field study of the behavior and social relations of howling monkeys. Comp. Psychol. Monog., 10 (2) : 1–168.

Carrillo Rodriguez, C.
    1955. Contribución a la biología del venado cola blanca, *Odocoileus virginianus,* en México. Univ. Nac. Autónomo de Mex., Fac. de Ciencias, Dept. Biol., México, D.F. 65 pp.

Chapman, F. M.
    1896. Notes on birds observed in Yucatán. Bull. Amer. Mus. Nat. Hist., 8 : 271–290.

Christensen, G. C.
    1954. The chukar partridge in Nevada. Nevada Fish and Game Comm., Biol. Bull., No. 1. 77 pp.

Contreras Arias, A.
  1942. Mapa de las provincias climatolo-
        gicas de la Republica Mexicana.
        Sec. Agric. Fomento, Inst. Geográ-
        fico, México, D.F. 54 pp.
Cowan, J. B.
  1952. Life history and productivity of a
        population of western mourning
        doves in California. Calif. Fish and
        Game, 38 : 505–521.

Dalquest, W. W.
  1949. The white-lipped peccary in the
        state of Veracruz, Mexico. An. Inst.
        Biol., México, D.F., 20 : 1–3.
  1950. Records of mammals from the Mex-
        ican state of San Luis Potosí. Loui-
        siana State Univ. Mus. Zoöl., Occ.
        Papers, No. 23. 15 pp.
  1953. Mammals of the Mexican state of
        San Luis Potosí. Louisiana State
        Univ. Studies, Biol. Sci. Ser., No. 1.
        229 pp.
Dalquest, W. W., and J. H. Roberts
  1951. Behavior of young grisons in cap-
        tivity. Amer. Midl. Nat., 46 : 359–
        366.
Davie, O.
  1889. Nests and eggs of North American
        birds. Hann and Adair, Columbus.
        455 pp.
Davis, L. I.
  1952. Winter bird census at Xilitla, San
        Luis Potosí, Mexico. Condor, 54 :
        345–355.
Davis, W. B.
  1944a. Notes on summer birds of Guerrero.
        Condor, 46 : 9–14.
  1944b. Notes on Mexican mammals. Jour.
        Mamm., 25 : 370–403.
Davis, W. B., and P. W. Lukens, Jr.
  1958. Mammals of the Mexican state of
        Guerrero exclusive of Chiroptera
        and Rodentia. Jour. Mamm., 39 :
        347–369.
Dickey, D. R., and A. J. van Rossem
  1938. The birds of El Salvador. Field
        Mus. Nat. Hist., Zoöl. Ser., vol. 23.
        609 pp.

Evenden, F. G., Jr.
  1952. Notes on Mexican bird distribution.
        Wilson Bull., 64 : 112–113.

Ferrel, C. M., H. R. Leach, D. F. Tillotson
  1953. Food habits of the coyote in Cali-

fornia. Calif. Fish and Game, 39 :
        301–341.
Friedmann, H., L. Griscom, and R. T. Moore
  1950. Distributional check-list of the birds
        of Mexico. Part 1. Pac. Coast Avi-
        fauna, No. 29. 202 pp.
Friedmann, H., and F. D. Smith, Jr.
  1955. A further contribution to the orni-
        thology of northeastern Venezuela.
        Proc. U. S. Nat. Mus., 104 : 463–
        524.

Gadow, H.
  1908. Through southern Mexico. Witherby
        and Co., London. 527 pp.
Gaumer, G. F.
  1917. Mamiferos de Yucatán. Dept. Ta-
        lleres Gráficos, Secretaría de Fo-
        mento, Mexico. 331 pp.
Gill, T.
  1951. Land hunger in Mexico. Chas. La-
        throp Pack Forestry Foundation,
        Washington, D.C. 86 pp.
Goldman, E. A.
  1913. Descriptions of new mammals from
        Panama and Mexico. Smithson. Misc.
        Coll., 60 : 1–20.
  1920. Mammals of Panama. Smithson.
        Misc. Coll., 69 : 1–309.
  1928. The Kaibab or white-tailed squirrel.
        Jour. Mamm., 9 : 127–129.
  1938. List of the gray foxes of Mexico.
        Jour. Wash. Acad. Sci., 28 : 494–
        498.
  1943. The races of the ocelot and margay
        in Middle America. Jour. Mamm.,
        24 : 372–385.
Goodwin, G. G.
  1954. Mammals from Mexico collected by
        Marian Martin for the American
        Museum of Natural History. Amer.
        Mus. Novit., No. 1689. 16 pp.
Gorsuch, D. M.
  1934. Life history of the Gambel quail in
        Arizona. Univ. Ariz., Biol. Sci. Bull.,
        No. 2. 89 pp.
Gray, P. N. (ed.)
  1932. Records of North American big
        game. Derrydale Press, New York.
        178 pp.
Grinnell, J.
  1928. A distributional summation of the
        ornithology of Lower California.
        Univ. Calif. Publ. Zoöl., 32 : 1–300.
Grinnell, J., H. C. Bryant, and T. I. Storer
  1918. The game birds of California. Univ.
        Calif. Press, Berkeley. 642 pp.

Grinnell, J., J. S. Dixon, and J. M. Linsdale
  1937. Fur-bearing mammals of California. Univ. Calif. Press, Berkeley. 2 vols. 777 pp.
Grinnell, J., and T. I. Storer
  1924. Animal life in the Yosemite. Univ. Calif. Press, Berkeley. 752 pp.
Griscom, L.
  1932. The distribution of bird-life in Guatemala. Bull. Amer. Mus. Nat. Hist., 64 : 1–439.
Gudger, E. W.
  1946. Does the jaguar use his tail as a lure in fishing. Jour. Mamm., 27 : 37–49.
Gullion, G. W.
  1953. Territorial behavior of the American coot. Condor, 55 : 169–186.
  1954. The reproductive cycle of American coots in California. Auk, 71 : 366–412.
  1956a. Let's go desert quail hunting. Nevada Fish and Game Comm., Biol. Bull., No. 2. 76 pp.
  1956b. Evidence of double-brooding in Gambel quail. Condor, 58 : 232–234.

Halloran, A. F.
  1954a. The dwarf antelope of the Yuma flats. Arizona Wildlife-Sportsman, 25 : 26–28.
  1954b. Bighorns south of the border. Arizona Wildlife-Sportsman, 25 : 42–44.
Harper, H. T., B. H. Harry, and W. D. Bailey
  1958. The chukar partridge in California. Calif. Fish and Game, 44 : 5–50.
Hart, C. M., B. Glading, and H. T. Harper
  1956. The pheasant in California. Chap. 3 in D. L. Allen (ed.), Pheasants in North America. The Stackpole Co., Harrisburg, Pa. 490 pp.
Haverschmidt, F.
  1947. Field notes on the black-bellied tree duck in Dutch Guiana. Wilson Bull., 59 : 209.
Hellmayr, C. E., and B. Conover
  1942. Catalogue of birds of the Americas. Field Mus. Nat. Hist., Zoöl. Ser., 13 (1) : 1–636.
Herrejón, M.
  1952. El cazador y la vida silvestre. Librería y Editorial "Pedagogía," México, D.F. 170 pp.
Hill, H. M., and I. L. Wiggins
  1948. Ornithological notes from Lower California. Condor, 50 : 155–161.

Hochbaum, H. A.
  1944. The canvasback on a prairie marsh. Amer. Wildlife Inst., Washington, D.C. 201 pp.
  1955. Travels and traditions of waterfowl. Univ. Minn. Press, Minneapolis. 301 pp.
Hornaday, W. T.
  1909. Camp-fires on desert and lava. Chas. Scribner's Sons, New York. 366 pp.
Howell, A. H.
  1901. Revision of the skunks of the genus *Chincha*. N. Amer. Fauna, No. 20. 62 pp.
Hubbs, C. L.
  1955. Black scoters reported from Baja California. Condor, 57 : 121–122.
Humboldt, A. von
  1900. Personal narrative of travels to the equinoctial regions of America, during the years 1799–1804. Thomasina Ross ed., London. 3 vols., 1,468 pp.
Hunter, W. P. (ed.)
  1838. Natural history of the quadrupeds of Paraguay and the River La Plata. Translated from the Spanish of Don Felix de Azara. A. and C. Black, Edinburgh. 340 pp.

Imaz Baume, A.
  1938. Cacería. Publ. by the author, México, D.F. 601 pp.
Ingles, L. G.
  1956. Meat for Mayan tables. Pacific Discovery, 9 : 4–12.

Jennings, W. S., and J. T. Harris
  1953. The collared peccary in Texas. Texas Game and Fish Comm., FA Report Ser., No. 12. 31 pp.

Kellogg, R., and E. A. Goldman
  1944. Review of the spider monkeys. Proc. U.S. Nat. Mus., 96 : 1–45.
Kortright, F. H.
  1942. The ducks, geese and swans of North America. Amer. Wildlife Inst., Washington, D.C. 476 pp.

Lawrence, G. N.
  1874. The birds of western and northwestern Mexico, based upon collections made by Col. A. J. Grayson, Capt. J. Xantus and Ferd. Bischoff, now in the museum of the Smithsonian Institution, at Washington, D.C. Mem. Boston Soc. Nat. Hist., 2 : 265–319.

Lay, D. W.
1942. Ecology of the opossum in eastern Texas. Jour. Mamm., 23 : 147–159.

León, N.
1887. Historia geografía y estadística de la municipalidad de Quiroga en 1884. Imprenta del Gobierno ó Cargo de José R. Bravo, Morelia. 74 pp.

Leopold, A. S.
1948. The wild turkeys of Mexico. Trans. N. Amer. Wildlife Conf., 13 : 393–400.
1950. Vegetation zones of Mexico. Ecology, 31 : 507–518.
1952. Zonas de vegetación en Mexico. Bol. Soc. Mex. Geografía y Estadística, 73 : 47–93.
1954. Dichotomous forking in the antlers of white-tailed deer. Jour. Mamm., 35 : 599–600.

Leopold, A. S., and R. A. McCabe
1957. Natural history of the Montezuma quail in Mexico. Condor, 59 : 3–26.

Leopold, A. S., and R. H. Smith
1953. Numbers and winter distribution of Pacific black brant in North America Calif. Fish and Game, 39 : 95–101.

Leopold, L. B. (ed.)
1953. Round River; from the journals of Aldo Leopold. Oxford Univ. Press, New York. 173 pp.

Liers, E. E.
1951. Notes on the river otter (Lutra canadensis). Jour. Mamm., 32 : 1–9.

Lindsey, A. A.
1946. The nesting of the New Mexican duck. Auk, 63 : 483–492.

Lint, K. C.
1952. Breeding ocellated turkeys in captivity. Bull. Zoöl. Soc. San Diego, No. 27. 23 pp.

López, C. M., and C. López
1911. Caza Mexicana. Librería de la Vda. de C. Bouret, México, D.F. 629 pp.

Lowery, G. H., Jr., and W. W. Dalquest
1951. Birds from the state of Veracruz, Mexico. Univ. Kansas Publ., Mus. Nat. Hist., 3 : 531–649.

Lowery, G. H., Jr., and R. J. Newman
1951. Notes on the ornithology of southeastern San Luis Potosí. Wilson Bull., 63 : 315–322.

Lumholtz, C.
1902. Unknown Mexico. Chas. Scribner's Sons, New York. 2 vols. 1,013 pp.
1912. New trails in Mexico. Chas. Scribner's Sons, New York. 411 pp.

Lundell, C. L.
1934. Preliminary sketch of the phytogeography of the Yucatán Peninsula. Carnegie Inst. Wash. Publ., 436 : 257–321.

McCabe, R. A.
1949. The scream of the mountain lion. Jour. Mamm., 30 : 305–306.

McCullough, C. Y.
1955. Breeding record of javelina, Tayassu angulatus, in southern Arizona. Jour. Mamm., 36 : 146.

Major, C. I. F.
1897. The otter of Central America. Ann. Mag. Nat. Hist., Ser. 6, 19 : 618–620.

Marsh, E. G., Jr.
1937. Biological survey of the Santa Rosa and Del Carmen Mountains of northern Coahuila, Mexico. U. S. Nat. Park Serv., mimeo. rep. 73 pp.

Martin del Campo, R.
1944. Huevos subfosiles de grulla en el Valle de México. An. Inst. Biol., México, D.F., 15 : 313–318.
1948. Contribución para el conocimiento de la fauna oritológica del Estado de Guerrero. An. Inst. Biol., México, D.F., 19 : 241–266.

Martínez, M.
1945. Las pinaceas Mexicanas. An. Inst. Biol., México, D.F., 16 : 1–345.

Mearns, E. A.
1907. Mammals of the Mexican boundary of the United States. Bull. U. S. Nat. Mus., 56, Pt. 1. 530 pp.

Merriam, C. H.
1898. Life zones and crop zones of the United States. U. S. Dept. Agric., Div. Biol. Survey Bull., 10. 79 pp.

Mexican check-list of birds
1950. See Friedmann, H., L. Griscom, and R. T. Moore.

Miller, G. S., Jr., and R. Kellogg
1955. List of North American recent mammals. Bull. U. S. Nat. Mus., 205. 954 pp.

Miller, L.
1943. Notes on the Mearns quail. Condor, 45 : 104–109.

Miller, W. DeW.
1905. List of birds collected in southern Sinaloa, Mexico, by J. H. Batty, during 1903–1904. Bull. Amer. Mus. Nat. Hist., 21 : 339–369.

Miranda, F.
  1952.   La Selva del Ocote. Publ. Ateneo de
          Chiapas, Tuxtla Gutiérrez, Chiapas.
          15 pp.
Moore, R. T.
  1938.   A new race of wild turkey. Auk, 55 :
          112–115.
Moore, R. T., and D. R. Medina
  1957.   The status of the chachalacas of
          western Mexico. Condor, 59 : 230–
          234.

Neff, J. A.
  1940.   Notes on nesting and other habits
          of the western white-winged dove
          in Arizona. Jour. Wildlife Mgmt.,
          4 : 279–290.
  1947.   Notes on some birds of Sonora, Mex-
          ico. Condor, 49 : 32–34.
Nelson, E. W.
  1899.   Revision of the squirrels of Mexico
          and Central America. Proc. Wash.
          Acad. Sci., 1 : 15–110.
  1901.   A new species of Galictis from Mex-
          ico. Proc. Biol. Soc. Wash., 14 : 129–
          130.
  1904.   A winter expedition in southwestern
          Mexico. Nat. Geog. Mag., 15 : 341–
          356.
  1909.   The rabbits of North America. N.
          Amer. Fauna, No. 29. 314 pp.
  1921.   Lower California and its natural re-
          sources. Nat. Acad. Sci., Vol. 16,
          first memoir. 194 pp.
  1925.   Status of the pronghorned antelope,
          1922–24. U. S. Dept. Agric., Dept.
          Bull., No. 1346. 64 pp.
  1932.   A new subspecies of Colinus nigro-
          gularis (Gould). Proc. Biol. Soc.
          Wash., 45 : 169–172.
Nelson, E. W., and E. A. Goldman
  1932.   Two new cacomistles from Mexico,
          with remarks on the genus Jentinkia.
          Jour. Wash. Acad. Sci., 22 : 484–488.
Nordhoff, C. B.
  1922.   Notes on some water-fowl. Condor,
          24 : 64–65.

Oates, E. W.
  1901.   Catalogue of the collection of bird's
          eggs in the British Museum. Brit.
          Mus. Nat. Hist., London. Vol. 1.
          252 pp.

Pattie, J. O.
  1905.   Pattie's personal narrative of a voy-
          age to the Pacific and in Mexico,
          June 20, 1824—August 30, 1830.
          Early Western Travels, 1748–1846,
          18 : 1–324. Arthur H. Clark Co.,
          Cleveland.
Paynter, R. A., Jr.
  1955.   The ornithogeography of the Yu-
          catán Peninsula. Peabody Mus. Nat.
          Hist., Bull. 9. 347 pp.
Pearson, A. K., and O. P. Pearson
  1955.   Natural history and breeding be-
          havior of the tinamou, Nothoprocta
          ornata. Auk, 72 : 113–127.
Phillips, J. C.
  1922–1926.   A natural history of the ducks.
          Houghton Mifflin Co., Boston and
          New York. 4 vols. 1,585 pp.

Reynolds, H. C.
  1945.   Some aspects of the life history and
          ecology of the opossum in central
          Missouri. Jour. Mamm., 26 : 361–
          379.
Richardson, W. B.
  1942.   Ring-tailed cats (Bassariscus astu-
          tus): their growth and development.
          Jour. Mamm., 23 : 17–26.
Ridgway, R., and H. Friedmann
  1946.   The birds of North and Middle
          America. Bull. U. S. Nat. Mus., 50,
          Pt. 10. 484 pp.
Ruxton, G. F.
  1849.   Adventures in Mexico and the Rocky
          Mountains. John Murray, London.
          332 pp.

Salvin, O.
  1860.   History of the derbyan mountain-
          pheasant (Oreophasis derbianus).
          Ibis, 2 : 248–253.
Salvin, O., and F. D. Godman
  1879–1904.   Biologia Centrali-Americana:
          Aves. [London.] 4 vols. Vol. 3
          (1897–1904). 510 pp.
Saunders, D. C.
  1951.   Territorial songs of the white-winged
          dove. Wilson Bull., 63 : 330–332.
Saunders, G. B.
  1953.   The tule goose (Anser albifrons
          gambelli), blue goose (Chen cae-
          rulescens) and mottled duck (Anas
          fulvigula maculosa) added to the list
          of the birds of Mexico. Auk, 70 : 84–
          85.
Saunders, G. B., and D. C. Saunders
  1949.   Report on migratory waterfowl in-
          vestigations in Mexico: January–

Saunders, G. B., and D. C. (*Continued*)
May, 1949. U. S. Fish and Wildlife
Serv., Washington, D.C. 107 pp.,
mimeo.

Schäfer, E.
1954. Zur Biologie des Steisshühnes *Notho-
cercus bonapartei*. Jour. für Ornitol-
ogie, 95 : 219–232.

Sclater, P. L., and O. Salvin
1859. On the ornithology of Central America. Part 3. Ibis, 1 : 213–234.

Sharp, A. J.
1946. Informe preliminar sobre algunos
estudios fitogeográficos efectuados
en México y Guatemala. Rev. Soc.
Mex. Hist. Nat., 7 : 35–40.

Simpson, L. B.
1938. California in 1792: The expedition
of José Longinos Martínez. Hunting-
ton Lib., San Marino. 111 pp.

Skutch, A. F.
1945. Incubation and nestling periods of
Central American birds. Auk, 62 : 8–
37.
1949. Life history of the ruddy quail-dove.
Condor, 51 : 3–19.

Small, J. A.
1956. Mexican safari. Field and Stream,
60 (10) : 50–53, 89–93, 112.

Sowls, L. K.
1955. Prairie ducks: A study of their behavior, ecology and management.
The Stackpole Co., Harrisburg, Pa.
193 pp.

Sperry, C. C.
1941. Food habits of the coyote. U. S.
Dept. Int., Fish and Wildlife Serv.,
Wildlife Res. Bull., No. 4. 70 pp.

Stager, K. E.
1954. Birds of the Barranca de Cobre region of southwestern Chihuahua,
Mexico. Condor, 56 : 21–32.

Standley, P. C.
1920–1926. Trees and shrubs of Mexico.
Contr. U. S. Nat. Herbarium, Vol.
23. 5 parts, 1,721 pp.

Stilwell, H.
1948. Is Mexico slaughtering our waterfowl? Field and Stream, 53 : 19–21,
108–111.

Sutton, G. M.
1944. At a bend in a Mexican river. Audubon Mag., 46 : 344–351.

Sutton, G. M., and T. D. Burleigh
1940. Birds of Valles, San Luis Potosí,
Mexico. Condor, 42 : 259–262.

Sutton, G. M., and O. S. Pettingill, Jr.
1942. Birds of the Gómez Farías region,
southwestern Tamaulipas. Auk, 59 :
1–34.

Taber, F. W.
1945. Contribution on the life history
and ecology of the nine-banded
armadillo. Jour. Mamm., 26 : 211–
226.

Tamayo, J. L.
1949. Geografía general de Mexico. Ta-
lleres Gráficos de la Nación, México,
D.F. 2 vols. 1,208 pp.

Taylor, W. P., W. B. McDougall, C. C. Presnall,
and K. P. Schmidt
1945. Preliminary ecological survey of the
northern Sierra del Carmen, Coahuila, Mexico. Texas Coöp. Wildlife
Res. Unit. 48 pp., mimeo.

Taylor, W. P., C. T. Vorhies, and P. B. Lister
1935. The relation of jack rabbits to grazing in southern Arizona. Jour. For.,
33 : 490–498.

Tozzer, A. M. (ed.)
1941. Landa's relación de las cosas de
Yucatán. Pap. Peabody Mus. Vol.
18. 394 pp.

Traylor, M. A., Jr.
1941. Birds from the Yucatán Peninsula.
Field Mus. Nat. Hist., Zoöl. Ser.,
24 : 195–225.

Van Rossem, A. J.
1945. A distributional survey of the birds
of Sonora, Mexico. Louisiana State
Univ. Mus. Zoöl., Occas. Papers, No.
21. 379 pp.

Van Tyne, J.
1935. The birds of northern Petén, Guatemala. Univ. Mich. Mus. Zoöl., Misc.
Publ. No. 27. 46 pp.

Villa R., B.
1948. Mamiferos del Soconusco, Chiapas.
An. Inst. Biol., México, D.F., 19 :
485–528.
1951. Jabalíes y berrendos. Dept. de Caza,
Mexico, Bol. de Divulgación No. 2.
30 pp.
1953a. Mamiferos silvestres del Valle de
México. An. Inst. Biol., México, D.F.,
23 : 269–492.
1953b. Nota acerca de la duración del
periodo de gestación de una venada
cola blanca (*Odocoileus virginianus
mexicanus*) de Tepecuacuilco, Gro.

Villa R., B. (*Continued*)
An. Inst. Biol., México, D.F., 24 : 459–460.

1954a. Distribución actual de los castores en México. An. Inst. Biol., México, D.F., 25 : 443–450.

1954b. Contribución al conocimiento de las epocas de caida y nacimiento de la cornamenta y de su terciopelo en venados cola blanca (*Odocoileus virginianus*) de San Cayetano, Estado de México, Mexico. An. Inst. Biol., México, D.F., 25 : 451–461.

Vogt, W.
1945. Unsolved problems concerning wildlife in Mexican national parks. Trans. N. Amer. Wildlife Conf., 10 : 355–358.

1946. Mexican natural resources, their past, present and future. Pan Amer. Union, Washington, D.C.

Wagner, H. O.
1949. Beitrag zur Anatomie und Biologie der Steisshühner (Tinamidae). *In* Carl Winter, Ornithologie als biologische Wissenschaft. Universitätsverlag, Heidelberg, pp. 240–246.

1953a. Die Hockohühner der Sierra Madre de Chiapas, Mexiko. Veröff. Mus. Bremen, Reihe A, 2 (2) : 105–128.

1953b. Beitrag zur Biologie und Domestizierungsmöglichkeit des Pfauentruthuhnes (*Agriocharis ocellata* Cuvier). Veröff. Mus. Bremen, Reihe A, 2 (2) : 135–140.

1956. Freilandbeobachtungen an Klam-meraffen. Zeitschrift für Tierpsychologie, 13 (2) : 302–313.

Walkinshaw, L. H.
1949. The sandhill cranes. Cranbrook Inst. Sci., Bull. No. 29. 202 pp.

Warner, D. W., and B. E. Harrell
1957. The systematics and biology of the singing quail, *Dactylortyx thoracicus*. Wilson Bull., 69 : 123–148.

Wetmore, A.
1943. The birds of southern Veracruz, Mexico. Proc. U. S. Nat. Mus., 93 : 215–340.

Worcester, H. M.
1955. Hunting the lawless. Amer. Wildlife Associates, Berkeley. 293 pp.

Wright, A. H.
1914. Early records of the wild turkey. Auk, 21 : 334–358.

Wright, P. L.
1948. Breeding habits of captive long-tailed weasels (*Mustela frenata*). Amer. Midl. Nat., 39 : 338–344.

Young, S. P., and E. A. Goldman
1944. The wolves of North America. Amer. Wildlife Inst., Washington, D.C. 636 pp.

1946. The puma, mysterious American cat. Amer. Wildlife Inst., Washington, D.C. 358 pp.

Zinser, J.
1936. The Mexican wildlife situation. Trans. N. Amer. Wildlife Conf., 1 : 6–11.

1944. Mexico's conservation program. Trans. N. Amer. Wildlife Conf., 9 : 29–33.

Index

Index